British Catalogue of Music

1978

A record of music and books about music recently published in Great Britain, based upon the material deposited at the Copyright Receipt Office of the British Library, arranged according to a system of classification with a Composer and Title Index, a Subject Index, and a List of Music Publishers.

The British Library BIBLIOGRAPHIC SERVICES DIVISION

The British Catalogue of Music is compiled within

The British Library

BIBLIOGRAPHIC SERVICES DIVISION

Store Street London WC1E 7DG

Telephone: 01-636 1544

Telex: 21462

ISBN 0–900220–74–0

ISSN 0068–1407

British Library Cataloguing in Publication data

British Catalogue of Music
1978

1. Music–Bibliography
I British Library Bibliographic Services Division
016.78   ML118

ISBN 0–900220–74–0
ISSN 0068–1407

Produced by computer-controlled phototypesetting by Computaprint Ltd London
and additional phototypesetting by Bishopsgate Press Ltd London
Printed in Great Britain by Whitstable Litho Ltd, Whitstable, Kent

Preface

The British Catalogue of Music is a record of new music—with the exception of certain types of popular music—published in Great Britain. In addition, it records foreign music available in this country through a sole agent and books about music. It is based on the works deposited at the Copyright Receipt Office of the British Library where copies of all new publications must be sent by law and is the most complete list of current British music available. The Catalogue is presented in three sections:

Classified Section
Composer and Title Index
Subject Index

Instruments, musical forms

While the Classified Section displays the works systematically according to the instrument or combination for which a work is written, the Subject Index lists the principle musical forms and musical character and it shows by means of the class symbol where works having such forms or musical character are to be found in the Classified Section. For example, in the Subject Index under the word Sonatas the following entries may be found:

Sonatas: Arrangements for 2 pianos	QNUK/AE
Sonatas: Organ	RE
Sonatas: Piano duets, 4 hands	QNVE
Sonatas: Violin solos, Unaccompanied	SPME

It will be seen that this group of entries enables you to assemble all the works in sonata form no matter for what instrument the music is, or was originally, written. Under the word Violin the following may be found:

Violin	S
Violin: Accompanying female voices: Choral works	FE/S
Violin: Books	AS
Violin & orchestra	MPS
Violin & string orchestra	RXMPS

This group directs you first to the place S in the Classified Section, where music for the violin is found, including works composed originally for other instruments and arranged for violin. It also directs you to works in which the violin figures in combination with other instruments. It thus provides at one and the same time the link between an instrument and its place in the Classified Section and an exhaustive guide to all the works in which that particular instrument figures. It should be borne in mind that class symbols which include () "brackets" or / "stroke" precede letters in the arrangement. Thus:

	A
is followed by	A(....)
which is followed by	A/....
which is followed by	AA
which is followed by	AB
which is followed by	B. etc.

Music literature

Books about music which normally appear in the *British National Bibliography* are also included in this catalogue. They occur in the sequences lettered A and B of the Classified Section. They are indexed in exactly the same way as musical works in the Composer and Title Index and are designated by the qualification "Books" in the Subject Index. Thus, in the second group above, the entry Violin: Books, directing you to AS, indicates that books about the violin will be found at that place.

Composers

When the composer or author of a work is known, look under his name in the Composer and Title Index. The information given here, including the publisher and price, will be adequate for most purposes. If, on the other hand, the fullest information about a work is required, turn to the entry in the Classified Section. This may be found by means of the class symbol (group of letters) at the end of the entry in the Composer and Title Index.

Titles, series, editors and arrangers

Entries are made in the Composer and Title Index under the titles of all works, so that, if you do not know the composer or author, a work can be found by looking up its title in the Composer and Title Index. If you do not know either the composer or the title, it may still be possible to trace the work if the name of the editor or arranger is known and, in the case of vocal works, the author of the words.

Prices

Prices given are those current at the time of the first recording of an entry in this catalogue. In a few cases prices of parts are not given but can be obtained on application to the publishers.

Abbreviations

Most of the abbreviations used in describing musical works are self-explanatory. The size of a musical work is indicated by one of the following conventional symbols: *8vo* for works up to 10½ in height, *4to* for works over 10½in to 12 in. in height, and *fol.* for works over 12 in. in height. The abbreviation *obl.* (oblong) is added to show when a work is of unusual proportions, and a single sheet is designated by the abbreviations *s.sh.* The abbreviations used for the description of books in the sections A and B are those in use in the *British National Bibliography*.

Patrick Mills
Editor
British Catalogue of Music

Outline of the Classification

The following outline is given for general information only. Users are advised to consult the Subject Index to discover the exact location of required material in the Classified Section.

MUSICAL LITERATURE

A	General Works
	Common sub-divisions
A(B)	Periodical
A(C)	Encyclopaedias
A(D)	Composite works, symposia, essays by several writers
A(E)	Anecdotes, personal reminiscences
A(K)	Economics
A(M)	Persons in music
A(MM)	Musical profession
A(MN)	Music as a career
A(P)	Individuals
A(Q)	Organisations
A(QT)	Terminology
A(QU)	Notation
A(R)	Printing
A(S)	Publishing
A(T)	Bibliographies
A(U)	Libraries
A(V)	Musical education
A(X)	History of music
A(Y)	Music of particular localities
A/AM	Theory of music
A/CC	Aesthetics
A/CY	Technique of music
A/D	Composition
A/E	Performance
A/F	Recording
A/FY	Musical character
A/G	Folk music
A/GM	Music associated with particular occupations
A/H	Dance music
A/HM	Ballet music
A/J	Music accompanying drama
A/JR	Film music
A/KD	Music to accompany social customs
A/L	Religious music
A/LZ	Elements of music
A/R	Harmony
A/S	Forms of music
A/Y	Fugue
AB	Works on vocal music
AC	Works on opera
ACM	Works on musical plays
AD-AX	Works on music for particular vocal or instrumental performers, enumerated like D-X below
B	Works on individual composers (including libretti and other verbal texts of particular musical works)
BZ	Works on non-European music

MUSIC: SCORES AND PARTS

C/AY	Collections not limited to work of particular composer, executant, form or character
C/AZ	Collections of a particular composer not otherwise limited
C/G-C/Y	Collections illustrating music of particular form, character, etc., enumerated like A/G-A/Y above
CB	Vocal music
CC	Opera. Vocal scores with keyboard
CM	Musical plays. Vocal score with keyboard
D	Choral music
DC	Oratorios, Cantatas, Masses
DF	Liturgical, Service music
DH	Motels, Anthems, Hymns
DW	Songs, etc.
E	Choral music with instruments other than keyboard
EZ	Choral music unaccompanied
F	Choral music. Female voices
G	Choral music. Male voices
J	Unison vocal works
K	Vocal solos
L	Instrumental music
M	Orchestral music
N	Chamber music
PVV	Music for individual instruments and instrumental groups
PW	Keyboard instruments
Q	Piano
R	Organ
RW	String instruments
S	Violin
SQ	Viola
SR	Cello
SS	Double bass
TQ	Harp
TS	Guitar
U	Wind instruments
V	Woodwind
VR	Flute
VS	Recorder
VT	Oboe
VU	Saxophone
VV	Clarinet
VW	Bassoon
W	Brass
WS	Trumpet
WT	Horn
WU	Trombone
WX	Bass tuba
X	Percussion instruments
Z	Non-European music

Classified section

This section contains entries under Subjects, Executants and Instruments according to a system of classification, a synopsis of which appears in the preliminary pages. The Composer and Title Index and the Subject Index which follow this section are the key to both the classification and to this section.

The following are used for sizes of musical works:

8vo. for works up to 10½ in. in height.
4to. for works between 10½in. and 12 in. in height.
fol. for works over 12 in. in height.
obl. indicates a work of unusual proportions.
s.sh. means a single sheet.

A — MUSICAL LITERATURE
Craft, Robert
Current convictions : views and reviews / [by] Robert Craft. — London : Secker and Warburg, 1978. — x,338p : music ; 22cm.
Originally published: New York : Knopf, 1977. — Index.
ISBN 0-436-11300-7 : £6.50
(B78-11191)

Fenton, Ian
Looking at music / [by] Ian Fenton. — London : Coventure, 1977. — 28p : ill(chiefly col), music, ports ; 29cm.
ISBN 0-904576-42-6 : £2.93
(B78-14493)

Goehr, Alexander
Musical ideas and ideas about music / by Alexander Goehr. — London : Birkbeck College, [1978]. — 14p ; 25cm. — (Birkbeck College. Foundation orations ; 1976)
'An oration delivered at Birkbeck College, London, 2nd December 1976 in celebration of the 153rd anniversary ; chairman the Right Honourable Lord Denning of Whitchurch, President of the College'.
Sd : £0.25
(B78-32354)

Heath, Edward
Music : a joy for life / [by] Edward Heath. — London : Sidgwick and Jackson, 1978. — 208p : ill(some col), facsims, music, plan, ports(some col) ; 25cm.
Text on inside covers. — Originally published: 1976. — Index.
Pbk : £3.95
ISBN 0-283-98349-3
(B78-33160)

My favourite music stories / edited by Yehudi Menuhin ; with line decorations by Peter McClure. — Guildford [etc.] : Lutterworth Press, 1977. — 160p : ill, music ; 23cm.
ISBN 0-7188-2308-7 : £2.95
(B78-18540)

Palmer, King
Music / [by] King Palmer. — 4th ed. — London : Teach Yourself Books, 1978. — viii,152p : ill, music ; 18cm. — (Teach yourself books)
Previous ed.: published as 'Teach yourself music'. London : English Universities Press, 1965. — Index.
ISBN 0-340-05666-5 Pbk : £1.50
(B78-16899)

Ramsbottom, Edward
Sounds and music / [by] Edward Ramsbottom and Joan Redmayne ; illustrated by Pat Nessling. — London [etc.] : Macmillan, 1978. — 16p : chiefly col ill ; 25cm. — (First ideas)
ISBN 0-333-23169-4 Sd : £0.48
(B78-18538)

Westerman, Gerhart von
Concert guide : a handbook for music-lovers / by Gerhart von Westerman ; preface by John Russell ; foreword by Wilhelm Furtwängler ; translated [from the German] and edited by Cornelius Cardew. — London : Sphere, 1973. — 488p : ill, music ; 18cm.
This translation originally published: London : Thames and Hudson, 1963. — Translation of: 'Knaurs Konzertführer'. München : Droemersche Verlagsanstalt, 1951. — Index.
ISBN 0-7221-9003-4 Pbk : £0.90
(B78-09117)

A(B/T/WT) — Periodicals. Bibliographies. Lists
Meggett, Joan M
Music periodical literature : an annotated bibliography of indexes and bibliographies / [compiled] by Joan M. Meggett. — Metuchen ; London : Scarecrow Press ; [Folkestone] : [Distributed by Bailey and Swinfen], 1978. — ix,116p ; 23cm.
Index.
ISBN 0-8108-1109-X : Unpriced
(B78-23111)

A(BC) — Directories
International music guide. — London : Tantivy Press [etc.].
1978 / edited by Derek Elley. — 1977. — 304p : ill, ports ; 21cm.
Index.
ISBN 0-498-02107-6 Pbk : £3.25
ISSN 0140-7147
(B78-07707)

A(C) — Encyclopaedias
The concise encyclopedia of music and musicians / edited by Martin Cooper. — 4th ed. (revised). — London : Hutchinson, 1978. — xix,481p : ill, music ; 23cm.
Previous ed.: 1975.
£6.50
(B78-20430)

Jacobs, Arthur
The new Penguin dictionary of music / [by] Arthur Jacobs. — 4th ed. — London : Allen Lane, 1978. — 458p : music ; 23cm.
This ed. originally published: Harmondsworth : Penguin, 1977.
ISBN 0-7139-1121-2 : £5.50
(B78-27519)

Michels, Ulrich
dtv-Atlas zur Musik : Tafeln und Texte / [von] Ulrich Michels ; graphische Gestaltung der Abbildungen Gunther Vogel. — 2.Aufl. — Kassel [etc.] ; London : Bärenreiter [etc.].
Previous ed.: Munich : Deutscher Taschenbuch Verlag, 1977.
Bd 1. Systematischer Teil ; [und], Historischer Teil : Von den Anfängen bis zur Renaissance. — 1978. — 282p : col ill, 2 col maps, col music ; 18cm.
Bibl.: p.266-271. — Index.
Pbk : £3.58
ISBN 3-7618-0554-3 (Bärenreiter)
ISBN 3-423-03022-4 (dtv)
(B78-19397)

A(C/YBD) — Encyclopaedias. Classical Greece
Michaelides, Solon
The music of ancient Greece : an encyclopaedia / by Solon Michaelides. — London : Faber, 1978. — xvi,365,[1]p,x leaves of plates : ill, music ; 25cm.
Index.
ISBN 0-571-10021-x : £15.00
(B78-04320)

A(D) — Essays
Ehmann, Wilhelm
Voce et tuba : gesammelte Reden und Aufsätze, 1934-1974 / [von] Wilhelm Ehmann ; herausgegeben von Dietrich Berke, Christiane Bernsdorff-Engelbrecht und Helmut Kornemann. — Kassel [etc.] ; London ([32 Great Titchfield St., W.1]) : Bärenreiter Kassel, 1976. — xix,666p : music, port ; 24cm.
List of sound discs: p.621-631.
Pbk : Unpriced
ISBN 3-7618-0561-6
(B78-03573)

A(D/XNS40) — Essays, 1937-1976
Carter, Elliott
The writings of Elliott Carter : an American composer looks at modern music / compiled, edited, and annotated by Else Stone and Kurt Stone. — Bloomington ; London : Indiana University Press, 1977. — xvii,390p : music, port ; 24cm.
Bibl.: p.369-370. — Index.
ISBN 0-253-36720-4 : £12.95
(B78-33159)

A(DD) — Quotations
An **encyclopedia** of quotations about music / compiled and edited by Nat Shapiro. — Newton Abbot [etc.] : David and Charles, 1978. — xiii,418p ; 22cm.
Also published: Garden City, N.Y. : Doubleday, 1978. — Index.
ISBN 0-7153-7611-x : £6.95 : CIP rev.
(B78-19438)

A(DE) — Questions & answers
Ray, Robin
Robin Ray's music quiz. — London : Batsford, 1978. — 96p : ill, facsim, music, ports ; 26cm.
With answers.
ISBN 0-7134-1492-8 : £3.50
(B78-35466)

A(KKR) — Patronage. Royal patronage
Hogwood, Christopher
Music at court / [by] Christopher Hogwood. — London : Folio Society, 1977. — 128p : ill(some col), facsims(some col), music, ports(some col) ; 25cm.
Ill. on lining papers. — Bibl.: p.128.
£4.95
(B78-08477)

A(QU) — Notation
Read, Gardner
Music notation : a manual of modern practice / by Gardner Read. — [2nd ed.]. — London : Gollancz, 1978. — xi,482p : music ; 22cm.
This ed. originally published: Boston, Mass. : Allyn and Bacon, 1969 ; London : Gollancz, 1974. — Bibl.: p.454-455. — Index.
ISBN 0-575-02554-9 Pbk : £3.95
(B78-30828)

A(TC) — Bibliographies of scores
British catalogue of music. — London : British Library, Bibliographic Services Division.
1977. — 1978. — [4],128p ; 31cm.
Index.
ISBN 0-900220-68-6 : £11.00
ISSN 0068-1407
(B78-24790)

Wiltshire Library and Museum Service
Music for orchestras / [Wiltshire Library & Museum Service]. — Trowbridge (Bythesea Rd, Trowbridge, [Wilts.]) : [Wiltshire County Council] Library and Museum Service, [1978]. — [22]p ; 22x9cm.
ISBN 0-86080-010-5 Sd : £0.20
(B78-23116)

York Minster. *Library*
A catalogue of the printed music published before 1850 in York Minster Library / compiled by David Griffiths. — York ([Dean's Park, York YO1 2JD]) : [The Library], 1977. — xxi,118p,[4]leaves of plates : ill, facsims, port ; 30cm. — (York Minster. Library. Sectional catalogues ; 1)
Index.
Pbk : £1.50
(B78-20765)

A(TC/YT/XFYH22) — Bibliographies of scores. United States, 1768-1889
Dichter, Harry
Handbook of early American sheet music, 1768-1889 / by Harry Dichter and Elliott Shapiro. — New York : Dover Publications [etc.] ; London : Constable, 1977. — iii-xxix,287p,[66]p of plates : facsims, music ; 24cm.
Originally published: as 'Early American sheet music, its lure and its lore, 1768-1889'. New York : Bowker, 1941. — 'The picture selection has been revised and expanded, and a number of corrections have been made' - title page verso. — Bibl.: p.259. — Index.
ISBN 0-486-23364-2 Pbk : £4.70
(B78-30339)

A(U) — Librarianship
Redfern, Brian
Organising music in libraries / [by] Brian Redfern. — Revised and rewritten ed. — London : Bingley [etc.].
In 2 vols. — Previous ed.: 1966.
Vol.1 : Arrangement and classification. — 1978. — 105p ; 23cm.
Bibl.: p.99-101. — Index.
ISBN 0-85157-231-6 : £3.25
(B78-50319)

A(V/YD/XN31) — England, 1920-1950
Ibberson, Mary
For joy that we are here : Rural Music Schools, 1929-1950 / [by] Mary Ibberson. — London : Bedford Square Press for the Rural Music Schools Association, 1977. — [6],97p : ill, ports ; 22cm.
ISBN 0-7199-0930-9 : £2.75
(B78-03572)

A(VC) — Teaching
Music education review : a handbook for music teachers. — London : Chappell.
Vol.1 : [1977] / general editor Michael Burnett. — 1977. — ix,211p : music ; 23cm.
At head of title: University of London, Institute of Education. — Bibl.
Pbk : £5.95
ISBN 0-903443-29-9
ISSN 0140-6493

A(VC/T) — Teaching. Bibliographies
Grindea, Carola
Music books for schools : an annotated list / compiled by Carola Grindea and Christopher Walter. — Oxford : School Library Association, 1977. — 32p ; 21cm. — (School Library Association. Book lists)
Index.
ISBN 0-900641-30-4 Sd : £1.30(£0.90 to members)
(B78-18775)

A(VF) — Schools
Musikalische Grundausbildung in der Musikschule. — Mainz ; London [etc.] : Schott.
Lehrerhandbuch. Teil 1 : Didaktik und Methodik / herausgegeben von Lore Auerbach, Hans Wilhelm Köneke, Wolfgang Stumme unter Mitarbeit von ... [anderen]. — 1978. — 240p : ill, form, music ; 24cm.
Bibl.: p.216-229.
Pbk : £9.50
ISBN 3-7957-2621-2
(B78-33930)

A(VQ) — Professional education
Committee of Enquiry into the Training of Musicians
Training musicians : a report to the Calouste Gulbenkian Foundation on the training of professional musicians / [Committee of Enquiry into the Training of Musicians]. — London (98 Portland Place, W1N 4ET) : The Foundation, UK and Commonwealth Branch, 1978. — 143p ; 22cm.
ISBN 0-903319-11-x Pbk : £1.50
(B78-18539)

A(VX/D) — Musicology. Essays
Seeger, Charles
Studies in musicology, 1935-1975 / [by] Charles Seeger. — Berkeley [etc.] ; London : University of California Press, 1977. — vii,357,[2]p,(2 fold) : ill, map, music, ports ; 27cm.
Bibl.: p.345-353. — Index.
ISBN 0-520-02000-6 : £11.75
(B78-11189)

A(WB/WT) — Concert promotion. Lists
Crampton, Stephen
Music matters : a check-list for local music groups / by Stephen Crampton and Kenneth May. — London (26 Bedford Sq., WC1B 3HU) : Standing Conference for Amateur Music, [1978]. — 16p : ill ; 15x21cm.
Bibl.: p.14-15.
Sd : Unpriced
(B78-20433)

A(X) — History
Baker, Richard, *b.1925*
The magic of music / [by] Richard Baker. — London : Sphere, 1976 [i.e. 1978]. — 128p,[16]p of plates : ill, music, ports ; 20cm.
Originally published: London : Hamilton, 1975. — Bibl.: p.118. — Index.
ISBN 0-7221-1422-2 Pbk : £1.25
(B78-33932)

Blackwood, Alan, *b.1932*
The pageant of music : an introduction to the history of music / [by] Alan Blackwood ; foreword by Percy M. Young ; illustrations by Christine Skilton. — London : Barrie and Jenkins, 1977. — 137p : ill ; 23cm.
Index.
ISBN 0-214-20423-5 : £3.95
(B78-04318)

A(XCE601) — History, 900-1500
Caldwell, John, *b.1938*
Medieval music / [by] John Caldwell. — London : Hutchinson, 1978. — 304p : music ; 24cm.
Bibl.: p.260-274. — Index.
ISBN 0-09-120900-5 : £12.50
(B78-17613)

A(XCH701) — History, 1300-1900
Colles, Henry Cope
The growth of music : a study in musical history / by H.C.
Colles. — 4th ed. — London [etc.] : Oxford University Press,
1978. — xvi,523p : music ; 20cm.
Previous ed.: 1956. — Index.
ISBN 0-19-316116-8 : £4.50
ISBN 0-19-316115-x Pbk : £2.95
(B78-20435)

A(XLK88) — History, 1890-1977
Griffiths, Paul
A concise history of modern music from Debussy to Boulez / [by]
Paul Griffiths. — [London] : Thames and Hudson, 1978. —
216p : ill, facsims, music, ports ; 22cm. — ([The world of art
library])
Bibl.: p.203-206. — Index.
ISBN 0-500-18167-5 : £5.50
(B78-21398)

A(Y) — MUSIC OF PARTICULAR LOCALITIES
A(YB/XG101) — Europe, 1800-1900
Longyear, Rey Morgan
Nineteenth-century Romanticism in music / [by] Rey M.
Longyear. — 2nd ed. — Englewood Cliffs ; London [etc.] :
Prentice-Hall, 1973. — xiv,289p : music ; 23cm. — (Prentice Hall
history of music series)
Also published simultaneously in a hardback edition, now out of print. —
Previous ed.: Englewood Cliffs ; Hemel Hempstead : Prentice-Hall, 1969. —
Bibl. — Index.
ISBN 0-13-622647-7 Pbk : £5.05
(B78-22843)

A(YC) — Great Britain
Cole, Hugo
The changing face of music / by Hugo Cole. — London :
Gollancz, 1978. — 160p ; 23cm.
Bibl.: p.149-153. — Index.
ISBN 0-575-02496-8 : £7.95
(B78-35470)

A(YC/BC) — Great Britain. Directories
Music trades international directory. — [Watford] : [Wheatland
Journals].
1978. — [1978]. — 108p : ill ; 30cm.
Cover title: Music trades directory. — Fold. cover. — Ill. on inside front
cover.
Pbk : £3.00
ISSN 0307-8523
(B78-11702)

A(YC/WE/Q) — Great Britain. Festivals. Organizations
British Federation of Music Festivals
Year book / the British Federation of Music Festivals
(incorporating The Music Teachers' Association). — London (106
Gloucester Place, W1H 3DB) : [The Federation].
1978. — [1978]. — 121p : ill ; 21cm.
Sd : £1.50
ISSN 0309-8044
(B78-17612)

A(YC/XPQ17) — Great Britain, 1955-1971
Twenty British composers / edited by Peter Dickinson. — London :
J. and W. Chester for the Feeney Trust, 1975. — vii,84p,plate :
music, port ; 23cm.
List of works: p.59-84.
ISBN 0-9502767-3-1 : Unpriced
(B78-33938)

A(YDM/X) — Ireland. History
Acton, Charles
Irish music & musicians / written by Charles Acton. — Dublin
([65 Middle Abbey St., Dublin 1]) : Eason and Son Ltd, 1978. —
[28]p(2 fold) : ill(some col), music, ports(some col) ; 25cm. —
(The Irish heritage series ; 15)
ISBN 0-900346-22-1 Sd : £0.90
(B78-33934)

A(YH/XDZA153) — France, 1581-1733
Anthony, James R
French baroque music : from Beaujoyeulx to Rameau / [by]
James R. Anthony. — Revised ed. — London : Batsford, 1978. —
xi,458p,[8]p of plates : ill, music, port ; 22cm.
Previous ed.: 1973. — Bibl.: p.389-414. — Index.
ISBN 0-7134-1076-0 : £12.50
(B78-26886)

A(YT) — United States
American Music Conference, 1st, University of Keele, 1975
First American Music Conference [held at] Keele University,
England, Friday, April 18-21, 1975. — [Keele] ([Keele, Staffs. ST5
5BG]) : [University of Keele, Department of Music], [1977?]. —
[3],201p : 1 ill, music ; 27cm.
Sd : Unpriced
(B78-30830)

Clarke, Garry E
Essays on American music / [by] Garry E. Clarke. — Westport,
Conn. ; London : Greenwood Press, 1977. — xviii,259,[1]p :
music ; 22cm. — (Contributions in American history ; no.62 ISSN
0084-9214)
Bibl.: p.233-245. — Index.
ISBN 0-8371-9484-9 : £12.95
(B78-09696)

A(Z) — MUSIC IN RELATION TO OTHER SUBJECTS
Parrott, Ian
The music of Rosemary Brown / by Ian Parrott. — London
[etc.] : Regency Press, 1978. — 92p,leaf of plate,4p of plates :
music, ports ; 23cm.
Bibl.: p.91-92. — Index.
£2.40
Also classified at AQ/E(P)
(B78-19809)

A(Z/T) — Music-related to women. Bibliographies
Skowronski, JoAnn
Women in American music : a bibliography / by JoAnn
Skowronski. — Metuchen ; London : Scarecrow Press ;
[Folkestone] : [Distributed by Bailey and Swinfen], 1978. — viii,
183p ; 23cm.
Index.
ISBN 0-8108-1105-7 : £6.80
(B78-24791)

A(ZD) — Therapeutics - influenced by music
Music therapy in the community : papers read at the conference
held in London on the 16th October 1976. — London (48
Lanchester Rd, N6 4TA) : British Society for Music Therapy,
[1977?]. — [2],37p ; 26cm.
Bibl.: p.14.
Sd : Unpriced
(B78-12810)

A/AM(P) — Shenkier, Heinrich
Narmour, Eugene
Beyond Schenkerism : the need for alternatives in music analysis /
[by] Eugene Narmour. — Chicago ; London : University of
Chicago Press, 1977. — xi,238p : ill, music ; 24cm.
Bibl.: p.215-220. — Index.
ISBN 0-226-56847-4 : £14.00
(B78-03570)

A/B — PHYSICS OF MUSIC
Kenney, A R
Sounds of music / [by] A.R. Kenney. — Sunbury-on-Thames
[etc.] : Nelson, 1978. — 24p : ill, port ; 19x25cm. — (Science at
work)
ISBN 0-17-438332-0 Sd : £0.45
(B78-29834)

Rigden, John S
Physics and the sound of music / [by] John S. Rigden. — New
York ; London [etc.] : Wiley, 1977. — xiii,286p : ill, music ;
24cm.
With answers to selected problems. — Index.
ISBN 0-471-02433-3 Pbk : £8.85
(B78-02609)

A/C — Appreciation
Thomson, William
Music for listeners / [by] William Thomson. — Englewood Cliffs ;
London [etc.] : Prentice-Hall, 1978. — xx,490p : ill, facsims,
maps, music, ports ; 25cm.
Index.
ISBN 0-13-608026-x : £8.70
(B78-29828)

A/C(VF) — Appreciation. Schools
Bennett, Roy
Enjoying music / [by] Roy Bennett. — London : Longman.
Book 2. — 1978. — 64p : ill, facsims, music, ports ; 19x25cm.
Text on inside covers.
ISBN 0-582-22180-3 Sd : £0.95
(B78-37863)

A/CC — AESTHETICS
A/CC(P) — Pound, Ezra
Pound, Ezra
Ezra Pound and music : the complete criticism / edited with
commentary by R. Murray Schafer. — London : Faber, 1978. —
xiii,530p : facsims, music, port ; 24cm.
Originally published: New York : New Directions, 1977. — Index.
ISBN 0-571-11233-1 : £25.00
(B78-08474)

A/CS — PSYCHOLOGY
Davies, John Booth
The psychology of music / [by] John Booth Davies. — London :
Hutchinson, 1978. — 240p : ill, music ; 24cm. — ([Hutchinson
university library])
Bibl.: p.219-234. — Index.
ISBN 0-09-129500-9 : £8.95
(B78-11194)

A/D — COMPOSITION
Cope, David
New music composition / [by] David Cope. — New York :
Schirmer Books ; London : Collier Macmillan, 1977. — xiii,351p :
ill, music ; 24cm.
Bibl.: p.333-340. — Index.
ISBN 0-02-870630-7 Pbk : £6.75

(B78-06259)

A/D(M) — Composers
The **musician's** world : letters of the great composers / edited by
Hans Gal. — London : Thames and Hudson, 1978. — 462p ;
23cm.
Originally published: 1965. — Bibl.: p.453-455. — Index.
ISBN 0-500-27130-5 Pbk : £2.95

(B78-35467)

A/D(M/C) — Composers. Encyclopaedias
The **dictionary** of composers / edited by Charles Osborne. —
London [etc.] : Bodley Head, 1977. — 380p : ill, facsims, ports ;
24cm.
ISBN 0-370-30016-5 : £5.95

(B78-20434)

Gilder, Eric
The dictionary of composers and their music : every listener's
companion arranged chronologically and alphabetically / [by] Eric
Gilder, June G. Port. — New York ; London : Paddington Press,
1978. — 431p ; 25cm.
Half title: Composers and their music.
ISBN 0-448-22364-3 : £6.95

(B78-26881)

A/D(M/YEM/XLQ51) — Composers. Austria, 1895-1945
Rognoni, Luigi
The second Vienna school : expressionism and dodecaphony / [by]
Luigi Rognoni ; translated from the Italian by Robert W. Mann.
— London : J. Calder : [Distributed by Calder and Boyars], 1977.
— xxix,417p,fold plate : ill(incl 1 col), music, ports ; 23cm.
Translation of: 'La scuola musicale di Vienna'. Torino : Einaudi, 1966. —
Bibl.: p.402-410. — Index.
ISBN 0-7145-3528-1 : £12.50

(B78-06256)

A/D(VC) — Composition. Teaching
Meyer-Denkmann, Gertrud
Experiments in sound : new directions in musical education for
young children / [by] Gertrud Meyer-Denkmann ; adapted for use
in English schools by Elizabeth and John Paynter. — London :
Universal Edition, 1977. — [5],52p,[4]p of plates,leaf of plate :
ill(some col) ; 24cm.
Bibl.: p.52.
ISBN 0-900938-49-8 Pbk : £3.50

(B78-10119)

A/D(VF) — Composition. Schools
Paynter, John
Sound tracks / devised and written by John Paynter ; designed
and illustrated by Eve Mathews. — Cambridge [etc.] : Cambridge
University Press.
[1] : Pattern music. — 1978. — 1v. : ill(chiefly col), music ; 30cm.
Booklet (iii,12p.), sheet ([2]sides), 5 folders ([24]p.) in plastic envelope. —
Bibl.
ISBN 0-521-20581-6 : £1.95

(B78-23589)

[2] : Rites and ceremonies. — 1978. — 1v. : ill(chiefly col), music ; 30cm.
Booklet (iii,12p.) sheet ([2]sides), 5 folders ([28]p.) in plastic envelope. —
Bibl.
ISBN 0-521-20579-4 : £1.95

(B78-23590)

[4] : Magic songs. — 1978. — 1v. : ill(some col), music, port ; 30cm.
Booklet (iii,12p.), sheet ([2]sides), 5 folders ([26]p.) in plastic envelope. —
Bibl.
ISBN 0-521-20578-6 : £1.95

(B78-23592)

A/D(YTLD/M) — Composers. Afro-American composers
The **black** composer speaks / edited by David N. Baker, Lida M.
Belt and Herman C. Hudson. — Metuchen ; London : Scarecrow
Press ; [Folkestone] : [Distributed by Bailey and Swinfen], 1978.
— vi,506p : ports ; 23cm.
'A project of the Afro-American Arts Institute, Indiana University'. — Bibl.
— Index.
ISBN 0-8108-1045-X : £17.00

(B78-22844)

A/E — PERFORMANCE
A/EC(P) — Stokowski, Leopold. Biographies
Robinson, Paul
Stokowski / [by] Paul Robinson ; discography by Bruce Surtees.
— London : Macdonald and Jane's, 1977. — [3],154p,[8]p of
plates : 1 ill, music, ports ; 23cm. — (The art of the conductor)
Also published: Toronto : Lester and Orpen, 1977. — Bibl.: p.121. — List
of sound discs: p.123-152. — Index.
ISBN 0-354-04232-7 : £4.95

(B78-01681)

A/EC(P) — Toscanini, Arturo. Biographies
Sachs, Harvey
Toscanini / [by] Harvey Sachs. — London : Weidenfeld and
Nicolson, 1978. — x,380p,[16]p of plates : ill, 2 facsims, music,
plan, ports ; 25cm.
Also published: Philadelphia : Lippincott, 1978. — Bibl.: p.355-360. —
Index.
ISBN 0-297-77492-1 : £10.00

(B78-38607)

A/EC(P/E) — Beecham, Sir Thomas, bt. Anecdotes
Beecham stories : anecdotes, sayings and impressions of Sir Thomas
Beecham / compiled and edited by Harold Atkins and Archie
Newman ; with a foreword by Yehudi Menuhin. — London :
Robson, 1978. — 96p,[4]p of plates : ill, ports ; 23cm.
ISBN 0-86051-044-1 : £3.50 : CIP rev.

(B78-26892)

A/FD — RECORDED MUSIC
A/FD(QB/WT) — Clarion records. Lists
Carter, Sydney Horace
A catalogue of 'Clarion' & 'Ebonoid' records / compiled by
Sydney H. Carter ; arranged in alphabetical order by E. Bayly,
Snr ; a history of their manufacture by Frank Andrews ; edited by
Ernie Bayly. — Bournemouth (19 Glendale Rd, Bournemouth
BH6 4JA) : 'Talking machine review', 1977. — [98]p : ill, facsims,
ports ; 26cm.
ISBN 0-902338-29-3 Sd : £2.00
Also classified at A/FD(QB/WT)

(B78-20766)

A/FD(QB/WT) — Ebonoid Records. Lists
Carter, Sydney Horace
A catalogue of 'Clarion' & 'Ebonoid' records / compiled by
Sydney H. Carter ; arranged in alphabetical order by E. Bayly,
Snr ; a history of their manufacture by Frank Andrews ; edited by
Ernie Bayly. — Bournemouth (19 Glendale Rd, Bournemouth
BH6 4JA) : 'Talking machine review', 1977. — [98]p : ill, facsims,
ports ; 26cm.
ISBN 0-902338-29-3 Sd : £2.00
Primary classification A/FD(QB/WT)

(B78-20766)

A/FD(WT) — Recorded music. Lists
Music master. — Hastings (1 De Cham Ave., Hastings, Sussex) :
John Humphries.
1978 / [compiled by Michael Preston]. — 1978. — 7-659p ; 31cm.
English text, English, French, German and Spanish preliminaries.
ISBN 0-904520-06-4 : £30.00
ISSN 0308-9347

(B78-11519)

A/FD(WT/T) — Lists. Bibliographies
Gray, Michael H
Bibliography of discographies / by Michael H. Gray and Gerald
D. Gibson. — New York ; London : Bowker.
Vol.1 : Classical music, 1925-1975. — 1977. — xi,164p ; 26cm.
Index.
ISBN 0-8352-1023-5 : £15.00

(B78-09309)

A/FD(XKS101) — Recorded music, 1877-1977
Gelatt, Roland
The fabulous phonograph, 1877-1977 / [by] Roland Gelatt. — 2nd
revised ed. — London : Cassell, 1977. — 349p,[32]p of plates : ill,
facsims, ports ; 22cm.
Previous ed.: Philadelphia : Lippincott, 1955 ; London : Cassell, 1956. —
Index.
ISBN 0-304-29904-9 : £6.50

(B78-03423)

A/FD(YDL) — Recorded music. Scotland
Scottish Arts Council
Recordings of artists working in Scotland / [Scottish Arts
Council]. — Edinburgh (19 Charlotte Sq., Edinburgh EH2 4DF) :
The Council, 1978. — 34p ; 21cm.
ISBN 0-902989-45-6 Sd : Unpriced

(B78-35031)

A/FD/JT(P/X) — Desert Island Discs. History
Plomley, Roy
'Desert island discs' / [by] Roy Plomley. — [London] : Fontana,
1977. — 224p,8p of plates : ports ; 18cm.
Originally published: London : Kimber, 1975.
ISBN 0-00-634227-2 Pbk : £0.85

(B78-08479)

A/FF(WT) — Stereophonic records. Lists
Greenfield, Edward
The Penguin stereo record guide / [by] Edward Greenfield,
Robert Layton, Ivan March ; edited by Ivan March. — 2nd ed. —
Harmondsworth [etc.] : Penguin, 1977. — xxvii,1169p ; 20cm. —
(A Penguin handbook)
Previous ed.: 1975.
Pbk : £4.50
ISBN 0-14-046223-6

(B78-23118)

A/FF/ER — Stereophonic records. Discothéques
Swindells, Adrienne P
    Running a disco / [by] Adrienne P. Swindells ; illustrated by
Colin Stone. — St Albans : Hart-Davis Educational, 1977. —
48p : ill, ports ; 22cm. — (Scanners)
ISBN 0-247-12630-6 Sd : £0.65

        (B78-15126)

A/FY — MUSICAL CHARACTER
A/G(B) — Folk music. Periodicals
    Folk news. — London (28 Gordon Mansions, Torrington Place,
WC1E 7HF) : Folk News Publications.
Vol.1, no.1- ; June 1977-. — [1977]-. — ill, ports ; 42cm.
Monthly. — 24p. in 1st issue.
Sd : £0.20
ISSN 0140-0851

        (B78-00387)

A/G(VF) — Folk music. Schools
    Folk music in school / edited by Robert Leach and Roy Palmer. —
Cambridge [etc.] : Cambridge University Press, 1978. — vi,162p :
ill, facsims, music, plan ; 24cm. — (The resources of music series)
Bibl.: p.154-158. — List of sound discs: p.148-154. — Index.
ISBN 0-521-21595-1 : £4.95
ISBN 0-521-29206-9 Pbk : £2.80

        (B78-29835)

A/G(YDM) — Folk music. Ireland
Breathnach, Breandán
    Folk music and dances in Ireland / [by] Breandán Breathnach. —
Revised ed. — Dublin [etc.] (25 Lower Abbey St., Dublin 1) :
Mercier Press Ltd, 1977. — viii,152p : ill, facsims, music, port ;
19cm.
Includes 2 songs in Irish. — Previous ed.: Dublin : Talbot Press, 1971. —
Bibl.: p.151-152. — Index.
ISBN 0-85342-509-4 Pbk : £2.10
Also classified at 793.3'19415

        (B78-34736)

McMahon, Tony
    Irish traditional music / text Tony McMahon ; illustrations Terry
Myler. — [Tallaght] : Folens, [1978]. — [1],32p : col ill, col
ports ; 25cm. — (Irish environmental library series ; no.41)
Sd : Unpriced

        (B78-15122)

Ó Canainn, Tomás
    Traditional music in Ireland / [by] Tomás Ó Canainn. — London
[etc.] : Routledge and Kegan Paul, 1978. — x,145p,[4]p of plates :
1 ill, music, ports ; 24cm.
Index.
ISBN 0-7100-0021-9 Pbk : £3.60 : CIP rev.

        (B78-31597)

A/GB — Popular music
Attwood, Tony
    Pop workbook / [by] Tony Attwood and Paul Farmer. —
London : Edward Arnold, 1978. — 96p : ill, ports ; 24cm.
Bibl. — List of sound discs: p.83-84. — Index.
ISBN 0-7131-0155-5 Sd : £1.75 : CIP rev.

        (B77-28559)

Tobler, John
    Pop quest : so you think you know all about rock 'n' pop / [by]
John Tobler & Cathy McKnight. — London : Independent
Television Books : Arrow Books, 1978. — 125p : ill, facsim ;
18cm. — (Look-in books)
'In association with Yorkshire Television'.
ISBN 0-09-917570-3 Pbk : £0.65

        (B78-20431)

A/GB(DD/B/T) — Popular music. Articles. Periodicals.
    Bibliographies
    Popular music periodicals index. — Metuchen ; London : Scarecrow
Press ; [Folkestone] : [Distributed by Bailey and Swinfen].
1976 / compiled by Dean Tudor and Linda Biesenthal. — 1977. — 262p ;
23cm.
Index.
ISBN 0-8108-1079-4 : £8.50

        (B78-50320)

A/GB(WE) — Popular music. Festivals
Great Britain. *Working Group on Pop Festivals*
    Pop festivals and their problems : second report of the Working
Group on Pop Festivals. — London : H.M.S.O., 1978. — vii,38p ;
25cm.
ISBN 0-11-751254-0 Sd : £0.85

        (B78-16620)

A/GB(YC/BC) — Popular music. Great Britain. Directories
    Kemp's music & recording industry year book (international). —
London : Kemps.
1978 / [editor David I. Price]. — [1978]. — [4],372p : ill, maps ; 21cm.
ISBN 0-905255-30-5 Pbk : £5.50
ISSN 0305-7100

        (B78-09409)

A/GB(YT/BC) — Popular music. United States. Directories
Wootton, Richard
    Honky tonkin' : a guide to music USA. — 2nd ed. / [by] Richard
Wootton. — London (21 Melbourne Court, Anerley Rd, Penge,
S.E.20) : The author, 1978. — 179p : ill, maps, ports ; 19cm.
Previous ed.: / by Richard Wootton and Charlie McKissack. 1977.
ISBN 0-9506108-0-1 Pbk : £2.50

        (B78-28695)

A/GB(YT/X) — Popular music. United States. History
Ewen, David
    All the years of American popular music / [by] David Ewen. —
Englewood Cliffs ; London [etc.] : Prentice-Hall, 1977. — xviii,
850p ; 25cm.
Index.
ISBN 0-13-022442-1 : Unpriced

        (B78-20432)

A/GB/FD(T) — Popular music. Recorded music. Bibliographies
    Annual index to popular music record reviews. — Metuchen ;
London : Scarecrow Press ; [Folkestone] : [Distributed by Bailey
and Swinfen].
1976 / by Dean Tudor, Linda Biesenthal, Nancy Tudor. — 1977. — 578p ;
23cm.
Spine title: Popular music record reviews. — Index.
ISBN 0-8108-1070-0 : £17.00
ISSN 0092-3486

        (B78-20767)

A/GB/FD(XPQ22) — Recorded music, 1955-1976
Cable, Michael
    The pop industry inside out / [by] Michael Cable. — London :
W.H. Allen, 1977. — viii,228p : 1 ill ; 23cm.
Index.
ISBN 0-491-02381-2 : £4.95

        (B78-03111)

A/GBS(B) — Soul music. Periodicals
    Deeper and deeper soul magazine. — Birkenhead (18 Stretton
Close, Holmlands Estate, Prenton, Birkenhead, Merseyside) : K.
Murray.
[No.1]- ; [July 1977]-. — 1977-. — ill, ports ; 26cm.
Quarterly. — [2],14p. in 1st issue.
Sd : £0.25
ISSN 0140-4350

        (B78-06258)

A/GBS/FD(B) — Soul music. Recorded music. Periodicals
    Soul cargo. — [Newcastle-under-Lyme] ([67 Albert Terrace,
Wolstanton, Newcastle-under-Lyme, Staffs.]) : [C. Savory].
No.1-. — [1977]-. — ill ; 26cm.
Six issues a year. — [2],24p. in 1st issue.
Sd : £0.30
ISSN 0140-7422

        (B78-05414)

A/GC(B) — Country music. Periodicals
    Country music round up. — North Hykeham : Country Music
Round Up Publishing Co. ; Barking, Essex (Roding Trading
Estate, Barking, Essex) : Distributed by A.M.D. Magazine
Distributors Ltd.
[Vol.1, no.1]- ; [Dec. 1976]-. — [1976]-. — ill, ports ; 42cm.
Monthly. — 24p. in vol.1, no.10.
Sd : £0.20
ISSN 0140-5721

        (B78-03571)

A/GC(C) — Country music. Encyclopaedias
Dellar, Fred
    The illustrated encyclopedia of country music / [by Fred Dellar,
Roy Thompson, Douglas B. Green]. — London (27 Old
Gloucester St., WC1N 3AF) : Salamander Books Ltd, 1977. —
256p : ill(some col), ports(some col) ; 31cm.
Spine title: Country music. — Ill. on lining papers. — Index.
ISBN 0-86101-004-3 : £5.95

        (B78-05399)

A/GJ — Childhood
Evans, David, *b.1940 (May)*
    Sharing sounds : musical experiences with young children / [by]
David Evans. — London [etc.] : Longman, 1978. — vii,199p : ill,
music ; 21cm. — (Longman early childhood education)
Bibl.: p.192-194. — Index.
ISBN 0-582-25006-4 : Unpriced
ISBN 0-582-25008-0 Pbk : £2.50

        (B78-31364)

A/GR — Activities
Willson, Robina Beckles
    Musical merry-go-round : musical activities for the very young /
[by] Robina Beckles Willson ; illustrated by Gunvor Edwards. —
London : Heinemann, 1977. — 128p : ill, music ; 22cm.
Index.
ISBN 0-434-97257-6 : £3.50

        (B78-01459)

A/GS — Games
Wishart, Trevor
Sounds fun 2 : a second book of musical games / [by] Trevor
Wishart. — London : Universal Edition, 1977. — 45p : ill ; 22cm.
ISBN 0-900938-47-1 Sd : £0.75

(B78-11209)

A/HK(X) — Rock 'n' roll. History
Marcus, Greil
Mystery train : images of America in rock 'n' roll music / [by]
Greil Marcus. — London [etc.] : Omnibus Press, 1977. — xiii,279,
[9]p ; 20cm.
Originally published: New York : Dutton, 1975. — Index.
ISBN 0-86001-311-1 Pbk : Unpriced

(B78-06253)

A/HKQ(B) — Punk rock. Periodicals
Rock on!. — London : IPC Magazines.
No.1- ; May 1978-. — 1978-. — ill(some col), ports(some col) ; 30cm.
Monthly. — [32]p. in 1st issue.
Sd : £0.25
ISSN 0141-7177

(B78-26241)

Trick. — London (43 Bow La., EC4M 9DT) : Wishcastle Ltd.
No.1- ; Nov. 1977-. — [1977]-. — ill, ports ; 42cm.
Monthly. — 24p. in 1st issue.
Sd : £0.20
ISSN 0140-7929

(B78-02606)

A/HKR(C) — Rock. Encyclopaedias
Logan, Nick
The illustrated 'New musical express' encyclopedia of rock /
[authors Nick Logan and Bob Woffinden]. — [1978 ed.]. —
London (27 Old Gloucester St., WC1N 3AF) : Salamander Books
Limited, 1977. — 256p : ill(chiefly col), ports(chiefly col) ; 30cm.
Previous ed.: London : Hamlyn, 1976. — Index.
ISBN 0-86101-009-4 Pbk : £3.95

(B78-12095)

A/HKR(T) — Rock. Bibliographies
Noyce, John Leonard
Rock music index / compiled by John L. Noyce and Alison
Skinner. — Brighton : Noyce, 1977. — [15]p ; 30cm.
Bibl.: p.[1].
Sd : £1.20

(B78-02933)

A/HKR/FD(WT) — Rock. Recorded music. Lists
Anderson, Ian, *b.1946*
Rock record collectors guide / by Ian Anderson. — London (77
New Bond St., W.1) : MRP Books, 1977. — [6],177p,[32]p of
plates : ill, ports ; 20cm.
ISBN 0-905590-04-x Pbk : £2.99

(B78-02937)

A/JT(WT) — Radio. Lists
British Broadcasting Corporation
Catalogue of music broadcast on Radio 3 and Radio 4 / British
Broadcasting Corporation. — London : B.B.C.
1974 / research and compiled by Myra Grimley and Mary Wiegold ; edited
by Stephen Plaistow. — 1977. — [3],301p ; 30cm.
ISBN 0-563-17369-6 Pbk : £4.00

(B78-20763)

A/KD(X) — Social aspects. History
Brace, Geoffrey
Listen! music and civilization / [by] Geoffrey Brace and Ian
Burton. — Cambridge [etc.] : Cambridge University Press, 1978.
— vi,74p : ill(some col), facsims, music, ports(some col) ;
21x22cm.
ISBN 0-521-21153-0 Pbk : £2.25

(B78-22160)

A/LZ — ELEMENTS OF MUSIC
Toch, Ernst
The shaping forces in music : an inquiry into the nature of
harmony, melody, counterpoint, form / [by] Ernst Toch. — [1st
ed., reprinted] ; with a new introduction by Lawrence Weschler ;
and a new complete checklist of Toch's works. — New York :
Dover Publications ; London : Constable, 1977. — xxvii,260p :
music, port ; 22cm.
Originally published: New York : Criterion Music, 1948. — List of works:
p.239-257. — Index.
ISBN 0-486-23346-4 Pbk : £2.50

(B78-06255)

A/M — Rudiments
Lally, Maureen
Listen, sing and play / [by] Maureen Lally. — Dublin :
Educational Company of Ireland.
2 : First class, lessons 11-20, second class, lessons 21-30. Workbook. —
1978. — [2],23p : ill, music ; 19x25cm.
Fill-in book.
Sd : £0.48

(B78-24450)

3 : classes 3 and 4, lessons 31-45. Workbook. — 1978. — [2],23p : ill,
music ; 19x24cm.
Fill-in book.
Sd : £0.48

(B78-21396)

A/PN — Twelve tone music
Forte, Allen
The structure of atonal music / [by] Allen Forte. — New Haven ;
London : Yale University Press, 1977. — ix,224p : ill, music ;
26cm.
Originally published: 1973. — Bibl.: p.213. — Index.
ISBN 0-300-02120-8 Pbk : £4.50

(B78-24451)

Perle, George
Serial composition and atonality : an introduction to the music of
Schoenberg, Berg and Webern / by George Perle. — 4th ed.,
revised. — Berkeley [etc.] ; London : University of California
Press, 1977. — ix,158p : music ; 26cm.
Previous ed.: Berkeley : University of California Press, 1972. — Index.
ISBN 0-520-03395-7 : £8.75

(B78-16384)

Perle, George
Twelve tonality / [by] George Perle. — Berkeley [etc.] ; London :
University of California Press, 1977. — xi,174p : music ; 27cm.
Index.
ISBN 0-520-03387-6 : £10.25

(B78-17614)

A/R — Harmony
Mears, Caroline
Music for today / [by] Caroline Mears. — Cape Town ; Oxford
[etc.] : Oxford University Press, 1977[i.e.1978]. — [5],133p :
music ; 22x31cm.
ISBN 0-19-570082-1 : £9.50

(B78-12984)

Schoenberg, Arnold
Theory of harmony / [by] Arnold Schoenberg ; translated [from
the German] by Roy E. Carter. — London : Faber : Faber Music,
1978. — iii-xxi,441p : music ; 26cm.
'... translation, based on the Third Edition (1922) [of "Harmonielehre".
Vienna : Universal Edition, 1922]' - title page verso. — Index.
ISBN 0-571-10933-0 : £22.50 : CIP rev.

(B78-12985)

A/R(XMA60) — Harmony, 1901-1960
Persichetti, Vincent
Twentieth century harmony : creative aspects and practice / by
Vincent Persichetti. — London : Faber, 1978. — 287p : music ;
24cm.
Originally published: New York : Norton, 1961 ; London : Faber, 1962. —
Index.
ISBN 0-571-11216-1 Pbk : £2.95

(B78-11195)

A/S — MUSICAL FORM
Kohs, Ellis B
Musical form : studies in analysis and synthesis / [by] Ellis B.
Kohs. — Boston [Mass.] [etc.] ; London : Houghton Mifflin, 1976.
— xix,341p : music ; 25cm.
Bibl.: p.331-332. — Index.
ISBN 0-395-18613-7 : £10.95

(B78-25371)

AB — MUSICAL LITERATURE. VOCAL MUSIC
AB/E — Performance
Hewitt, Graham
How to sing / [by] Graham Hewitt ; illustrated by Shirley
Bellwood. — London : Elm Tree Books : E.M.I. Music
Publishing, 1978. — vi,94p : ill, music ; 25cm.
ISBN 0-241-89897-8 : £3.95 : CIP rev.
ISBN 0-241-89915-x Pbk : £1.95

(B78-04325)

Linwood-Christopher, Mabel
The amateur singer : a series of practical hints on the use of the
voice for conductors, soloists and choristers / [by] Mabel
Linwood-Christopher. — [Cardiff] ([9 Museum Place, Cardiff]) :
[Welsh Amateur Music Federation], [1977]. — 54p in various
pagings : ill, music ; 22cm.
List of songs: (9p.). — Contents: Stance and breathing - Use of resonators -
Diction - Words and music - Notes on notes - Repertoire.
Sd : Unpriced

(B78-06264)

Rose, Arnold
The singer and the voice : vocal physiology and technique for
singers / [by] Arnold Rose. — 2nd ed. — London : Scolar Press,
1978. — 267p : ill ; 21cm.
This ed. originally published: London : Faber, 1971. — Bibl.: p.262-263. —
Index.
ISBN 0-85967-446-0 : £8.00
ISBN 0-85967-447-9 Pbk : £3.95

(B78-36279)

AC — MUSICAL LITERATURE. OPERA

May, Robin
A companion to the opera / by Robin May. — Guildford [etc.] :
Lutterworth Press, 1977. — 364p,[16]p of plates : ill, ports ;
21cm.
Bibl.: p.347-348. — Index.
ISBN 0-7188-2123-8 : £5.95

(B78-01674)

Swanston, Hamish
In defence of opera / [by] Hamish F.G. Swanston. —
Harmondsworth [etc.] : Penguin, 1978. — 314p ; 19cm. — (A
pelican original)
Also published: London : Allen Lane, 1978. — Bibl.: p.305-307. — Index.
ISBN 0-14-022005-4 Pbk : £1.25

(B78-05403)

Swanston, Hamish
In defence of opera / [by] Hamish F.G. Swanston. — London :
Allen Lane, 1978. — 314p ; 23cm.
Also published: Harmondsworth : Penguin, 1978. — Bibl.: p.305-307. —
Index.
ISBN 0-7139-1063-1 : £6.50

(B78-09697)

Westerman, Gerhart von
Opera guide / [by] Gerhart von Westerman ; edited with an
introduction by Harold Rosenthal ; translated [from the German]
by Anne Ross. — London : Sphere, 1973. — 580p : music ; 18cm.
This translation and adaptation originally published: London : Thames and
Hudson, 1964. — Adapted from 'Knaurs Opernfuhrer'. Munich :
Droemersche Verlagsanstalt, 1952. — Index.
ISBN 0-7221-9004-2 Pbk : £0.90

(B78-05404)

AC(WB/P) — Afflisio, Giuseppe. Biographies

Afflisio, Giuseppe
Vita di Giuseppe Afflisio = Lebensgeschichte des Giuseppe
Afflisio / aus dem Nachlass von Bernhard Paumgartner ;
herausgegeben von Gerhard Croll und Hans Wagner. — Kassel
[etc.] ; London ([17 Bucklersbury, Hitchin, Herts.]) : Bärenreiter,
1977. — 104p ; 21cm. — (Internationale Stiftung Mozarteum
Salzburg. Schriftenreihe ; Bd 7)
Parallel Italian text and German translation.
Pbk : £4.48
ISBN 3-7618-0573-x

(B78-19963)

AC(XE182) — History, 1600-1781

Robinson, Michael Finlay
Opera before Mozart / [by] Michael F. Robinson. — 3rd ed. —
London : Hutchinson, 1978. — 168p : music ; 22cm.
Previous ed.: 1972. — Bibl.: p.161-162. — Index.
ISBN 0-09-136221-0 Pbk : £3.25

(B78-40352)

AC(Z) — Opera - related to literary forms

Conrad, Peter, b.1948
Romantic opera and literary form / [by] Peter Conrad. —
Berkeley [etc.] ; London : University of California Press, 1977. —
ix,185p : ill ; 21cm. — (Quantum books)
Bibl.: p.179-180. — Index.
ISBN 0-520-03258-6 : £5.50

(B78-12986)

AC/E(M/XJK100/EM) — Opera. Singers, 1850-1949. Illustrations

The great opera stars in historic photographs : 343 portraits from
the 1850s to the 1940s / edited by James Camner. — New York :
Dover Publications [etc.] ; London : Constable, 1978. — [6],199p :
chiefly ill,ports ; 29cm.
Index.
ISBN 0-486-23575-0 Pbk : £4.35

(B78-31599)

AC/E(YDKPL) — Opera. Performance. Gwynedd. Llandudno

Jones, Ivor Wynne
Opera at Llandudno / by Ivor Wynne Jones. — Llandudno ([c/o
I.W. Jones, 'Pegasus', 71 Llandudno Rd, Penrhyn Bay,
Llandudno, Gwynedd LL30 3HN]) : Welsh National Opera
Company, 1978. — Folder([4]p) : 1 ill, facsim, ports ; 21cm.
Unpriced

(B78-28696)

ACF — MUSICAL LITERATURE. OPERETTA

ACF(YD/XK55) — Operetta. England, 1860-1914

Hyman, Alan
Sullivan and his satellites : a survey of English operettas,
1860-1914 / [by] Alan Hyman. — London [etc.] : Chappell : Elm
Tree Books, 1978. — xvi,224p ; ill, ports ; 26cm.
Bibl.: p.215-216. — Index.
ISBN 0-903443-24-4 : £7.50

(B78-26888)

ACM — MUSICAL LITERATURE. MUSICAL PLAYS

ACM(C) — Musical plays. Encyclopaedias

Green, Stanley, b.1923
Encyclopaedia of the musical / [by] Stanley Green. — London :
Cassell, 1977. — vii,488p ; 24cm.
Originally published: as 'Encyclopaedia of the musical theatre'. New York :
Dodd, Mead, 1976. — Bibl.: p.472-477. — List of sound discs: p.478-488.
ISBN 0-304-29930-8 : £7.95

(B78-03575)

ACM(XKF112) — Musical plays, 1866-1977

Jackson, Arthur
The book of musicals : from 'Show Boat' to 'A Chorus Line' / by
Arthur Jackson ; foreword by Clive Barnes. — London : Mitchell
Beazley, 1977. — 208p : ill(some col), facsims(some col), music,
ports ; 30cm.
'A Webb & Bower book' - title page verso. — Ill. on lining papers. — Bibl.:
p.202-203. — List of films: p.198-199. — List of sound discs: p.200-202. —
Index. — Includes a section on cinema musicals.
ISBN 0-85533-116-x : £7.95

(B78-16385)

ACM/D — Musical plays. Composition

Engel, Lehman
The making of a musical / [by] Lehman Engel. — New York :
Macmillan ; London : Collier Macmillan, 1977. — xvii,157p :
music ; 22cm.
Index.
ISBN 0-02-536070-1 : £6.75

(B78-32355)

ACM/E(YT/X) — Musical plays. United States. History

Laufe, Abe
Broadway's greatest musicals / [by] Abe Laufe. — Newton Abbot
[etc.] : David and Charles, 1978. — [9],519p,[14]p of plates :
ports ; 23cm.
Originally published: New York : Funk and Wagnalls, 1977. — Bibl.:
p.432-433. — Index.
ISBN 0-7153-7712-4 : £9.50

(B78-37865)

ACM/FD(XL596) — Musical plays. Recorded music, 1897-1976

Rust, Brian Arthur Lovell
London musical shows on record, 1897-1976 / [compiled] by
Brian Rust with Rex Bunnett. — Harrow (177 Kenton Rd,
Harrow, Middx HA3 0HA) : General Gramophone Publications
Ltd, 1977. — [2],672p ; 22cm.
ISBN 0-902470-07-8 : £11.00

(B78-02935)

ACMBN(WT) — Stories. Lists

Drone, Jeanette Marie
Index to opera, operetta and musical comedy synopses in
collections and periodicals / by Jeanette Marie Drone. —
Metuchen ; London : Scarecrow Press ; [Folkestone] : [Distributed
by Bailey and Swinfen], 1978. — v,171p ; 23cm.
Bibl.: p.165-171.
ISBN 0-8108-1100-6 : £5.95

(B78-19781)

AD — MUSICAL LITERATURE. CHORAL MUSIC

AD(X) — History

Choral music : a symposium / edited by Arthur Jacobs. —
Harmondsworth [etc.] : Penguin, 1978. — 448p : music ; 18cm. —
(A pelican original)
Originally published: 1963. — Bibl.: p.405-413. — List of works: p.415-426.
— List of sound discs: p.427-440. — Index.
ISBN 0-14-020533-0 Pbk : £1.25

(B78-35474)

AD/E — Performance

Nicholson, Sydney H
Practical methods in choir training / by Sydney H. Nicholson. —
Croydon (Addington Palace, Croydon CR9 5AD) : Royal School
of Church Music, [1977]. — [1],28p : music ; 22cm. — (Royal
School of Church Music. Handbooks ; no.2)
ISBN 0-85402-069-1 Sd : £0.65

(B78-01055)

AD/E(P) — Lane, Edgar A. Biographies

Lane, Margaret, b.1899
Edgar A. Lane : musician, 1865-1938 : memories of Edgar Alfred
Lane / [compiled by Margaret Lane]. — [Swanage] : ['Purbeck
mail'], [1976?]. — 36p : ill, facsims, ports ; 21cm.
Sd : Unpriced

(B78-09112)

AD/L(XFYK101) — Religious choral music, 1770-1870

Donakowski, Conrad L
A muse for the masses : ritual and music in an age of democratic
revolution, 1770-1870 / [by] Conrad L. Donakowski. — Chicago ;
London : University of Chicago Press, 1977. — xii,435p : ill ;
24cm.
Bibl.: p.393-410. — Index.
ISBN 0-226-15621-4 : £15.40

(B78-11190)

AD/LD(B) — Church music. Periodicals
Music in worship : a quarterly journal for Christians. — Garston
(c/o The editor, 78 Trevellance Way, Garston, Herts. WD2 6LZ) :
'Music in worship'.
[No.1]- ; Sept. 1977-. — [1977]-. — music ; 30cm.
Sheet ([2]p.) as 1st issue.
Sd : £0.15
ISSN 0141-657x

(B78-23593)

AD/LD(X) — Church music. History
Routley, Erik
The Church and music / [by] Erik Routley. — Revised ed. —
[London] : Duckworth, 1978. — 262p ; 23cm. — ([Studies in
theology])
This ed. originally published: 1967. — Bibl.: p.255-256. — Index.
ISBN 0-7156-0062-1 : £12.50
Also classified at ADF(X)

(B78-30831)

AD/LD(YD/D) — Church music. England. Essays
English church music : a collection of essays. — Croydon
(Addington Palace, Croydon CR9 5AD) : Royal School of Church
Music.
1978. — [1978]. — 64p,[2]leaves of plates : 1 ill, music, port ; 22cm.
ISBN 0-85402-075-6 Pbk : £1.70

(B78-29836)

AD/LD/E — Church music. Performance
Royal School of Church Music
RSCM chorister training scheme. — [Croydon] ([Addington
Palace, Croydon, Surrey CR9 5AD]) : [R.S.C.M.].
Part 1. General outline and junior singer training. — 1977 [i.e. 1978]. — [2],
48p : music ; 21cm. — (Training manual ; no.1)
ISBN 0-85402-070-5 Sd : £0.80

(B78-22161)

Part 1. Senior singer training and chorister training. — 1977 [i.e. 1978]. —
[2],48p : music ; 21cm. — (Training manual ; no.2)
ISBN 0-85402-074-8 Sd : £0.80

(B78-22162)

Part 2. Handbook for ex-trebles and young choirmen / [by] Michael
Rhodes. — [1978]. — [2],16p : music ; 21cm.
Bibl.: p.7.
ISBN 0-85402-073-x Sd : £0.55

(B78-22164)

Part 2. Training for ex-trebles and young choirmen / by Michael Rhodes. —
[1978]. — [2],32p : music ; 21cm. — (Training manual ; no.3)
ISBN 0-85402-071-3 Sd : £0.80

(B78-22165)

AD/LSK(X) — Choral music. Salvation Army. History
Boon, Brindley
Sing the happy song! : (a history of Salvation Army vocal
music) / by Brindley Boon. — London : Salvationist Publishing
and Supplies, 1978. — [5],176p ; 22cm.
Bibl.: p.169. — Index.
ISBN 0-85412-321-0 Pbk : Unpriced

(B78-34738)

ADF(X) — Liturgical music. History
Routley, Erik
The Church and music / [by] Erik Routley. — Revised ed. —
[London] : Duckworth, 1978. — 262p ; 23cm. — ([Studies in
theology])
This ed. originally published: 1967. — Bibl.: p.255-256. — Index.
ISBN 0-7156-0062-1 : £12.50
Primary classification AD/LD(X)

(B78-30831)

ADFF(YD/XCT116) — Roman Catholic liturgy. England, 1460-1575
Benham, Hugh
Latin church music in England, c.1460-1575 / by Hugh Benham.
— London : Barrie and Jenkins, 1977. — xiii,247p : music ; 23cm.
Bibl.: p.232-236. — Index.
ISBN 0-214-20059-0 : £10.00

(B78-26889)

ADGTCX — Syro-Maronite Church liturgy
Hage, Louis
Maronite music / [by] Louis Hage. — London : Longman for the
University of Essex, 1978. — 13,12,[4]p,[2]p of plates : ill, music ;
22cm. — (Carreras Arab lecture ; 7th)
'... delivered in November 1973'. — Second title page in Arabic. — English
and Arabic text. — Two-way paging. — Bibl.: p.13.
ISBN 0-582-78085-3 Sd : £0.75

(B78-35472)

ADR(YDL/WT) — Psalms. Scotland. Lists
Heaney, E L
Alphabetical index of the Scottish metrical psalms : first line of
every 4-line verse of the Psalms in metre / [compiled by E.L.
Heaney]. — Glasgow (23 Nairn St., Glasgow G3 8SE) : [The
compiler], [1977]. — [1],56p ; 21cm.
Sd : £0.50

(B78-15373)

ADW(XCH101) — Songs, 1200-1300. Carmina burana
[Carmina Burana. Selections]. Songs from 'Carmina Burana' /
translated [from the Latin] into Scots verse by J.K. Annand. —
Loanhead (Edgefield Rd, Loanhead, Midlothian) : Macdonald
Publishers, 1978. — 40p ; 22cm.
ISBN 0-904265-20-x Pbk : Unpriced

(B78-30833)

ADW/G(YDLZS/P) — Folk songs. Skye. Tolmie, Frances.
Biographies
Bassin, Ethel
The old songs of Skye : Frances Tolmie and her circle / [by]
Ethel Bassin ; edited by Derek Bowman. — London [etc.] :
Routledge and Kegan Paul, 1977. — xxi,227p,[9]p of plates : ill,
facsims, maps(on lining papers), music, ports ; 24cm.
Index.
ISBN 0-7100-8546-x : £5.95

(B78-03578)

ADW/G(YT/TC) — Folk songs. United States. Bibliographies of
scores
Coffin, Tristram Potter
The British traditional ballad in North America / by Tristram
Potter Coffin. — Revised ed. [reprinted] / with a supplement by
Roger de V. Renwick. — Austin ; London : University of Texas
Press, 1977. — xvii,297p ; 24cm. — (American Folklore Society.
Bibliographical and special series)
Revised ed. originally published: Philadelphia : American Folklore Society,
1963. — Bibl.: p.287-294. — Index.
ISBN 0-292-70719-3 : £11.25

(B78-01317)

ADW/GB/L(S) — Popular songs. Religious music. Publishing
Acott, Dennis
The Christian songwriters' handbook / general editor Eric A.
Thorn ; prepared by Dennis Acott and Mal Grosch. — Maidstone
(65 Grace Ave., Maidstone, Kent) : Third Day Enterprises, 1977.
— [1],12p ; 21cm.
'The substance of this book was originally published as a series of articles in
"Psalm" magazine' - back cover.
ISBN 0-9505912-0-3 Sd : £0.40

(B78-10624)

ADW/GMC — Shanties
Hugill, Stan
Sea shanties / [by] Stan Hugill ; with drawings by the author. —
London : Barrie and Jenkins, 1977. — viii,156p,[8]p of plates : ill,
music ; 22cm.
ISBN 0-214-20329-8 Pbk : £2.95

(B78-01680)

AJFDW(VC) — Female voices. Children's voices. Songs, etc. Teaching
Jenkins, David, b.1944
Children's overture : an introduction to music listening and
creative musical activities for young children / [by] David Jenkins
& Mark Visocchi. — [Oxford] : Oxford University Press, 1978. —
[2],32p : music ; 25cm.
Sound disc (2s. 7in. 33 1/3 rpm) in pocket.
ISBN 0-19-321388-5 Sd : £2.75

(B78-33673)

AJFDW/GJS — Female voices, Children's voices. School songs
Haddon, Celia
Great days and jolly days : the story of girls' school songs / by
Celia Haddon. — London [etc.] : Hodder and Stoughton, 1977. —
128p : ill, facsims, ports ; 26cm.
Ill., music on lining papers.
ISBN 0-340-22230-1 : £3.50

(B78-01679)

AK — MUSICAL LITERATURE. VOCAL SOLOS
AK/FD(XM15) — Solo voice. Recorded music, 1900-1915
Scott, Michael
The record of singing to 1914 / [by] Michael Scott. — London :
Duckworth, 1977. — xii,243p : ill, ports ; 29cm.
Bibl.: p.235-236. — Index.
ISBN 0-7156-1030-9 : £12.50

(B78-03582)

AKDW — Songs, etc
Baker, Nicholas
Songs to sing in the bath : waterproof cartoons / by Nick Baker.
— London : Allison and Busby, 1976. — [24]p : chiefly ill(some
col) ; 21cm.
ISBN 0-85031-190-x Sd : £0.75

(B78-08476)

AKDW(XCDXK451) — Songs, etc. 850-1300
Dronke, Peter
The medieval lyric / [by] Peter Dronke. — 2nd ed. — London :
Hutchinson, 1978. — 288p : music ; 23cm.
Previous ed.: 1968. — Bibl.: p.246-276. — Index.
ISBN 0-09-132080-1 : £5.95

(B78-09116)

AKDW(XKK101/T) — Songs, etc. 1870-1970. Bibliographies
Gooch, Bryan N S
Musical settings of late Victorian and modern British literature : a catalogue / [compiled by] Bryan N.S. Gooch and David S. Thatcher ; editorial assistant Odean Long. — New York ; London ([2 Holly Bush Hill, NW3 6SH]) : Garland Publishing, Inc., 1976. — [5],xxv,1112p ; 23cm. — (Garland reference library of the humanities ; vol.31)
Index.
ISBN 0-8240-9981-8 : £55.35
(B78-14028)

AKDW(YDM) — Songs, etc. Ireland
Comic songs of Ireland / collected and annotated by James N. Healy ; music written out by Con O'Donovan. — Dublin [etc.] (25 Lower Abbey St., Dublin 1) : Mercier Press, 1978. — 48p : music ; 18cm.
ISBN 0-85342-529-9 Sd : £0.80
(B78-39785)

Love songs of the Irish / collected and annotated by James N. Healy ; music written out by Con O'Donovan. — Dublin [etc.] (25 Lower Abbey St., Dublin 1) : Mercier Press, 1977. — 80p : music ; 18cm.
ISBN 0-85342-497-7 Pbk : £1.10
(B78-39234)

AKDW(YDQC) — Songs, etc. Cork
Comic songs of Cork and Kerry / collected and annotated by James N. Healy ; music written out by Con O'Donovan. — Dublin [etc.] (25 Lower Abbey St., Dublin 1) : Mercier Press, 1978. — 48p : music ; 18cm.
ISBN 0-85342-498-5 Sd : £0.80
Also classified at AKDW(YDQK)
(B78-39235)

AKDW(YDQK) — Songs, etc. Kerry
Comic songs of Cork and Kerry / collected and annotated by James N. Healy ; music written out by Con O'Donovan. — Dublin [etc.] (25 Lower Abbey St., Dublin 1) : Mercier Press, 1978. — 48p : music ; 18cm.
ISBN 0-85342-498-5 Sd : £0.80
Primary classification AKDW(YDQC)
(B78-39235)

AKDW/G(YDCM) — Folk songs. Kent
The Folkestone fiery serpent, and other Kentish poems : a selection / [made] by C.H. Bishop. — Maidstone (Springfield, Maidstone, Kent) : Kent County Library, 1977. — [3],68p ; 22cm.
ISBN 0-905155-13-0 Sd : £0.50
(B78-11199)

AKDW/G(YDHNB) — Folk songs. Black country
Raven, Jon
The urban & industrial songs of the Black Country and Birmingham / [by] Jon Raven. — Wolverhampton (68 Limes Rd, Tottenhall, Wolverhampton WV6 8RB) : Broadside, 1977. — xxi, 258p : music ; 23cm.
Bibl.: p.xii-xiv. — List of sound discs: p.xii. — Index.
ISBN 0-9503722-2-6 : £7.75
(B78-20442)

AKDW/G(YF) — Folk songs. Czechoslovakia
Tschache, Helmut
Lieder und Volksmusik aus der Tschechoslowakei : Materialien für den Musikunterricht in den Sekundarstufen / [von] Helmut Tschache. — Mainz ; London [etc.] : Schott, 1978. — 58p : ill, maps, music ; 28cm.
Bibl. — Lists of sound discs.
Sd : £4.80
(B78-33161)

AKDW/G(YTLD/XA1867) — Afro-American folk songs. To 1867
Epstein, Dena J
Sinful tunes and spirituals : black folk music to the Civil War / [by] Dena J. Epstein. — Urbana [etc.] ; London : University of Illinois Press, 1977. — xix,433p : ill, facsims, music, ports ; 24cm. — (Music in American life)
Bibl.: p.374-415. — Index.
ISBN 0-252-00520-1 : £12.60
(B78-15754)

AKDW/GB(WT) — Popular songs. Lists
Havlice, Patricia Pate
Popular song index / [compiled] by Patricia Pate Havlice. — Metuchen ; London : Scarecrow Press ; [Folkestone] : [Distributed by Bailey and Swinfen].
1st supplement. — 1978. — 386p ; 23cm.
Bibl.: p.5-9.
ISBN 0-8108-1099-9 : £12.75
(B78-27098)

AKDW/GB/E(EM/M) — Popular songs. Singers. Illustrations
Supersonic annual. — London : IPC Magazines.
1978. — 1977. — 78p : ill(some col), ports(some col) ; 28cm. — (A Fleetway annual)
Cover title.
ISBN 0-85037-356-5 : £1.65
(B78-02605)

AKDW/GB/E(M) — Popular songs. Singers
Top pop scene. — Maidenhead : Purnell, 1977. — 3-62p : ill(some col), ports ; 27cm.
Text, ill. on lining papers.
ISBN 0-361-03889-5 : £1.00
(B78-04317)

Top pop scene. — Maidenhead : Purnell.
[1978]. — 1978. — [60]p : ill(some col), chiefly ports(some col) ; 27cm.
Ill., ports. on lining papers.
ISBN 0-361-04141-1 : £1.35
(B78-26880)

Watson, Pat
Inside the pop scene / by Pat Watson. — Gloucester : Thornhill Press, 1977. — 45p : ill, ports ; 22cm.
Bibl.: p.45.
ISBN 0-904110-57-5 Pbk : £1.50
(B78-14832)

AKDW/GB/E(P) — Abba
Lindvall, Marianne
Abba : the ultimate pop group / [by] Marianne Lindvall. — London : Pop Universal Ltd : Souvenir Press, 1977. — 96p,fold plate : ill, ports(chiefly col) ; 28cm.
Also published: Edmonton, Alta : Hurtig, 1977.
ISBN 0-285-62312-5 Pbk : £2.95
(B78-17616)

AKDW/GB/E(P) — Abba. Biographies
Edgington, Harry
Abba / [by] Harry Edgington and Peter Himmelstrand. — Revised ed. — London : Magnum Books, 1978. — 176p,[16]p of plates : ports ; 18cm.
Previous ed.: London : Everest, 1977.
ISBN 0-417-03370-2 Pbk : £0.95
(B78-28698)

AKDW/GB/E(P) — Beatles
Cowan, Philip
Behind the Beatles songs / by Philip Cowan ; illustrated by Robert Rankin. — London (159 Wardour St., W.1) : Polytantric Press, [1978?]. — 63p : ill ; 26cm.
List of sound discs: p.50-53.
ISBN 0-905150-09-0 Pbk : £2.50
(B78-28699)

AKDW/GB/E(P) — Beatles. Biographies
Davies, Hunter
The Beatles : the authorized biography / [by] Hunter Davies. — [New ed.]. — London [etc.] : Mayflower, 1978. — 400p,[40]p of plates : facsims, ports ; 18cm.
Previous ed.: London : Heinemann, 1968. — List of sound discs: p.387-396.
ISBN 0-583-11530-6 Pbk : £1.25
(B78-26244)

Larkin, Rochelle
The Beatles, yesterday, today, tomorrow / [by] Rochelle Larkin. — New York ; London [etc.] ([161 Fulham Rd, S.W.3]) : Scholastic Book Services, 1977. — [3],108p : ill, ports ; 18cm.
Originally published: 1974.
Pbk : Unpriced
(B78-06261)

AKDW/GB/E(P) — Buchanan, Jack. Biographies
Marshall, Michael, b.1930
Top hat & tails : the story of Jack Buchanan / [by] Michael Marshall. — London : Elm Tree Books, 1978. — xvi,271p : ill, ports ; 24cm.
Bibl.: p.259-261. — List of sound discs : p.253-258. — Index.
ISBN 0-241-89602-9 : £6.95 : CIP rev.
(B78-06268)

AKDW/GB/E(P) — Crosby, Bing
Thompson, Charles
The complete Crosby / [by] Charles Thompson. — Revised and augmented ed. — London : W.H. Allen, 1978. — viii,280p,[32]p of plates : ill, ports ; 23cm.
Previous ed.: published as 'Bing'. 1975.
ISBN 0-491-02335-9 : £5.95
(B78-20440)

AKDW/GB/E(P) — Crosby, Bing. Biographies
Thomas, Bob
The one and only Bing / [by] Bob Thomas. — London : Joseph, 1977. — [8],152p : ill, ports ; 28cm.
Originally published: United States : Associated Press?, 1977?. — List of films: p.110-130. — List of sound discs: p.146-151.
ISBN 0-7181-1698-4 : £5.50
(B78-09699)

Thompson, Charles
    Bing : the authorised biography / [by] Charles Thompson. —
    Large print [ed.]. — Litton : Magna Print Books, 1976. — 525p ;
    23cm.
    Originally published: London : W.H. Allen, 1975.
    ISBN 0-86009-048-5 : £4.75

(B78-04324)

AKDW/GB/E(P) — Edward H. Dafis
Wyn, Hefin
    Doedd neb yn becso dam : hanes, lluniau a chaneuon Edward H.
    Dafis / gan Hefin Wyn. — [Penygroes, Gwynedd] ([Ffordd
    Llanllyfni, Penygroes, Gwynedd LL54 6DB]) : [Sain (Recordiau)
    Cyf.], 1977. — 79p : ill, ports ; 21cm.
    Sd : £1.50

(B78-09115)

AKDW/GB/E(P) — Lynn, Dame Vera. Biographies
Lynn, *Dame* Vera
    Vocal refrain : an autobiography / by Vera Lynn. — Large print
    ed. — Litton : Magna Print Books, 1976. — 349p ; 23cm.
    Originally published: London : W.H. Allen, 1975.
    ISBN 0-86009-046-9 : £4.25

(B78-05405)

AKDW/GB/E(P) — Sinatra, Frank. Biographies
Frank, Alan
    Sinatra / [by] Alan Frank. — London [etc.] : Hamlyn, 1978. —
    176p : ill(some col), facsims, ports(some col) ; 30cm.
    Ill. on lining papers. — Bibl.: p.175. — List of films: p.152-168. — List of
    sound discs: p.169-175. — Index.
    ISBN 0-600-38317-2 : £4.50

(B78-37100)

Wilson, Earl
    Sinatra / [by] Earl Wilson. — London : Star Books, 1978. — xv,
    380p,[8]p of plates : ill, ports ; 18cm.
    Originally published: New York : Macmillan ; London : W.H. Allen, 1976.
    ISBN 0-352-30194-5 Pbk : £1.25

(B78-22166)

AKDW/GB/E(P) — Tucker, Sophy. Biographies
Freedland, Michael
    Sophie : the Sophie Tucker story / [by] Michael Freedland. —
    London : Woburn Press, 1978. — [9],221p,leaf of plate,[8]p of
    plates : facsims, ports ; 23cm.
    ISBN 0-7130-0153-4 : £6.50

(B78-05406)

AKDW/GB/E(P) — Wings
Pascall, Jeremy
    Paul McCartney & Wings / [by] Jeremy Pascall ; [edited by
    Pamela Harvey]. — [Secaucus] : Chartwell Books ; [London] :
    Phoebus, [1977]. — 96p : ill(some col), ports(some col) ; 31cm.
    Ports on lining papers.
    ISBN 0-89009-125-0 : £2.95

(B78-01677)

AKDW/GB/E(P/B) — Abba. Periodicals
    Abba magazine. — Knutsford : Poster Plus Ltd ; London :
    Distributed by Seymour Press.
    No.1- ; [Dec. 1977]-. — 1977-. — ill, ports(some col) ; 21cm.
    Monthly. — 32p. in 3rd issue.
    Sd : £0.40
    ISSN 0141-8394

(B78-30832)

AKDW/GB/E(P/B) — Previn, Dory
Previn, Dory
    Midnight baby : an autobiography / [by] Dory Previn. —
    London : Corgi, 1978. — 140p ; 18cm.
    Originally published: New York : Macmillan, 1976 ; London : Elm Tree
    Books, 1977.
    ISBN 0-552-10643-7 Pbk : £0.75

(B78-18542)

AKDW/GB/FD(P) — Sinatra, Frank. Recorded music
Ridgway, John, *b.1943*
    The Sinatrafile / by John Ridgway. — Birmingham (Miramar,
    Rowney Green La., Alvechurch, Birmingham B48 7QF) : John
    Ridgway Books.
    Part 2 : [Commercial]. — 1978. — x,309p : facsims, ports ; 25cm.
    Limited ed. of 1000 copies. — Bibl.: p.265. — Index.
    ISBN 0-905808-02-9 : £14.00
    ISBN 0-905808-03-7 Pbk : £12.00

(B78-23594)

AKDW/GB/FD(XPM16) — Popular songs. Recorded music,
    1952-1977
Rice, Jo
    The Guinness book of British hit singles : (the Guinness book of
    records records) / [compiled by] Jo and Tim Rice ; with ...
    [others]. — Enfield : Guinness Superlatives, 1977. — ii-ix,277p :
    col map, ports ; 21cm.
    Index.
    ISBN 0-900424-77-x : £4.95
    ISBN 0-900424-83-4 Pbk : £3.75

(B78-02936)

AKDW/GB/FD(XPQ24) — Popular songs. Recorded music,
    1955-1978
    British records charts, 1955-1978 / compiled by Tony Jasper. —
    [Revised and updated ed.]. — London : Macdonald and Jane's,
    1978. — 288p ; 23cm.
    '... [Top Twenty] British singles charts, week by week ... from 1955 to 1978
    ... published by ... "Music week" magazine ...' - jacket. — Previous ed.:
    published as '20 years of British record charts, 1955-1975'. London : Queen
    Anne Press, 1975.
    ISBN 0-354-08523-9 : £4.95

(B78-37424)

AKDW/GBS/E(P) — Wonder, Stevie. Biographies
Elsner, Constanze
    Stevie Wonder / [by] Constanze Elsner. — London : Everest,
    1977. — 360p,[8]p of plates : ports ; 23cm.
    List of sound discs: p.329-351. — Index.
    ISBN 0-905018-51-6 : £4.95

(B78-15755)

AKDW/GC/E(P) — Rogers, Jimmie. Biographies
Paris, Mike
    Jimmie the Kid : the life of Jimmie Rodgers / [by] Mike Paris
    and Chris Comber. — London : Eddison Press : 'Old time music'
    Magazine, 1977. — 211p : ill, facsims, ports ; 23cm. — (Eddison
    musicbooks)
    Bibl.: p.204-206. — List of sound discs: p.171-196. — Index.
    ISBN 0-85649-019-9 : £3.95

(B78-33931)

AKDW/GCW(BC) — Country 'n' western music. Directories
British Country Music Association
    Yearbook / British Country Music Association. — Newton Abbot
    (PO Box 2, Newton Abbot, Devon TQ12 4HT) : The Association.
    1978. — 1978. — [1],80p : ill, ports ; 21cm.
    Pbk : Unpriced
    ISSN 0308-4698

(B78-21397)

AKDW/GCW/E(P) — Cash, Johnny. Biographies
Cash, Johnny
    Man in black / [by] Johnny Cash. — London [etc.] : Hodder and
    Stoughton, 1977. — 5-244p,[8]p of plates : ill, ports ; 18cm.
    Originally published: Grand Rapids : Zondervan, 1975 ; London : Hodder
    and Stoughton, 1976.
    ISBN 0-340-22173-9 Pbk : £0.95

(B78-02614)

AKDW/GM — Songs. Occupational groups
    Victoria's inferno : songs of the old mills, mines, manufactories,
    canals and railways / edited by Jon Raven. — Wolverhampton
    (68 Limes Rd, Tettenhall, Wolverhampton [W. Midlands]) :
    Broadside, 1978. — 192p : ill, music ; 19cm.
    Bibl.: p.182-192. — List of sound discs : p.192.
    ISBN 0-9503722-3-4 Pbk : £0.95

(B78-29838)

AKDW/HHW — Blues
Garon, Paul
    Blues & the poetic spirit / [by] Paul Garon ; with a preface by
    Franklin Rosemont. — London : Eddison Press, 1975. — 178p :
    ill, facsims, ports ; 22cm. — (Eddison blues books ; [3])
    Bibl.: p.169-174. — Index.
    ISBN 0-85649-018-0 : £3.50

(B78-30829)

AKDW/HHW(X) — Blues. History
Murray, Albert
    Stomping the blues / [by] Albert Murray. — London [etc.] :
    Quartet Books, 1978. — [7],264p : ill, facsims, ports ; 26cm.
    Originally published: New York : McGraw-Hill, 1976. — Index.
    ISBN 0-7043-2172-6 : £4.95
    ISBN 0-7043-3200-0 Pbk : £2.50

(B78-22168)

AKDW/HK/E(P) — Presley, Elvis
    Elvis Presley - 1935-1977 : a tribute to the king. — Wednesbury (2
    Engine La., Wednesbury, W. Midlands) : 'Bavie' Publications.
    Cover title: Goodbye.
    [1]. — 1977. — [30]leaves : ill, ports ; 30cm.
    Sheet (1 side : port.) as insert.
    Pbk : £3.00

(B78-12098)

    [2]. — 1977. — [33]leaves : ill, ports ; 30cm.
    Sheet (1 side : port.) as insert.
    Pbk : £3.00

(B78-12099)

    [3]. — 1977. — [33] leaves : 1 ill, ports ; 30cm.
    Cover title: Goodbye.
    Pbk : £3.00
    Also classified at 821'.9'14

(B78-06988)

    [4]. — 1977. — [31]leaves : ill, ports ; 30cm.
    Sheet (1 side : port.) as insert.
    Pbk : £3.00

(B78-12100)

    [5]. — 1977. — [32]leaves : ill, ports ; 30cm.
    Sheet (1 side : port.) as insert.
    Pbk : £3.00

(B78-12101)

AKDW/HK/E(P) — Presley, Elvis. Biographies
Yancey, Becky
My life with Elvis / [by] Becky Yancey ; with Cliff Linedecker. — London : W.H. Allen, 1977. — xviii,360p : ill, ports ; 22cm.
Also published: New York : St Martin's Press, 1977.
ISBN 0-491-02084-8 : £5.95
(B78-01678)

AKDW/HK/E(P/DE) — Presley, Elvis. Questions & answers
Nash, Bruce M
The Elvis Presley quizbook / [by] Bruce M. Nash. — New York : Warner Books ; [London] : Distributed by New English Library, 1978. — 205p,[8]p of plates : ports ; 18cm.
With answers.
ISBN 0-446-89823-6 Pbk : £0.90
(B78-33163)

AKDW/HKQ — Punk rock
Hennessy, Val
In the gutter / by Val Hennessy. — London [etc.] : Quartet Books, 1978. — 95p : chiefly ill(some col) ; 26cm. — (Quartet diversions)
ISBN 0-7043-3230-2 Pbk : £1.95
(B78-24013)

AKDW/HKQ/E(P) — Sex Pistols
The Sex Pistols : the inside story / compiled and edited by Fred and Judy Vermorel. — London : Star Books, 1978. — 224p,[8]p of plates : ill, facsims, ports ; 18cm.
ISBN 0-426-18585-4 Pbk : £0.75
(B78-35475)

AKDW/HKR(B) — Rock. Periodicals
Face out. — [Wendover] ([c/o Chris Furse, 25 Lionel Ave., Wendover, Aylesbury, Bucks.]) : ['Face out'].
No.1- ; [Apr. 1978]-. — [1978]-. — 26cm.
Irregular. — [11]p. in 1st issue.
Sd : Unpriced
ISSN 0141-6987
(B78-26879)

AKDW/HKR(C) — Encyclopaedias
Logan, Nick
The illustrated 'New musical express' encyclopedia of rock / [text Nick Logan, Bob Woffinden]. — Revised ed. — London [etc.] : Hamlyn, 1978. — 256p : ill(chiefly col), ports(some col) ; 31cm.
'A Salamander book'. — Col. ill. on lining papers. — Previous ed.: 1976. — Index.
ISBN 0-600-33171-7 : £5.95
(B78-15752)

AKDW/HKR(X) — Rock. History
Pascall, Jeremy
The illustrated history of rock music / [by] Jeremy Pascall. — London [etc.] : Hamlyn, 1978. — 3-222p : ill(chiefly col), ports(chiefly col) ; 30cm.
Col. port., col. ill. on lining papers. — Index.
ISBN 0-600-37605-2 : £5.95
(B78-39779)

AKDW/HKR(Z) — Rock-in relation in sociology
Frith, Simon
The sociology of rock / [by] Simon Frith. — London : Constable, 1978. — 255p ; 23cm. — (Communication and society)
Bibl.: p.241-247. — Index.
ISBN 0-09-460220-4 : £7.50
ISBN 0-09-462290-6 Pbk : £3.95
(B78-31211)

AKDW/HKR/E(M) — Rock. Singers
Farren, Mick
Rock 'n roll circus : the illustrated rock concert / by Mick Farren & George Snow. — London : Pierrot Publishing Ltd ; London (219 Eversleigh Rd, SW11 5UY) : Distributed by Big O Publishing Ltd, 1978. — 3-117p : ill(some col), facsims, ports(some col) ; 26cm.
ISBN 0-905310-10-1 Pbk : £3.95
(B78-31595)

AKDW/HKR/E(MN) — Songs, etc. Rock. Singing. Careers
How t'make it as a rockstar / [editor Zip Lecky, assistant editor Tony Benyon]. — London : IPC Magazines, 1977. — 36p : chiefly ill(some col) ; 30cm.
Sd : £0.40

AKDW/HKR/E(P) — Bolan, Marc
Marc Bolan : a tribute / [compiled and edited by Ted Dicks and Paul Platz]. — London (19 Poland St., W1V 3DD) : Essex House Publishing, 1978. — [127]p : ill, facsims, music, ports ; 28cm.
List of sound discs (2p.).
ISBN 0-906445-01-9 Pbk : £2.95
(B78-39784)

AKDW/HKR/E(P) — Bolan, Marc. Biographies
Marc Bolan : a tribute / [compiled and edited by Ted Dicks and Paul Platz]. — London (19 Poland St., W1V 3DD) : Essex House Publishing ; London : Springwood Books, 1978. — [127]p : ill, facsims, music, ports ; 29cm.
List of sound discs (2p.).
ISBN 0-906445-00-0 : £5.95
ISBN 0-905947-11-8 (Springwood Books)
(B78-39783)

AKDW/HKR/E(P) — Dylan, Bob. Biographies
Alexander, Robert
Bob Dylan : an illustrated history / produced by Michael Gross ; with a text by Robert Alexander. — London : Elm Tree Books, 1978. — [10],150p : ill, ports ; 28cm.
Bibl.: p.148-149.
ISBN 0-241-10038-0 Pbk : £3.95
(B78-33164)

AKDW/HKR/E(P) — Genesis. Biographies
Gallo, Armando
Genesis : the evolution of a rock band / [by] Armando Gallo. — London : Sidgwick and Jackson, 1978. — 145,[6]p : ill(some col), facsims, ports(some col) ; 28cm.
List of sound discs: p.[2]-[6]. — Index.
ISBN 0-283-98439-2 : £7.50
ISBN 0-283-98440-6 Pbk : £4.50
(B78-25373)

AKDW/HKR/E(P) — Stewart, Rod. Biographies
Burton, Peter
Rod Stewart : a life on the town / by Peter Burton. — London : New English Library, 1977. — 120p : ill(chiefly col), ports(some col) ; 27cm.
List of sound discs: p.91-94. — Includes the songs of Rod Stewart.
ISBN 0-450-03429-1 Pbk : £3.50
(B78-06262)

AKDW/HKR/E(P) — Wakeman, Rick. Biographies
Wooding, Dan
Rick Wakeman : the caped crusader / [by] Dan Wooding ; foreword by Elton John. — London : Hale, 1978. — 192p : ill, facsim, ports ; 26cm.
List of sound discs: p.189. — List of films: p.189. — Index.
ISBN 0-7091-6487-4 : £4.95
(B78-22170)

AKDW/HKR/E(P) — Who, The. Biographies
A decade of The Who : an authorised history in music, paintings, words and photographs / [text Steve Turner ; paintings and drawings John Davis]. — London : Elm Tree Books [for] Fabulous Music Ltd, 1977. — 3-239p : ill(some col), music, ports ; 28cm.
List of sound discs: p.238-239. — Includes 'lyrics of over eighty of their songs ... accompanied by the music for forty of them' - back cover.
ISBN 0-241-89809-9 Pbk : £4.50
(B78-00388)

AKDW/HKR/E(P) — Who, The. Tommy
Barnes, Richard
The story of 'Tommy' / [by] Richard Barnes & Pete Townshend. — Twickenham (The Boathouse, Ranelagh Drive, Twickenham, Middx TW1 1QZ) : Eel Pie Publishing Ltd, 1977. — [1],129p : ill(chiefly col), facsims(some col), ports(chiefly col) ; 31cm.
ISBN 0-906008-02-6 : £6.95
ISBN 0-906008-01-8 Pbk : Unpriced
(B78-18545)

AKDW/HKR/E(P) — Wonder, Stevie. Biographies
Fox Cumming, Ray
Stevie Wonder / [by] Ray Fox Cumming. — London (44 Hill St., W1X 8LB) : Mandabrook Books, 1977. — 123,[1]p ; 18cm.
'"Daily mirror" pop club' - cover. — List of sound discs: p.122-123.
ISBN 0-427-00418-7 Pbk : £0.60
(B78-50321)

Haskins, James
The story of Stevie Wonder / [by] James Haskins. — London [etc.] : Panther, 1978. — 93p,[16]p of plates : ports ; 18cm.
Originally published: New York : Lothrop, Lee and Shepard, 1976. — List of sound discs: p.82-90. — Index.
ISBN 0-586-04541-4 Pbk : £0.65
(B78-06263)

AKDW/HKR/E(P/YT/XQQ) — Rolling Thunder Revue. United States, 1975
Shepard, Sam
Rolling Thunder logbook / by Sam Shepard. — Harmondsworth [etc.] : Penguin, 1978. — [8],184p : ill, ports ; 26cm.
Cover title: Bob Dylan starring in Rolling Thunder logbook. — Originally published: New York : Viking Press, 1977.
ISBN 0-14-004750-6 Pbk : £1.75
(B78-20439)

AKDW/HKR/FD(P/WT) — Dylan, Bob. Recorded music. Lists
Hoggard, Stuart
  Bob Dylan : an illustrated discography / [by] Stuart Hoggard &
  Jim Shields. — [Oxford] ([113 Thame Rd, Oxford]) : Transmedia
  Express, [1978]. — 108,[23]p : ill, ports ; 20cm.
  Bibl.: p.[8]. — Index.
  ISBN 0-906344-00-x Pbk : £1.90

(B78-17915)

**AKDW/JR/FD(YT/WT) — Film songs. Recordings. United States.
                    Lists**
Pitts, Michael R
  Hollywood on record : the film stars' discography / by Michael
  R. Pitts and Louis H. Harrison. — Metuchen ; London :
  Scarecrow Press ; [Folkestone] : [Distributed by Bailey and
  Swinfen], 1978. — xi,411p : ports ; 23cm.
  ISBN 0-8108-1093-x : £13.60

(B78-27785)

AKDW/JV(YDBL) — Music hall. Lambeth
  Lambeth and Music Hall : a treasury of Music Hall memorabilia :
  including articles, biographies, photographs, engravings and
  reproductions of original material / compiled by Eva O'Rourke.
  — [London] ([Leisure Centre, Loughborough Park, S.W.9]) :
  London Borough of Lambeth Directorate of Amenity Services,
  1977. — Portfolio : ill, facsims, ports ; 25x33cm.
  Twenty-two items. — Bibl.
  ISBN 0-905208-02-1 : £1.00

(B78-20450)

AKDW/JV/E(P) — Leno, Dan. Biographies
Brandreth, Gyles
  The funniest man on earth : the story of Dan Leno / [by] Gyles
  Brandreth. — London : Hamilton, 1977. — x,105p,16p of plates :
  ill, facsims, ports ; 23cm.
  Bibl.: p.100-101. — List of sound discs: p.96-97. — Index.
  ISBN 0-241-89810-2 : £4.50

(B78-01692)

AKDW/K/G — Ballads
  The Penguin book of folk ballads of the English-speaking world /
  edited by Albert B. Friedman. — Harmondsworth [etc.] : Penguin,
  1977. — xxxv,470p : music ; 20cm.
  This collection originally published: as 'The Viking book of folk ballads of
  the English-speaking world'. New York : Viking Press, 1956. — Bibl.:
  p.459-463. — Index. — Includes music of some ballads.
  ISBN 0-14-004241-5 Pbk : £1.75

(B78-08525)

AKDW/K/G(YDJD) — Ballads. Lancashire
  Ballads and songs of Lancashire / collected, compiled, and edited,
  with notes, by John Harland. — 3rd ed. / corrected, revised, and
  enlarged by T.T. Wilkinson. — Wakefield : EP Publishing.
  Facsimile reprint of: 3rd ed. Manchester : Heywood, 1882.
  Part 2 : Modern. — 1976. — xxv p,p209-554,plate : port ; 20cm.
  ISBN 0-7158-1182-7 : £5.25

(B78-02615)

AKDW/K/G(YDM) — Ballads. Ireland
  Ballads from the pubs of Ireland / edited by James N. Healy with
  music and commentary ; illustrations by the author. — 3rd ed. —
  Dublin [etc.] (25 Lower Abbey St., Dublin 1) : Mercier Press,
  1976. — 144p : ill, music ; 18cm.
  This ed. originally published: 1968.
  Pbk : £1.50

(B78-37866)

  The first book of Irish ballads / edited by Daniel O'Keeffe ; with
  notes and music by James N. Healy. — Revised ed. — Cork (4
  Bridge St., Cork) : Mercier Press, 1976. — 136p : music ; 19cm.
  Revised ed. originally published: 1968.
  ISBN 0-85342-080-7 Pbk : £1.50

(B78-37867)

  The second book of Irish ballads / edited by James N. Healy. —
  3rd ed. ; ... with additional notes and music. — Cork (4 Bridge
  St., Cork) : Mercier Press, 1976. — 134p : music ; 19cm.
  Includes 3 songs in Irish. — Third ed. originally published: 1968.
  ISBN 0-85342-081-5 Pbk : £1.50

(B78-37868)

AKDW/K/GNCC — Coal mining
  Come all ye bold miners : ballads and songs of the coalfields /
  compiled by A.L. Lloyd. — New, revised and enlarged ed. —
  London : Lawrence and Wishart, 1978. — 384p : music ; 23cm.
  Previous ed.: 1952. — Index. — Includes music of several songs.
  ISBN 0-85315-412-0 : £10.00

(B78-39786)

AKDW/KC(YDM) — Songs. Sea. Ireland
  Irish ballads and songs of the sea / edited, with musical
  arrangements and illustrations, by James N. Healy. — Cork (4
  Bridge St., Cork) : Mercier Press, 1976. — 143p : ill, music ;
  19cm.
  Includes 3 songs in Irish. — This collection originally published: 1967. —
  Index.
  ISBN 0-85342-074-2 Pbk : £1.50

(B78-34739)

AKFL/E(P) — Callas, Maria. Biographies
Rémy, Pierre Jean
  Maria Callas : a tribute / [by] Pierre-Jean Rémy ; translated from
  the French by Catherine Atthill. — London : Macdonald and
  Jane's, 1978. — 192p : ill, facsim, ports ; 26cm.
  Translation of: 'Callas'. Paris : Ramsay, 1978. — List of sound discs :
  p.189-192.
  ISBN 0-354-04315-3 : £6.95

(B78-35471)

AKGN/FD(P/WT) — Ruffo, Titta. Recordings. Lists
Mathews, Emrys G
  Titta Ruffo : a centenary discography / [by] Emrys G. Mathews.
  — Llandeilo (['Neuadd Deg', Penybanc, Llandeilo, Dyfed SA19
  7TA]) : The author, 1978. — [26]p : facsim, port ; 21cm.
  Originally published: 1977.
  Sd : £0.60

(B78-27784)

AL — MUSICAL LITERATURE. INSTRUMENTAL MUSIC
AL/B — Instruments
Remnant, Mary
  Musical instruments of the West / [by] Mary Remnant. —
  London : Batsford, 1978. — 240p : ill ; 24cm.
  Bibl.: p.230-235. — Index.
  ISBN 0-7134-0569-4 : £10.00

(B78-24452)

AL/B(WJ) — Instruments. Catalogues
Victoria and Albert Museum
  Catalogue of musical instruments [in the] Victoria and Albert
  Museum. — London : H.M.S.O.
  Vol.2 : Non-keyboard instruments / [by] Anthony Baines. — 2nd ed. —
  1978. — xi,123p,[95]p of plates : ill ; 25cm.
  Previous ed.: 1968. — Bibl.: p.109-111. — Index.
  ISBN 0-11-290263-4 Pbk : £8.75

(B78-36278)

AL/B(X) — Instruments. History
Geiringer, Karl
  Instruments in the history of Western music / [by] Karl
  Geiringer. — 3rd (revised and enlarged) ed. — London [etc.] :
  Allen and Unwin, 1978. — 3-318p,leaf of plate,lxvii p of plates :
  ill(some col), music, ports ; 23cm.
  Previous ed.: i.e. 2nd ed. 1945. — Bibl.: p.301-308. — Index.
  ISBN 0-04-781005-x : £10.50

(B78-37097)

AL/B(YDB) — Instruments. London. Victoria & Albert Museum
Victoria and Albert Museum
  Musical instruments at the Victoria & Albert Museum : an
  introduction / [by] Carole Patey ; [for the] Victoria & Albert
  Museum Education Department. — London : H.M.S.O., 1978. —
  30p : ill ; 15x21cm.
  Bibl.: p.30.
  ISBN 0-11-290274-x Sd : £0.95

(B78-39230)

AL/BC — Instruments. Manufacture
Dalby, Stuart
  Make your own musical instruments / [by] Stuart Dalby. —
  London : Batsford, 1978. — 93p : ill ; 26cm.
  ISBN 0-7134-0545-7 : £3.95

(B78-26243)

Tolley, Bryan
  Musical instruments / [by] Bryan Tolley ; illustrated by Frank
  Capon. — Hove : Wayland, 1978. — 64p : col ill ; 22cm. —
  (Beginning crafts)
  Cover title: Making musical instruments.
  ISBN 0-85340-529-8 : £1.75

(B78-31598)

AL/BC(T) — Instruments. Manufacture. Bibliographies
Woodrow, Martin
  Make your own musical instruments : a bibliography / compiled
  by Martin Woodrow. — Stevenage (14 Wisden Rd, Stevenage,
  Herts.) : Clover Publications, 1977. — 31p ; 21cm.
  Index.
  Sd : £2.40

AL/CY — Technique
  Tensions in the performance of music : a symposium / edited by
  Carola Grindea ; foreword by Yehudi Menuhin ; preface by Allen
  Percival. — London : Kahn and Averill, 1978. — 128p ; 21cm.
  ISBN 0-900707-44-5 : £3.00

(B78-16900)

AL/E(YD/XCKF) — Minstrelsy. England, 1306
Bullock-Davies, Constance
  Menestrellorum multitudo : minstrels at a royal feast / by
  Constance Bullock-Davies. — Cardiff : University of Wales Press,
  1978. — xli,188p,plate : port ; 22cm.
  Includes transcript of MS. E101/369/6 in the Public Record Office.
  ISBN 0-7083-0656-x : £7.50

(B78-12983)

ALF(XFQ31) — Concertos, 1715-1745
Hutchings, Arthur
The baroque concerto / by Arthur Hutchings. — 3rd revised ed. — London [etc.] : Faber, 1978. — 363p : maps, music ; 22cm.
This ed. originally published: 1973. — Bibl.: p.351-356. — Index.
ISBN 0-571-10865-2 Pbk : £3.95 : CIP rev.

(B78-30835)

AM — MUSICAL LITERATURE. ORCHESTRAL MUSIC
AMM — Symphony orchestra
Downes, Edward
Everyman's guide to orchestral music / [by] Edward Downes. — London [etc.] : Dent, 1978. — xxix,1058p : ill, music, ports ; 25cm.
Originally published: as 'The New York Philharmonic guide to the symphony'. New York : Walker, 1976. — Index.
ISBN 0-460-03030-2 : £15.00 : CIP rev.

(B78-03579)

Raynor, Henry
The orchestra : a history / by Henry Raynor. — New York : Scribner's ; London : Hale, 1978. — 207p,[16]p of plates : ill, music, ports ; 23cm.
Index.
ISBN 0-7091-6333-9 : £4.50

(B78-12988)

AMM/E(QB/B) — Philharmonia Orchestra. Periodicals
Con brio. — London (13 De Walden Court, 85 New Cavendish St., W.1) : New Philharmonia Club.
No.1- ; 1976-. — [1976]-. — 30cm.
Published at irregular intervals. — 10p. in No.4.
Sd : Unpriced
ISSN 0140-8771

(B78-06990)

AMM/E(QB/B) — Scottish National Orchestra. Periodicals
Scottish National Orchestra
SNO scene. — Glasgow (150 Hope St., Glasgow G2 2TH) : Scottish National Orchestra Society.
No.1- ; June 1977-. — 1977-. — ill, facsims, ports ; 30cm.
Monthly. — 10p. in No.4.
Sd : £3.00 yearly
ISSN 0140-9379

(B78-06989)

AMM/E(QB/X) — Hallé Orchestra. History
Kennedy, Michael, *b.1926*
Hallé, 1858-1976 : a brief survey of the orchestra's history, travels and achievements / [by] Michael Kennedy]. — [Revised ed.]. — [Manchester] ([30 Cross St., Manchester M2 7BA]) : [Hallé Concerts Society], [1977]. — 75p : ill, ports ; 21cm.
Previous ed.: 1968. — List of sound discs: p.62-74.
Sd : £0.75

(B78-06265)

AMT — MUSICAL LITERATURE. JAZZ
Coker, Jerry
Listening to jazz / [by] Jerry Coker. — Englewood Cliffs ; London [etc.] : Prentice-Hall, 1978. — xii,148p : ill, music ; 21cm.
'A spectrum book'. — Lists of sound discs.
ISBN 0-13-537217-8 : £6.55
ISBN 0-13-537209-7 Pbk : £2.50

(B78-24453)

AMT(C) — Encyclopaedias
Case, Brian
The illustrated encyclopedia of jazz / [authors Brian Case and Stan Britt, editor Trisha Palmer]. — London (27 Old Gloucester St., WC1N 3AF) : Salamander Books, 1978. — 224p : ill(chiefly col), ports(some col) ; 31cm. — (A Salamander book)
Ill. on lining papers. — Index.
ISBN 0-86101-013-2 : £6.95

(B78-22169)

Feather, Leonard
The encyclopedia of jazz / by Leonard Feather ; appreciations by Duke Ellington, Benny Goodman and John Hammond. — [Completely revised, enlarged ed.]. — London [etc.] : Quartet Books, 1978. — 527p : music, ports ; 27cm.
Previous ed.: London : Barker, 1961. — Bibl.: p.524-527. — Index.
ISBN 0-7043-2173-4 : £9.95

(B78-25374)

White, Mark
The observer's book of jazz / [by] Mark White. — London : F. Warne, 1978. — 192p : ill, ports ; 15cm. — (The observer's pocket series)
Ill. on lining papers. — Bibl.: p.183-184. — List of sound discs: p.171-182. — Index.
ISBN 0-7232-1588-x : £1.25

(B78-35477)

AMT(M) — Musicians
Hentoff, Nat
Jazz is / by Nat Hentoff. — London : W.H. Allen, 1978. — 3-288p : ports ; 24cm.
Originally published: New York : Random House, 1976. — Bibl.: p.286. — Index.
ISBN 0-491-02312-x : £5.95

(B78-08478)

White, Mark
The observer's book of big bands / [by] Mark White. — London : F. Warne, 1978. — 192p : ill, 2 facsims, ports ; 15cm. — (Observer's pocket series ISSN 0305-4837)
Bibl.: p.184-185. — List of sound discs: p.177-184. — Index.
ISBN 0-7232-1589-8 : £1.25

(B78-37101)

AMT(M/XMS14) — Musicians, 1917-1930
Lyttleton, Humphrey
Basin Street to Harlem : jazz masters and masterpieces, 1917-1930 / [by] Humphrey Lyttleton. — London : Robson, 1978. — 214p,[8]p of plates, ports ; 23cm. — (The best of jazz)
Bibl.: p.204-205. — List of sound discs: p.206-208. — Index.
ISBN 0-903895-91-9 : £5.25 : CIP rev.

(B78-27526)

AMT(M/XQ18) — Musicians, 1960-1977
Wilmer, Valerie
As serious as your life : the story of the new jazz / [by] Valerie Wilmer ; with photographs by the author. — London : Allison and Busby, 1977. — 296p,[16]p of plates : ports ; 21cm.
Bibl.: p.283-285. — Index.
ISBN 0-85031-224-8 : £6.50

(B78-11201)

AMT(M/YTLD) — Afro-American musicians
Wilmer, Valerie
As serious as your life : the story of the new jazz / [by] Valerie Wilmer ; with photographs by the author. — London [etc.] : Quartet Books, 1977. — 296p,[16]p of plates : ports ; 20cm.
Bibl.: p.283-285. — Index.
ISBN 0-7043-3164-0 Pbk : £2.95

(B78-05410)

AMT(P) — Bolden, Buddy. Biographies
Marquis, Donald M
In search of Buddy Bolden, first man of jazz / [by] Donald M. Marquis. — Baton Rouge ; London : Louisiana State University Press, 1978. — xxi,176p,[30]p of plates : ill, facsims, maps, ports ; 24cm.
Bibl.: p.153-170. — Index.
ISBN 0-8071-0356-x : £7.00

(B78-33167)

AMT(P) — Ellington, Duke. Biographies
Ellington, Mercer
Duke Ellington in person : an intimate memoir / by Mercer Ellington ; with Stanley Dance. — London : Hutchinson, 1978. — xii,236p,[24]p of plates : 2 ill, facsim, ports ; 23cm.
Also published: Boston, Mass. : Houghton Mifflin, 1978. — List of compositions: p.222-224. — List of recordings: p.225-226. — Index.
ISBN 0-09-132750-4 : £5.95

(B78-34740)

Jewell, Derek
Duke : a portrait of Duke Ellington / [by] Derek Jewell. — [New ed.]. — London : Sphere, 1978. — 302p,[16]p of plates : ports ; 18cm.
Previous ed.: London : Elm Tree Books, 1977. — Bibl.: p.288. — List of recordings: p.286-288. — Index.
ISBN 0-7221-5022-9 Pbk : £1.95

(B78-33939)

AMT(P) — Lewis, George. Biographies
Bethell, Tom
George Lewis : a jazzman from New Orleans / [by] Tom Bethell. — Berkeley [etc.] ; London : University of California Press, 1977. — ix,387p : ill, ports ; 23cm.
Bibl.: p.371-379. — List of sound discs: p.292-363. — Index.
£8.75
ISBN 0-520-03213-8

AMT(X) — History
Collier, James Lincoln
The making of jazz : a comprehensive history / [by] James Lincoln Collier. — London [etc.] : Hart-Davis MacGibbon, 1978. — iii-xv,543p : ill, music, ports ; 24cm.
Bibl.: p.511-515. — Index.
ISBN 0-246-11092-9 : £10.00

(B78-33166)

Gridley, Mark C
Jazz styles / [by] Mark C. Gridley. — Englewood Cliffs ; London [etc.] : Prentice-Hall, 1978. — x,421p : ill, music, ports ; 24cm.
Bibl.: p.407-409. — List of sound discs: p.355-406. — Index.
ISBN 0-13-509885-8 : £9.45
ISBN 0-13-509877-7 Pbk : £6.55

(B78-31600)

The **story** of jazz : from New Orleans to Rock Jazz / edited by Joachim-Ernst Berendt ; with contributions from Werner Burkhardt ... [et al.] ; [translated from the German]. — London : Barrie and Jenkins [etc.], 1978. — 192p : ill, ports ; 23x25cm.
Translation of: 'Die Story des Jazz'. Stuttgart : Deutsche Verlags-Anstalt, 1975. — Bibl.: p.182-183. — List of sound discs: p.184-192.
ISBN 0-214-20379-4 : £5.50

(B78-09118)

AMT(XQ10/C) — History, 1960-1969. Encyclopaedias
Feather, Leonard
The encyclopedia of jazz in the sixties / by Leonard Feather ; foreword by John Lewis. — London [etc.] : Quartet Books, 1978. — 312p : ill, ports ; 26cm.
Originally published: New York : Horizon Press, 1966. — Bibl.: p.311-312. — List of sound discs: p.309-310.
ISBN 0-7043-2174-2 : £9.95

(B78-26893)

AMT(XR9/C) — History, 1970-1978. Encyclopaedias
Feather, Leonard
The encyclopedia of jazz in the seventies / by Leonard Feather and Ira Gitler ; introduction by Quincy Jones. — London [etc.] : Quartet Books, 1978. — 394p : ill, ports ; 26cm.
Originally published: New York : Horizon Press, 1976. — Bibl.: p.391-393.
ISBN 0-7043-2175-0 : £9.95

(B78-26894)

AMT(YTLD/B) — Periodicals
Black music & jazz review. — Sutton : IPC Specialist and Professional Press.
Supersedes: Black music.
Vol.1, issue 1- ; Apr. 1978-. — [1978]-. — ill, ports ; 31cm.
Monthly. — 3-58p. in 1st issue.
Sd : £0.40
ISSN 0141-7738

(B78-26878)

AMT(YTRN/M) — New Orleans. Musicians
Rose, Al
New Orleans jazz : a family album / [by] Al Rose and Edmond Souchon. — Revised [ed.]. — Baton Rouge ; London : Louisiana State University Press, 1978. — viii,338p : ill, facsims, ports ; 29cm.
Previous ed.: Baton Rouge : Louisiana State University Press, 1967. — Index.
ISBN 0-8071-0374-8 : £17.50

(B78-23597)

AMT/FD(M) — Recordings. Musicians
Selections from the gutter : jazz portraits from the 'Jazz record' / edited by Art Hodes and Chadwick Hansen. — Berkeley [etc.] ; London : University of California Press, 1977. — xiv,233p : ill, ports ; 26cm.
ISBN 0-520-02999-2 : £8.75

(B78-05409)

APW — MUSICAL LITERATURE. KEYBOARD INSTRUMENTS
AQ/BT — Piano. Maintenance
Johnson, Michael
Tune and repair your own piano : a practical and theoretical guide to the tuning of all keyboard stringed instruments, and to the running repair of the piano / [by] Michael Johnson and Robin Mackworth-Young. — London [etc.] : Harcourt Brace Jovanovich, 1978. — [7],82p : ill ; 19cm.
ISBN 0-15-191383-8 : Unpriced
ISBN 0-15-691468-9 Pbk : £2.20

(B78-24454)

Smith, Eric, *b.1940*
Pianos in practice / [by] Eric Smith. — London : Scolar Press, 1978. — [9],100p : ill ; 18x26cm.
Bibl.: p.96. — Index.
ISBN 0-85967-393-6 : £8.00
ISBN 0-85967-394-4 Pbk : £3.95

(B78-28704)

AQ/E — Piano. Performance
Last, Joan
Interpretation in piano study / [by] Joan Last. — London [etc.] : Oxford University Press, 1978. — xiii,141p : music ; 20cm.
Originally published: as 'Interpretation for the piano student'. 1960. — Index.
ISBN 0-19-318424-9 Pbk : £2.50

(B78-26895)

AQ/E(P) — Brown, Rosemary
Parrott, Ian
The music of Rosemary Brown / by Ian Parrott. — London [etc.] : Regency Press, 1978. — 92p,leaf of plate,4p of plates : music, ports ; 23cm.
Bibl.: p.91-92. — Index.
£2.40
Primary classification A(Z)

(B78-19809)

AQ/E(VC) — Piano. Performance. Teaching
Booth, Victor
We piano teachers / [by] Victor Booth. — [Revised ed.] / revised by Adele Franklin ; preface by Margaret Hubicki. — London : Hutchinson, 1978. — 135p,leaf of plate,viii p of plates : ill, facsim, music, port ; 22cm.
This ed. originally published: Richmond, Vic. ; London : Hutchinson, 1971. — Bibl.: p.129-131. — Index.
ISBN 0-09-106191-1 Pbk : £2.95

(B78-40354)

Enoch, Yvonne
Group piano-teaching / [by] Yvonne Enoch. — London [etc.] : Oxford University Press, 1978. — viii,114p : form, music ; 19cm.
Originally published: 1974. — Bibl.: p.114. — List of music: p.111-113.
ISBN 0-19-318423-0 Pbk : £2.95

(B78-26247)

AQ/E(VC/P) — Van-Jung Page, Lucy
Lucy Van-Jung Page, 1892-1972 : recollections of pupils and friends. — [Oxford] ([26 Chalfont Rd, Oxford]) : [Miss C.J. Gibson], 1977. — [5],133p,plate : port ; 22cm.
Pbk : Unpriced

(B78-09119)

AQ/ED — Piano. Accompaniment
Duckenfield, Bridget
The care and nurture of your pianist partner or lesser spotted accompanist / by Bridget Duckenfield. — Ross-on-Wye (P.O. Box 4, Ross-on-Wye, [Herefordshire] HR9 6EB) : Hydatum, 1978. — [2],18p : ill(chiefly col), music ; 24cm.
ISBN 0-905682-10-6 Sd : £1.25

(B78-33940)

AQ/ED(P/XQG11) — Moore, Gerald. Biographies, 1967-1977
Moore, Gerald, *b.1899*
Farewell recital : further memoirs / [by] Gerald Moore. — London : Hamilton, 1978. — [11],178p,[8]p of plates : ill, ports ; 23cm.
Index.
ISBN 0-241-89817-x : £4.95 : CIP rev.

(B77-33371)

AQ/FH(Q/BC) — Player Piano Group. Directories
Player Piano Group
Membership list / the Player Piano Group. — [Brentford] ([358 High St., Brentford, Middx]) : [The Group].
Jan. 1977. — [1977]. — [1],14p ; 21cm.
Sd : Unpriced

(B78-01685)

AQR/E — Harpsichord. Performance
Nurmi, Ruth
A plain & easy introduction to the harpsichord / [by] Ruth Nurmi. — Albuquerque : University of New Mexico Press ; London : Distributed by Heinemann, 1974. — xiv,248p : ill, music ; 26cm.
Bibl. — Index.
ISBN 0-434-52470-0 : £9.50

(B78-28705)

AR(B) — Organs. Periodicals
British Institute of Organ Studies
BIOS journal. — Oxford (130 Southfield Rd, Oxford OX4 1PA) : Positif Press.
Vol.1 : 1977 / editor Michael Sayer. — 1977. — 120p : ill, facsims ; 22cm.
Bibl.
ISBN 0-9503892-8-5 Pbk : Unpriced
ISSN 0141-4992

(B78-20443)

AR(YDB/B) — Organ. London. Periodicals
London Association of Organists
Newsletter / London Association of Organists. — London (c/o P. Lea-Cox, St Jude-on-the-Hill, Central Sq., N.W.11) : [The Association].
Issue no.1- ; 1976-. — [1976]-. — 21cm.
Three issues a year. — [8]p. in 2nd issue.
Sd : Unpriced
ISSN 0309-6955

(B78-09120)

AR/B(YGB/XBH) — Organ. Instruments. Budapest, 300
Kaba, Melinda
Die römische Orgel von Aquincum (3. Jahrhundert) / [von] Melinda Kaba ; mit einem Beitrag von Erno Gegus 'Spektralanalytische Untersuchung der Bestandteile der Orgel von Aquincum' ; [aus dem Ungarischen übertragen von Tilda und Paul Alpári]. — Kassel [i.e. Cassel] [etc.] ; London : Bärenreiter, 1976. — 144p : ill ; 25cm. — (Musicologia Hungarica. Neue Folge ; 6)
Index.
£11.20
ISBN 3-7618-0541-1

(B78-03580)

AR/BC(P) — Duddyngton, Antony
Blewett, P R W
Antony Duddyngton, organ maker : the Duddyngton manuscripts at All Hallows-by-the-Tower, London / [this booklet by P.R.W. Blewett] ; [with transcripts by H.C. Thompson]. — [South Croydon] ([22 Edgar Rd, Sanderstead, South Croydon CR2 0NG]) : [Rev. P. Blewett], [1977]. — [14]p(2 fold) : facsims ; 24cm.
Bibl.: p.[13].
ISBN 0-906257-00-x Sd : £0.50

(B78-33169)

AR/E — Organ. Performance
Ashburnham, George
The 2nd pocket organ tutor / by George Ashburnham. — Sutton (22 Effingham Close, Sutton, Surrey SM2 6AG) : Ashburnham School of Music, [1978]. — 116p : ill, music ; 22cm.
Index.
£9.14

(B78-36280)

Supper, Walter
Die Orgeldisposition : eine Heranführung / [von] Walter Supper. — Grossausgabe ; mit einem Vorwort von Christhard Mahrenholz. — Kassel [i.e. Cassel] [etc.] ; London : Bärenreiter, 1977. — 3-268,[1]p : ill ; 24cm.
This ed. originally published: 1950. — Index.
Pbk : £13.44
ISBN 3-7618-0559-4

(B78-01682)

ARPV/B(B) — Electric organ. Instruments. Periodicals
Electronic organ review. — [Heathfield] ([Waldron, Heathfield, Sussex TN21 0QS]) : [Electronic Organ Review].
Nov.1976-. — [1976]-. — ill, ports ; 21cm.
Monthly. — [3],48p. in Nov. 1977 issue.
Sd : £0.50(£5.00 yearly)
ISSN 0141-0466

(B78-11202)

ARPV/E(B) — Electric organ. Periodicals
Home organist and leisure music. — London : Cover Publications Ltd ; London (181 Queen Victoria St., EC4V 4DD) : Distributed by Independent Magazines Ltd.
Vol.1, no.1- ; Aug.-Sept. 1977-. — 1977-. — ill, music, ports ; 30cm.
Six issues a year. — 82p. in 1st issue. — 'Farfisa news', Summer 1977 : 11th ed. (folder ([4]p.)) as insert.
Sd : £4.35 yearly
ISSN 0140-7902
Also classified at 786.7

(B78-06991)

ARS(B) — Accordion. Periodicals
Box and fiddle. — [Stranraer] ([c/o The editor, 50 Mount Vernon Rd, Stranraer]) : National Association of Accordion and Fiddle Clubs.
No.1- ; Oct. 1977-. — [1977]-. — ill, ports ; 44cm.
Monthly. — 8p. in 1st issue.
Sd : £0.10
ISSN 0140-6329
Also classified at AS(B)

(B78-03581)

ARW — MUSICAL LITERATURE. STRING INSTRUMENTS
AS(B) — Violin. Periodicals
Box and fiddle. — [Stranraer] ([c/o The editor, 50 Mount Vernon Rd, Stranraer]) : National Association of Accordion and Fiddle Clubs.
No.1- ; Oct. 1977-. — [1977]-. — ill, ports ; 44cm.
Monthly. — 8p. in 1st issue.
Sd : £0.10
ISSN 0140-6329
Primary classification ARS(B)

(B78-03581)

AS(VG/YDED) — Violin. Primary schools. Hertfordshire
Rural Music Schools Association
The Suzuki investigation in Hertfordshire : a report of the investigation, sponsored by the Calouste Gulbenkian Foundation and by the Leverhulme Trust, into the feasibility of introducing the Suzuki Talent Education method of teaching the violin into state schools in Britain / [Rural Music Schools Association]. — London : Bedford Square Press, 1977. — 19p ; 21cm.
ISBN 0-7199-0941-4 Sd : Unpriced

(B78-38994)

AS/BC(YD/M) — Violin. Manufacture. England. Violin makers
The **violin** makers : portrait of a living craft / [edited] by Mary Anne Alburger ; with a foreword by Watson Forbes. — London : Gollancz, 1978. — 240p,[31]p of plates : ill, ports ; 24cm.
Taped interviews with 28 craftsmen. — Ill. on lining papers. — Bibl.: p.239. — Index.
ISBN 0-575-02442-9 : £9.50

(B78-28706)

ASR/E(P) — Casals, Pablo
Blum, David
Casals and the art of interpretation / [by] David Blum. — London : Heinemann Educational, 1977. — xvi,223p,[4]p of plates : music, ports ; 23cm.
Bibl.: p.212-214. — Index.
ISBN 0-435-81150-9 : £8.50

(B78-06993)

AT — MUSICAL LITERATURE. PLUCKED STRING INSTRUMENTS
AT/B(XCSK301) — Plucked instruments, 1350-1790
Gill, Donald
Gut-strung plucked instruments contemporary with the lute / by Donald Gill. — Richmond, Surrey (c/o The Administrator, 71 Priory Rd, Kew Gardens, Richmond, Surrey TW9 3DH) : Lute Society, 1976. — [1],24p ; 21cm. — (Lute Society. Booklets ; no.2
ISSN 0140-6353)
Bibl.: p.21-24.
Sd : Unpriced

(B78-01683)

ATQ/E(P) — Roberts, John. Biographies
Roberts, E Ernest
John Roberts, telynor Cymru / gan E. Ernest Roberts ; trosiad i'r Gymraeg [o'r Saesneg] gan Selyf Roberts. — Dinbych [i.e. Denbigh] : Gwasg Gee, 1978. — 124p,leaf of plate,[12]p of plates : ill, facsims, music, ports ; 22cm.
Includes a translation of John Roberts' letters to Francis Hindes Groome, edited by Dorah E. Yates.
Pbk : £1.50

(B78-33170)

ATQS/B — Irish harp. Instruments
Rimmer, Joan
The Irish harp / [by] Joan Rimmer. — 2nd ed. — Cork (4 Bridge St., Cork) : Mercier Press for the Cultural Relations Committee, 1977. — [8],79p : ill, facsim ; 22cm. — (Irish life and culture ; 16)
Second title page in Irish. — Previous ed.: 1969.
ISBN 0-85342-151-x Pbk : £1.50

(B78-35478)

ATS/B — Guitar. Gibson guitar
Bishop, Ian Courtney
The Gibson guitar from 1950 / [by] Ian Courtney Bishop. — London (20 Denmark St., WC2H 8NE) : Musical New Services Ltd, 1978. — iv,95p : ill, ports ; 26cm.
'A "Guitar" magazine project'. — Originally published: 1977.
Pbk : Unpriced

ATS/B — Guitar. Instruments
Evans, Tom, *b.1948*
Guitars : music, history, construction and players from the Renaissance to rock / [by] Tom and Mary Anne Evans. — New York ; London : Paddington Press, 1977. — 479p : ill, facsims, music, ports ; 26cm.
Ill. on lining papers. — Bibl.: p.452-461. — Index.
ISBN 0-448-22240-x : £10.95

(B78-25375)

ATS/BC — Guitars. Construction
Sloane, Irving
Classic guitar construction : diagrams, photographs and step-by-step instructions / [by] Irving Sloane. — London [etc.] : Omnibus Press, 1976. — 3-95p : ill, plans, port ; 25cm.
Originally published: New York : Dutton, 1966. — Bibl.: p.95.
ISBN 0-86001-232-8 Pbk : £2.95

(B78-01684)

ATS/BT — Guitar. Maintenance
Sloane, Irving
Guitar repair : a manual of repair for guitars and fretted instruments / [by] Irving Sloane. — London : Omnibus Press, 1976. — 95p : ill ; 28cm.
Originally published: New York : Dutton, 1973 ; London : Nelson, 1974. — Index.
ISBN 0-86001-157-7 Pbk : £2.95

(B78-19402)

ATS/CY — Guitar. Technique
Bobri, Vladimir
The Segovia technique / [by] Vladimir Bobri. — New York : Collier Books ; London : Collier Macmillan, 1977. — ix,94p : ill, ports ; 23cm.
Originally published: New York : Macmillan ; London : Collier Macmillan, 1972. — Bibl.: p.82-87. — Index.
ISBN 0-02-079240-9 Pbk : £4.50

(B78-01056)

ATS/E — Guitar. Performance
Pearse, John
Frets and fingers : a guitar player's manual / [by] John Pearse. — New York ; London : Paddington Press, 1978. — 208p : ill, music ; 26cm.
ISBN 0-7092-0625-9 : £4.95

(B78-34741)

ATS/E(M) — Guitarists
Tobler, John
Guitar heroes / [by] John Tobler. — London [etc.] : Marshall Cavendish, 1978. — 88p : ill, ports(some col) ; 30cm.
Port. on lining papers. — Lists of sound discs.
ISBN 0-85685-438-7 : £2.95

(B78-39236)

ATS/ED — Guitar. Accompaniment
Green, E
Finger style folk : a guitar tutor for folk song accompaniment / by E. Green and G. Higson. — Blackpool (45 Riverside Drive, Hambleton, Blackpool FY6 9EH) : Wyre Publications, 1976. — [1],iii,57p : ill, music, ports ; 30cm.
Sd : Unpriced

(B78-06266)

AU — MUSICAL LITERATURE. WIND INSTRUMENTS
AUMM(QB/X) — Middlesex Yeomanry Association Military Band. History
Thrower, Arthur Harry
A brief history of the Middlesex Yeomanry (Duke of Cambridge's Hussars) Association Military Band / [by] Arthur H. Thrower. — London ([44 South Easling Rd, W.5]) : The author, 1978. — [1], 8p ; 20cm.
Sd : Unpriced

(B78-30834)

AUMM(X) — Military bands. History
Cassin-Scott, Jack
Military bands and their uniforms / [by] Jack Cassin-Scott & John Fabb. — Poole : Blandford Press, 1978. — 3-158p : ill(some col), facsim, music, ports(1 col) ; 24cm.
Col. ill. on lining papers. — List of sound discs: p.141-144. — Index.
ISBN 0-7137-0895-6 : £6.95

(B78-26675)

AUMM/E(B) — Military bands. Performance. Periodicals
Marching band news. — Beaconsfield (64 London End, Beaconsfield, Bucks.) : 'Marching band news'.
No.1- ; Apr. 1978-. — [1978]-. — ill, ports ; 22cm.
Monthly. — 8p. in 1st issue.
Sd : £2.50 yearly
ISSN 0141-7169

(B78-26891)

AV/BC(M/WT) — Manufacture. Instrument makers. Lists
Langwill, Lyndesay Graham
An index of musical wind-instrument makers / by Lyndesay G. Langwill. — 5th ed. ; revised, enlarged and illustrated. — Edinburgh (7 Dick Place, Edinburgh EH9 2JS) : The author, 1977. — xvi,308p : ill, facsims ; 26cm.
Previous ed.: 1974. — Bibl.: p.196-201.
£10.00

(B78-14459)

AVS/E — Recorder. Performance
Goodyear, Stephen F
The recorder / [by] Stephen F. Goodyear. — Sevenoaks [etc.] : Teach Yourself Books, 1978. — xii,175p,[4]p of plates : ill, music ; 18cm. — (Teach yourself books)
Bibl.: p.160-161. — Index.
ISBN 0-340-22247-6 Pbk : £1.25 : CIP rev.

(B78-25376)

Rowland-Jones, A
Introduction to the recorder : a tutor for adults / [by] A. Rowland-Jones. — London [etc.] : Oxford University Press, 1978. — [4],60p : ill, music ; 25cm.
Text, ill., music on inside back cover.
ISBN 0-19-322341-4 Sp : £1.95

(B78-23598)

AVV/B — Clarinet. Instruments
Rutland, Jonathan Patrick
The clarinet / by J.P. Rutland ; illustrated by Bob Warburton. — London [etc.] : F. Watts, 1978. — 48p : ill, facsim, music, ports ; 18x23cm.
Bibl.: p.46. — Index.
ISBN 0-85166-641-8 : £1.95

(B78-50000)

AVV/E — Clarinet. Performance
Rehfeldt, Phillip
New directions for clarinet / [by] Phillip Rehfeldt. — Berkeley [etc.] ; London : University of California Press, 1977. — viii, 135p : ill, music ; 28cm. — (The new instrumentation)
Sound disc (2s. 7in. 33 1/3 rpm) in pocket. — Bibl.: p.134-135. — List of music: p.124-134.
ISBN 0-520-03379-5 Sp : £10.50

(B78-27527)

Thurston, Frederick
Clarinet technique / by Frederick Thurston. — 3rd ed. — London [etc.] : Oxford University Press, 1977. — viii,94p : ill, music ; 19cm.
Previous ed.: 1964. — Bibl.: p.61-94.
ISBN 0-19-318610-1 Pbk : £1.95

(B78-05412)

AVV/E(M) — Clarinet. Musicians
Weston, Pamela
More clarinet virtuosi of the past / [by] Pamela Weston. — London (1 Rockland Rd, SW15 2LN) : The author, 1977. — 392p,32p of plates : ill, facsims, music, ports ; 22cm.
Bibl.: p.371-374. — Index.
Pbk : £5.40

(B78-00390)

AVY/E(B) — Bagpipes. Performance. Periodicals
The international piper. — Cockenzie (Seton Works, Edinburgh Rd, Cockenzie, East Lothian EH32 0HQ) : International Piper Ltd.
Vol.1, no.1- ; May 1978-. — [1978]-. — ill, maps, music, ports ; 27cm.
Monthly. — 24p. in 1st issue.
Sd : £0.35
ISSN 0141-7150

(B78-26248)

AWM(QB/YC/BC) — Brass bands. Great Britain. Directories
Directory of British brass bands : associations, societies, contests. — [Rochdale] ([28 Marigold St., Rochdale OL11 1RJ]) : [British Federation of Brass Bands].
Vol.2 : 1978-79. — [1978]. — [1],80p : ill ; 21cm.
Sd : £1.00
ISSN 0307-6261

(B78-27525)

AWS/B — Trumpet. Instruments
Bate, Philip
The trumpet and trombone : an outline of their history, development and construction / [by] Philip Bate. — 2nd ed. — London : E. Benn [etc.], 1978. — xix,300p,[23]p of plates : ill, music, port ; 23cm. — (Instruments of the orchestra)
Previous ed.: 1966. — Bibl.: p.274-283. — Index.
ISBN 0-510-36412-8 : £8.50
Also classified at AWU/B

(B78-09121)

AWT/B — Horn. Instruments
Merewether, Richard
The horn, the horn- / by Richard Merewether. — London (116 Long Acre, WC2E 9PA) : Paxman Musical Instruments Ltd, 1978. — 7-54p : ill, music ; 21cm. — (Hornplayer's companion series)
Sd : £1.50

(B78-15125)

Morley-Pegge, Reginald
The French horn : some notes on the evolution of the instrument and of its technique / [by] R. Morley-Pegge. — 2nd ed. — London : E. Benn [etc.], 1978. — xvii,222p,[8]leaves of plates(1 fold),[2]p of plates : ill, music ; 23cm. — (Instruments of the orchestra) (A Benn study : music)
Text on versos of 7 leaves of plates. — This ed. originally published: Tonbridge : Benn, 1973. — Bibl.: p.183-189. — Index.
£7.50
ISBN 0-510-36601-5
ISBN 0-510-36600-7 Pbk : £4.95

AWU/B — Trombone. Instruments
Bate, Philip
The trumpet and trombone : an outline of their history, development and construction / [by] Philip Bate. — 2nd ed. — London : E. Benn [etc.], 1978. — xix,300p,[23]p of plates : ill, music, port ; 23cm. — (Instruments of the orchestra)
Previous ed.: 1966. — Bibl.: p.274-283. — Index.
ISBN 0-510-36412-8 : £8.50
Primary classification AWS/B

(B78-09121)

AX — MUSICAL LITERATURE. PERCUSSION INSTRUMENTS
AX/B — Percussion. Instruments
Holland, James
Percussion / [by] James Holland. — London : Macdonald and Jane's, 1978. — xii,283p : ill, music, plans, ports ; 22cm. — (Yehudi Menuhin music guides)
Bibl.: p.269-270. — List of sound discs: p.271-277. — Index.
ISBN 0-354-04173-8 : £6.95
ISBN 0-354-04174-6 Pbk : £3.95

(B78-39787)

AX/BC — Manufacture
Goddard, Arthur
A selection of musical instruments to make for children / by Arthur Goddard. — [London] ([Trident House, Brooks Mews, W1Y 2PN]) : Trident Television Ltd, 1976. — [27]p : col ill ; 21cm.
'From the Yorkshire Television series "The Music Man" ...'.
Sd : £0.25

(B78-05413)

AX/GR(VE) — Percussion. Activities. Pre-school children
Blades, James
    Ready to play : stories with percussion sounds / [by] James
    Blades and Carole Ward. — London : British Broadcasting
    Corporation, 1978. — 64p : ill, music ; 24cm.
    On cover: 'Play School'.
    ISBN 0-563-17610-5 Pbk : £1.50
                                                                (B78-38609)

AXS — Bells
Yolen, Jane
    Ring out! : a book of bells / [by] Jane Yolen ; drawings by
    Richard Cuffari. — London : Evans Bros, 1978. — 128p : ill ;
    24cm.
    Originally published: New York : Seabury Press, 1974. — Bibl.: p.123-124.
    — Index.
    ISBN 0-237-44875-0 : £3.50
                                                                (B78-31602)

AXSR/BC(P) — Hatch, Joseph. Biographies
Hilton, John Anthony
    Joseph Hatch : the Ulcombe bellfounder / by John Hilton. —
    Oxford ([36 Great Clarendon St., Oxford]) : J. Hannon and Co.,
    [1978]. — [1],12p ; 21cm.
    Originally published: Tonbridge : The author, 1965.
    £2.50
    Sd : £0.60
                                                                (B78-18095)

AXSR/E — Church bells. Performance
Lewis, Harold
    Bell ringing, minimus : three and four bell methods / collected by
    H. Lewis & G. Fowler. — Oxford (36 Great Clarendon St.,
    Oxford) : J. Hannon and Co., 1977. — [3],30p ; 21cm.
    Sd : £1.50
                                                                (B78-17617)

**AXSR/E(YDDES/QB) — Church bells. Performance. Saffron
                  Walden. Saffron Walden Society of Change Ringers**
Stacey, Harold Clifford
    The Saffron Walden Society of Change Ringers / by H.C. Stacey.
    — Saffron Walden : Saffron Walden Society of Change Ringers ;
    Oxford (36 Great Clarendon St., Oxford) : Distributed by J.
    Hannon & Co., 1976. — [3],44 leaves ; 30cm.
    Pbk : £3.50
                                                                (B78-16903)

AXT/E(VG) — Glockenspiel. Performance. Primary schools
Russell-Smith, Geoffry
    Start making music : a primary teacher's guide : a complete self
    tutor for the absolute beginner - with instructional tape recording,
    reading, playing and teaching music for the non-specialist primary
    teacher / by Geoffry Russell-Smith. — London : Universal
    Edition, 1977. — [3],56p : ill, music ; 31cm.
    Accompanied by: sound cassette.
    ISBN 0-900938-48-x Sd : £6.00
                                                                (B78-12102)

AY/BC — Other instruments. Manufacture
Sawyer, David
    Vibrations : making unorthodox musical instruments / [by] David
    Sawyer. — Cambridge [etc.] : Cambridge University Press, 1977.
    — 102p : ill ; 25cm. — (Resources of music)
    Bibl.: p.102.
    ISBN 0-521-20812-2 Pbk : £4.00
                                                                (B78-04323)

B — INDIVIDUAL COMPOSERS
BBCADE — Bach, Johann Sebastian. Religious cantatas
Whittaker, William Gillies
    The cantatas of Johann Sebastian Bach : sacred and secular / [by]
    W. Gillies Whittaker. — London [etc.] : Oxford University Press.
    In 2 vols. — Originally published: 1959.
    Vol.1. — 1978. — xiv,717p : music ; 22cm.
    ISBN 0-19-315238-x Pbk : £6.95(set of 2 vols)
                                                                (B78-39233)

BBG(N) — Bartók, Béla. Biographies
Dommett, Kenneth
    Bartók / [by] Kenneth Dommett. — Sevenoaks : Novello, 1978.
    — 23p ; 19cm. — (Novello short biographies)
    Bibl.: p.22-23. — List of works: p.21-22.
    Sd : £0.30

BBJ(D) — Beethoven, Ludwig van. Essays
Beethoven studies / edited by Alan Tyson. — London [etc.] :
    Oxford University Press.
    2. — 1977 [i.e. 1978]. — xi,200p : music ; 24cm.
    List of works: p.193-196. — Index.
    ISBN 0-19-315315-7 : £9.50 : CIP rev.
                                                                (B77-28782)

BBJ(N) — Beethoven, Ludwig van. Biographies
Kendall, Alan, b.1939
    The life of Beethoven / [by] Alan Kendall. — London [etc.] :
    Hamlyn, 1978. — 144p : ill(some col), facsims, music, ports(some
    col) ; 30cm.
    Bibl.: p.141. — List of works: p.136-141. — Index.
    ISBN 0-600-31431-6 : £4.50
                                                                (B78-26882)

Orga, Ateş
    Beethoven : his life and times / [by] Ateş Orga. — Tunbridge
    Wells : Midas Books [etc.], 1978. — 176p : ill, facsims, ports ;
    26cm.
    Bibl.: p.5. — Index.
    ISBN 0-85936-082-2 : £6.50
                                                                (B78-26883)

Solomon, Maynard
    Beethoven / [by] Maynard Solomon. — London : Cassell, 1978.
    — xvi,400p : ill, facsims, map, ports ; 24cm.
    Originally published: New York : Schirmer Books, 1977. — Bibl.: p.372-385.
    — Index.
    ISBN 0-304-30034-9 : £8.95
                                                                (B78-26884)

BBJAC(ZC) — Beethoven, Ludwig van. Fidelio - expounding love
Singer, Irving
    Mozart & Beethoven : the concept of love in their operas / [by]
    Irving Singer. — Baltimore ; London : Johns Hopkins University
    Press, 1977. — xii,155,[1]p ; 24cm.
    Index.
    ISBN 0-8018-1987-3 : £7.00
    Primary classification BMSAC(ZC)
                                                                (B78-15123)

BBJARXNS — Beethoven, Ludwig van. String quartets
Kerman, Joseph
    The Beethoven quartets / [by] Joseph Kerman. — London [etc.] :
    Oxford University Press, 1978. — [6],386,viii p : music ; 24cm.
    Originally published: New York : Knopf ; London : Oxford University
    Press, 1967. — Bibl.: p.383-386. — List of works: p.i-iii. — Index.
    ISBN 0-19-315145-6 Pbk : £3.95
                                                                (B78-37869)

Radcliffe, Philip
    Beethoven's string quartets / [by] Philip Radcliffe. — 2nd ed. —
    Cambridge [etc.] : Cambridge University Press, 1978. — 192p :
    music ; 21cm.
    Previous ed.: London : Hutchinson, 1965. — Index.
    ISBN 0-521-21963-9 : £6.95
    ISBN 0-521-29326-x Pbk : £1.95
                                                                (B78-29840)

BBNO(D) — Bialas, Günter. Essays
Meilensteine eines Komponistenlebens : kleine Festschrift zum 70.
    Geburtstag von Günter Bialas / herausgegeben von Gotthard
    Speer und Hans-Jürgen Winterhoff. — Kassel [etc.] ; London ([32
    Gt Titchfield St., W1P 7AD]) : Bärenreiter, 1977. — 125p :
    music, ports ; 29cm.
    'Herausgegeben im Auftrag des Arbeitskreises für Schlessisches Lied und
    Schlessische Musik' - title page verso. — Bibl.: p.121. — List of sound discs:
    p.121.
    £10.08
    ISBN 3-7618-0572-1
                                                                (B78-19399)

BBPLAC — Blake, David. Toussaint. Librettos
Ward, Anthony
    Toussaint, or, The aristocracy of the skin : opera in 3 acts and 22
    scenes / text by Anthony Ward ; music by David Blake. —
    Sevenoaks : Novello, 1977. — xii,59p ; 21cm.
    Pbk : £1.70
                                                                (B78-06260)

BBRO — Boulez, Pierre
Boulez, Pierre
    Pierre Boulez, conversations with Célestin Deliège / [translated
    from the French] ; foreword by Robert Wangermée. — London
    ([48 Great Marlborough St., W1V 2BN]) : Eulenburg Books,
    1976. — 123p ; 24cm.
    Translation of: 'Par volonté et par hasard'. Paris : Éditions du Seuil, 1975.
    ISBN 0-903873-21-4 : £3.00
    ISBN 0-903873-22-2 Pbk : £1.50
                                                                (B78-11192)

BBTAQ — Brahms, Johannes. Piano music
Matthews, Denis
    Brahms piano music / [by] Denis Matthews. — London : British
    Broadcasting Corporation, 1978. — 76p : music ; 20cm. —
    (British Broadcasting Corporation. BBC music guides)
    Index.
    ISBN 0-563-12981-6 Pbk : £1.00
                                                                (B78-28703)

BBTNAMME — Brian, Havergal. Symphonies
MacDonald, Malcolm, b.1948
   The symphonies of Havergal Brian / [by] Malcolm MacDonald.
   — London : Kahn and Averill.
In 3 vols.
Vol.2 : Symphonies 13-29. — 1978. — 288p : music ; 23cm.
ISBN 0-900707-43-7 : £6.25

(B78-23596)

BBUAC — Britten, Benjamin, Baron Britten. The little sweep.
   Librettos
Crozier, Eric
   The little sweep ... / by Eric Crozier ; music by Benjamin Britten.
   — London : Boosey and Hawkes, [1978]. — 39p ; 21cm.
Originally published: in 'Let's make an opera'. London : Hawkes and Son,
1949.
Sd : Unpriced

(B78-28697)

BBUEAMME — Bruckner, Anton. Symphonies
Barford, Philip
   Bruckner symphonies / [by] Philip Barford. — London : British
   Broadcasting Corporation, 1978. — 68p : music ; 20cm. —
   (British Broadcasting Corporation. BBC music guides)
ISBN 0-563-12767-8 Pbk : £1.00

(B78-33165)

Simpson, Robert
   The essence of Bruckner : an essay towards the understanding of
   his music / by Robert Simpson. — 2nd ed. — London : Gollancz,
   1977. — 206p,plate : music, port ; 23cm.
Previous ed.: 1967. — Index.
ISBN 0-575-01189-0 : £4.95

(B78-10360)

BBX — Byrd, William
Kerman, Joseph
   The music of William Byrd / [by Joseph Kerman, Philip Brett,
   Oliver Neighbour]. — London [etc.] : Faber.
In 3 vols.
Vol.3 : The consort and keyboard music of William Byrd / [by] Oliver
Neighbour. — 1978. — 3-272p : music ; 25cm.
Bibl.: p.13-17. — Index.
ISBN 0-571-10566-1 : £15.00 : CIP rev.

(B78-19401)

BCBRS — Carter, Elliott
   Elliott Carter : a 70th birthday tribute. — [New York] : Associated
   Music Publishers ; London (140 Strand, WC2 1HG) : G. Schirmer
   Limited, 1978. — 16p : ports ; 16x21cm.
List of works: p.12-15.
Sd : Unpriced

(B78-26885)

BCBX(N) — Cavalli, Francesco. Biographies
Glover, Jane
   Cavalli / [by] Jane Glover. — London : Batsford, 1978. — 191p,
   [4]p of plates : facsims, music ; 25cm.
Bibl.: p.171-181. — List of works: p.170. — Index.
ISBN 0-7134-1007-8 : £8.50

(B78-26885)

BCE(N) — Chopin, Frédéric. Biographies
Jordan, Ruth
   Nocturne : a life of Chopin / [by] Ruth Jordan. — London :
   Constable, 1978. — 286p,leaf of plate,12p of plates : ill, facsims,
   ports ; 23cm.
Bibl.: p.277-280. — Index.
ISBN 0-09-462330-9 : £6.95

(B78-26246)

BCMWACM — Coward, Sir Noël. Cowardy custard. Librettos
Frow, Gerald
   The Mermaid's 'Cowardy custard' : an entertainment / devised by
   Gerald Frow, Alan Strachan, Wendy Toye ; featuring the words
   and music of Nöel Coward. — New York ; London [etc.] :
   French, [1977]. — 96p : plan ; 22cm. — (French's musical
   library)
Six men, 6 women.
ISBN 0-573-68079-5 Sd : £1.80

(B78-21400)

BCQRACPP — Crocker, John. Potty pantomime. Librettos
Crocker, John, b.1925
   Potty pantomime / by John Crocker ; with lyrics and music by
   Eric Gilder. — London : [Evans Bros], [1978]. — [4],16p : music ;
   21cm. — (Evans one act plays)
Eight characters.
ISBN 0-237-75031-7 Sd : £0.40

(B78-37098)

BDEAC — Davies, Peter Maxwell. The martyrdom of St Magnus.
   Librettos
Davies, Peter Maxwell
   The martyrdom of St Magnus : a chamber opera in nine scenes /
   [by] Peter Maxwell Davies ; libretto by the composer after the
   novel 'Magnus' by George Mackay Brown. — London : Boosey
   and Hawkes, 1977. — 31p ; 19cm.
Sd : £1.00

(B78-06987)

BDL(N/EM) — Delius, Frederick. Biographies. Illustrations
   Delius : a life in pictures / [compiled by] Lionel Carley and Robert
   Threlfall. — Oxford : Oxford University Press, 1977. — [4],99p,8p
   of plates : ill(some col), facsims, music, ports(some col) ; 31cm.
ISBN 0-19-315437-4 : £6.95

(B78-05402)

BDL(TC) — Delius, Frederick. Bibliographies of scores
Threlfall, Robert
   A catalogue of the compositions of Frederick Delius : sources and
   references / [by] Robert Threlfall. — London : Delius Trust :
   Distributed by Boosey and Hawkes, 1977. — 206p : facsims, port ;
   26cm.
Limited ed. of 1000 numbered copies. — Index.
ISBN 0-85162-028-0 : £10.00

(B78-03908)

BDL/JM — Delius, Frederick. Hassan
Redwood, Dawn
   Flecker and Delius : the making of 'Hassan' / [by] Dawn
   Redwood. — London (14 Barlby Rd, W10 6AR) : Thames
   Publishing, 1978. — 103p : ill, facsims, music, ports ; 21cm.
Facsims., ports on lining papers.
ISBN 0-905210-06-9 : £5.50

(B78-29853)

BDRAC — Donizetti, Gaetano. La favorita. Librettos
Royer, Alphonse
   La favorita : drama in four acts / music by Gaetano Donizetti ;
   libretto by Alphonse Royer and Gustave Vaëz ; Italian translation
   [from the French] by Francesco Jannetti, literal English
   translation [from the Italian] by William Weaver. — New York ;
   London ([140 Strand, WC2R 1HH]) : G. Schirmer, 1977. — vii
   p,18 leaves ; 27cm. — (G. Schirmer's collection of opera librettos)
Parallel Italian text and English translation. — Leaves printed on both sides.
Sd : Unpriced

(B78-26887)

BDXAMME — Dvořák, Antonin. Symphonies
Layton, Robert
   Dvořák symphonies and concertos / [by] Robert Layton. —
   London : British Broadcasting Corporation, 1978. — 68p : music ;
   20cm. — (British Broadcasting Corporation. BBC music guides)
ISBN 0-563-12676-0 Pbk : £1.00
Also classified at BDXAMPF

(B78-29839)

BDXAMPF — Dvořák, Antonin. Concertos
Layton, Robert
   Dvořák symphonies and concertos / [by] Robert Layton. —
   London : British Broadcasting Corporation, 1978. — 68p : music ;
   20cm. — (British Broadcasting Corporation. BBC music guides)
ISBN 0-563-12676-0 Pbk : £1.00
Primary classification BDXAMME

(B78-29839)

BEP(N/XLJ32) — Elgar, Sir Edward, bt. 1889-1920
Young, Percy Marshall
   Alice Elgar : enigma of a Victorian lady / [by] Percy M. Young.
   — London : Dobson, 1978. — 201p,[20]p of plates : ill(some col),
   facsims, ports(some col) ; 23cm.
Ill. on lining papers. — Bibl.: p.194. — Index.
ISBN 0-234-77482-7 : £7.50

(B78-35468)

BEP/FD — Elgar, Sir Edward. Recorded music
Knowles, John, b.1948
   Elgar's interpreters on record : an Elgar discography / compiled
   by John Knowles. — [Malvern] ([c/o F.B. Greatwich, 20
   Geraldine Rd, Malvern, Worcs. WR14 3PA]) : The Elgar Society,
   1977. — 68,[1]p ; 21cm.
Sd : £1.00

(B78-33481)

BFKSACM — Fiske, John. England expects. Librettos
Richards, Gavin
   England expects : a musical entertainment for all those sick with
   sacrifice / by Gavin Richards ; music by John Fiske. — London
   (97 Ferme Park Rd, Crouch End, N8 9SA) : Journeyman Press ;
   London : Belt and Braces Roadshow Co., 1977. — 64p : ill,
   ports ; 21cm.
Fifteen men, 6 women, supers.
ISBN 0-904526-25-9 Pbk : £1.20

(B78-01675)

BFUR(N) — French, Percy. Biographies
Healy, James N
Percy French and his songs / by James N. Healy ; illustrations and musical arrangements by the author. — Dublin [etc.] ([25 Lower Abbey St., Dublin 1]) : Mercier Press, 1977. — xxviii, 172p : ill, music, port ; 19cm.
Originally published: 1966. — Bibl.: p.172. — Includes the words of many of French's songs.
ISBN 0-85342-394-6 Pbk : £1.70

(B78-33936)

BGRT(B) — Grainger, Percy Aldridge. Periodicals
The **Grainger** journal / the Percy Grainger Society. — Kenilworth (c/o D. Tall, 21 Laburnum Ave., Kenilworth, Warks CV8 2DR) : Percy Grainger Society.
No.1- ; Spring 1978-. — [1978]-. — ill, music, ports ; 22cm.
Two issues a year. — [1],36p. in 1st issue.
Sd : Unpriced
ISSN 0141-5085

(B78-37094)

BGYU(N) — Gurney, Ivor. Biographies
Hurd, Michael
The ordeal of Ivor Gurney / [by] Michael Hurd. — Oxford [etc.] : Oxford University Press, 1978. — xi,230p,[8]p of plates : ill, facsim, map, music, ports ; 23cm.
Bibl.: p.217. — Index.
ISBN 0-19-211752-1 : £5.95 : CIP rev.

(B78-29833)

BHE(N) — Haydn, Joseph. Biographies
Landon, Howard Chandler Robbins
Haydn : chronicle and works / [by] H.C. Robbins Landon. — [London] : [Thames and Hudson].
In 5 vols.
Haydn at Eszterháza, 1766-1790. — [1978]. — 799p,[20]p of plates : ill(incl 1 col), facsims, music, ports ; 27cm.
List of works: p.795-799. — Index.
ISBN 0-500-01168-0 : £30.00

(B78-40350)

BHND — Hoddinott, Alun
Deane, Basil
Alun Hoddinott / [by] Basil Deane. — [Cardiff] : University of Wales Press [for] the Welsh Arts Council, 1978. — 74p : music ; 24cm. — (Composers of Wales ; 2)
Bibl.: p.74. — List of works: p.67-72. — List of sound discs: p.73.
ISBN 0-7083-0695-0 Pbk : £1.50

(B78-39781)

BHS(N) — Howells, Herbert. Biographies
Palmer, Christopher
Herbert Howells : a study / by Christopher Palmer ; foreword by Sir David Willcocks. — Sevenoaks : Novello, 1978. — 87p : music, ports ; 22cm.
List of works: p.84-87.
Pbk : £1.20

(B78-33933)

BIV — Ives, Charles
Charles Ives Centennial Festival-Conference, *New York and New Haven, 1974*
An Ives celebration : papers and panels of the Charles Ives Centennial Festival-Conference / edited by H. Wiley Hitchcock, Vivian Perlis. — Urbana [etc.] ; London : University of Illinois Press, 1977. — xi,282p : facsims, music, port ; 27cm. — (Music in American life)
Index.
ISBN 0-252-00619-4 : £8.40

(B78-16383)

BJFAC — Janáček, Leoš. Opera
Ewans, Michael
Janáček's tragic operas / [by] Michael Ewans. — London : Faber, 1977. — 3-284p : music ; 23cm.
Bibl.: p.272. — List of music: p.273-277. — Index.
ISBN 0-571-10959-4 : £7.95 : CIP rev.

(B77-23620)

BKDN(N) — Kern, Jerome. Biographies
Freedland, Michael
Jerome Kern / [by] Michael Freedland. — London : Robson, 1978. — [5],182p,[8]p of plates : ill, facsim, ports ; 23cm.
Index.
ISBN 0-86051-011-5 : £4.50 : CIP rev.

(B78-20441)

BKTM — Krenek, Ernst
Krenek, Ernst
Horizons circled : reflections on my music / [by] Ernst Krenek, with contributions by Will Ogdon and John L. Stewart. — Berkeley [etc.] ; London : University of California Press, 1974. — ix,167p,[6]p of plates : ill, music, ports ; 23cm.
List of works: p.155-167.
ISBN 0-520-02338-2 : £6.80

(B78-06254)

BLJ(B) — Liszt, Franz. Periodicals
Liszt Society
The Liszt Society journal. — London (78 Wimbledon Park Side, SW19 5LH) : The Society.
Supersedes: Liszt Society. Newsletter.
Vol.1- ; 1975-. — [1976]-. — music, ports ; 31cm.
Published at irregular intervals. — 37p. in 1st issue.
£3.50(for members)
ISSN 0141-0792

(B78-11193)

BME(N) — Mahler, Gustav. Biographies
Gartenberg, Egon
Mahler : the man and his music / [by] Egon Gartenberg. — London : Cassell, 1978. — x,406p,[32]p of plates : ill, facsim, music, ports ; 24cm.
Bibl.: p.379-386. — Index.
ISBN 0-304-30058-6 : £8.95

(B78-25369)

BMGH — Mathias, William
Boyd, Malcolm, *b.1932*
William Mathias / [by] Malcolm Boyd. — [Cardiff] : University of Wales Press [for] the Welsh Arts Council, 1978. — 88p : music ; 24cm. — (Composers of Wales ; 1)
Bibl.: p.88. — List of works: p.75-84. — List of sound discs: p.85-87.
ISBN 0-7083-0672-1 Pbk : Unpriced

(B78-15753)

BMJ(N/YDL/XHJ) — Mendelssohn, Felix. Scotland, 1829
Jenkins, David, *b.1944*
Mendelssohn in Scotland / [by] David Jenkins & Mark Visocchi. — London : Chappell : Elm Tree Books, 1978. — 116p : ill, 2 facsims, 2 maps, plan, ports ; 29cm.
'The authors have woven together Mendelssohn's and Klingemann's original material against an historical background ...' - jacket. — Bibl.: p.113. — Index.
ISBN 0-903443-18-x : £5.95

(B78-19674)

BMS — Mozart, Wolfgang Amadeus
McLeish, Kenneth
Mozart / [by] Kenneth and Valerie McLeish. — London : Heinemann, 1978. — [5],84p : ill, facsims, music, ports ; 21cm. — (Composers and their world)
Bibl.: p.75. — Index.
ISBN 0-434-95125-0 : £2.50

(B78-29831)

BMS(N) — Mozart, Wolfgang Amadeus. Biographies
Eibl, Joseph Heinz
Wolfgang Amadeus Mozart, Chronik eines Lebens / zusammengestellt von Joseph Heinz Eibl. — 2.Aufl. — Kassel [etc.] ; London : Bärenreiter [etc.], 1977. — 151p : geneal table ; 18cm.
Previous ed.: Kassel ; London : Bärenreiter, 1965. — Bibl.: p.150-151. — Index.
Pbk : £1.90
ISBN 3-7618-0562-4

(B78-21399)

Kenyon, Nicholas
Mozart : the young musician / by Nicholas Kenyon ; illustrated by Peter Dennis. — London : Macdonald Educational, 1978. — 48p : ill(chiefly col), facsims, music, col port ; 29cm. — (Macdonald famous people)
Index.
ISBN 0-356-05916-2 : £1.95

(B78-30826)

Raynor, Henry
Mozart / [by] Henry Raynor. — London [etc.] : Macmillan, 1978. — 152p : ill(some col), facsims, music, plans, ports(some col) ; 25cm.
Bibl.: p.149. — Index.
ISBN 0-333-21615-6 : £5.95 : CIP rev.

(B77-22045)

BMSAC — Mozart, Wolfgang Amadeus. Don Giovanni
Abert, Hermann
Mozart's 'Don Giovanni' / [by] Hermann Abert ; translated [from the German] by Peter Gellhorn. — London (48 Great Marlborough St., W1V 2BN) : Eulenburg Books, 1976. — 138p : music ; 24cm.
Translation of: the essay on 'Don Giovanni' originally published in 'W.A. Mozart' / von Hermann Abert ; neubearbeitete und erweiterte Ausgabe von Otto Johns 'Mozart'. 6.Aufl. Leipzig : Breitkopf und Härtel, 1923-24.
ISBN 0-903873-19-2 : £3.00
ISBN 0-903873-11-7 Pbk : £1.50

(B78-11196)

BMSAC — Mozart, Wolfgang Amadeus. Don Giovanni. Librettos
Da Ponte, Lorenzo
Don Giovanni, KV527 : Dramma giocoso im zwei Akten / [von
Wolfgang Amadeus Mozart] ; Text von Lorenzo da Ponte. —
Kassel [etc.] ; London ([32 Gt Titchfield St., W1P 7AD]) :
Bärenreiter. — (Internationale Stiftung Mozarteum Salzburg.
Mozarts italienische Texte mit deutscher Übersetzung ; Bd 4)
Textbuch italienisch-deutsch / wortgetreue deutsche Übersetzung von
Walther Dürr. — 1977. — 207p ; 19cm.
Parallel Italian text and German translation. — Italian text from: 'Wolfgang
Amadeus Mozart. Neue Ausgabe sämtlicher Werke. Serie II. Bühnenwerke.
Werkgruppe 5. Band 17. "Il dissoluto punito ossia il Don Giovanni"' /
presented by Wolfgang Plath and Wolfgang Rehm.
Pbk : £2.24
ISBN 3-7618-0563-2
(B78-17615)

Higgins, John, b.1934
The making of an opera : 'Don Giovanni' at Glyndebourne / [by]
John Higgins ; with special photography by Roger Wood. —
London : Secker and Warburg, 1978. — xiii,272p : ill, facsims,
ports ; 25cm.
Index. — Includes: Don Giovanni, or, The libertine's punishment : opera in
two acts / music by Wolfgang Amadeus Mozart ; libretto by Lorenzo da
Ponte ; English translation [from the Italian] by Ellen H. Bleiler.
ISBN 0-436-19595-x : £7.95
Primary classification BMSAC/E
(B78-33162)

BMSAC — Mozart, Wolfgang Amadeus. Opera
Osborne, Charles, b.1927
The complete operas of Mozart : a critical guide / by Charles
Osborne. — London : Gollancz, 1978. — 349p,leaf of plate,[14]p
of plates : ill, facsims, music, ports ; 24cm.
Bibl.: p.341. — Index.
ISBN 0-575-02221-3 : £7.50
(B78-33935)

**BMSAC(ZC) — Mozart, Wolfgang Amadeus. Operas - expounding
love**
Singer, Irving
Mozart & Beethoven : the concept of love in their operas / [by]
Irving Singer. — Baltimore ; London : Johns Hopkins University
Press, 1977. — xii,155,[1]p ; 24cm.
Index.
ISBN 0-8018-1987-3 : £7.00
Also classified at BBJAC(ZC); 782.1'092'4
(B78-15123)

BMSAC/E — Mozart, Wolfgang Amadeus. Don Giovanni. Production
Higgins, John, b.1934
The making of an opera : 'Don Giovanni' at Glyndebourne / [by]
John Higgins ; with special photography by Roger Wood. —
London : Secker and Warburg, 1978. — xiii,272p : ill, facsims,
ports ; 25cm.
Index. — Includes: Don Giovanni, or, The libertine's punishment : opera in
two acts / music by Wolfgang Amadeus Mozart ; libretto by Lorenzo da
Ponte ; English translation [from the Italian] by Ellen H. Bleiler.
ISBN 0-436-19595-x : £7.95
Also classified at BMSAC
(B78-33162)

BMSADW — Mozart, Wolfgang Amadeus. Songs, etc
Arien, Szenen, Ensembles / [von] Wolfgang Amadeus Mozart. —
Kassel [etc.] ; London ([32 Gt Titchfield St., W1P 7AD]) :
Bärenreiter. — (Internationale Stiftung Mozarteum Salzburg.
Mozarts italienische Texte mit deutscher Übersetzung ; Bd 3)
Textbuch italienisch-deutsch / wortgetreue deutsche Übersetzungen von
Stefan Kunze. — 1977. — 119p ; 19cm.
Parallel Italian text and German translation. — Italian texts from:
'Wolfgang Amadeus Mozart. Neue Ausgabe sämtlicher Werke. Serie II.
Bühnenwerke. Werkgruppe 7. Arien, Szenen, Ensembles und Chöre mit
Orchester. Bd 1-4' / presented by Stefan Kunze.
Pbk : £1.68
ISBN 3-7618-0556-x
(B78-26890)

**BMSAMPQF — Mozart, Wolfgang Amadeus. Piano & orchestra.
Concertos**
Girdlestone, Cuthbert Morton
Mozart's piano concertos / [by] C.M. Girdlestone. — 3rd ed. —
London : Cassell, 1978. — 509p : music ; 23cm.
Previous ed.: 1958. — Index.
ISBN 0-304-30043-8 : £6.50
(B78-22846)

Radcliffe, Philip
Mozart piano concertos / [by] Philip Radcliffe. — London :
British Broadcasting Corporation, 1978. — 72p : music ; 20cm. —
(British Broadcasting Corporation. BBC music guides)
Index.
ISBN 0-563-12771-6 Pbk : £1.00
(B78-33168)

**BMSAMPSF — Mozart, Wolfgang Amadeus. Violin & orchestra.
Concertos**
King, Alexander Hyatt
Mozart wind and string concertos / [by] A. Hyatt King. —
London : British Broadcasting Corporation, 1978. — 76p : music ;
20cm. — (British Broadcasting Corporation. BBC music guides)
Index.
ISBN 0-563-12770-8 Pbk : £1.00
Also classified at BMSAMPUF
(B78-28702)

**BMSAMPUF — Mozart, Wolfgang Amadeus. Wind instrument &
orchestra. Concertos**
King, Alexander Hyatt
Mozart wind and string concertos / [by] A. Hyatt King. —
London : British Broadcasting Corporation, 1978. — 76p : music ;
20cm. — (British Broadcasting Corporation. BBC music guides)
Index.
ISBN 0-563-12770-8 Pbk : £1.00
Primary classification BMSAMPSF
(B78-28702)

BMTPAC — Musgrave, Thea. Mary, Queen of Scots
Musgrave, Thea
Mary, Queen of Scots : an opera in three acts / libretto and music
by Thea Musgrave. — Sevenoaks : Novello, 1976. — [5],56p :
geneal table ; 20cm.
Libretto.
Sd : £1.00
(B78-12097)

BPEB(N) — Parry, Joseph. Biographies
Richards, W Mansel
Dr Joseph Parry, 1841-1903 / [compiled by W. Mansel Richards
and pupils of Cyfarthfa High School]. — [Merthyr Tydfil] ([c/o
Town Hall, Merthyr Tydfil, M. Glam.]) : [W.M. Richards], 1977.
— [8]p : 2 ill, music, port ; 22cm.
Bibl.: p.[3]. — List of selected works: p.[6]-[7].
Sd : Unpriced
(B78-03577)

BPECACM — Patrick, John. Noah's animals. Librettos
Patrick, John, b.1907
Noah's animals : a musical allegory in three acts / by John
Patrick. — New York ; London [etc.] : French, 1976. — 69p : ill,
plans ; 22cm. — (French's musical library)
Eleven men, 10 women, supers.
ISBN 0-573-68078-7 Sd : £1.65
(B78-02612)

BPNN(N) — Porter, Cole. Biographies
Schwartz, Charles
Cole Porter : a biography / by Charles Schwartz. — London :
W.H. Allen, 1978. — xvii,365p,[16]p of plates : ill, ports ; 24cm.
Originally published: New York : Dial Press, 1977. — Bibl.: p.334-344. —
List of musical works: p.271-323. — List of sound discs: p.324-333. —
Index.
ISBN 0-491-02292-1 : £6.50
(B78-22845)

BPO(N) — Poulenc, Francis. Biographies
Audel, Stéphane
My friends and myself : conversations [with] Francis Poulenc /
assembled by Stéphane Audel ; translated [from the French] by
James Harding. — London : Dobson, 1978. — 152p,leaf of
plate,[8]p of plates : 1 ill, ports ; 23cm.
Translation of: 'Moi et mes amis'. Genève : La Palatine, 1963. — Index.
ISBN 0-234-77251-4 : £4.95
(B78-39780)

BPU(N) — Puccini, Giacomo. Biographies
Weaver, William, b.1923
Puccini : the man and his music / [by] William Weaver ; picture
editor Gerald Fitzgerald. — London : Hutchinson, 1978. — x,
150p : ill(some col), facsims, music, ports(some col) ; 24cm. —
(Metropolitan Opera Guild. Composer series)
Originally published: New York : Dutton, 1977. — Bibl.: p.ix.
ISBN 0-09-132380-0 : £5.50
(B78-20437)

BRC(N) — Rachmaninoff, Sergei. Biographies
Piggott, Patrick
Rachmaninov / [by] Patrick Piggott. — London : Faber, 1978. —
110p : ill, facsim, music, ports ; 22cm. — (The great composers)
Bibl.: p.104. — List of works: p.105-106. — Index.
ISBN 0-571-10265-4 : £3.95 : CIP rev.
(B77-12592)

BRK(N) — Rodgers, Richard. Biographies
Nolan, Frederick
The sound of their music : the story of Rodgers & Hammerstein /
[by] Frederick Nolan. — London [etc.] : Dent, 1978. — 272p : ill,
ports ; 24cm.
Bibl.: p.265-266. — Index.
ISBN 0-460-04315-3 : £6.50 : CIP rev.
(B78-09114)

BRU — Rubbra, Edmund
Edmund Rubbra : composer-essays / edited by Lewis Foreman ; with an introduction by Sir Adrian Boult, & three specially commissioned drawings of Dr Rubbra by Richard Walker ... — Rickmansworth (22 Pheasant Way, Rickmansworth, Herts.) : Triad Press, 1977. — 112p : ill, facsims, music, ports ; 30cm.
Facsims on lining papers. — Limited ed. of 250 numbered copies. — Bibl.: p.97-102. — List of sound discs: p.102-107. — Index.
ISBN 0-902070-21-5 : £9.95 : CIP rev.

(B77-18309)

BSET(N) — Schoenberg, Arnold. Biographies
Small, Christopher, b.1927
Schoenberg / [by] Christopher Small. — Sevenoaks : Novello, 1977. — 28p ; 19cm. — (Novello short biographies)
List of works: p.27-28.
Sd : £0.47

(B78-02607)

BSF(N) — Schubert, Franz. Biographies
Reed, John, b.1909
Schubert / [by] John Reed. — London : Faber, 1978. — 106p : ill, facsims, music, ports ; 23cm. — (The great composers)
Bibl.: p.96. — Index.
ISBN 0-571-10327-8 : £3.95 : CIP rev.

(B77-22755)

Woodford, Peggy
Schubert : his life and times / [by] Peggy Woodford. — Tunbridge Wells : Midas Books [etc.], 1978. — 159p : ill, facsims, ports ; 26cm.
Bibl.: p.6. — Index.
ISBN 0-85936-095-4 : £6.50

(B78-40351)

BSGNC — Scriabin, Alexander
Macdonald, Hugh, b.1940
Skryabin / [by] Hugh Macdonald. — London [etc.] : Oxford University Press, 1978. — 71p : music ; 22cm. — (Oxford studies of composers ; 15)
List of works: p.69-71.
ISBN 0-19-315438-2 Pbk : £2.95

(B78-35469)

BSGNHACM — Sharkey, Jack. Not the Count of Monte Cristo?! Librettos
Reiser, Dave
'Not the Count of Monte Cristo?!' : a musical comedy in three acts for 3 players and a piano / by Dave Reiser & Jack Sharkey. — New York ; London [etc.] : French, 1978. — 65p : plan ; 19cm.
ISBN 0-573-68085-x Sd : £1.65

(B78-12096)

BSGNHACM — Sharkey, Jack. Pushover. Librettos
Easton, Ken
Pushover : a choral play in one act about Samson, Judge of Israel / book, music & lyrics by Ken Easton and Jack Sharkey. — New York ; London [etc.] : French, 1977. — 27p ; 19cm.
Two men, 3 women, supers.
ISBN 0-573-62425-9 Sd : £1.20

(B78-03576)

BSGNHACM — Sharkey, Jack. Turnabout. Librettos
Easton, Ken
Turnabout : a musical version of the Book of Esther / book, music and lyrics by Ken Easton and Jack Sharkey. — [French's acting ed.]. — New York ; London [etc.] : French, 1978. — 49p ; 19cm.
Six men, 18 women, supers.
ISBN 0-573-62527-1 Sd : £1.65

(B78-20438)

BSGR(TC) — Shostakovich, Dmitrii Dmitrievich. Bibliographies of scores
MacDonald, Malcolm, b.1948
Dmitri Shostakovich, a complete catalogue / compiled by Malcolm MacDonald. — London : Boosey and Hawkes, 1977. — 47p : music, ports ; 25cm.
Index.
Pbk : £1.50

(B78-02934)

BSGRAMME — Shostakovich, Dmitrii Dmitrievich. Symphonies
Ottaway, Hugh
Shostakovich symphonies / [by] Hugh Ottaway. — London : British Broadcasting Corporation, 1978. — 68p : music ; 20cm. — (British Broadcasting Corporation. BBC music guides)
Index.
ISBN 0-563-12772-4 Pbk : £1.00

(B78-28701)

BSU(N) — Strauss, Richard. Biographies
Del Mar, Norman
Richard Strauss : a critical commentary on his life and works / by Norman Del Mar. — London : Barrie and Jenkins.
In 3 vols.
Vol.1. — 1978. — xv,462p,[6] leaves of plates : facsim, music, ports ; 23cm.
Originally published: 1962. — Bibl.: p.442-444. — Index.
£8.95
ISBN 0-214-15735-0

(B78-27521)

Vol.2. — 1978. — xi,452p,[8] leaves of plates : ill, facsims, music, ports ; 23cm.
Originally published: 1969. — Index.
£8.95
ISBN 0-214-16008-4

(B78-27522)

Vol.3. — 1978. — xxi,552p,leaf of plate,[10]p of plates : ill, facsims, music, plans, ports ; 23cm.
Originally published: 1972. — Bibl.: p.510-511. — List of works: p.478-504. — List of sound discs: p.507-509. — Index to vols 1-3.
£8.95
ISBN 0-214-65158-4

(B78-27523)

Jefferson, Alan
Richard Strauss / [by] Alan Jefferson. — Sevenoaks : Novello, 1978. — 27p ; 19cm. — (Novello short biographies)
List of works: p.26-27.
Sd : £0.30

(B78-31596)

BSU(N/XNL5) — Strauss, Richard. Biographies, 1931-1935
Strauss, Richard
A confidential matter : the letters of Richard Strauss and Stefan Zweig, 1931-1935 / translated from the German by Max Knight ; foreword by Edward E. Lowinsky. — Berkeley [etc.] ; London : University of California Press, 1977. — xxxi,122p : ill, facsims, music, ports ; 23cm.
Translation of: 'Briefwechsel zwischen Richard Strauss und Stefan Zweig'. Frankfurt am Main : Fischer, 1957.
ISBN 0-520-03036-2 : £6.75

(B78-04319)

BSUAC — Strauss, Richard. Ariadne auf Naxos. Librettos
Hofmannsthal, Hugo von
Ariadne auf Naxos : Oper in einem Akt nebst einem Vorspiel / von Hugo von Hofmannsthal ; Musik von Richard Strauss. — London [etc.] : Boosey and Hawkes, [1977]. — 32p ; 26cm.
Libretto. — Originally published: Berlin : s.n., 1912.
Sd : £0.85

BSUAC — Strauss, Richard. Electra. Librettos
Hofmannsthal, Hugo von
Elektra : tragedy in one act / by Hugo von Hofmannsthal ; English version [translated from the German] by Alfred Kalisch ; music by Richard Strauss. — London [etc.] : Boosey and Hawkes, [1977]. — 67p ; 26cm.
Parallel German and English libretto.
Pbk : £9.00

BSV(N) — Stravinsky, Igor. Biographies
McLeish, Kenneth
Stravinsky / [by] Kenneth and Valerie McLeish. — London : Heinemann, 1978. — [5],83p : ill, facsims, music, ports ; 21cm. — (Composers and their world)
Bibl.: p.76. — Index.
ISBN 0-434-95126-9 : £2.50

(B78-30825)

BSVAMM/HM/R — Stravinsky, Igor. Rite of spring. Harmony
Forte, Allen
The harmonic organization of 'The rite of spring' / [by] Allen Forte. — New Haven ; London : Yale University Press, 1978. — vii,151p : 1 ill, music ; 24cm.
ISBN 0-300-02201-8 : £10.80

(B78-38605)

BSW(N) — Sullivan, Sir Arthur Seymour. Biographies
Allen, Reginald
Sir Arthur Sullivan : composer & personage / by Reginald Allen in collaboration with Gale R. D'Luhy. — New York : Pierpont Morgan Library ; London [etc.] : Chappell, 1975. — iii-xxviii, 215p : ill, facsims, music, ports ; 29cm.
Jacket title: The life and work of Sir Arthur Sullivan. — Bibl.: p.207-208. — Index.
ISBN 0-87923-145-9 : £12.95

(B78-05721)

BVE(N) — Verdi, Giuseppe. Biographies
Hume, Paul
Verdi : the man and his music / [by] Paul Hume ; picture editor Gerald Fitzgerald. — London : Hutchinson, 1978. — x,182p : ill(some col), facsims, ports(1 col) ; 24cm. — (Metropolitan Opera Guild. Composer series)
Originally published: New York : Dutton, 1977. — Bibl.: p.ix.
ISBN 0-09-132390-8 : £5.50

(B78-08475)

Osborne, Charles, *b.1927*
Verdi / [by] Charles Osborne. — London [etc.] : Macmillan, 1978.
— 152p : ill(some col), facsims, music, ports(2 col) ; 25cm.
Bibl.: p.149. — List of works: p.149. — Index.
ISBN 0-333-21483-8 : £5.95 : CIP rev.

(B77-21346)

Southwell-Sander, Peter
Verdi : his life and times / [by] Peter Southwell-Sander ; with a
foreword by Sir Geraint Evans. — Tunbridge Wells : Midas
Books, 1978. — 160p : ill, facsims, music, ports ; 26cm.
Bibl.: p.7. — Index.
ISBN 0-85936-096-2 : £6.50 : CIP rev.

(B78-03574)

BVEAC — Verdi, Giuseppe. Opera
Budden, Julian
The operas of Verdi / [by] Julian Budden. — London : Cassell.
In 3 vols.
2 : From 'Il trovatore' to 'La forza del destina'. — 1978. — ix,532p :
music ; 24cm.
Index.
ISBN 0-304-30056-x : £17.50

(B78-39231)

Godefroy, Vincent
The dramatic genius of Verdi : studies of selected operas / by
Vincent Godefroy. — London : Gollancz.
In 2 vols.
Vol.2. — 1977. — 348p : music ; 23cm.
ISBN 0-575-02166-7 : £7.50

(B78-02610)

BVJ(N) — Vivaldi, Antonio. Biographies
Kendall, Alan, *b.1939*
Vivaldi / [by] Alan Kendall. — London : Chappell : Elm Tree
Books, 1978. — 128p,[8]p of plates : ill(some col), facsims, music,
plan, ports ; 32cm.
List of works: p.110-120. — Bibl.: p.121-122. — Index.
ISBN 0-903443-26-0 : £8.95

(B78-18541)

BWC(N) — Wagner, Richard. Biographies
Chancellor, John
Wagner / [by] John Chancellor. — London : Weidenfeld and
Nicolson, 1978. — x,310p,[8]p of plates : ill, ports ; 23cm.
Bibl.: p.299-301. — Index.
ISBN 0-297-77429-8 : £8.50

(B78-20436)

Wagner, Cosima
Cosima Wagner's diaries. — London : Collins.
Vol.1 : 1869-1877 / edited and annotated by Martin Gregor-Dellin and
Dietrich Mack ; translation [from the German] and with an introduction by
Geoffrey Skelton. — 1978. — 1199p,[16]p of plates : ill, ports ; 24cm.
Translation of: 'Die Tagebücher'. Bd 1 : 1869-1877. München : Piper, 1976.
— Index.
ISBN 0-00-216130-3 : £15.00

(B78-34737)

BWC(Z) — Wagner, Richard - related to Friedrich Nietzche
Fischer-Dieskau, Dietrich
Wagner and Nietzsche / [by] Dietrich Fischer-Dieskau ; translated
from the German by Joachim Neugroschel. — London : Sidgwick
and Jackson, 1978. — [8],232p ; 24cm.
This translation originally published: New York : Seabury Press, 1976. —
Translation of: 'Wagner und Nietzsche'. Stuttgart : Deutsche
Verlags-Anstalt, 1974. — Index.
ISBN 0-283-98434-1 : £7.50
Also classified at 193

(B78-39782)

BWCAC — Wagner, Richard. Opera
Garten, Hugh Frederic
Wagner the dramatist / by H.F. Garten. — London : J. Calder,
1977. — 159p : ill, ports ; 23cm. — ([Opera library])
Bibl.: p.151-155. — Index.
ISBN 0-7145-3620-2 : £5.95

(B78-09113)

BWCAC — Wagner, Richard. Rienzi
Deathridge, John
Wagner's 'Rienzi' : a reappraisal based on a study of the sketches
and drafts / [by] John Deathridge. — Oxford : Clarendon Press,
1977. — xvii,199p,III leaves of plates : facsim, music ; 28cm. —
(Oxford monographs on music)
Bibl.: p.191-193. — Index.
ISBN 0-19-816131-x : £12.00 : CIP rev.

(B77-08491)

BWKRACM — Webber, Andrew Lloyd. Evita
Webber, Andrew Lloyd
Evita : the legend of Eva Peron, 1919-1952 / by Andrew Lloyd
Webber and Tim Rice. — London : Elm Tree Books, 1978. —
[121]p : ill, ports ; 27cm.
Ports. on lining papers. — Bibl.: p.[120].
ISBN 0-241-89890-0 : £3.95 : CIP rev.

(B78-12401)

BWNTSACM — Wise, Jim. Yankee ingenuity. Librettos
Bimonte, Richard
Yankee ingenuity
Yankee ingenuity : a musical / music by Jim Wise ; book and
lyrics by Richard Bimonte. — French's acting ed. — New York ;
London [etc.] : French, 1977. — 83p : plans ; 22cm. — (French's
musical library)
Eight men, 4 women. — Music available separately. — 'Based on "Fashion"
by Anna Cora Mowatt'.
ISBN 0-573-68082-5 Sd : £1.65

(B78-12987)

BWPDACN — Wood, David. Old Father Time. Librettos
Wood, David, *b.1944*
Old Father Time : a family musical / book, music and lyrics by
David Wood. — London [etc.] : French, 1978. — [5],73p : plans ;
22cm.
Seven men, 5 women, supers.
ISBN 0-573-05046-5 Pbk : £1.20

(B78-39232)

BZ — LITERATURE ON NON-EUROPEAN MUSIC
Eight urban musical cultures : tradition and change / edited by
Bruno Nettl. — Urbana [etc.] ; London : University of Illinois
Press, 1978. — [9],320p : ill, facsims, music ; 24cm.
ISBN 0-252-00208-3 : £10.50

(B78-39229)

BZB — Asia
Malm, William Paul
Music cultures of the Pacific, the Near East, and Asia / [by]
William P. Malm. — 2nd ed. — Englewood Cliffs [etc.] ;
London : Prentice-Hall, 1977. — [1],xviii,236p : ill, map, music ;
23cm. — (Prentice-Hall history of music series)
Previous ed.: 1967. — Bibl. — Lists of sound discs. — Index.
ISBN 0-13-608000-6 : £7.95
ISBN 0-13-607994-6 Pbk : £4.75

(B78-04322)

BZCW/PR — Arab music. Modes
Wright, O
The modal system of Arab and Persian music, AD 1250-1300 / by
O. Wright. — Oxford [etc.] : Oxford University Press, 1978. — ix,
302p : music ; 26cm. — (London Oriental series ; vol.28)
Bibl.: p.293-296. — Index.
ISBN 0-19-713575-7 : £32.00 : CIP rev.
Also classified at BZE/PR

(B77-07528)

BZE/PR — Iran. Modes
Wright, O
The modal system of Arab and Persian music, AD 1250-1300 / by
O. Wright. — Oxford [etc.] : Oxford University Press, 1978. — ix,
302p : music ; 26cm. — (London Oriental series ; vol.28)
Bibl.: p.293-296. — Index.
ISBN 0-19-713575-7 : £32.00 : CIP rev.
Primary classification BZCW/PR

(B77-07528)

BZHPADGVF — Japan. Buddhism. Liturgical music
Giesen, Walter
Zur Geschichte des buddhistischen Ritualgesangs in Japan :
Traktate des 9. bis 14. Jahrhunderts zum shomyo der
Tendai-Sekte / [von] Walter Giesen. — Kassel [etc.] ; London
([32 Gt Titchfield St., W1P 7AD]) : Bärenreiter, 1977. — [11],
355p : ill, music ; 24cm. — (Studien zur traditionellen Musik
Japans ; Bd 1)
Bibl.: p.317-320. — Index.
Pbk : £12.60

(B78-35473)

C/AY — GENERAL COLLECTIONS
C/AYD — Collections. England
Musica Britannica : a national collection of music. — London :
Stainer and Bell, for the Musica Britannica Trust.
Vol.40 : Music for mixed consort / edited and reconstructed by Warwick
Edwards. — 1977. — xxv,163p ; fol.
ISBN 0-85249-436-x : Unpriced
Also classified at NVP/AYD

(B78-50001)

For SATB soloists and SATB chorus with orchestra.
Vol.41 : Confitebor tibi, Domine [by] Samuel Wesley ; transcribed and
edited by John Marsh. — 1978. — xix,214p ; fol.
Unpriced
Also classified at EMDR

(B78-50697)

C/AZ — Collected works of individual composers
Berlioz, Hector
[Works]. New edition of the complete works. — Kassel ; London :
Bärenreiter.
Vol.9 : Grande messe des morts ; edited by Jürgen Kindermann. — 1978. —
xvii,177p ; fol.
Unpriced
Also classified at EMDGKAV

(B78-50698)

Liszt, Franz
[Works]. Liszt Society publications. — London : Schott.
Vol.7 : Unfamiliar piano pieces. — 1978. — [9],74p ; 4to. —
£3.00
Also classified at QPJ

(B78-50322)

Nietzsche, Friedrich
[Works]. Der musikalische Nachlass / [von] Friedrich Nietzsche ;
herausgegeben im Auftrag der Schweizerischen Musikforschenden
Gesellschaft von Curt Paul Janz. — Basel ; [London] :
Bärenreiter, 1978. — x,352p ; fol.
Unpriced

(B78-50699)

Purcell, Henry
[Works]. The works of Henry Purcell. — Sevenoaks : Novello.
Volume 8 : Ode on St Cecilia's Day, 1692 ; edited under the supervision of
the Purcell Society by Peter Dennison. — 1978. — xvii,93p ; 8vo.
£10.00
Also classified at EMDX

(B78-50002)

CB — VOCAL MUSIC
CB/AY(XCH 301) — Collections, 1200-1500
Invitation to medieval music. — London : Stainer and Bell.
Works by Busnois, Dunstable, Van Ghizeghem, Gulielmus, Hert, Morton,
Ockeghem, Soursby and Wrede.
4 : Music of the mid-fifteenth century (ii) : an advanced selection of 11
compositions for 1-3 voices and/or instruments newly transcribed and edited
by Brian Trowell. — 1978. — 48p ; 8vo.
ISBN 0-85249-317-7 : £1.25

(B78-50004)

CB/J — Stage music
Davies, Peter Maxwell
Miss Donnithorne's maggot : for mezzo-soprano and chamber
ensemble / [by] Peter Maxwell Davies ; text (and foreword) by
Randolph Stowe. — London : Boosey and Hawkes, 1977. — 58p ;
fol.
Facsimile of the composer's manuscript.
£7.00

(B78-50003)

Orton, Richard H
Mug grant / [by] Richard Orton. — Birmingham : Arts Lab
Music, 1978. — [8]p ; 4to.
For three male performers with mugs.
Unpriced

(B78-50701)

CC — OPERA. VOCAL SCORES
Arne, Thomas Augustine
[Thomas and Sally. *Vocal score*]. Thomas and Sally : a dramatic
pastoral in two acts / [by] Thomas Arne ; edited by Roger Fiske.
— London : Schott, 1977. — [7],52p ; 4to.
Duration 55 min.
Unpriced

(B78-50323)

Cavalli, Francesco
[L'egisto. *Vocal score*]. L'egisto : opera in three acts and a
prologue / [by] Francesco Cavalli ; libretto by Giovanni Faustini,
English translation by Geoffrey Dunn and Raymond Leppard,
German translation by Karl Robert Marz, performing edition
realized by Raymond Leppard. — London : Faber Music, 1977.
— [9],235p ; 4to.
Text in Italian, English and German. — Duration 140 min.
Unpriced

(B78-50324)

Einem, Gottfried von
[Kabale und liebe. Op.44. *Vocal score*]. Kabale und Liebe : Oper
in 2 teilen (9 Bildern) nach Friedrich von Schiller / [von]
Gottfried von Einem ; Libretto von Boris Blacher und Lotte
Ingrisch. — London : Boosey and Hawkes, 1978. — [6],429p ;
4to.
Duration 135 min.
Unpriced

(B78-50006)

Gagliano, Marco da
[La Dafne. *Vocal score*]. La Dafne / [by] Marco da Gagliano ... ;
newly transcribed and edited with a translation of the composer's
preface by James Erber. — London : Cathedral Music, 1978. — x,
49p ; 8vo.
Libretto by O. Rinuccini. — Text in Italian.
Unpriced

(B78-50325)

Monteverdi, Claudio
[L'incoronazione di Poppea. Vocal score]. L'incoronazione di
Poppea = The coronation of Poppea : opera in two acts and
prologue / [by] Claudio Monteverdi ; realized by Raymond
Leppard, libretto by Francesco Busenello, English translation by
Geoffrey Dunn, German translation by Karl Robert Marz, vocal
score by Courtney Kenny ; with a preface by Raymond Leppard.
— New ed. — London : Faber Music, 1977. — [14],221p ; 4to.
Text in Italian, English and German - Duration 150 min.
Unpriced

(B78-50007)

Musgrave, Thea
[Mary, Queen of Scots. *Vocal score*]. Mary, Queen of Scots : opera
in three acts / [by] Thea Musgrave ; libretto by the composer
based on Moray, a play by Amalia Elguera, vocal score, piano
reduction by Giles Swayne. — Sevenoaks : Novello, 1978. — [16],
302p ; 4to.
£15.00

(B78-50008)

Smetana, Bedřich
[The bartered bride. *Vocal score*]. The bartered bride : a comic
opera in three acts / [by] Bedřich Smetana ; libretto by Karel
Sabina ; English version by Joan Cross and Eric Crozier. —
Revised English libretto. — London : Boosey and Hawkes, 1978.
— iv,241p ; 8vo.
Unpriced

(B78-50702)

Tippett, *Sir* Michael
[The ice break. *Vocal score*]. The ice break : an opera in three
acts / words and music by Michael Tippett ; vocal score by
Michael Tippett, German translation by Ken W. Bartlett. —
London : Schott, 1977. — [8],358p ; 4to.
£13.00

(B78-50009)

Vaughan Williams, Ralph
[Hugh the drover. *Vocal score*]. Hugh the drover or Love in the
stocks : a romantic ballad opera in two acts / by Ralph Vaughan
Williams ; libretto by Harold Child. — New ed. based on the
1959 edition as revised in accordance with the composer's
directions ... — London : Curwen : Faber Music, 1977. — xii,
206p ; 4to.
With a foreword by Michael Kennedy and a synopsis by the composer.
Unpriced

(B78-50010)

Wagner, Richard
[Der Ring des Nibelungen. Die Walküre]. Die Walküre / [by]
Richard Wagner ; complete vocal and orchestral score. — New
York : Dover ; [London] : [Constable], 1978. — [8],710p ; 4to.
Originally published Leipzig, Peters, circa 1910 ; this republication contains
a new English translation of the introductory matter.
ISBN 0-486-23566-1 : Unpriced
Primary classification CQC

CF — OPERETTAS. VOCAL SCORES
Straus, Oscar
[Ein Walzertraum. *Vocal score*]. A waltz dream : operetta in three
acts / music by Oscar Straus ; adapted and arranged by Ronald
Hanmer, original book and lyrics by Felix Dörmann and Leopold
Jacobson, new book by Bernard Dunn, new lyrics by Michael
Flanders and Edmund Tracey. — London : Weinberger, 1978. —
227p ; 4to.
Unpriced

(B78-50326)

Offenbach, Jacques
[Monsieur Choufleuri restera chez lui de. *Vocal score*]. Salon
Blumenkohl/Monsieur Choufleuri restera chez lui de ... :
Buffo-Operette in einem Akt deutsch nach Karl Fr. Wiltmann von
Heinz Balthes und Paul Vasil, opéra bouffe en un acte de St.
Rémy, E. L'Epine, Hector Crémieux et Ludovic Halévy,
musikalische Revision, neue Instrumentation und praktische
Bearbeitung von Caspar Richter. — Berlin : Bote und Bock ;
[London] : [Associated music], 1978. — 77p ; 4to.
Text in French and German.
£11.50

(B78-50703)

CM — MUSICAL PLAYS. VOCAL SCORES
Schmidt, Harvey
[The fantasticks. *Vocal score*]. The fantasticks : book and lyrics by
Tom Jones / music by Harvey Schmidt ; suggested by a play 'Les
Romanesques' by Edmund Rostand, edited by Robert H. Noeltner
and Ken Collins. — Revised ed. — New York ; [London] :
Chappell, 1978. — 168p ; 4to.
Unpriced

(B78-50327)

CN — Children's musical plays with keyboard accompaniment
Boyle, Rory
[Augustine. *Vocal score*]. Augustine : an opera in one or two acts
for children / [by] Rory Boyle ; libretto by David Taylor. —
London : Chester Music, 1977. — [4],79p ; 4to.
Duration 50 min.
Unpriced

(B78-50704)

Gardner, John
[Bel and the dragon. Op.120. *Vocal score*]. Bel and the dragon :
an opera for children / [by] John Gardner ; libretto by Timothy
Kraemer. — London : Oxford University Press, 1978. — [2],93p ;
8vo.
Duration 60 min.
ISBN 0-19-336202-3 : Unpriced

(B78-50709)

Oliver, Donald
Almost caught red-pawed (or The cat who cried over spilt milk) :
a musical play for children / by Annette Harper and [music by]
Donald Oliver. — New York ; [London] : Chappell, 1978. —
45p ; 4to.
Unpriced

(B78-50705)

Oliver, Donald
The cookie lady : a musical play for children / by Annette Harper
and [music by] Donald Oliver. — New York ; [London] :
Chappell, 1978. — 47p ; 4to.
Unpriced

(B78-50706)

Oliver, Donald
The runaways : a musical play for children / by Annette Harper
and [music by] Donald Oliver. — New York ; [London] :
Chappell, 1978. — 47p ; 4to.
Unpriced

(B78-50707)

Wade, Darrell
Dismal land and the giant : a one act musical play for juniors /
by Darrell Wade. — Gnosall ((16 Anchor Way, Danes Green,
Gnosall)) : Viking, 1978. — 4to.
For unison voices and piano with optional instruments.
Unpriced

(B78-50011)

Wade, Darrell
Mr Mulberry's toyshop : a one act musical play for infants or
lower juniors / by Darrell Wade. — Gnosall (16 Anchor Way,
Danes Green, Gnosall) : Viking, 1977. — 8p ; 4to.
Unpriced

(B78-50012)

Wade, Darrell
Mrs Pennyweather's garden : a musical play for infants (with
optional percussion) / by Darrell Wade. — Gnosall (16 Anchor
Way, Danes Green, Gnosall) : Viking, 1978. — 4to.
Unpriced

(B78-50328)

Wade, Darrell
A storm in a teacup : a one act musical play for infants or lower
juniors / by Darrell Wade. — Gnosall : Viking, 1978. — 12p ;
4to.
Unpriced

(B78-50708)

CP — Revues. Vocal scores
Blake, Howard
[The new national song book. *Vocal score*]. The new national song
book / by Howard Blake. — South Croydon : Lengnick, 1978. —
54p ; 4to.
£1.95

(B78-50013)

CQC — OPERA. FULL SCORES
Arne, Thomas Augustine
Thomas and Sally : dramatic pastoral in two acts / [by] Thomas
Arne, libretto by Isaac Bickerstaffe, edited by Roger Fiske. —
London : Eulenburg, 1977. — xvii,104p ; 8vo. — (Edition
Eulenburg ; no.926)
Miniature score.
Unpriced

(B78-50329)

Einem, Gottfried von
Kabale und Liebe : Oper in 2 Teilen (9 Bildern) nach Friedrich
von Schiller / [von] Gottfried von Einem ; Libretto von Boris
Blacher und Lotte Ingrisch ; Op.44. — London : Boosey and
Hawkes, 1978. — [6],671p ; 8vo. — (Hawkes pocket scores ; 906)
Miniature score. — Duration 135 min.
Unpriced

(B78-50710)

Tavener, John
A gentle spirit : an opera in one act for soprano, tenor and
chamber orchestra / [by] John Tavener ; libretto by Gerard
McLarnon, based on Dostoievsky. — London : Chester Music,
1978. — [2],78p ; 4to.
Duration 45 min.
Unpriced

(B78-50711)

Wagner, Richard
[Der Ring des Nibelungen. Die Walküre]. Die Walküre / [by]
Richard Wagner ; complete vocal and orchestral score. — New
York : Dover ; [London] : [Constable], 1978. — [8],710p ; 4to.
Originally published Leipzig, Peters, circa 1910 ; this republication contains
a new English translation of the introductory matter.
ISBN 0-486-23566-1 : Unpriced
Also classified at CC

(B78-50712)

CQM — MUSICAL PLAYS. FULL SCORES
CQM/LF — Musical plays. Christmas
Möckl, Franz
Ein Kind ist uns geboren : das Ottowinder Christspiel, für
Sprecher, Soli ad lib. (Sopran, Tenor, Bariton) - Kinderstimmen,
Frauen - , gemischten Chor und Gemeindegesang -
Instrumentalkreis (Stabspiele, Schlagzeng) - Orgel (wahlweise oder
zusätzlich auch Streicher, Holz und Blechbläser) / [von] Franz
Möckl. — Mainz ; London : Schott, 1977. — 52p ; obl. 4to.
Duration 75 min.
£8.00

(B78-50014)

CQN — Children's musical plays. Full scores
Winters, Geoffrey
The three pigs : for group music making / words and music by
Geoffrey Winters. — Sevenoaks : Novello, 1977. — 18p ; 4to.
With recorder, glockenspiel, percussion and piano - Duration 15 min.
£1.20

(B78-50330)

CQPF — MASQUES. FULL SCORES
Davies, Peter Maxwell
Le jongleur de Notre Dame : a masque, for mime, baritone,
chamber ensemble and children's band / [by] Peter Maxwell
Davies ; text by the composer. — London : Chester Music, 1978.
— 66p ; 4to.
Unpriced

(B78-50713)

DAC — OPERATIC CHORAL WORKS. CHORAL SCORES
Monteverdi, Claudio
[L'incoronazione di Poppea. *Choral score*]. L'incoronazione di
Poppea / [by] Claudio Monteverdi ; realized by Raymond
Leppard, English translation by Gegffrey Dunn, German
translation by Karl Robert Marz. — London : Faber Music, 1978.
— 19p ; 8vo.
Text in Italian, English and German.
Unpriced

(B78-50331)

DACM — MUSICAL PLAYS. CHORAL WORKS. CHORAL SCORES
DACN — Children's musical plays. Choral scores
Boyle, Rory
[Augustine. *Choral score*]. Augustine : an opera in one or two acts
for children / [by] Rory Boyle ; libretto by David Taylor. —
London : Chester Music, 1977. — 24p ; 8vo.
Unpriced

(B78-50714)

DE — RELIGIOUS CANTATAS WITH KEYBOARD ACCOMPANIMENT
Chapple, Brian
[Cantica. *Vocal score*]. Cantica : for soprano and tenos soloists, chorus and orchestra / [by] Brian Chapple ; [text from Psalms 102, 40 and 96]. — London : Chester Music, 1978. — [2],58p ; 4to.
Facsimile of the composer's autograph. — Text in Latin.
Unpriced

(B78-50715)

Hoddinott, Alan
[Sinfonia fidei. *Vocal score*]. Sinfonia fidei : a cantata for soprano and tenor soloists, chorus and orchestra / [by] Alan Hoddinott ; Latin verse selected by Christopher Fry. — London : Oxford University Press, 1978. — 56p ; 8vo.
ISBN 0-19-336842-0 : Unpriced

(B78-50716)

Hurd, Michael
[Pilgrim. *Vocal score*]. Pilgrim : a musical morality in popular style for unison voices (with divisions) and piano with guitar chord symbols / words and music by Michael Hurd ; based on and incorporating text from John Bunyan's 'Pilgrim's progress'. — Sevenoaks : Novello, 1978. — [6],33p ; 8vo.
Duration 18 min.
£0.86

(B78-50332)

Kelly, Bryan
[At the round earth's imagined corners. *Vocal score*]. At the round earth's imagined corners : cantata for tenor solo, SATB and string orchestra / [by] Bryan Kelly. — Sevenoaks : Novello, 1977. — 44p ; 8vo.
Unpriced

(B78-50015)

Maconchy, Elizabeth
[Heloïse and Abelard. *Vocal score*]. Heloïsw and Abelard : a dramatic cantata for soprano, tenor and baritone soloists, chorus and orchestra / [by] Elizabeth Maconchy. — London : Chester Music, 1978. — [2],109p ; 4to.
Unpriced

(B78-50717)

Tate, Phyllis
[Saint Martha and the dragon. *Vocal score*]. Saint Martha and the dragon : a dramatic legend set to music, for narrator, soprano and tenor soloists, chorus, children's chorus (with percussion) and chamber orchestra / music by Phyllis Tate ; poem by Charles Causley. — London : Oxford University Press, 1978. — [8],80p ; 4to.
Duration 43 min. — Piano reduction by Alan Boustead.
ISBN 0-19-338397-7 : Unpriced

(B78-50718)

DE/LQ — All Saints
Leighton, Kenneth
Sequence for All Saints : for SATB choir, baritone solo and organ, words from English Hymnal 731 / music by Kenneth Leighton, opus 75. — Wendover : Roberton, 1978. — 43p ; 8vo.
Partly based on Song 67 by Orlando Gibbons ; additional text by Isaac Watts.
£1.20

(B78-50719)

DFF — ROMAN LITURGY WITH KEYBOARD ACCOMPANIMENT
Fauré, Gabriel
[Choral music. *Selections*]. Messe basse and other sacred works : for female or boys voices and organ or piano / [by] Gabriel Fauré ; edited by Desmond Ratcliffe, English words translated or adapted by the editor. — Sevenoaks : Novello, 1977. — [5],41p ; 8vo.
Text in Latin and English.
Unpriced

(B78-50016)

DG — Ordinary of the Mass. Vocal scores
Bruckner, Anton
[Mass, no.2, E minor, (1896). *Vocal score*]. Mass no.2, E minor, for eight part choir and wind instruments (1896 version) / [by] Anton Bruckner. — Revised version of the edition of Kurt Soldan by James Erber. — London : Peters, 1977. — [2],48p ; 8vo.
Unpriced

(B78-50720)

Hovhaness, Alan
[Simple mass. Op.282. *Vocal score*]. Simple mass. Op.282 : for four-part unison chorus and soprano, alto, tenor and bass solos with organ accompaniment / [by] Alan Hovhaness. — New York ; London : Associated Music, 1977. — 30p ; 8vo.
Text in English.
£1.80

(B78-50333)

DGB — Kyrie
Mozart, Wolfgang Amadeus
[Kyrie, K.322, E flat major. *Vocal score*]. Kyrie, (K.322), for four-part chorus of mixed voices with piano accompaniment / [by] Wolfgang Amadeus Mozart ; edited by H.C. Robbins Landon. — New York ; London : Schirmer, 1977. — 10p ; 8vo.
Unpriced

(B78-50017)

Mozart, Wolfgang Amadeus
[Kyrie, K.323, C major. *Vocal score*]. Kyrie, (K.323), for four-part chorus of mixed voices with piano accompaniment / [by] Wolfgang Amadeus Mozart ; edited by H.C. Robbins Landon. — New York ; London : Schirmer, 1977. — 14p ; 8vo.
Unpriced

(B78-50018)

Mozart, Wolfgang Amadeus
[Kyrie, K.341, D minor. *Vocal score*]. Kyrie, K.341, for four-part chorus of mixed voices with piano accompaniment / [by] Wolfgang Amadeus Mozart ; edited by H.C. Robbins Landon. — New York ; London : Schirmer, 1977. — 18p ; 8vo.
Unpriced

(B78-50019)

DGE — Sanctus
Argento, Dominick
[The masque of angels. Sanctus. *arr*]. Sanctus : double chorus and piano or organ from the opera 'The masque of angels' / [by] Dominick Argento ; text by John Olon-Serymgeour. — [New York] ; [London] : Boosey and Hawkes, 1978. — 22p ; 8vo.
Unpriced

(B78-50721)

DGKAV — Requiem masses
Nunes Garcia, Jose Mauricio
[Requiem mass. *Vocal score*]. Requiem mass for four-part chorus of mixed voices and alto, tenor and bass solos with piano accompaniment / [by] Jose Mauricio Nuñes-García ; edited by Dominique-René de Lerma. — New York ; London : Associated Music, 1977. — 53p ; 8vo.
£2.40

(B78-50334)

Tavener, John
[Little requiem for Father Malachy Lynch. *Vocal score*]. Little requiem for Father Malachy Lynch / [by] John Tavener. — London : Chester Music, 1978. — 9p ; 8vo. — (Contemporary church music series)
S.A.T.B. and organ.
Unpriced

(B78-50722)

DGM — ANGLICAN LITURGY WITH KEYBOARD ACCOMPANIMENT
Royal School of Church Music
Singing on Saturday : a selection of music and readings. — Croydon : Royal School of Church Music, 1978. — 39p ; 8vo.
£1.90

(B78-50335)

DGNQ — Morning Prayer. Te Deum
Handel, George Frideric
[Utrecht Te Deum. *Vocal score*]. The Utrecht Te Deum (1713) : for chorus of mixed voices and soloists with organ or piano accompaniment / [by] George Frideric Handel ; edited and with keyboard reduction by William Herrmann. — New York ; London : Schirmer, 1977. — v,65p ; 8vo.
£2.40

(B78-50336)

DGPP — Evening Prayer. Canticles
Harvey, Jonathan
Magnificat and Nunc dimittis : for choir and organ (1978) / [by] Jonathan Harvey. — London : Faber Music, 1978. — [3],39p ; obl. 8vo.
Duration 12 min.
£1.50

(B78-50337)

Mendelssohn, Felix
[Magnificat & Nunc dimittis, op.69, nos.3, 1]. Magnificat and
Nunc dimittis / [by] Felix Mendelssohn ; edited by Maurice
Bevan. — London (36 Ralelagh Gdns., W.6) : Cathedral Music,
1978. — 28p ; 8vo.
For SATB and organ.
Unpriced

(B78-50338)

DGT — LITURGIES OF DENOMINATIONS OTHER THAN ROMAN & ANGLICAN
DGU — Jewish religious music
Gottlieb, Jacob
Hakol kol Yaacov = The voice is the voice of Jacob :
compositions for cantor and choir / by Yankel der Heizeriker ;
edited by Dr Isaac Gottlieb. — Limited ed. — Tel-Aviv ; London
(18 Station Tce, N.W.10) : Sinai Publishing House, 1977. — xv,
117p ; 4to.
ISBN 0-9506345-0-6 : Unpriced

(B78-50724)

DH — MOTETS, ANTHEMS, HYMNS, ETC. WITH KEYBOARD ACCOMPANIMENT
Elgar, *Sir* **Edward,** *bart*
[Selections. *arr*]. Seven anthems / [by] Edward Elgar. —
Sevenoaks : Novello, 1978. — [3],51p ; 8vo.
£1.30

(B78-50725)

Hemingway, Roger
The sea of faith, Dover Beach / words by Matthew Arnold ... ;
music by Roger Hemingway ; anthem for SATB with divisions,
and organ. — Sevenoaks : Novello, 1978. — 14p ; 8vo.
£0.45

(B78-50726)

Peter, Johann Friedrich
[Herr, wie sind deine Werke so gross. *arr*]. Lord, thy creations,
how great they are = Herr, wie sind deine Werke so gross :
S.A.T.B. with accompaniment / [by] Johann Friedrich Peter ; ed.
and arr. by Karl Koreger ; German text from Psalm 92 ; English
version by K.K. — New York ; [London] : Boosey and Hawkes,
1978. — 7p ; 8vo. — (Moramus editions)
Unpriced

(B78-50339)

Peter, Johann Friedrich
[Ihre Priester will ich mit Heil kleiden. *arr*]. I will clothe thy
priests with salvation = Ihre Priester will ich mit Heil kleiden :
S.A.T.B. with accompaniment / [by] Johann Friedrich Peter ;
edited and arranged by Karl Kroeger, German text from Psalm
132, English version by K. K. — [New York] ; [London] : Boosey
and Hawkes, 1978. — 8p ; 8vo. — (Moramus edition)
With piano.
Unpriced

(B78-50340)

Peter, Johann Friedrich
[Kommt danket dem Helden. *arr*]. Come thank now Jehovah =
Kommt danket dem Helden : double chorus ; SATB with
accompaniment / [by] Johann Friedrich Peter ; ed. & arr. by Karl
Kroeger ; German hymn by Johann Daniel Herrnschmidt ;
English version by K.K. — New York ; [London] : Boosey and
Hawkes, 1978. — 11p ; 8vo. — (Moramus edition)
Unpriced

(B78-50341)

Peter, Johann Friedrich
[Unser Herr Jesus Christus. *arr*]. Our dear Lord Jesus Christ =
Unser Herr Jesus Christus : SATB with accompaniment / [by]
Johann Friedrich Peter ; ed. & arr. by Karl Kroeger ; German
text from 1 Thessalonians 5 ; English version by K.K. — New
York ; [London] : Boosey and Hawkes, 1978. — 11p ; 8vo. —
(Moramus edition)
Unpriced

(B78-50342)

Vivaldi, Antonio
[Gloria. Gloria. Ryom 589. *Vocal score*]. Gloria for SATB with
keyboard or orchestra, from the cantata of the same name / [by]
Antonio Vivaldi ; keyboard realisation by Louis Pichierri. —
Wendover : Roberton, 1978. — 11p ; 8vo.
£0.20

(B78-50020)

Walton, *Sir* **William**
Antiphon : S.A.T.B. / by William Walton ; words by George
Herbert. — London : Oxford University Press, 1978. — 4p ; 8vo.
ISBN 0-19-350366-2 : Unpriced

(B78-50021)

Watson, Ronald
All my hope on God is founded / [by] Ronald Watson ; words ...
J. Neander (1650-1680). — Brundall (Deacon House, Brundall) :
Braydeston Press : William Elkin, 1978. — 11p ; 8vo.
SATB.
Unpriced

(B78-50022)

DH/AY — Collections
Be known to us : a collection of general anthems for mixed voices /
edited by Betty Pulkingham. — Poole (57 Dorchester Rd,
Lytchett Minster) : Celebration Publishing, 1978. — [6],65p ; 8vo.
ISBN 0-906309-03-4 : Unpriced

(B78-50727)

In wonder, love and praise : a collection of fourteen anthems /
editor, Martin Ellis. — Sevenoaks : Novello, 1978. — 83p ; 8vo.
— (Church choir library ; vol.1)
Unpriced

(B78-50728)

With a joyful voice : a collection of anthems. — Sevenoaks :
Novello, 1978. — 49p ; 8vo.
Works by Gray, Gordon Cameron, Ireland, Palestrina, Cope, S.S. Wesley,
Thiman, John Wood, Brockless, Martin Shaw, Morley and William Fox.
£1.45

(B78-50729)

DH/LF/AY — Christmas. Collections
Come, Christmas : an anthology of standard Christmas carols, new
carols and favourite excerpts from major choral works. —
Sevenoaks : Novello, [1978]. — 96p ; 8vo.
£1.45

(B78-50730)

DJ — MOTETS WITH KEYBOARD ACCOMPANIMENT
DJ/LF — Christmas
Dering, Richard
[Cantica sacra senis vocibus. Quem vidistis pastores?]. Quem
vidistis pastores? : Motet for Christmas for six voices / [by]
Richard Dering ; edited by Anthony G. Petti. — London :
Chester Music, 1978. — 8p ; 8vo.
Unpriced

(B78-50731)

DK — ANTHEMS WITH KEYBOARD ACCOMPANIMENT
Croft, William
God is gone up with a merry noise : full anthem with verse for
SSAATB / by William Croft ; edited by Watkins Shaw, text from
Psalm 47. — Sevenoaks : Novello, 1978. — 14p ; 8vo. — (Novello
early church music ; 34)
£0.43

(B78-50343)

Mathias, William
Arise, shine, for your light has come : S.A.T.B. / [by] William
Mathias ; op.77 no.2 ; [text from] the third Book of Isaiah (Isaiah
60). — London : Oxford University Press, 1978. — 12p ; 8vo. —
(Oxford anthems ; A327)
With organ.
ISBN 0-19-350367-0 : Unpriced

(B78-50732)

DK/LEZ — Advent
How, Martin
Advent message / [by] Martin How. — London : Weinberger,
1978. — 4p ; 8vo.
For 3-part chorus.
Unpriced

(B78-50733)

DK/LNB — Trinity
Batten, Adrian
[Holy, holy, holy]. Holy, Lord God almighty : verse anthem for
Trinity Sunday / [by] Adrian Batten ... ; edited by Maurice
Bevan. — London (36 Ranelagh Gdns., W.6) : Cathedral Music,
1978. — 8p ; 8vo.
Unpriced

(B78-50344)

DM — HYMNS WITH KEYBOARD ACCOMPANIMENT
DM/AY — Collections
Christian hymns / [compiled by] Paul E.G. Cook, Graham
Harrison. — Bridgend : Evangelical Movements of Wales ;
Worthing : Henry E. Walter, 1977. — [1016]p ; 8vo.
Unpriced

(B78-50024)

Praise for today. — London : Psalms and Hymns Trust, 1974. —
[200]p ; 8vo.
General editor, R.W. Thompson, music editor, E.P. Sharpe.
Unpriced

(B78-50734)

Sixteen hymns of today for use as simple anthems / selected and edited by John Wilson. — Croydon : Royal School of Church Music, 1978. — 48p ; 8vo.
Unpriced

(B78-50345)

DM/LF — Christmas
Rorem, Ned
Shout the glad tidings : S.A.T.B. / [by] Ned Rorem ; [words by] Muhlenberg - 1826 (from the Hymnal). — [New York] ; [London] : Boosey and Hawkes, 1978. — 7p ; 8vo.
Unpriced

(B78-50735)

DM/LSD/AY — Anglican church. Collections
Anglican hymn book : Robin Sheldon, musical editor. — [Revised ed., with supplement]. — London (Wine Office Court, E.C.4) : Vine Books, 1977. — [948]p ; 8vo.
£4.85

(B78-50736)

DP — CAROLS WITH KEYBOARD ACCOMPANIMENT
DP/LF — Christmas
Carter, Andrew
A maiden most gentle : (a Christmas carol) ; S.A.T.B., French tune / arranged by Andrew Carter, under paraphrased from the Venerable Bede. — London : Oxford University Press, 1978. — 4p ; 8vo. — (Oxford choral songs ; X266)
ISBN 0-19-343067-3 : Unpriced

(B78-50737)

Davis, Diane
Yeldall carol, This is the day / [by] Diane Davis. — Reading (Yeldall Manor, Hare Hatch, Reading) : Celebration Services, 1974. — 3p ; 8vo.
SATB and piano.
Unpriced

(B78-50025)

Hughes, David E
Ring bells ring / words and music by David E. Hughes. — Porthcawl (2 Highfield Close) : David E. Hughes, 1978. — s.sh ; 8vo.
Unpriced

(B78-50738)

Kelly, Bryan
Watt's cradle song : S.A.T.B. / [by] Bryan Kelly ; [text by] Isaac Watts. — London : Oxford University Press, 1978. — [2]p ; 8vo. — (Oxford choral songs ; X264)
With piano.
ISBN 0-19-343065-7 : Unpriced

(B78-50739)

Ledger, Philip
Two carols / arranged by Philip Ledger. — London : Oxford University Press, 1978. — 11p ; 8vo. — (Oxford choral songs ; X265)
For mixed voices. — Contents: Silent night : unaccompanied - 2: On Christmas night : accompanied.
ISBN 0-19-343066-5 : Unpriced
Also classified at EZDP/LF

(B78-50740)

Mathias, William
Nativity carol : S.A.T.B. : [by] William Mathias / op.77, no.3 ; words traditional, adapted William Mathias. — London : Oxford University Press, 1978. — 9p ; 8vo. — (Oxford choral songs ; X263)
With organ or piano duet.
ISBN 0-19-343064-9 : Unpriced

(B78-50741)

Petrokino, Paul
[Workers' carol. *arr].* The workers' carol / tune by Paul Petrokino ; arranged for unison voices, descant and treble recorders and piano by Pamela Breese, words by Morris Martin. — Wendover : Roberton, 1978. — 3p ; 8vo.
SATB and piano.
Unpriced

(B78-50026)

Pockriss, Lee
[Happy birthday, Jesus. *arr].* Happy birthday, Jesus / words by Estelle Levitt ; music by Lee Pockriss ; arranged by Jacques Rizzo. — [New York] ; [London] : Chappell, 1978. — 8vo.
S.A.T.B. (7p.), S.A.B. (7p.).
Unpriced

(B78-50742)

DR — PSALMS WITH KEYBOARD ACCOMPANIMENT
Jackson, Francis
Praise God in his sanctuary : S.A.T.B. / [by] Francis Jackson ; Psalm 150. — York : Banks, 1978. — 10p ; 8vo. — (Eboracum choral series ; 84)
Unpriced

(B78-50743)

Latrobe, Christian Ignatius
[Original anthems. Make a joyful noise unto the Lord. *Vocal score].* Psalm 100, Make a joyful noise unto the Lord / [by] Christian I. Latrobe ; edited and arranged by Karl Kroeger. — [New York] ; [London] : Boosey and Hawkes, 1978. — 35p ; 8vo. — (Noramus edition)
For SATB soli and chorus with organ or piano. — Duration 10 min.
Unpriced

(B78-50346)

DTF — LORD'S PRAYER WITH KEYBOARD ACCOMPANIMENT
Fanshawe, David
[African Sanctus. Lord's Prayer. *arr].* The Lord's Prayer ... : S.A.T.B. and piano with optional guitar and drums / by David Fanshawe ; arranged by Jacques Rizzo. — [New York] ; [London] : Chappell, 1978. — 10p ; 8vo.
Unpriced

(B78-50347)

Fanshawe, David
[African Sanctus. Lord's Prayer. *arr].* The Lord's Prayer ... : S.A.B. and piano with optional guitar and drums / by David Fanshawe ; arranged by Jacques Rizzo. — [New York] ; [London] : Chappell, 1978. — 10p ; 8vo.
Unpriced

(B78-50348)

DW — SONGS, ETC. WITH KEYBOARD ACCOMPANIMENT
Bavicchi, John
[Three American choruses. *Vocal score].* Three American choruses : for SATB voices, piano and optional brasses / [by] John Bavicchi. — New York ; [London] : Oxford University Press, 1978. — 15p ; 8vo.
Contents: 1: Inscription on the Liberty Bell - 2: Words of Igor Sikorsky - 3: From an American pioneer movement.
Unpriced

(B78-50027)

Bizet, Georges
[Valse avec choeur. *Vocal score].* Valse avec choeur = Walzermit Chor : pour choeur mixte et petit orchestra = für gemischten Chor und kleines Orchester / [par] Georges Bizet ; edité par Fritz Weisse, Fassung für Chor nit Klavierbegleitung zugleich Klavierauszug. — Mainz ; London : Schott, 1978. — 31p ; 4to.
£8.00

(B78-50744)

Brahms, Johannes
[Intermezzo, piano, op.117, no.1, E flat major. *arr].* Wiegenlied : for mixed chorus and piano four hands / [by] Brahms ; arr. by Gordon Binkerd, [text from] a Scottish song [in] a translation by Johann von Herder. — [New York] ; [London] : Boosey and Hawkes, 1977. — 11p ; 4to.
Duration 4 min.
Unpriced

(B78-50349)

Lehár, Franz
Six rhymes from Mother Goose : for four-part chorus of mixed voices and piano accompaniment / [by] Thom Ritter George. — New York ; London : Schirmer, 1977. — 31p ; 8vo.
£1.60

(B78-50350)

Livingston, Jay
[The lemon drop kid. Silver bells. *arr].* Silver bells : SATB and piano / words and music by Jay Livingston and Ray Evans, arranged by Chuck Cassey. — New York : Warner ; [London] : [Blossom], 1978. — 8p ; 8vo.
Unpriced

(B78-50351)

McCarthy, John
Oh, father : an English music hall medley, for four-part chorus of mixed voices with piano accompniment / [by] John McCarthy. — Wendover : Roberton, 1977. — 23p ; 8vo.
£0.32

(B78-50745)

Payne, Harold
[Music speaks louder than words. *arr].* Music speaks louder than words : SATB chorus and piano with optional guitar, bass and drums / words and music by Harold Payne, Edgar Pease III and Michael Scarpiello ; arranged by Paris Rutherford. — New York : Warner ; [London] : [Blossom], 1978. — 11p ; 8vo.
Unpriced

(B78-50352)

Rodgers, Richard
[Love me tonight. Mimi. *arr].* Mimi : SATB chorus and piano / music by Richard Rodgers ; words by Lorenz Hart ; arranged by Pat Rutherford. — New York : Warner ; [London] : [Blossom], 1978. — 11p ; 8vo.
Unpriced

(B78-50746)

Sullivan, *Sir* **Arthur Seymour**
[Songs. *Selections : arr*]. The authentic Gilbert & Sullivan
songbook : 92 unabridged selections from all 14 operas reproduced
from early vocal scores / collected by Malcolm Binney and Peter
Lavender, selected and with plot summaries by James Spero. —
New York : Dover ; [London] : [Constable], 1977. — xi,399p ;
4to.
ISBN 0-486-23482-7 : £5.35

(B78-50028)

Turok, Paul
Chorus of the frogs : for four-part chorus of mixed voices with
piano accompaniment / [by] Paul Turok ; op.16, text from 'The
frogs' of Aristophanes. — New York ; London : Schirmer, 1977.
— 19p ; 8vo.
£0.45

(B78-50353)

DW/AY — Collections
The **great** song book / edited by Timothy John ; music edited by
Peter Hankey ; illustrated by Tomi Ungerer. — London ;
Tonbridge : Benn, 1978. — 112p ; 4to.
ISBN 0-510-00037-1 : Unpriced

(B78-50747)

DW/LC — Spirituals
Ferguson, Edwin Earle
Ev'ry time I feel the spirit : spiritual for four-part chorus of mixed
voices with accompaniment for organ and optional handbells /
arranged by Edwin Early Ferguson. — Wendover : Roberton,
1978. — 8p ; 8vo.
£0.20

(B78-50748)

Hudson, Hazel
The Daniel quodlibet (based on three negro spirituals) : for two
female, two male or one female and one male voices / arr. by
Hazel Hudson. — London : Edwin Ashdown, 1978. — 7p ; 8vo.
— (Ashdown vocal duets ; 390)
With piano. — Duration 1 1/2 min.
Unpriced
Primary classification FDW/LC

(B78-50394)

DW/LF — Christmas
Lombardo, Mario
Guess what time of year it is! : for SATB chorus with piano
accompaniment / music by Mario Lombardo ; lyrics by Bill
Margaretten. — [New York] ; [London] : Chappell, 1978. — 7p ;
8vo.
Unpriced

(B78-50749)

**DX — SECULAR CANTATAS WITH KEYBOARD
        ACCOMPANIMENT**
Hurd, Michael
[The phoenix and the turtle. *Vocal score*]. The phoenix and the
turtle : for mezzo-soprano solo, SATB timpani (2) and string
orchestra / [by] Michael Hurd ; words by William Shakespeare.
— Sevenoaks : Novello, 1977. — [4],24p ; 8vo.
Duration 13 mins.
£0.78

(B78-50029)

Hurd, Michael
[Shepherd's calendar. *Vocal score*]. Shepherd's calendar : choral
symphony for baritone solo, SATB and orchestra / [by] Michael
Hurd ; words by John Clare, 1793-1864. — Sevenoaks : Novello,
1978. — 55p ; 8vo.
Duration 30 min.
£1.45

(B78-50354)

**E — CHORAL WORKS WITH ACCOMPANIMENT OTHER
      THAN KEYBOARD**
EMDE — With orchestra. Religious cantatas
Penderecki, Krzysztof
Canticum canticorum Salomonis. Liberprimus : for 16-part vocal
ensemble and orchestra / [by] Krzysztof Penderecki. — Mainz ;
[London] : Schott, 1975. — [4],44p ; fol.
Duration 17 min.
£30.00

(B78-50030)

EMDGKAV — With orchestra. Roman liturgy. Requiems
Berlioz, Hector
[Works]. New edition of the complete works. — Kassel ; London :
Bärenreiter.
Vol.9 : Grande messe des morts ; edited by Jürgen Kindermann. — 1978. —
xvii,177p ; fol.
Unpriced
Primary classification C/AZ

Fauré, Gabriel
Requiem, Op.48 / [by] Gabriel Fauré ; edited by Roger Fiske and
Paul Inwood. — London : Eulenburg, 1978. — xxii,118p ; 8vo. —
(Edition Eulenburg ; no.1096)
Unpriced

(B78-50031)

EMDH — With orchestra. Motets, Anthems, Hymns, etc
Tavener, John
Ultimos ritos. En honor de San Juan de la Cruz / [de] John
Tavener. — London : Chester Music, 1972 [i.e. 1974]. — [7],
118p ; 4to.
Unpriced

(B78-50750)

EMDR — With orchestra. Psalms
Musica britannica : a national collection of music. — London :
Stainer and Bell, for the Musica Britannica Trust.
For SATB soloists and SATB chorus with orchestra.
Vol.41 : Confitebor tibi, Domine [by] Samuel Wesley ; transcribed and
edited by John Marsh. — 1978. — xix,214p ; fol.
Unpriced
Primary classification C/AYD

EMDX — With orchestra. Secular cantatas
Buller, John
The mime of Mick, Nick and the Maggies : on part 2 of
'Finnegans Wake' / by James Joyce ; for singers, speaker and 13
instrumentalists by John Buller. — New York ; London :
Schirmer, 1978. — viii,210p ; 4to.
Duration 70 min.
£17.50

(B78-50355)

Delius, Frederick
An arabesque = Eine Arabeske : for baritone solo, mixed chorus
and orchestra = für Bariton-Solo, gemischter Chor und
Orchester / [by] Frederick Delius. — London : Boosey and
Hawkes, 1978. — [4],34p ; 8vo. — (Hawkes pocket scores ; 909)
A reprint in reduced format of the full score originally published by
Universal Edition, Vienna, in 1920 but incorporating some corrections. —
English text translated by Philip Heseltine from Jens Peter Jacobsen's poem.
Unpriced

(B78-50751)

Delius, Frederick
Sea drift / [by] Frederick Delius ; poem by Walt Whitman,
German translation by Jelka Rosen, a reprint of the full score
edited and revised by Sir Thomas Beecham. — London : Boosey
and Hawkes, 1977. — 83p ; 8vo. — (Hawkes pocket scores ;
no.43)
Text in English and German. — Duration 23 min. — Misreadings and
errors in Beecham's 1951 edition have been corrected.
Unpriced

(B78-50032)

Purcell, Henry
[Works]. The works of Henry Purcell. — Sevenoaks : Novello.
Volume 8 : Ode on St Cecilia's Day, 1692 ; edited under the supervision of
the Purcell Society by Peter Dennison. — 1978. — xvii,93p ; 8vo.
£10.00
Primary classification C/AZ

(B78-50002)

Wimberger, Gerhard
Memento vivere : für Mezzosopran, Bariton, 3 Sprechstimmen,
gemischten Chor und Orchester / [von] Gerhard Wimberger ;
nach Texten von Kurt Marti, Abraham Clara, Paul Fleming,
Andreas Gryphius u.a. — Kassel ; London : Bärenreiter, 1977. —
112p ; 4to.
£12.60

(B78-50356)

ENUDG — With wind, strings & keyboard. Ordinary of the Mass
Valls, Francisco
Missa scala aretina : para 11 voces in 3 cores, instrumentos y
continuo = for 11 voices in 3 choirs, instruments and continuo /
[por] Francisco Valls ; publicado del MS.M. 1489 de la Biblioteca
Central de Barcelona = edited from Barcelona Biblioteca Central
MS M. 1489 by Jose Lopez-Calo, S.J. — Sevenoaks : Novello,
1978. — [22],170p ; 8vo.
Introduction in Spanish and English.
£3.15

(B78-50752)

**ENUXPNNDE — With brass, strings & keyboard octet. Religious
             cantatas**
Janáček, Leoš
[Lord, have mercy upon us]. Hospodine. Höre mich, Herr : suli,
coro, organo, arpa, trombe, 4 tromboni e tuba / [von] Leoš
Janáček. — Praha : Editio Dupraphone ; Kassel ; London :
Bärenreiter, 1977. — 4to.
Score (19p.) & harp part.
£3.00

(B78-50753)

ENWXPDR — With brass & keyboard. Psalms
Schütz, Heinrich
[Psalmen Davids sampt etlichen Moteten und Concerten. Alleluia].
Alleluia. Lobet den Herren = Alleluia. Worship Jehovah : for 8
solo voices and double choir, with instruments / [by] Heinrich
Schütz ; edited by Paul Steinitz. — London : Oxford University
Press, 1978. — [2],45p ; 4to.
Duration 10 min.
ISBN 0-19-338088-9 : Unpriced

(B78-50358)

ENYDDW — With wind, strings, keyboard & percussion. Songs, etc
Pehkonen, Elis
Pop into the middle ages : new settings of medieval lyrics for
group music making / by Elis Pehkonen. — Sevenoaks : Novello,
1977. — [4],20p ; 4to.
Duration 9 min.
£0.94

(B78-50033)

ENYESDP/LF — With recorder, strings & keyboard. Carols.
                          Christmas
Odom, John
The last month of the year : eight carols for voices,
Orff-instruments, recorders and guitars / [by] John Odom. —
London : Schott. — (Ensembles with Orff instruments)
Score ([5], 9p.) & 4 parts, with a vocal score.
1 : Hodie, Vhristus natus est. — 1978. — 4to.
Unpriced

(B78-50754)

2 : Children go where I send thee. — 1978. — 4to.
Unpriced

(B78-50755)

3 : Virgin Mary, meek and mild. — 1978. — 4to.
Unpriced

(B78-50756)

4 : O magnum mysterium. — 1978. — 4to.
Unpriced

(B78-50757)

5 : Noël. — 1978. — 4to.
Unpriced

(B78-50758)

6 : The last month of the year. — 1978. — 4to.
Unpriced

(B78-50759)

7 : What you gonna call yo' pretty little baby?. — 1978. — 4to.
Unpriced

(B78-50760)

8 : A Christmas gloria. — 1978. — 4to.
Unpriced

(B78-50761)

ENYEXPDG — With brass, strings & percussion. Ordinary of the
                          Mass
Riethmuller, Heinrich
Tempelhofer Messe / [von] Heinrich Riethmuller. — Hamburg ;
London : Simrock, 1974. — 8vo & 4to.
For chorus, congregation and instrumental ensemble. — Chorus score (7p.),
Melody edition (7p.) & 4 parts. — Text in German.
£4.96

(B78-50034)

ENYLDW — With keyboard & percussion. Songs, etc
Nelson, Ron
Four pieces after the seasons : S.A.T.B. with instrumental
accompaniment / [by] Ron Nelson ; words by Thomas E.
Ahlburn. — [New York] ; [London] : Boosey and Hawkes. —
(Brown university choral series)
Duration 3 1/2 min.
1 : Early May. — 1977. — [4],15p ; 8vo.
£0.50

(B78-50035)

2 : Wonder and wild honey. — 1977. — [1],10p ; 8vo.
£0.40

(B78-50036)

3 : Late September. — 1977. — [1],10p ; 8vo.
£0.40

(B78-50037)

4 : Winter journeyings. — 1977. — [1],10p ; 8vo.
£0.40

(B78-50038)

ETSPLRDGS — With guitar & organ. Anglican liturgy. Communion
Pulkingham, Betty
The King of glory : series 3 (mixolydian) / by Betty Pulkingham.
— Poole (57 Dorchester Rd, Lytchett Minster, Poole) :
Celebration Services, 1976. — 8vo.
For SATB voices with organ and guitar. — Score (31p.) & congregational
part (8p.).
Unpriced

(B78-50040)

EUMDE — With wind band. Religious cantatas
Nelson, Ron
Processional and prayer of Emperor of China on the Altar of
Heaven, December 21, 1539 / [by] Ron Nelson. — [New York] ;
[London] : Oxford University Press, 1977. — 4to.
For chorus & wind band - Score (32p.) & 24 parts.
Unpriced

(B78-50041)

EUMMDW — With military band. Songs, etc
Surinach, Carlos
Celebraciones medievales : Spanish divertissements of the Middle
Ages, for concert band with four-part chorus of mixed voices /
[by] Carlos Surinach, English translation by Joseph Machlis. —
New York ; London : Associated Music, 1977. — 103p ; 4to.
Duration 16 min. — Score (103p.) & choral score (29p.). — Text in Spanish
and English.
£4.55

(B78-50359)

EWMDW/JR — With brass band. Film songs
Lerner, Sammy
[I'm Popeye the sailor man. arr]. I'm Popeye the sailor man / by
Sammy Lerner ; arranged by John Stuart. — New York :
Warner ; [London] : [Blossom], 1978. — 4to. — (Supersound
series for young bands)
For chorus & wind band. Score (8p.) & 49 parts, with several copies of
various parts.
Unpriced

(B78-50762)

EWNDH/LF — With brass ensemble. Motets, Anthems, Hymns, etc
Praetorius, Michael
[Musae Sioniae. Tl.2. Selections]. Weihnachtskonzerte : für zwei
vierstimmige Chöre / [von] Michael Praetorius ; herausgegeben
von Manfred Glonatzki. — Kassel ; London : Bärenreiter, 1977.
— 16p ; 8vo. — (Werkreihe für Bläser und Sanger)
Contents: 1: Nun komm, der Heiden Heiland - 2: In dulci jubilo.
£2.24

(B78-50360)

EWNDW — With brass ensemble. Songs, etc
Venetian ceremonial motets / edited by Denis Stevens. —
Sevenoaks : Novello, 1977. — [12],24p ; 8vo.
Contents: 1: Venetia, mundi splendor - Michael cui stenodomus / by
Johannes Ciconia - 2: Ducalis sedes inclita - Stirps Mocenigo / by Antonio
Romano - 3: Plaude, decus / by Christofero de Monte.
£1.10

(B78-50763)

EWSPDW — With trumpet & piano. Songs, etc
Hovhaness, Alan
[Symphony no.24, 'Majnun'. Letters in the sand. arr]. Letters in
the sand : SATB with trumpet solo and piano / [by] Alan
Hovhaness ; words from 'Salaman and Absal' by Jami, tr. by
Edward Fitzgerald. — New York ; London : Associated Music,
1977. — 11p ; 8vo.
£0.35

(B78-50361)

Hovhaness, Alan
[Symphony no.24, 'Majnun'. Majnun answered. arr]. Majnun
answered ... : SATB with trumpet solo and piano / [by] Alan
Hovhaness. — New York ; London : Associated Music, 1977. —
6p ; 8vo.
£0.30

(B78-50362)

EXRPLRDH — With timpani & organ. Motets, Anthems, Hymns, etc
Wyton, Alec
A hymne to God the Father / words by John Donne ; music by
Alec Wyton : anthem for speaker, SATB with divisions, brass
(optional), timpani and organ. — Sevenoaks : Novello, 1978. —
19p ; 8vo.
Score for voices, timpani and organ.
£0.47

(B78-50363)

EZ — UNACCOMPANIED CHORAL WORKS
EZDE — Religious cantatas
Beyer, Frank Michael
Canticum Mose et Agni : für Doppelchor a cappella (1976) /
[von] Frank Michael Beyer ; [Text von] Mose (Exodus), Kap.15,
v, 1-4, 9, 10, 14, 16-18 [und] Offenbarung des Johannes, Kap.15,
v, 1-4. — Berlin ; London : Bote und Bock, 1977. — [2],34p ; 4to.
£4.80

(B78-50364)

Holst, Gustav
A choral fantasia, Op.51 / [by] Gustav Holst ; poem by Robert
Bridges ; foreword by Imogen Holst. — London : Eulenburg,
1977. — [4],31p ; 8vo. — (Edition Eulenburg ; no.1098)
For chorus and orchestra with a concertante organ part - Miniature score -
Text in English and German.
£1.00

(B78-50042)

Tavener, John
Canticle of the Mother of God / by John Tavener. — London :
Chester Music, 1977. — 13p ; 8vo. — (Contemporary church
music series)
For soprano solo and SSATBB chorus - Greek and Hebrew text.
Unpriced

(B78-50764)

EZDE/LF — Religious cantatas. Christmas
Brown, Christopher
  Hodie salvator apparuit : a sequence for Christmas, op.28 / [by]
  Christopher Brown. — London : Chester Music, 1976. — [2],54p ;
  4to.
  For double choir with S.A.T.B. solo.
  Unpriced
                                                              (B78-50765)

EZDE/LM — Religious cantatas. Ascension
Payne, Anthony
  A littel Ascensiontide cantata : for unaccompanied chorus SATB /
  words attributed to Cynewulf ; music by Anthony Payne. —
  London : Chester Music, 1978. — [1],17p ; 4to. — (Contemporary
  church music series)
  Unpriced
                                                              (B78-50766)

EZDE/LN — Religious cantatas. Whitsun
Payne, Anthony
  A little Whitsuntide cantata : for unaccompanied chorus SATB /
  words by Emily Brontë ; music by Anthony Payne. — London :
  Chester Music, 1978. — [1],16p ; 4to. — (Contemporary church
  music series)
  Unpriced
                                                              (B78-50767)

EZDG — Roman liturgy. Ordinary of the Mass
Shepherd, John
  The Western Wind mass / by John Shepherd ; edited and
  arranged for modern use by Anthony G. Petti. — London :
  Chester Music, 1976. — [4],40p ; 8vo.
  For S.A.T.B.
  Unpriced
                                                              (B78-50768)

Tallis, Thomas
  Mass, Puer natus est nobis / [by] Thomas Tallis ; reconstructed
  and edited by Sally Dunkley and David Wulstan. — Oxford :
  Oxenford Imprint : Dist. Blackwell's Music Shop, 1977. — ii,45,iii
  p ; 8vo. — (Voces musicales ; series I, 1)
  Unpriced
                                                              (B78-50365)

Taverner, John
  [Masses. *Selections*]. Six-part masses / [by] John Taverner ;
  transcribed and edited by Hugh Benham. — London : Stainer and
  Bell, 1978. — xix,260p ; 8vo. — (Early English church music ;
  20)
  ISBN 0-85249-477-7 : Unpriced
                                                              (B78-50769)

EZDGB — Roman liturgy. Ordinary of the Mass. Kyrie
Shepherd, John, b.1520
  Paschal Kyrie / [by] John Shepherd ; edited by David Wulstan.
  — Oxford : Oxenford Imprint : Blackwell's Music Shop, 1978. —
  3p ; 8vo.
  S.S.A.A.T.B.
  Unpriced
                                                              (B78-50770)

EZDGC — Roman liturgy. Ordinary of the Mass. Gloria
Jenni, Donald
  Gloria for four-part chorus of mixed voices a cappella / [by] D.
  Jenni. — New York ; London : Associated Music, 1977. — 8p ;
  8vo.
  English text.
  £0.30
                                                              (B78-50366)

EZDGKH/LF — Roman liturgy. Divine Office. Matins. Christmas
Palestrina, Giovanni Pierluigi da
  [Motettorum ... portim quinis ... vocibus ... liber primus. O
  magnum mysterium]. O magnum mysterium / [by] G.P. da
  Palestrina ; transcribed by R. Barnes. — London (36 Ranelagh
  Gdns., W.6) : Cathedral Music, 1978. — 6p ; 8vo.
  For S.S.A.A.T.B.
  Unpriced
                                                              (B78-50367)

Rorem, Ned
  O magnum mysterium : S.A.T.B. / [by] Ned Rorem. — [New
  York] ; [London] : Boosey and Hawkes, 1978. — 7p ; 8vo.
  Unpriced
  Primary classification EZDJ/LF

EZDGKHM/LH — Misereres
Allegri, Gregorio
  [Miserere]. Miserere mei, Deus : for nine voices / [by] Gregorio
  Allegri. — London : Chester Music, 1976. — 25p ; 8vo.
  Unpriced
                                                              (B78-50771)

EZDGKK — Roman liturgy. Divine Office. Vespers. Magnificat
Lasso, Orlando di
  Magnificat septimi toni for mixed voices and instruments / [by]
  Orlandus Lassus ; edited by Denis Stevens. — London : Oxford
  University Press, 1978. — [1],16p ; 8vo.
  For S.S.A.A.T.T.B..
  ISBN 0-19-337335-1 : Unpriced
                                                              (B78-50773)

White, Robert
  Magnificat / [by] Robert White ; reconstructed and edited by
  Sally Dunkley. — Oxford : Oxenford Imprint : Blackwell's Music
  Shop, 1978. — 19,ii p ; 8vo. — (Voces musicales ; ser. 1 : 4)
  S.S.A.A.T.B.
  Unpriced
                                                              (B78-50772)

EZDGMM — Anglican liturgy. Preces & responses
Doveton, Robin
  Preces and responses (SATB) / [by] Robin Doveton. — London
  (36 Ranelagh Gdns., W.6) : Cathedral Music, 1978. — 6p ; 8vo.
  Unpriced
                                                              (B78-50368)

Ebdon, Thomas
  Preces and responses / [by] Thomas Ebdon. — London (36
  Ranelagh Gdns., W.6) : Cathedral Music, 1977. — 4p ; 4to.
  S.A.T.B.
  Unpriced
                                                              (B78-50369)

EZDH — Motets, Anthems, Hymns, etc
Briegel, Wolfgang Carl
  [Evangelischer Blumengarten. Machet die Töre weit]. Machet die
  Töre weit : Du König der Ehren, wir danken Dir : für
  vierstimmigen gemischten Chor / herausgegeben von Konrad
  Ameln und Harold Kummerling. — Kassel ; London :
  Bärenreiter, 1977. — 8p ; 8vo. — (Chor-Archiv)
  £0.84
                                                              (B78-50370)

Chorbajian, John
  Vital spark of heavenly flame. (The dying Christian to his soul) :
  for full chorus of mixed voices a cappella / [by] John Chorbajian ;
  words by Alexander Pope. — New York ; London : Schirmer,
  1977. — 8p ; 8vo.
  Unpriced
                                                              (B78-50043)

Howells, Herbert
  Antiphon : S.A.T.B. (unacc.) / by Herbert Howells ; words by
  George Herbert. — London : Oxford University Press, 1978. —
  11p ; 8vo.
  ISBN 0-19-350365-4 : Unpriced
                                                              (B78-50044)

Howells, Herbert
  Come, my soul : SATB unacc. / [by] Herbert Howells ; [words
  by] J. Newton ... — London : Oxford University Press, 1978. —
  8p ; 8vo. — (Oxford anthems ; A.323)
  Unpriced
                                                              (B78-50371)

Routh, Francis
  At the round earth's imagined corners : for unaccompanied voices
  S.M. S.A.T.B. / [by] Francis Routh ; words by John Donne ... —
  london : Radcliffe, 1978. — 8p ; 8vo.
  Unpriced
                                                              (B78-50774)

Rubbra, Edmund
  Agnus Dei. Jesus, Lamb of God : op.143 / [by] Edmund Rubbra.
  — London : Lengnick, 1978. — [3p] ; 8vo.
  For S.A.T.B.
  £0.12
                                                              (B78-50775)

Rubbra, Edmund
  Emblem XI. How shall my tongue express ...? : Motet / [by]
  Edmund Rubbra ; op. 155 : [words by] Francis Quarles ... —
  London : Lengnick, 1978. — 8p ; 8vo. — (St. Nicholas series)
  For unaccompanied S.A.T.B.
  £0.18
                                                              (B78-50372)

EZDH/AY — Motets, Anthems, Hymns, etc. Collections
Six easy three-part anthems / edited by Anthony Greening. —
  Croydon : Royal School of Church Music, 1978. — 20p ; 8vo.
  Unpriced
                                                              (B78-50373)

EZDH/LF — Motets, Anthems, Hymns, etc. Christmas
Praetorius, Michael
[Musae Sioniae. Tl.2. *Selections*]. Weihnachtskonzerte : für zwei
vierstimmige Chöre / [von] Michael Praetorius ; herausgegeben
von Manfred Glowatzki. — Kassel ; London : Bärenreiter, 1977.
— 24p ; 8vo. — (Chor-Archiv)
Contents: 1: Nun komm, der Heiden Heiland - 2: In dulci jubilo.
£1.96

(B78-50374)

Praetorius, Michael
[Polyhymnia caduceatrix et panegyrica. Wie schön leuchtet der
Morgenstern]. How brightly beams the morning star = Wie schön
leuchtet der Morgenstern : for four-part chorus of mixed voices,
five solo voices and optional keyboard accompaniment / [by]
Michael Praetorius ; words and melody by Philipp Nicolai,
English text, composite ; edited by C. Buell Agey. — New York ;
London : Schirmer, 1977. — 16p ; 8vo.
English and German text.
£0.35

(B78-50375)

EZDJ — Motets
Berkeley, Sir Lennox
Judica me. Op.96 : for unaccompanied chorus, SSATBB / [by]
Lennox Berkeley. — London : Chester Music, 1978. — 9p ; 4to.
— (Contemporary church music series)
Unpriced

(B78-50776)

Jackson, Francis
Alleluia, laudate pueri dominum : S.S.A.A.T.T.B.B. / [by] Francis
Jackson ; [text from] Psalm 113 (Latin version). — York : Banks,
1978. — 8p ; 8vo. — (Eboracum choral series ; 42)
Text in Latin.
Unpriced

(B78-50777)

Reaney, Gilbert
Two anonymous alleluias from the Worcester Fragments,
(Worcester Cathedral Library, Add. ms. 68) / edited by Gilbert
Reaney. — Lustleigh : Antico Edition, 1977. — 13p ; 4to.
Three soloists and choir.
Unpriced

(B78-50045)

Shepherd, John, b.1520
Libera nos, salva nos : two settings / [by] John Shepherd ; edited
by David Wulstan. — Oxford : Oxenford : Blackwell's Music
Shop (dist.), 1978. — 6p ; 8vo.
Unpriced

(B78-50778)

Tallis, Thomas
[Cantiones, 1575. Derelinquat impius]. Derelinquat impius / [by]
Thomas Tallis ; edited by R. Barnes. — London : Cathedral
Music, 1978. — 7p ; 8vo.
Unpriced

(B78-50376)

Victoria, Tomás Luis de
[Liber primus qui missas ... aliaque cumplectitut, 1576. Nigra
sum]. Nigra sum de beata virgine : for six-part chorus of mixed
voices unaccompanied / by Tomás Luis de Victoria ; edited by
Vahe Aslanian, text from the Song of Solomon. — Wendover :
Roberton, 1978. — 7p ; 8vo. — (Lawson-Gould sacred choral
series)
£0.20

(B78-50779)

Victoria, Tomás Luis de
[Motecta. Ave Maria]. Ave Maria. In Annuntiationis B. Maria
Virginis, / [by] Tomás Luis de Victoria ; transcribed and edited by
Andrew Giles. — London (36 Ranelagh Gdns. W.6) : Cathedral
Music, 1977. — 14p ; 8vo.
For double choir SATB-SATB. — Originally a minor third lower. — Text
in Latin. — From the 1572 edition.
Unpriced

(B78-50377)

Victoria, Tomás Luis de
[Motecta. Doctor bonus]. Doctor bonus. In festo sancti Andreae /
[by] Tomás Luis de Victoria ; transcribed and edited by Andrew
Giles. — London : Cathedral Music, 1977. — 6p ; 8vo.
Includes the variant ending from the editions of 1583, 1585. — For S.A.T.B.
— Text in Latin.
Unpriced

(B78-50378)

EZDJ/AY — Motets. Collections
The Chester books of motets : sacred renaissance motets with Latin
texts / edited by Anthony G. Petti. — London : Chester.
4 : The German school for 4 voices. — 1977. — 44p ; 4to.
Unpriced

(B78-50780)

5 : The Flemish school for 4 voices. — 1977. — 45p ; 4to.
Unpriced

(B78-50781)

EZDJ/LF — Motets. Christmas
Rorem, Ned
O magnum mysterium : S.A.T.B. / [by] Ned Rorem. — [New
York] ; [London] : Boosey and Hawkes, 1978. — 7p ; 8vo.
Unpriced
Also classified at EZDGKH/LH

(B78-50782)

EZDJ/LK — Motets. Good Friday
Rossini, Gioacchino Antonio
[Stabat mater. Quando corpus]. Quando corpus ... : for four-part
chorus of mixed voices / [by] Gioacchino Rossini ; edited by
Leonard Van Camp. — Wendover : Roberton, 1976. — 8p ; 8vo.
Duration 4 min.
£0.20

(B78-50783)

EZDJ/LL — Motets. Easter
Shepherd, John, b.1520
Haec dies / [by] John Shepherd ; edited by David Wulstan. —
Oxford : Oxenford Imprint : Blackwell's Music Shop, 1978. —
3p ; 8vo.
S.S.A.A.T.B.
Unpriced

(B78-50784)

EZDK — Anthems
Dearnley, Christopher
Let thy hand be strengthened / [by] Christopher Dearnley ; text
from Psalm 89 .... — London : Cathedral Music, 1978. — s. sh. ;
8vo. — (St. Paul's series ; no.1)
For S.A.T.B.
Unpriced

(B78-50379)

Tye, Christopher
English sacred music / [by] Christopher Tye ; transcribed and
edited by John Morehen. — London : Stainer and Bell, for the
British Academy. — (Early English church music ; 19)
Vol.1. — 1977. — xvi,352p ; 8vo.
ISBN 0-85249-449-1 : Unpriced

(B78-50046)

EZDM — Hymns
Clarke, Jeremiah
[Bishop Thorpe. arr]. By cool Siloam's shady rill / [Jeremiah
Clarke's tune ; arranged] for unaccompanied mixed chorus,
S.A.T.B. a cappella [by] Louie L. White, [words by] Reginald
Heber. — New York : Galaxy ; [London] : [Stainer and Bell],
1978. — 10p ; 8vo.
This melody attributed to Clarke was called 'Bishop Thorpe' in Edward
Millar's 'Psalms of David'.
Unpriced

(B78-50380)

EZDM/AYE — Hymns. Collections. Germany
Nun jauchzt dem Herren, alle Welt : Chorsätze zu Gemeinsamen
Kirchenliedern / herausgegeben von Kunibertas Dubrovolskis und
Ulrich W. Zimmer. — Kassel ; London : Bärenreiter, 1977. —
24p ; 8vo.
£3.20

(B78-50381)

EZDP/LF — Carols. Christmas
Gardner, John
Sunny bank carol : S.A.T.B. (unacc.), opus 141 / [by] John
Gardner ; words traditional. — London : Oxford University Press,
1978. — [2]p ; 8vo. — (Oxford choral songs ; X262)
ISBN 0-19-343063-0 : Unpriced

(B78-50785)

Ledger, Philip
Two carols / arranged by Philip Ledger. — London : Oxford
University Press, 1978. — 11p ; 8vo. — (Oxford choral songs ;
X265)
For mixed voices. — Contents: Silent night : unaccompanied - 2: On
Christmas night : accompanied.
ISBN 0-19-343066-5 : Unpriced
Primary classification DP/LF

Lindley, Simon
Come sing and dance : S.A.T.B. / [by] Simon Lindley ; words
adapted from an ancient carol. — York : Banks Music, 1978. —
3p ; 8vo. — (Eboracum choral series ; 87)
Unpriced

(B78-50786)

Potter, Archibald James
The storke : carol for S.A.T.B. / [music by] A.J. Potter ; words
traditional. — London : Edwin Ashdown, 1978. — 8p ; 8vo.
£0.20

(B78-50787)

Ridout, Alan
That virgin's child : for S.A.T.B. unacc. / by Alan Ridout ; words by John Gwyneth. — Harpenden : Williams School of Church Music, 1977. — 3p ; 8vo. — (Bourne series ; no.9)
Unpriced

(B78-50047)

Smith, Robert
Star of Bethlehem = Seren Bethlehem : three carols for S.A.T.B. unaccompanied / [by] Robert Smith ; English and Welsh words by Robert Smith. — Wendover : Roberton, 1978. — 32p ; 8vo.
Words in English and Welsh. — Contents: 1: There were in that country = 'Roedd yn y wlad honno - 2: Star of Bethlehem = Seren Bethlehem - 3: The holly = Y gelynnon.
£0.48

(B78-50788)

Sternfeld, Frederick William
[An old English carol. *arr*]. An old English carol : old English ballad tune / adapted by F.W. Sternfeld ; arranged for mixed voices, SATB, by C.R. Wilson. — london : Oxford University Press, 1978. — 3p ; 8vo. — (Oxford choral songs ; X267)
ISBN 0-19-343068-1 : Unpriced

(B78-50789)

Weiss, Donn
De tierra lejana venimos / Puerto Rican folk carol for four-part chorus of mixed voices unaccompanied ; arranged by Donn Weiss. — Wendover : Roberton, 1977. — 12p ; 8vo.
Text in English and Spanish.
£0.24

(B78-50790)

Wilkinson, Stephen
Galician carol, Panxoliña [sic] de Nadal : for four-part chorus of mixed voices unaccompanied / arranged by Stephen Wilkinson, melody from Cancionero musical (Pedrell), words from Cancionero popular gallego (Ballesteros) trans. J.B. Trend. — Wendover : Roberton, 1977. — 8p ; 8vo.
£0.18

(B78-50048)

EZDU — Madrigals
Josquin des Prés
[Selections]. Seven secular pieces : for four voices or instruments, ATTB / [by] Josquin des Prés ; [edited by] Bernard Thomas. — London : London Pro Musica, 1976. — [1],16p ; 4to. — (The art of the Netherlanders, 1470-1530 ; vol.6)
Unpriced
Also classified at LNSK/DU

(B78-50382)

Monteverdi, Claudio
[Madrigals. *Selections*]. Tenmadrigals : for mixed voices / [by] Claudio Monteverdi ; edited by Denis Stevens. — London : Oxford University Press, 1978. — [2],105p ; 8vo.
ISBN 0-19-343676-0 : Unpriced

(B78-50791)

Vento, Ivo de
[Newe teutsche Lieder, mit viern, fünff, und sechs Stimmen. *Selections*]. Eight lieder, 1570 : for four voices or instruments, ATTBB / [by] Ivo de Vento ; texts edited and translated by Alan Robson. — London : London Pro Musica, 1977. — [1],24p ; 4to. — (Anthologies of renaissance music ; vol.8)
With a 'turnover sheet', bearing a duplicate of pages 18, 19, 24 inserted.
Unpriced
Also classified at LNSK/DU

(B78-50383)

EZDU/AYD — Madrigals. Collections. England
The **Oxford** book of English madrigals / edited by Philip Ledger. — London : Oxford University Press, 1978. — 403p ; 8vo.
ISBN 0-19-343664-7 : Unpriced

(B78-50792)

EZDU/AYH — Madrigals. Collections. France
Thirty chansons, 1529 : for three instruments or voices / [edited by] Bernard Thomas. — London : London Pro Musica, 1977. — [1], 40p ; 4to. — (Parisian chanson ; vol.10)
Taken from Attaingnant's collection 'Quarante et deux chansons musicales. — Includes a separate appendix of six chansons for voice and lute, 1529.
Unpriced
Also classified at VSNTK/DU/AYH

(B78-50384)

EZDW — Songs, etc
Bach, Jan
Hair today : for mixed chorus (SAATBB) a cappella / [by] Jan Bach ; verses anonymous (Westminster 1671). — New York : New Galaxy Music ; [London] : [Stainer and Bell], 1978. — 8p ; 8vo.
Unpriced

(B78-50049)

Bent, Margaret
Two 14th-century motets in praise of music / edited by Margaret Bent. — Lustleigh : Newton Abbot, 1977. — [1],13p ; 4to.
1: Sub Arturo plebs - Fons citharizancium - In omnem terram - 2: Apollinis eclipsator - Zodiacum signis - In omnem terram.
Unpriced

(B78-50793)

Berkeley, *Sir* Lennox
The hill of the graces : for unaccompanied chorus, SSAATTBB / text by Edmund Spenser ; music by Lennox Berkeley, Op.91, no.2. — London : Chester Music, 1977. — 21p ; 8vo. — (Contemporary choral series)
Unpriced

(B78-50794)

Blyton, Carey
The misletoe bough, p.61 : traditional carol for SSATBB and piano woodwork or string orchestra and percussion / arranged by Carey Blyton, [words by Thomas H. Bagly]. — Wendover : Roberton, 1977. — 11p ; 8vo.
A song made popular by Sir Henry Bishop who first arranged it. — A musician is required to rap the woodwork of the closed top of a grand piano or the front of an upright piano at appropriate moments.
£0.20

(B78-50050)

Boyd, Anne
As I crossed a bridge of dreams : for unaccompanied chorus (12 or more singers divided into 3 SATB groups) / [by] Anne Boyd. — London : Faber Music, 1974. — [5],30p ; 8vo.
Duration 10 min.
Unpriced

(B78-50385)

Brown, Christopher
Aubade, op.17 : for mixed chorus / words by Herriot, Davenant and Spenser ; music by Christopher Brown. — London : Chester Music, 1977. — 29p ; 8vo. — (Contemporary choral series)
Unpriced

(B78-50795)

Clark, Keith
Three songs from 'A Shropshire lad' : for SATB choir unaccompanied with tenor solo / music by Keith Clark ; words by A.E. Houseman. — Wendover : Roberton, 1978. — 16p ; 8vo.
Tenor solo in no.1 - Staff & tonic sol-fa notation. - Contents: 1: With rue my heart is laden - 2: When I was one and twenty - 3: Far in a western brookland.
£0.24

(B78-50386)

De Cormier, Robert
She'll be comin' round the mountain : American folk song, for full chorus of mixed voices unaccompanied / arranged by Robert de Cormier. — Wendover : Roberton, 1975. — 23p ; 8vo. — (Robert de Cormier choral series)
£0.32

(B78-50051)

Dinerstein, Norman
Gather ye rosebuds : for four-part chorus of mixed voices a cappella / [by] Norman Dinerstein ; words by Robert Herrick. — New York ; London : Schirmer, 1977. — 20p ; 8vo.
Unpriced

(B78-50052)

Elgar, *Sir* Edward, *bart*
Four unaccompanied part-songs. Opus.53 : for SATB with divisions / [by] Edward Elgar. — Sevenoaks : Novello, 1978. — [1],37p ; 8vo.
£1.10

(B78-50796)

George, Thom Ritter
Would I might go far over sea : for four-part chorus of mixed voices a cappella / [by] Thom Ritter Walker ; [words by] Arthur O'Shaughnessy. — New York ; London : Chappell, 1977. — 8p ; 8vo.
Unpriced

(B78-50387)

Killmayer, Wilhelm
Speranza : für fünfstimmigen gemischten Chor a cappella / [von] Wilhelm Killmayer. — Mainz ; [London] : Schott, 1978. — 7p ; 8vo.
£0.72

(B78-50797)

Mathias, William
A royal garland : for unaccompanied mixed voices, op.77 / [by] William Mathias. — London : Oxford University Press, 1978. — 32p ; 8vo.
Duration 15 min.
ISBN 0-19-337440-4 : Unpriced

(B78-50798)

Smith, Robert
Music : for 4-part choir of mixed voices unaccompanied / music by Robert Smith ; words by Wilfred Owen. — Wendover : Roberton, 1978. — 8p ; 8vo.
Staff & tonic sol-fa notation.
£0.18

(B78-50053)

Trubitt, Allen
What any lover learns : for four-part chorus of mixed voices a cappella / [by] Allen Trubitt ; words by Archibald MacLeish. — New York ; London : Chappell, 1976. — 11p ; 8vo.
Unpriced

(B78-50054)

Tučapský, Antonin
Lands : two settings for unaccompanied mixed voice choir of poems by W.H. Auden, music by Antonin Tučapský. — Wendover : Roberton, 1977. — 23p ; 8vo. — (Roberton mixed voice series)
Duration 12 min. — Contents 1: If I could tell you. — 2: Lauds.
£0.32

(B78-50055)

EZDW/AY — Songs, etc. Collections
Invitation to the partsong. — London : Stainer and Bell.
3 : Shakespeare settings by Bishop, Cooke, Hatton, MacFarren, Stevens, Webbe ; a selection of four- and five-part works newly transcribed and edited by Geoffrey Bush and Michael Hurd. — 1978. — [1],49p ; 8vo.
ISBN 0-85249-491-2 : £1.25

(B78-50056)

Sing easy : twelve easy songs for mixed voices / edited by John Coates. — london : Oxford University Press, 1978. — [2],30p ; 8vo. — (Sing for pleasure ; book 8)
ISBN 0-19-330215-2 : Unpriced

(B78-50799)

EZDW/AYC — Songs, etc. Collections. Great Britain
Five traditional songs / arranged for unaccompanied mixed voices by John Rutter. — London : Oxford University Press, 1978. — 27p ; 8vo.
ISBN 0-19-343717-1 : Unpriced

(B78-50800)

EZDW/LC — Spirituals
Hughes, Brian
Two Old Testament spirituals / freely arranged for four-part mixed choir unaccompanied by Brian Hughes. — Wendover : Roberton, 1978. — 8p ; 8vo.
Contents: 1: Jonah - 2: Noah.
£0.18

(B78-50057)

West, John A
Shepherd, shepherd : spiritual for full chorus of mixed voices unaccompanied / arranged by John A. West. — Wendover : Roberton, 1978. — 7p ; 8vo. — (Lawson-Gould sacred choral series)
£0.20

(B78-50801)

West, John A
Sinner, please don't let this harvest pass : for four-part chorus of mixed voices a cappella / spiritual arranged by John A. West. — Wendover : Roberton, 1978. — 8p ; 8vo.
£0.20

(B78-50802)

EZDW/LF — Songs, etc. Christmas
Rorem, Ned
The oxen : S.A.T.B. / [by] Ned Rorem ; [words by] Thomas Hardy. — [New York] ; [London] : Boosey Hawkes, 1978. — 7p ; 8vo.
Unpriced

(B78-50803)

F — FEMALE VOICES, CHILDREN'S VOICES
FACN — Children's musical plays. Chorus score
Gardner, John
[Bel and the dragon. Op.120. Chorus score]. Bel and the dragon, opus 120 / music by John Gardner ; text by Timothy Kraemer. — London : Oxford University Press, 1978. — 8vo.
Chorus parts & 2 audience parts.
ISBN 0-19-336205-8 : Unpriced

(B78-50804)

FADM/AY — Hymns. Choral scores
Hosanna in the highest : a collection of descants for traditional hymns / by Betty Pulkingham. —. Lytchett Minster (Dorchester Rd) : Celebration Services, 1978. — [2],43p ; 8vo.
Melodies and descants.
ISBN 0-906309-07-7 : £1.50

(B78-50805)

FDE — Religious cantatas
Walker, Sue
The day the world was born / [by] Sue Walker. — Great Wakering : Mayhew McCrimmon, 1978. — 43p ; 8vo.
Children's voices and piano.
ISBN 0-85597-271-8 : £1.10

(B78-50806)

FDE/LF — Religious cantatas. Christmas
Swayne, Giles
[Alleluia!. Vocal score]. Alleluia! : a Christmas sequence for speaker, female or boys' voices, harp, piano and percussion / music by Giles Swayne. — Sevenoaks : Novello, 1978. — [4],36p ; 8vo.
Duration 17 min.
£1.05

(B78-50807)

FDE/LL — Religious cantatas. Easter
Cartwright, Kenneth
Resurrection jazz : a cantata for schools / [by] Kenneth Cartwright ; words by Leighton Stubbs. — London : Boosey and Hawkes, 1977. — 4to.
Vocal score (28p.), Choral score (12p.) & 3 optional parts.
Unpriced

(B78-50388)

FDH — Motets, Anthems, Hymns, etc
Parker, Alice
[Songs for Sunday. Search me O God]. Search me O God / [by] Alice Parker, [and], Creation hymn ; [by] Johann Steurlein ; psalm and hymn for two-part choir and piano ... — Wendover : Roberton, 1978. — 8p ; 8vo. — (Alice Parker choral series)
Creation hymn arranged by Alice Parker.
£0.18

(B78-50389)

Parry, William Howard
The spiritual railway : two-part or unison with piano and optional instruments / by W.H. Parry ; words trad. (slightly adapted). — London : Oxford University Press, 1978. — 7p ; 8vo. — (Oxford Choral Songs ; T.112)
ISBN 0-19-341512-7 : Unpriced

(B78-50058)

FDJ — Motets
Suidell, Padre
[Credo. Crucifixus. arr]. Crucifixus = (He was crucified) : for two-part chorus of women's voices with keyboard accompaniment / [by] Padre Suidell ; edited by Jack Boyd, English translation by J.B. — Wendover : Roberton, 1976. — 4p ; 8vo. — (Music 70 choral series)
Piano reduction by C.I. Latrobe.
£0.15

(B78-50808)

FDM — Hymns
Asprey, Jonathan
The celebration song / [by] Jonathan Asprey and Tim Whipple. — Poole (57 Dorchester Rd, Lychett Minster, Poole) : Celebration Services, 1975. — 6p ; 8vo.
Unpriced

(B78-50059)

FDP/LF — Carols. Christmas
Binkerd, Gordon
Song under the silver umbrella : for children's voices and accompaniment / [by] Gordon Binkerd. — [New York] ; [London] : Boosey and Hawkes.
Words by G.K. Chesterton.
1 : The Christ-Child : (S.A. and piano or harp). — 1978. — 12p ; 8vo.
Unpriced

(B78-50809)

Byrd, William
[Pavane, 'Earl of Salisbury', virginals. arr]. The 'Earl of Salisbury' carol, adapted from 'The Earl of Salisbury's Pavane', two-part / by William Byrd ; arr. Richard Graves, words by W. Ballet. — York : Banks, 1978. — 4p ; 8vo. — (Eboracum choral series ; 74)
Unpriced

(B78-50810)

Pockriss, Lee
[Happy birthday, Jesus. arr]. Happy birthday, Jesus / words by Estelle Levitt ; music by Lee Pockriss ; arranged by Jacques Rizzo. — [New York] ; [London] : Chappell, 1978. — 8vo.
SS.A. (7p.), two-part chorus (7p.).
Unpriced

(B78-50811)

Smith, Robert F
In excelsis gloria : two carols for three-part female voice choir and piano with optional recorders / by Robert F. Smith. — Wendover : Roberton, 1978. — 19p ; 8vo.
Staff & tonic sol-fa notation. — Contents: 1: When Christ was born of Mary free - 2: What child is this?.
£0.28

(B78-50390)

Whelan, E L
[Carol y doethion]. Carol y doethion = Carol of the kings [a]
Cysgu yn y gwair = Lord Emmanuel / y gerddoriaeth gan ...
E.L. Whelan ; geiriau gan ... Eirlys Jones a Carys Whelan. — Y
Bontfaen = Cowbridge (Hafod, St. Hilary, Cowbridge) : E.L.
Whelan, 1975. — 4p ; 4to.
Two part carols.
£0.25
                                                                (B78-50060)

Whelan, E L
[Clychau'r nadolig]. Clychau'r nadolig = Christmas bells [a]
Bethlehem / y gerddoriaeth gan ... E.L. Whelan ; geiriau gan ...
Eirlys Jones a Carys Whelan. — Y Bontfaen = Cowbridge
(Hafod, St. Hilary, Cowbridge) : E.L. Whelan, 1976. — 4p ; 4to.
Two-part carols.
£0.25
                                                                (B78-50061)

FDP/LL — Carols. Easter
Parker, Alice
[Songs for Sunday. This joyful Eastertide]. This joyful Eastertide :
two seasonal carols of praise, for two-part choir and piano /
arranged by Alice Parker. — Wendover : Roberton, 1978. — 7p ;
8vo. — (Alice Parker choral series)
£0.18
                                                                (B78-50391)

FDW — Songs, etc
Binkerd, Gordon
Song under the silver umbrella : for children's voices and
accompaniment / [by] Gordon Binkerd. — [New York] ;
[London] : Boosey and Hawkes.
Words by Thomas Moore.
5 : Child's song : (three-part children's chorus and piano). — 1978. — 11p ;
8vo.
Unpriced
                                                                (B78-50812)

6 : White fields : (S.A. and piano). — 1978. — 8p ; 8vo.
Unpriced
                                                                (B78-50813)

Chorbajian, John
A cradle song : for four-part chorus of women's voices with piano
accompaniment / [by] John Chorbajian ; [poem by] William
Blake. — New York ; London : Schirmer, 1977. — 16p ; 8vo.
Unpriced
                                                                (B78-50062)

Graves, Richard
Cornish flower song : two-part song / arranged with new words
by Richard Graves. — London : Bosworth and Co., 1978. — 8p ;
8vo.
Unpriced
                                                                (B78-50814)

Hughes-Jones, Llifon
Sleep = Cswg : for two-part choir and piano / by Llifon
Hughes-Jones ; English words by John Fletcher, Welsh words by
Lewys Moelwyn. — Wendover : Roberton, 1978. — 8p ; 8vo.
Staff & tonic sol-fa notation.
£0.20
                                                                (B78-50815)

Maw, Nicholas
Calico pie and other nonsense rhymes : songs and rounds for
children / [by] Nicholas Maw. — London : Boosey and Hawkes,
1978. — 8vo.
Vocal score ([3p.],43p.), Melody ed. ([2],22p.).
£2.60
                                                                (B78-50392)

Maw, Nicholas
Caroline Pink and other nonsense rhymes / [by] Nicholas Maw.
— London : Boosey and Hawkes, 1978. — 8vo.
Vocal score ([2],46p.), Melody ed. ([1],24p.).
£2.60
                                                                (B78-50393)

Silverman, Jerry
Jest 'fore Christmas : for two-part chorus of young voices with
piano and guitar accompaniment / music by Jerry Silverman ;
poem by Eugene Field. — New York ; London : Schirmer, 1977.
— 5p ; 8vo.
Unpriced
                                                                (B78-50063)

Winfrey, Robert
Let's build a city : for two-part chorus of young voices with piano
accompaniment / [by] Robert Winfrey. — New York ; London :
Schirmer, 1977. — 8p ; 8vo.
Unpriced
                                                                (B78-50064)

FDW/GJ — Children's songs
Lutoslawski, Witold
Three children's songs for three equal voices (SSA) / [by] Witold
Lutuslawski ; based on words by L. Kvzemoniecka and A. Barto,
edited by Marie Pooler. — London : Chester Music, 1977. — 4to.
Vocal score ([1],13p.) & chorus score (8p.).
Unpriced
                                                                (B78-50816)

FDW/JR — Songs, etc. Films
Schwartz, Arthur
[That's entertainment. That's entertainment. *arr*]. That's
entertainment : S.S.A. with piano / music by Arthur Schwartz ;
arranged by Dick Averre, lyrics by Howard Dietz. — New York ;
[London] : Chappell, 1978. — 12p ; 8vo.
Unpriced
                                                                (B78-50817)

FDW/LC — Spirituals
Dexter, Harry
Mary and Martha : negro spiritual / arranged for two-part singing
by Harry Dexter. — London : Edwin Ashdown, 1978. — 7p ;
8vo. — (Ashdown vocal duets ; no.392)
£0.20
                                                                (B78-50818)

Dexter, Harry
Wake up, Jacob : negro spiritual / arranged for two-part singing
with piano accompaniment by Harry Dexter. — London : Edwin
Ashdown, 1978. — 7p ; 8vo. — (Ashdown vocal duets ; no.391)
£0.20
                                                                (B78-50819)

Hudson, Hazel
The Daniel quodlibet (based on three negro spirituals) : for two
female, two male or one female and one male voices / arr. by
Hazel Hudson. — London : Edwin Ashdown, 1978. — 7p ; 8vo.
— (Ashdown vocal duets ; 390)
With piano. — Duration 1 1/2 min.
Unpriced
Also classified at GDW/LC; DW/LC
                                                                (B78-50394)

Hudson, Hazel
Feed my sheep : a quodlibet based on negro spirituals / arr. by
Hazel Hudson. — London : Ashdown, 1978. — 4p ; 8vo. —
(Ashdown vocal duets ; no.389)
Two part song.
Unpriced
                                                                (B78-50065)

Stockton, Robert
Let it shine : spiritual for 3-part chorus of female voices with
piano and optional percussion / arranged by Robert Stockton. —
Wendover : Roberton, 1977. — 8p ; 8vo. — (Music 70 choral
series)
£0.18
                                                                (B78-50395)

FDW/LF — Songs. Christmas
Lombardo, Mario
Guess what time of year it is! : for SATB chorus with piano
accompaniment / music by Mario Lombardo ; lyrics by Bill
Margaretten. — [New York] ; [London] : Chappell, 1978. — 7p ;
8vo.
Unpriced
                                                                (B78-50820)

FDW/XC/AY — Rounds. Collections
Rounds about rounds / collected and edited by Jane Yolen, musical
arrangements by Barbara Green, illustrated by Gail Gibbons. —
New York ; London : Franklin Watts, 1977. — 120p ; 4to.
ISBN 0-531-00125-3 : Unpriced
                                                                (B78-50396)

FE/LDM/AYE — With instruments. Hymns. Collections. Germany
Chormusik für Kinder / herausgegeben vom Landesverband der
evangelischen Kirchenmusiker Badens. — Kassel ; London :
Bärenreiter.
[1] : Advent, Weihnachten, Epiphanias. — 1976. — [1],48p ; 8vo. —
Unpriced
                                                                (B78-50397)

[2] : Lob und Dank. — 1977. — [1],41p ; 8vo. —
£3.36
                                                                (B78-50398)

FE/RXNRDW — With string quintet. Songs, etc
Holst, Gustav
Seven part-songs for female voices and strings / words by Robert
Bridges ; music by Gustav Holst, op.44. — Revised [ed.] 1973 /
by Imogen Holst. — Sevenoaks : Novello, [1974]. — [2],46p ; 4to.
Unpriced
                                                                (B78-50821)

FE/TSDP/LF/AY — With guitar. Carols. Christmas. Collections
Lindsay carol book / arranged by Douglas Coombes, 10 carols from
around the world with guitar chords. — Sandy : Lindsay Music,
1978. — 14p ; obl.8vo.
ISBN 0-85957-007-x : Unpriced

(B78-50822)

FEZDH — Unaccompanied voices. Motets, Anthems, Hymns, etc
Binkerd, Gordon
Song under the silver umbrella : for children's voices and
accompaniment / [by] Gordon Binkerd. — [New York] ;
[London] : Boosey and Hawkes.
Words by William Blake.
2 : Song of innocence : (three-part children's chorus). — 1978. — 8p ; 8vo.
Unpriced

(B78-50823)

FEZDJ — Unaccompanied voices. Motets
Victoria, Tomás Luis de
[Jesu dulcis memoria]. Jusu! the very thought is sweet : for 4-part
female choir unaccompanied / [by] T.L. de Victoria ; arr. Hilda
Morgan ; words by St Bernard of Clairvaux, trans. J.M. Neale. —
Wendover : Roberton, 1978. — 4p ; 8vo.
Attributed to Victoria in this publication. — Text in English and Latin.
£0.15

(B78-50824)

FEZDP/LF — Unaccompanied voices. Carols. Christmas
Miller, Thomas E
Sing we now Christmas : traditional French carol for 4-part
chorus of female voices unaccompanied / arranged by Thomas E.
Miller. — Wendover : Roberton, 1977. — 11p ; 8vo.
£0.20

(B78-50399)

Sing for joy : ten Christmas carols / arranged for 3-part female
voice choir unaccompanied by Cecil Cope. — Wendover :
Roberton, 1978. — 14p ; 8vo.
£0.28

(B78-50825)

FEZDW — Unaccompanied voices. Songs, etc
Cockshott, Gerald
My boy Billy : folk song collected by R. Vaughan Williams /
arranged for S.S.C. (unaccompanied) by Gerald Cockshott. —
Wendover : Roberton, 1977. — 7p ; 8vo.
Duration 1 3/4 min.
£0.18

(B78-50066)

Phillips, John Charles
O waly waly : for SSA unaccompanied, Somerset folk song /
collected Cecil Sharp, arranged John C. Phillips. — Wendover :
Roberton, 1978. — 4p ; 8vo.
£0.12

(B78-50400)

Schumann, Robert
[Romanzen für Frauenstimmen, Op.69. Tamburin schlägerin]. The
tambourine player = Tamburin schlägerin : for four-part chorus
of women's voices a cappella / [by] Robert Schumann ; op.69,
no.1, edited by Frank Mueller, English text by F.M. — New
York ; London : Schirmer, 1977. — 8p ; 8vo.
For SSAA. — Text in English and German.
£0.30

(B78-50401)

Weingarden, Louis
Three short sacred songs : for SSA chorus unaccompanied / [by]
Louis Weingarden. — New York ; [London] : Oxford University
Press, 1978. — 3p ; 8vo.
Unpriced

(B78-50402)

FEZDW/AY — Unaccompanied voices. Songs, etc. Collections
Help your patrol to make music / [compiled] by Susan Stevens. —
London : Girl Guides Association, 1978. — [1],24p ; obl.8vo.
Unpriced

(B78-50403)

FLDJ — Treble voices. Motets
Blow, John
Paratum cor meum Deus / [by] John Blow ; edited [from] Oxford
Ch.Ch.Mus. 14 f.108 by Christopher Dearnley. — London (36
Ranelagh Gdns. W.6) : Cathedral Music, 1977. — 6p ; 8vo.
For S.S. and continuo. — Text in Latin.
Unpriced

(B78-50404)

FLE/NYLDW — Treble voices. With keyboard & percussion. Songs,
etc
Kirk, Theron
Now's the time to sing : for three-part chorus of treble voices with
descant solo, piano four-hands accompaniment and percussion /
[by] Theron Kirk. — New York ; London : Schirmer, 1977. —
12p ; 8vo.
Unpriced

(B78-50067)

FLEZDGMM — Unaccompanied treble voices. Anglican liturgy.
    Preces and responses
McLeish, Craig
Preces and responses for trebles / [by] Craig McLeish. — London
(36 Ranelagh Gdns., W.6) : Cathedral Music, 1978. — 3p ; 8vo.
— (St. Paul's series ; no.9)
Unpriced

(B78-50405)

G — MALE VOICES
GDGS — Anglican liturgy. Communion
Doveton, Robin
A short Communion service : for ATB and organ / [by] Robin
Doveton. — London : Cathedral Music, 1978. — 7p ; 8vo.
Unpriced

(B78-50406)

GDH/LF — Motets, Anthems, Hymns, etc. Christmas
Gump, Richard
The gift of December : for four-part chorus of men's voices and
baritone solo with piano accompaniment / [by] Richard Gump ;
[words by] Rev. Ernest Bradley. — New York ; London :
Schirmer, 1977. — 12p ; 8vo.
Unpriced

(B78-50068)

GDP/LF — Carols. Christmas
Goedecke, Werner
Fröhliche Weihnachtszeit : eine Folge volkstümlicher
Weihnachtslieder für Männerchor und Klavier oder a cappella /
[von] Werner Goedecke. — Mainz ; [London] : Schott, 1977. —
18p ; 8vo.
£4.40

(B78-50070)

GDR — Psalms
Roberton, *Sir* **Hugh Stevenson**
Two Scottish psalm tunes / arranged for four-part male voice
choir by Hugh S. Roberton. — Wendover : Roberton, 1977. —
11p ; 8vo. — (Roberton male voice series)
Staff & tonic sol-fa notation. — Contents: 1: Old 124th, Now Israel may
say - 2: Come, let us to the Lord our God.
£0.20

(B78-50407)

GDW/LC — Spirituals
Hudson, Hazel
The Daniel quodlibet (based on three negro spirituals) : for two
female, two male or one female and one male voices / arr. by
Hazel Hudson. — London : Edwin Ashdown, 1978. — 7p ; 8vo.
— (Ashdown vocal duets ; 390)
With piano. — Duration 1 1/2 min.
Unpriced
Primary classification FDW/LC

(B78-50394)

GE/NYDPDW/G/AYE — With woodwind, strings, keyboard &
    percussion. Folk songs. Collections. Germany
Schönster Schatz leb wohl eine Reise durch Deutschland mit
Volksliedern und Tänzen : für Männerchor, zwei Klarinetten oder
andere Holzbläser, Streicher oder Tasteninstrumente und
Schlagzeug, Gitarre ad lib / [bearbeitet von] Karl Jaus. —
Mainz ; London : Schott, 1977. — 25p ; 8vo. — (Schott's
Chorverlag)
Duration 22 min.
£5.20

(B78-50071)

GEZDGKAD — Proper of the Mass. Graduals
Byrd, William
[Gradualia, lib.1. Ave verum corpus. *arr*]. Ave verum corpus : for
male voice choir unaccompanied / [by] William Byrd ; arr. Hilda
Morgan. — Wendover : Roberton, 1978. — 7p ; 8vo.
£0.20
Primary classification GEZDJ

GEZDGKAH/LEZ — Unaccompanied voices. Proper of the Mass. Communion. Advent
Morales, Cristoval
Ecce virgo concipiet / [by] Morales ; ed. Roger Lowman. — London : Cathedral Music, 1978. — 4p ; 8vo.
For ATTB.
Unpriced

(B78-50408)

GEZDGKB — Unaccompanied voices. Roman liturgy. Divine Office. Matins. Te Deum
Taverner, John
Te Deum / [by] John Taverner ; edited by David Wulstan. — Oxford : Oxenford Imprint : Distributed by Blackwell's Music Shop, 1977. — ii,16p ; 8vo. — (Voces musicales series ; I, 2)
For A.A.T.T.B.
Unpriced

(B78-50409)

GEZDGKH/LF — Unaccompanied voices. Roman liturgy. Divine Office. Matins. Christmas
Morales, Cristoval
O magnum mysterium / [by] Morales ; ed. R. Lowman. — London (36 Ranelagh Gdns., W.6) : Cathedral Music, 1978. — 3p ; 8vo.
For AATB.
Unpriced

(B78-50410)

GEZDGKJ/LF — Unaccompanied voices. Roman liturgy. Divine Office. Vespers. Christmas
Palestrina, Giovanni Pierluigi da
Hodie Christus natus est / [by] Giovanni Pierluigi Palestrina ... ; edited by Christopher Dearnley. — London : Cathedral Music, 1978. — 4p ; 8vo.
For AATB.
Unpriced

(B78-50411)

GEZDGMM — Unaccompanied voices. Anglican liturgy. Preces & responses
Ashfield, Robert
Responses for A.T.B. / [by] Robert Ashfield. — London : Cathedral Music, 1978. — 2p ; 8vo.
Unpriced

(B78-50412)

Doveton, Robin
[Preces and responses. arr]. Preces and responses / [by] Robin Doveton ; arr. men's voices. — London (36 Ranelagh Gdns W.6) : Cathedral Music, 1977. — 6p ; 8vo.
For A.T.B.
Unpriced

(B78-50413)

Jones, Michael Leighton
Preces and responses for men's voices / [by] Michael Leighton Jones. — Revised ed. — London (36 Ranelagh Gdns., W.6) : Cathedral Music, 1978. — 4p ; 4to.
Unpriced

(B78-50414)

GEZDGNR — Unaccompanied voices. Anglican liturgy. Morning Prayer. Benedicite
Batten, Adrian
[Short service for men. Benedicite]. Benedicite ... / [by] Adrian Batten ; edited by Maurice Bevan. — London (36 Ranelagh Gdns., W.6) : Cathedral Music, 1978. — 6p ; 8vo.
For AATB. — Originally in C major.
Unpriced

(B78-50415)

GEZDGPP — Unaccompanied voices. Anglican liturgy. Evening Prayer. Canticles
Dearnley, Christopher
Evening service for men's voices / [by] Christopher Dearnley. — London (36 Ranelagh Gdns., W.6) : Cathedral Music, 1978. — 2p ; 8vo.
For A.T.T.B.
Unpriced

(B78-50416)

Doveton, Robin
Magnificat and Nunc dimittis / [by] Robin Doveton. — London : Cathedral Music, 1977. — 6p ; 8vo.
For A.T.B.
Unpriced

(B78-50417)

Mundy, William
Evening service for men's voices 'in three parts' / [by] William (?) Mundy ; edited by Maurice Bevan. — London : Cathedral Music, 1977. — 17p ; 8vo.
For A.A.T.T.B.B. with optional organ.
Unpriced

(B78-50418)

GEZDH — Unaccompanied voices. Motets, Anthems, Hymns, etc
Loudová, Ivana
I speak in wisdom's voice (Ego sapienta) : for full chorus of men's voices a cappella / [by] Ivana Loudová ; English version by Jane May. — New York ; London : Schirmer, 1977. — 12p ; 8vo.
Unpriced

(B78-50419)

GEZDH/LF — Unaccompanied voices. Motets, Anthems, Hymns, etc. Christmas
Mendelssohn, Felix
[Perite autem. Op.115, no.2]. How brightly shine = Perite autem : for four part chorus of men's voices a cappella / [by] Felix Mendelssohn ; Op.115, no.2, edited by Frank Mueller, English text by F.M. — New York ; London : Schirmer, 1977. — 11p ; 8vo.
Text in English and Latin.
£0.35

(B78-50420)

GEZDJ — Motets
Byrd, William
[Gradualia, lib.1. Ave verum corpus. arr]. Ave verum corpus : for male voice choir unaccompanied / [by] William Byrd ; arr. Hilda Morgan. — Wendover : Roberton, 1978. — 7p ; 8vo.
£0.20
Also classified at GEZDGKAD

(B78-50826)

GEZDJ/LL — Unaccompanied voices. Motets. Easter
White, Robert
Regina coeli / [by] Robert White ; edited by Sarah Cobbold. — Oxford : Oxenfor Imprint, dist. Blackwell's Music Shop, 1978. — 5p ; 8vo. — (Voces musicales ; series I, 3)
Sources, Christ Church MSS. 970-81 and 983, no.44, Bodleian Rawl. Lit. d 4. — For A.A.T. Bar. B.
Unpriced

(B78-50421)

GEZDJ/LM — Unaccompanied voices. Motets. Ascension
Handl, Jacob
[Secundus tomus musici operis. Ascendo ad Patrem meum. arr]. Ascendo ad Patrem meum / [by] Jacob Handl ; arranged for AATTBB by R. Barnes, text from St John XX ... and St Luke XXIV ... — London : Cathedral Music, 1978. — 4p ; 8vo.
Unpriced

(B78-50422)

GEZDP/LF — Unaccompanied voices. Carols. Christmas
Plumstead, Mary
They all were looking for a king : for four-part male voice choir unaccompanied / words by George MacDonald ; music by Mary Plumstead. — Revised ed. — Wendover : Roberton, 1976. — 4p ; 8vo.
£0.15

(B78-50827)

GEZDW — Unaccompanied voices. Songs, etc
Johnston, Peter Fyfe
When the kye comes home : T.T.B.B. unacc. / arr. Peter F. Johnston, [words by] James Hogg. — York : Banks Music, 1977. — 6p ; 8vo. — (Eboracum choral series)
Unpriced

(B78-50072)

Lees, Heath
Iona boat song. For a dead king : traditional Scottish air for 4-part male chorus unaccompanied / arranged by Heath Lees ; words by Hugh S. Roberton. — Wendover : Roberton, 1978. — 4p ; 8vo.
£0.15

(B78-50828)

Pasfield, William Reginald
Jillian of Berry : four part song for male voices T.T.B.B. / music by W.R. Pasfield ; words from 'The knight of the burning pestle' (1610) by Beaumont and Fletcher. — London : Edwin Ashdown, 1978. — 6p ; 8vo. — (Enoch choral series ; no.358)
Unaccompanied - Originally published: London : Joseph Williams, 1961, with textual additions - Duration 1 min.
£0.20

(B78-50829)

Schubert, Franz
Das stille Lied : für vier Männerstimmen = for four men's voices / [von] Franz Schubert ; herausgegeben von, edited by, Walther Dürr. — Erstausgabe. — Kassel ; London : Bärenreiter, 1978. — 8p ; 8vo.
D.916. — Text by Johann Georg Soeyemund.
£0.90

(B78-50830)

Smetana, Bedřich
[The dower]. Die Mitgift [und] Gebet : zwei Männerchöre a cappella nach Texten von Josef Srb-Debrnov / [von] Bedřich Smetana ; herausgegeben von Jaromir Fiala, deutsche Übersetzung von Kurt Honolha. — Kassel ; [London] : Bärenreiter, 1977. — 7p ; 8vo. — (The nineteenth century)
£0.70

(B78-50423)

Sutermeister, Heinrich
Les sondards / [von] Heinrich Sutermeister ; texte français, Jean Samuel Cartet. — Mainz ; [London] : Schott, 1977. — 2p ; 8vo.
French text.
£0.20

(B78-50073)

GEZDW/LC — Unaccompanied voices. Spirituals
Hughes, Brian
Jonah : spiritual for unaccompanied male choir or quartet / freely arranged by Brian Hughes, words and tune adapted by Lucy Rider-Meyer. — Wendover : Roberton, 1978. — 4p ; 8vo.
£0.12

(B78-50074)

HY — SPEAKING CHORUS
Orff, Carl
Sprechstücke : für Sprecher, Sprechchor und Schlagwerk / [von] Carl Orff ; [Einführung von] Werner Thomas. — Mainz ; London : Schott, 1977. — 56p ; obl. 4to.
£7.20

(B78-50076)

HYE/VTPLTN — Speaker's chorus. With oboes & plucked string instruments
Hufschmidt, Wolfgang
Trio 3. / [von] Wolfgang Hufschmidt ; Texte für Sprecherin (nen) und Instrumente, ('Magnificat peregrini toni') ; [von] Wolfgang Hufschmidt. — Partitur-Fassung 1975-1977 mit Versionen für eine oder drei Sprecherinnen und oder 1-9 Oboeinstrumente und oder 1-9 Gitarren oder andere zupfinstrumente. — Kassel ; London : Bärenreiter, 1977. — 3 pt ; obl.fol.4to.
£22.40

(B78-50424)

J — VOICES IN UNISON
JDGNT — Anglican liturgy. Jubilate Deo
Asprey, Jonathan
Jubilate Deo : psalm 100 / [by] Jonathan Asprey. — [Poole] : Celebration Services, 1976. — 4p ; 8vo.
For voices in unison.
Unpriced

(B78-50077)

JDGS — Anglican liturgy. Communion
Fenton, Raymond
The Cerney setting of Series 3 Holy Communion / by Raymond Fenton. — South Cerney (All Hallows Church, South Cerney, Gloucestershire) : Raymond Fenton, 1977. — 19p ; 8vo.
Unpriced

(B78-50078)

Hesford, Bryan
Holy communion series III. Missa in simplicitate / [by] Bryan Hesford. — London : Cramer, 1978. — 7p ; 8vo. — (Cramer's library of church music ; no.24)
For cantor, choir, congregation and organ.
Unpriced

(B78-50831)

JDH — Motets, Anthems, Hymns, etc
Farra, Mimi
Hosanna Lord! / [by] Mimi Farra. — Poole : Celebration Services, 1975. — 3p ; 8vo.
Unison voices.
Unpriced

(B78-50079)

JDK — Anthems
Page, Jodi
Fear not, for I have redeemed you / [by] Jodi Page ; based on Isaiah 43. — Poole : Celebration Services, 1975. — 4p ; 8vo.
Voices in unison.
Unpriced

(B78-50080)

JDM — Hymns
Kennedy, Mikel
Never in my life / [by] Mikel Kennedy. — Poole (57 Dorchester Rd. Lytchett Minister, Poole) : Celebration Services, 1975. — 5p ; 8vo.
Unpriced

(B78-50081)

Pulkingham, Betty
Hail to the Lord's anointed / [by] Betty Pulkingham ; based on Psalm 72 words by James Montgomery. — Poole (57 Dorchester Rd. Lytchett Minister, Poole) : Celebration Services, 1974. — 3p ; 8vo.
Unpriced

(B78-50082)

JDTF — Lord's Prayer
Fanshawe, David
[African Sanctus. Lord's Prayer. *arr*]. The Lord's Prayer ... : unison chorus and piano / by David Fanshawe ; arranged by Jacques Rizzo. — New York ; [London] : Chappell, 1978. — 5p ; 8vo.
Unpriced

(B78-50425)

JDW/JV/AY — Music hall songs. Collections
Francis and Day's community book of music hall songs. — London : EMI Music.
No.1. — 1977. — [1],53p ; 8vo. —
Unpriced

(B78-50083)

No.2. — 1977. — [1],49p ; 8vo. —
Unpriced

(B78-50084)

JE/TSDM/LSB/AY — With guitar. Hymns. Roman Catholic Church. Collections
Celebration hymnal / guitar chord arrangements, Daniel Brown. — Vocal/guitar ed. [with] supplement. — Great Wakering : Mayhew-McCrimmon, 1978. — [257p] ; obl.8vo.
ISBN 0-85597-263-7 : Unpriced

(B78-50832)

JE/VSPDP/LF — With recorder & piano. Carols. Christmas
Petrokino, Paul
[Workers' carol. *arr*]. The workers' carol / tune by Paul Petrokino ; arranged for unison voices, descant and treble recorders and piano by Pamela Breese, words by Morris Martin. — Wendover : Roberton, 1978. — 4p ; 8vo.
Duration 2 1/2 min.
£0.12

(B78-50426)

JEZDGKB — Unaccompanied voices. Divine Office
Music for Evening Prayer from the Divine Office / [by] the Benedictine nuns of Stanbrook Abbey ; edited by Hildelith Cumming. — London : Collins, 1978. — 152p ; 8vo.
With a leaflet entitled 'Psalm tones' inserted.
ISBN 0-00-599593-0 : Unpriced

(B78-50833)

JEZDM/AY — Unaccompanied voices. Hymns. Collections
20th century folk hymnal / compiled by Kevin Mayhew. — Leigh-on-Sea ([55 Leigh Rd, Leigh-on-Sea]) : Kevin Mayhew.
Vol.1. — 1976. — [96]p ; 8vo.
ISBN 0-905725-27-1 : Unpriced

(B78-50427)

Vol.3. — 1976. — [96p] ; 8vo.
ISBN 0-905725-00-x : Unpriced

(B78-50428)

JEZDTD — Plainsong. Gregorian chant
New Jubilate Deo : simple Gregorian chants for the faithful to learn. — 2nd ed. — London : Catholic Truth Society, 1978. — 69p ; 8vo.
First edition called 'Jubilate Deo'.
Unpriced

(B78-50834)

JEZDW/AY — Unaccompanied voices. Songs, etc. Collections
Big red songbook / compiled by Mal Collins, David Harker and Geoff White. — London (Unit 10, Specner Court, Chalcot Rd, N.W.1) : Plato Press, 1977. — 128p ; 16mo.
ISBN 0-904383-12-1 : £1.00

(B78-50835)

Song smith. — Stoke on Trent (495 Uttoxeter Rd., Meir, Stoke on Trent) : Dave Wrench : Adrian Crosby.
Quarterly. — [14]p. in 1st issue.
No.1-. — [1977]-. — 4to.
Lists of records.
£1.00 for 4 issues
ISSN 0140-1882

(B78-50429)

JEZDW/AYX — Unaccompanied voices. Songs, etc. Australia
The Penguin Australian song book / compiled and with notes by John Manifold. — Harmondsworth : Penguin Books, 1977. — xi, 180p ; obl. 8vo.
ISBN 0-14-070004-8 : £1.25

(B78-50085)

**JFADM — Female voices, Children's voices. Melody part. Hymns.
Collections**
With cheerful voice : hymns for children with melodies, descant
recorder parts, and prayers. — 2nd ed. revised and enlarged. —
London : A. & C. Black, 1978. — 208p ; 8vo.
ISBN 0-7136-1368-8 : Unpriced

(B78-50086)

JFADW — Female voices, Children's voices. Songs, etc. Choral scores
Eröd, Iván
[Milchzahnlieder. *Choral score*]. Milchzahnlieder = Milktooth
songs / [von] Iván Eröd ; Gedichte von, German and English
text, by Richard Bletschacher. — London : Boosey and Hawkes,
1978. — 10p ; 8vo.
Unpriced

(B78-50836)

**JFADW/AY — Female voices, Children's voices. Songs, etc. Melody
part. Collections**
Ta-ra-ra boom-de-ay : songs for everyone / chosen by David
Gadsby and Beatrice Harrop, melody edition with chords for
guitar, parts for voice or instrument and drawings by Bernard
Cheese. — London : A. and C. Black, 1978. — [112]p ; 8vo.
ISBN 0-7136-1790-x : Unpriced

(B78-50837)

**JFDH — Female voices, Children's voices. Motets, Anthems, Hymns,
etc**
How, Martin
An Easter greeting : for unison voices with divisions and organ /
music by Martin How ; words adapted from Mrs C.F. Alexander.
— Wendover : Roberton, 1978. — 4p ; 8vo.
Duration 2 1/2 min.
£0.15

(B78-50838)

JFDM — Female voices, Children's voices. Hymns
Baggett, Ed
We really want to thank you, Lord / words and music by Ed
Baggett. — Reading (Yeldall Manor, Hare Hatch, Reading) :
Celebration Services, 1974. — 4p ; 4to.
Unpriced

(B78-50087)

Howard, Brian
If I were a butterfly / [by] Brian Howard. — Reading :
Celebration Services, 1974. — 4p ; 4to.
Unpriced

(B78-50088)

Page, Jodi
On tiptoe / [by] Jodi Page ; verses, Maggie Durran, refrain [from]
Romans 8, J.B. Phillips's translation. — Reading (Yeldall Manor,
Hare Hatch, Reading) : Celebration Services, 1974. — 3p ; 4to.
Unpriced

(B78-50089)

Race, Steve
[The day of the donkey, and other songs of praise. *Vocal score*].
The day of the donkey (and other songs of praise for juniors) /
words and music by Steve Race. — London : Weinberger, 1978.
— 25p ; 4to.
Unpriced

(B78-50839)

JFDW — Female voices, Children's voices. Songs, etc
All sorts : a collection of songs for the first school / [edited by]
Janyce Pringle. — Exeter : Wheaton, 1978. — 48p ; 4to.
ISBN 0-08-022187-4 : Unpriced

(B78-50840)

Binkerd, Gordon
Song under the silver umbrella : for children's voices and
accompaniment / [by] Gordon Binkerd. — [New York] ;
[London] : Boosey and Hawkes.
Words by James Stephens.
3 : An evening falls : (unison children's voices and piano). — 1978. — 8p ;
8vo.
Unpriced

(B78-50841)
4 : The merry man of Paris : (unison children's voices and piano). — 1978.
— 11p ; 8vo.
Unpriced

(B78-50842)

Burtch, Mervyn
[Songs of London town. *Selections*]. Highgate and The tower /
music by Mervyn Burtch ; words by Eleanor Farjeon. —
Wendover : Roberton, 1977. — 8p ; 8vo.
£0.18

(B78-50090)

Dale, Mervyn
Let the children sing / [by] Mervyn Dale ; words by Spike
Milligan. — London : Edwin Ashdown.
Book 1. — 1978. — 16p ; 4to.
Unpriced

(B78-50430)

Eröd, Iván
[Milchzahnlieder. *Vocal score*]. Milchzahnlieder = Milktooth
songs : für Gesang oder Kinderchor, mit Klavier oder
Kammerorchester = for solo voice, or children's chorus with
piano or chamber orchestra / [von] Iván Eröd ; Gedichte von,
German and English text, by Richard Bletschacher. — London :
Boosey and Hawkes, 1978. — vi,26p ; 8vo.
Unpriced
Primary classification KDW

Fraser, Shena
Cotton : unison song with optional descant and piano music / by
Shena Fraser ; words by Eleanor Farjeon. — Wendover :
Roberton, 1978. — 4p ; 8vo.
Staff & tonic sol-fa notation. — Duration 2 min.
£0.12

(B78-50091)

Harper, Don
Songs from Alice : Alice in Wonderland and Through the
looking-glass / words by Lewis Carroll set to music by Don
Harper with illustrations by Charles Folkard. — London : Adam
and Charles Black, 1978. — 48p : ill ; 4to.
ISBN 0-7136-1879-5 : Unpriced

(B78-50843)

Potter, Archibald James
Lovelie Jemmie / arr. A.J. Potter. — London : Ashdown, 1978.
— 4p ; 8vo. — (Ashdown unison songs ; no.106)
Song - Duration 3 1/2 minutes.
Unpriced

(B78-50092)

Ten of the best : a selection of songs from Novello popular cantatas.
— Sevenoaks : Novello, 1978. — 55p ; 8vo.
£1.20

(B78-50431)

Wade, Darrell
Singing together / by Darrell Wade. — Gnosall (16 Anchor Way,
Danes Green, Gnosall) : Viking.
10 little chickadees. — 1977. — 3p ; 8vo. —
Unpriced

(B78-50093)
10 little chickadees. — 1977. — 3p ; 8vo. —
Unpriced

(B78-50432)
Bed in summer ; words by R.L. Stevenson. — 1977. — 3p ; 8vo.
Unpriced

(B78-50094)
Bed in summer ; words by R.L. Stevenson. — 1977. — 3p ; 8vo.
Unpriced

(B78-50095)
Little Indians all are we. — 1977. — 3p ; 8vo. —
Unpriced

(B78-50433)
Marching song ; words by R.L. Stevenson. — 1977. — 3p ; 8vo.
Unpriced

(B78-50096)
Off to the circus. — 1977. — 3p ; 8vo. —
Unpriced

(B78-50097)
Rain ; words by R.L. Stevenson. — 1977. — 3p ; 8vo.
Unpriced

(B78-50098)
Summer sun ; words by R.L. Stevenson. — 1977. — 3p ; 8vo.
Unpriced

(B78-50099)
Swinging along. — 1977. — 3p ; 8vo. —
Unpriced

(B78-50100)
The 2 rats. — 1977. — 3p ; 8vo. —
Unpriced

(B78-50101)
The ferryman ; words by Christina Rossetti. — 1977. — 3p ; 8vo.
Unpriced

(B78-50102)
The moon ; words by R.L. Stevenson. — 1977. — 3p ; 8vo.
Unpriced

(B78-50103)
Window cleaning man ; words by M. Long. — 1977. — 3p ; 8vo.
Unpriced

(B78-50104)

**JFDW/AY — Female voices, Children's voices. Songs, etc.
Collections**
Forty songs for the class plus ten for the choir : a song book for
primary children / [by] Donald Maxwell-Timmins. —
Huddersfield : Schofield and Sims, 1978. — 103p ; 8vo.
Teacher's ed.
ISBN 0-7217-2529-5 : Unpriced

(B78-50844)

JFDW/GJ — Female voices, Children's voices. Children's songs
Spinks, Donald
Songs of speech / by Mary Warren and [music by] Donald
Spinks. — Leicester (Morris Rd, Clarendon Pk) : Taskmaster,
1977. — 14p ; 4to.
For children with speech and language disorders.
Unpriced

(B78-50845)

Smith, Pat
Silly things to sing / [by] Pat Smith [and] Dorothy Wheatley. —
Leeds : E.J. Arnold, 1978. — 24p ; 4to.
ISBN 0-560-02726-5 : Unpriced

(B78-50846)

The **funny** family : songs, rhymes and games for children / [edited
by] Alison McMorland, illustrations by Kevin Maddison. —
London : Ward Lock, 1978. — [119p] ; obl.4to.
Transcribing of the melodies, piano arrangements and guitar chords, Peter
Bullock.
ISBN 0-7062-3719-6 : £3.95

(B78-50847)

JFDW/GS — Female voices, Children's voices. Songs, etc. Games
Nelson, Esther L
Singing and dancing games for the very young / by Esther L.
Nelson ; illustrations by Minn Matsuda ; photographs by Shirley
Zeiberg. — New York : Sterling [etc.] ; London : Distributed by
Ward Lock, 1977. — 72p : obl.4to.
Index.
ISBN 0-7061-2558-4 : £3.50

(B78-50434)

JFDW/JN — Female voices, Children's voices. Songs, etc. Mime
Diamond, Eileen
The little gingerbread man : a song/mime for children / words
and music by Eileen Diamond. — London : Chappell, 1977. —
4p ; 4to.
Unpriced

(B78-50435)

JFDW/JR/AY — Female voices, Children's voices. Songs, etc. Films.
Collections
Walt Disney's musical colouring book. — london : Wise, 1977. —
40p ; 4to.
ISBN 0-86001-484-3 : Unpriced

(B78-50848)

JFE/LDW/AY — Female voices, Children's voices. With instruments.
Songs, etc. Collections
Sounds and music / [by] Geoffrey Winters. — London : Longman.
Book 1. — 1978. — 97p ; 8vo.
ISBN 0-582-24203-7 : Unpriced

(B78-50849)

JFE/LNDP/LF/AY — Female voices, Children's voices. With
instruments. Carols. Christmas. Collections
Merrily to Bethlehem : a very unusual carol book / 44 carols
chosen by David Gadsby and Ivor Golby with piano
accompaniments, chords for guitar, parts for voice on instrument
and drawings by Bernard Cheese. — London : A. and C. Black,
1978. — [82p] ; obl.4to.
ISBN 0-7136-1887-6 : Unpriced

(B78-50850)

JFE/NYEPDW — Female voices, Children's voices. With woodwind,
strings & percussion. Songs, etc
Orff, Carl
Musik für Kinder. — Mainz ; London : Schott. —
(Orff-Schulwerk)
8 : Paralipomena / [von] Gunild Keetman und Carl Orff. — 1970. — 96p ;
obl. 8vo.
Unpriced

(B78-50105)

JFE/NYHSDW — Female voices. Children's voices. With recorders
& percussion. Songs, etc
Pont, Kenneth
The lantern song : ten Chinese songs arranged for voices,
recorders and percussion by Kenneth Pont / words freely adapted
from the Chinese by Stephen Jones. — london : Oxford University
Press, 1978. — 21p ; 4to.
ISBN 0-19-330613-1 : Unpriced

(B78-50851)

JFE/NYHSDX — Female voices, Children's voices. With recorders &
percussion. Secular cantatas
Leaper, Kenneth
Three Victorian scenes / by Kenneth Leaper ; for children's
voices, piano with occasional recorder, melodicas, tuned and
untuned percussion. — London : Chappell, 1978. — 63p ; 4to.
Unpriced

(B78-50852)

JFE/TSDW — Female voices, Children's voices. With guitar. Songs,
etc
Chorus : the Puffin Colony Song book / edited by David Green,
assisted by ... [others] ; cartoons by Gerard Hoffnung ; diagrams
by Nigel Paige ; photographs by Corinne Butler. —
Harmondsworth : Puffin Books, 1977. — 126p ; 8vo.
Includes part songs, rounds, action songs, folk songs and singing dances. —
Index.
ISBN 0-14-030941-1 : £0.70

(B78-50436)

JFE/TSDW/G/AY — Female voices, Children's voices. With guitar.
Folk songs. Collections
Forty songs for the class plus ten for the choir : a song book for
primary children / [compiled by] Donald Maxwell-Timmins. —
Huddersfield : Schofield and Sims, 1978. — 80p ; 8vo.
ISBN 0-7217-2528-7 : Unpriced

(B78-50853)

JFE/UMMDGF — Female voices, Children's voices. With military
band. Roman liturgy. Agnus Dei
Mailman, Martin
A simple ceremony, 'In memorian John Barnes Chance', Op.53 :
for symphonic band and unison voices / [by] Martin Mailman ;
text from the Ordinary of the Mass. — New York ; [London] :
Boosey and Hawkes, 1978. — 4to. — (Q.M.B. Edition ; 405)
Duration 11 min. — Score (38p.) & 69 parts, with several copies of various
parts.
Unpriced

(B78-50854)

JFE/XNDW — Female voices, Children's voices. Percussion
ensemble. Songs, etc
Follow my leader : ten songs with percussion accompaniments for
young singers and players / arranged by Douglas Gillies. —
London : Oxford University Press, 1977. — 23p ; obl. 8vo.
ISBN 0-19-330364-7 : Unpriced

(B78-50106)

JFEZDW/GJ/AY — Unaccompanied female voices, children's voices.
Children's songs. Collections
Detholiad y babanod / gan Jennie Gordon. — Llandysal : Gwasg
Gomer, 1978. — 49p ; 4to.
Songs.
Unpriced

(B78-50855)

JFVBDW/AY — Boys' voices. Songs, etc. Collections
Boys' Brigade. *Glasgow Battalion*
Company section song book. — Glawgow (168 Bath St., G.2) :
Boys' Brigade, Glasgow Battalion, 1977. — 10p ; 8vo.
Compiled by a committee of Boys' Brigade officers. — Music arranged by
Douglas Rolland, edited by John Neil.
Unpriced

(B78-50856)

JN — SINGLE VOICES IN COMBINATION
JNAYE/VVPLWTDX — Vocal octet. With clarinet & trombone.
Secular cantatas
Globokar, Vinko
Airs de voyages vers l'interieur : für acht Stimmen, Klarinette,
Posaune und Elektronik / [von] Vinko Globokar, Text vom
Komponisten. — Frankfurt : Litolff : Peters, 1978. — 55p ; fol.
Multilingual text. — Reproduction of the composer's manuscript. — Study
score. — Duration 23 min.
Unpriced

(B78-50857)

JNAZE/MRDW — Vocal sextet. With chamber orchestra. Songs, etc
Ferneyhough, Brian
Transit : six solo voices and chamber orchestra / [by] Brian
Ferneyhough. — London : Peters, 1977. — 42p ; fol.
Unpriced

(B78-50107)

JNAZE/NYEVDW — Vocal sextet. With clarinet, strings &
percussion. Songs, etc
Terzakis, Dimitri
Notturni : für sechs Singstimmen, Violine, Klarinette,
Schlaginstramente / [von] Dimitri Terzakis. — Kassel ; London :
Bärenreiter, 1977. — 48p ; fol.
Poems by Sappho in German - Duration 20 min.
£16.80

(B78-50437)

JNDE/NXNQDW/JM — Vocal trio. With strings & keyboard
sextet. Songs, etc. Incidental music
Handel, George Frideric
[Comus. Incidental music]. Music for Comus : serenata a 9 / [by]
G.F. Handel ; edited by Colin Timms and Anthony Hicks. —
First modern ed. — London (23 Stanley Court, 1 Woodfield Rd,
W.5) : Acca Music, 1977. — 24p ; 4to.
Handel's newly discovered contributions to Milton's Comus.
Unpriced

(B78-50108)

JNDE/NXNT — Vocal trio. With strings & keyboard trio
Fortner, Wolfgang
That time / [von] Wolfgang Fortner ; [text von] Samuel Beckett.
— Mainz ; London : Schott, 1977. — 91p ; 8vo.
Cantata with three singers accompanied by guitar, harpsichord and piano -
Study score.
£12.00

(B78-50109)

JNEDW — Vocal duet . Songs, etc
Lawes, Henry
[Ayres and dialogues. Dialogue on a kiss]. A dialogue on a kiss :
for two solo voices and continuo / [by] Henry Lawes ; edited by
Richard McGrady. — London : Oxford University Press, 1978. —
8p ; 4to. — (Musica da camera ; 60)
ISBN 0-19-345494-7 : Unpriced

(B78-50858)

JNEDX — Vocal duet. Secular cantatas
Delius, Frederick
[Idyll 'Once I passed through a populous city'. Vocal score].
Prelude and idyll : for soprano and baritone with orchestra / [by]
Frederick Delius ; words adapted from Walt Whitman by Robert
Nichols, German translation by Jelka Delius. — London : Boosey
and Hawkes, 1978. — [2],25p ; 4to.
Text in English and German.
Unpriced

(B78-50438)

**JNFLDE/NYEXPNQDW — Soprano trio. With brass, strings,
keyboard & percussion sextet. Songs, etc**
Sackman, Nicholas
A pair of wings / [by] Nicholas Sackman. — London : Schott,
1978. — [6],24p ; obl.fol.
For 3 sopranos, harp, flute, viola, trombone and percussion - Poem by
Stephen Hawes.
£5.00

(B78-50439)

KDH — MOTETS, ANTHEMS, HYMNS, ETC. SOLOS
Davis, Diane
I am a rock / words and music by Diane Davis. — Reading
(Yeldall Manor, Hare Hatch, Reading) : Celebration Services,
1974. — 5p ; 4to.
Unpriced

(B78-50110)

Geiger, George
I believe in God : a sacred song / music by George Geiger ; lyrics
by Marcia Brown. — Carlstadt [N.J.] : Lewis Music ; [London] :
[Phoenix], 1977. — 4p ; 4to.
Unpriced

(B78-50111)

KDM — HYMNS. SOLOS
Chappell, Herbert
Teach me how to pray, Lord / music by Herbert Chappell ;
words by Julia Cleare. — London : Chappell, 1978. — 3p ; 4to.
Unpriced

(B78-50440)

KDW — SONGS, ETC. SOLOS
Berkeley, Sir Lennox
Another spring. Op.93 : three songs to poems by Walter de la
Mare / [by] Lennox Berkeley. — London : Chester Music, 1978.
— 9p ; 4to.
Contents: 1: Poetry - 2: Another spring - 3: Afraid.
Unpriced

(B78-50859)

Bricusse, Leslie
[The travelling music show. Selections : arr]. Leslie Bricusse and
Anthony Newley's The travelling music show. — London :
Tro-Essex, 1978. — [1],64p ; 4to.
Unpriced

(B78-50441)

Eccles, John
[Songs. Selections]. Eight songs / by John Eccles ; edited by
Michael Pilkington. — London : Stainer and Bell, 1978. — 32p ;
8vo.
ISBN 0-85249-463-7 : £1.50

(B78-50114)

Eröd, Iván
[Milchzahnlieder. Vocal score]. Milchzahnlieder = Milktooth
songs : für Gesang oder Kinderchor, mit Klavier oder
Kammerorchester = for solo voice, or children's chorus with
piano or chamber orchestra / [von] Iván Eröd ; Gedichte von,
German and English text, by Richard Bletschacher. — London :
Boosey and Hawkes, 1978. — vi,26p ; 8vo.
Unpriced
Also classified at JFDW

(B78-50860)

Gershwin, George
[Porgy and Bess. Selections : arr]. Porgy and Bess / [par] George
Gershwin ; selection piano-chant, Anglais-Francais, paroles
françaises de René Rouzand, paroles anglaises de Du Bose
Heyward. — Paris ; [London] : Chappell, 1978. — 28p ; 4to.
Unpriced

(B78-50442)

Gottlieb, Jack
Haiku souvenirs : for voice and piano / music by Jack Gottlieb ;
words by Leonard Bernstein. — New York : Amberson : Boosey
and Hawkes ; [London] : [Boosey and Hawkes], 1978. — 11p ;
4to.
Unpriced

(B78-50861)

Gounod, Charles
[Faust. Ah! je ris. arr]. Jewel song ... / music by Charles
Gounod ; words by Jules Barbier and Michel Carré, English text,
Margaret Pert. — London : Leonard, Gould and Bolttler, 1977.
— 11p ; 4to.
French and English text.
Unpriced

(B78-50115)

Gounod, Charles
[Faust. Avant de quitter ces lieux. arr]. Cavatina 'Avant de quitter
ces lieux' / music, Charles Gounod ; words by O. Pradère,
English text, Margaret Pert. — London : Leonard, Gould &
Bolttler, 1977. — 4p ; 4to.
This appears in Act 2 of the later version - Text in French and English.
Unpriced

(B78-50443)

Husa, Karel
Twelve Moravian songs : for voice and piano / [by] Karel Husa ;
English text by Ruth Martin. — New York ; London : Associated
Music, 1977. — [2],20p ; 4to.
£3.05

(B78-50444)

Moretti, Federico
Doce canciones = Twelve songs : with guitar accompaniment /
[by] Federico Moretti ; (London, c. 1812), with alternative piano
accompaniment by Manuel Rucker. — Complete facsimile ed. /
with an introduction and English translation of the Spanish texts
by Brian Jeffery. — london : Tecla, 1978. — xiv,56p ; 4to.
ISBN 0-8494-0140-2 : Unpriced
Primary classification KE/TSDW

Raphael, Mark
Two Thomas Moore songs : for solo voice and piano / by Mark
Raphael. — Wendover : Roberton, 1978. — 7p ; 4to.
Contents: 1: When through the piazetta - 2: At the mid-hour of night.
£0.50

(B78-50445)

Schwartz, Stephen
[The magic show. Selections : arr]. The magic show : vocal
selection ... / piano/vocal arrangements by ... Jack Perricone ;
words and music by Stephen Schwartz. — Melville ; Croydon :
Belwin Mills, 1978. — 64p ; 4to.
Unpriced

(B78-50446)

Silverman, Jerry
Jest 'fore Christmas / music by Jerry Silverman ; poem by Eugene
Field. — New York ; London : Schirmer, 1977. — 5p ; 4to.
For solo voice.
Unpriced

(B78-50116)

Silverman, Jerry
A visit from St Nicholas. (The night before Christmas) / [by]
Jerry Silverman ; [melody] based on 'Sweet Betsy from Pike',
poem by Clement Clark Moore. — New York ; London :
Schirmer, 1977. — 3p ; 4to.
Unpriced

(B78-50117)

Sullivan, Sir Arthur Seymour
[Selections. arr]. Sing along with Sullivan : a new anthology of
music for the voice / selected and edited by Terence Rees and
Roderick Spencer. — London : Cramer, 1977. — ii,79p ; 4to.
Unpriced

(B78-50447)

Swann, Donald
[Songs. Selections]. Singalive! : twelve songs and a cakewalk / [by]
Donald Swann and [words] Arthur Scholey. — Glasgow : Collins,
1978. — 110p ; 4to.
For voices and instruments. — Musical editor, Lyn Howe.
ISBN 0-00-599605-8 : Unpriced

(B78-50862)

Swann, Donald
The road goes ever on : a song cycle : poemsby J.R.R. Tolkein /
music by Donald Swann ; with decorations by J.R.R. Tolkien. —
2nd ed. — london : Allen and Unwin, 1978. — xi,75p ; 4to.
With optional S.A.T.B. chorus. — New foreword by the composer.
ISBN 0-04-784011-0 : £4.75
(B78-50863)

Thomson, Virgil
The courtship of the Yongli Bongli Bo [sic] : for voice and
piano / [by] Virgil Thomson ; [words by] Edward Lear. — New
York ; London : Schirmer, 1977. — 15p ; 4to.
£1.50
(B78-50448)

KDW/AYC — Collections. Great Britain
Association of English Singers and Speakers
A heritage of 20th century British song. — London : Boosey and
Hawkes.
Vol.2. — 1977. — [8],216p ; 4to. —
Unpriced
(B78-50118)

Early Georgian songs / edited by Michael Pilkington. — London :
Stainer and Bell.
Book 1 : Medium voice. — 1978. — 32p ; 8vo.
ISBN 0-85249-459-9 : £1.50
(B78-50112)

Book 2 : Low voice. — 1978. — 32p ; 8vo.
ISBN 0-85249-460-2 : £1.50
(B78-50113)

KDW/AYD — Collections. England
Association of English Singers and Speakers
A heritage of 20th century British song. — London : Boosey and
Hawkes.
Vol.1. — 1977. — [8],240p ; 8vo. —
Unpriced
(B78-50119)

KDW/AYDL — Collections. Scotland
Beloved Scotch & Irish songs & ballads / compiled by Alexander
Shealy, edited by Robert Kail. — Carlstadt : Ashley ; [London] :
[Phoenix], 1978. — 160p ; 4to. — (World's favorite series ;
no.105)
Unpriced
Primary classification KDW/AYDM
(B78-50120)

KDW/AYDM — Collections. Ireland
Beloved Scotch & Irish songs & ballads / compiled by Alexander
Shealy, edited by Robert Kail. — Carlstadt : Ashley ; [London] :
[Phoenix], 1978. — 160p ; 4to. — (World's favorite series ;
no.105)
Unpriced
Also classified at KDW/AYDL
(B78-50120)

KDW/AYUR — Collections. Paraguay
Jubilen da quarânia, 1927-1977 : 20 melhores quarânias de todus os
tempos. — São Paulo : Fermata da Brasil ; [London] : [Essex
Music], 1977. — 76p ; 4to.
Unpriced
(B78-50121)

KDW/AYXR — Collections. New Zealand
Traditional songs of the Maori / [compiled] by Mervyn McLean
and Margaret Orbell. — Wellington [N.Z.] [etc.] ; London : A.H.
and A.W. Reed, 1975. — 324p ; obl.4to.
Bibl.: p.320.
ISBN 0-589-00748-3 : Unpriced
(B78-50449)

KDW/G/AYDJ — Folk songs. Collections. Northern England
The Hexamshire lass : ballads and folk songs from the North
Country / edited and arranged by W. Gillies Whittaker ; with an
introduction by Harold Thomson. — London : Curwen : Faber
Music, 1978. — [5],29p ; 8vo.
Thirteen songs from Whittaker's collection of 1921.
Unpriced
(B78-50450)

KDW/GB — Popular songs
Abba. Arrival. — London : Bocu Music : Music Sales, 1977. —
40p : ill ; 4to.
Ten songs by members of the group 'Abba'.
Unpriced
(B78-50122)

Ange
['Par les fils de Mandrin'. *arr*]. 'Par les fils de Mandrin' / [par]
Ange. — Paris ; [London] : Chappell, 1977. — 39p : ports ; 4to.
— (Collection rock et folk ballade)
Music by members of the group 'Ange'. — English text printed seperately
and translated by Michael Quatermaine. — Contents: 1: Par les fils de
Mandrin - 2: Au café du Colibri - 3: Ainsi s'en ira la pluie - 4: Autour du
feu - 5: Saltimbanques - 6: Des yeux couleur d'enfants - 7: Atlantis - 8:
Hymne à la vie.
Unpriced
(B78-50123)

Bee Gees
[Main course. *arr*]. Main course : songs / by the Bee Gees. —
New York ; London : Wise : Music Sales, 1976. — 48p : ports ;
4to.
Ten songs composed by members of the group 'Bee Gees'.
ISBN 0-86001-254-9 : Unpriced
(B78-50124)

Boyce, Max
Max Boyce songbook. — London : EMI.
Vol.1. — 1975. — 16p ; 4to. —
Unpriced
(B78-50125)

Vol.2. — 1975. — 19p ; 4to. —
Unpriced
(B78-50126)

Chapman, Mike
Smokie's greatest hits / words and music by Nicky Chinn and
Mike Chapman. — London : Chappell, 1978. — 5p ; 4to.
Also includes 'Going back to Bradford' and 'Needles and pins'.
Unpriced
(B78-50127)

Gallagher, Benny
[Songs. *Selections : arr*]. Showdown and other songs / by
Gallagher and Lyle ; piano transcription, Roger Day. — London :
Rondor Music : Music Sales, 1978. — 52p ; 4to.
Popular songs. — Contents: All grown up - Back stage - Heartbreaker -
Hurts to learn - In your eyes - It's over - Next to you - Throw-away heart -
Showdown - You're the one.
Unpriced
(B78-50128)

Gallagher, Benny
[Breakaway. *arr*]. Breakaway / words and music by Benny
Gallagher and John Oates. — London : Wise : Music Sales, 1976.
— 52p ; 4to.
Ten songs for voice and piano.
ISBN 0-86001-278-6 : Unpriced
(B78-50129)

Hall, Daryl
[Songs. *Selections: arr*]. Best of Daryl Hall and John Oates / [by]
Daryl Hall and John Oates. — [New York] ; [London] : Chappell,
1977. — 71p ; 4to.
Thirteen songs for voice and piano.
Unpriced
(B78-50130)

Hall, Daryl
[Beauty on a back street. *arr*]. Beauty on a back street / by Daryl
Hall and John Oates. — [New York] ; [London] : Chappell, 1977.
— 64p ; 4to.
Songs for voice and piano. — Contents: 1: Don't change - 2: Why do lovers
break each other's heart - 3: Winged bull -4: The girl who used to be - 5:
Emptiness - 6: Love hurts, love heals - 7: You must be good for something -
8: Bigger than both of us - 9: Bad habits and infections.
Unpriced
(B78-50131)

King, Carole
Carole King : her greatest hits, songs of long ago. — Hollywood :
Screen gems-EMI Music : Colgems-EMI Music ; [London] :
[EMI], 1978. — 49p ; 4to.
Unpriced
(B78-50864)

King, Carole
Simple things : piano, vocal, chords / [by] Carole King ; editor,
Gary Morowitz. — Hollywood : Colgems-EMI ; [London] :
[EMI], 1977. — 71p ; 4to.
Unpriced
(B78-50132)

King, Carole
Welcome home : piano, vocal, chords / [by] Carole King. —
Hollywood : Colgems-EMI Music ; [London] : [EMI], 1978. —
56p ; 4to.
Unpriced
(B78-50865)

Lennon, John
[Songs. *Selections : arr].* Beatles album no.2 / words and music by John Lennon and Paul McCartney. — Paris ; [London] : Chappell, 1978. — 50p ; 4to. — (Collection rock & folk Chappell)
Eighteen songs.
Unpriced

(B78-50451)

Lennon, John
[Songs. *Selections: arr].* The Beatles : the singles collections, 1962-1970 / by John Lennon and Paul McCartney. — London : Wise : Music Sales, 1976. — 80p ; 4to.
Twenty-six songs - 'Something' is by George Harrison.
ISBN 0-86001-274-3 : Unpriced

(B78-50133)

Macaulay, Tony
The Tony Macaulay songbook. — London : Macaulay Music : Noel Gay Music, 1978. — 56p ; 4to.
Words and music mainly by Tony Macaulay.
Unpriced

(B78-50866)

McCartney, Paul
[Songs. *Selections : arr].* The best of McCartney / [arranged] for guitar. — [London] : MPL Communications : Music Sales, 1977. — 67p ; 4to.
Unpriced

(B78-50867)

McCartney, Paul
[Band on the run. *arr].* Band on the run / [by] Paul McCartney. — London : MPL : Music Sales, 1977. — 58p : ports ; 4to.
Ten songs for voice and piano.
ISBN 0-86001-479-7 : Unpriced

(B78-50134)

McCartney, Paul
[London town. *arr].* London town / [songs by] Paul McCartney [composed for the group] Wings. — London : Music Sales, 1978. — [1],63p ; 4to.
Denny Laine contributes to a number of the songs.
Unpriced

(B78-50868)

McCartney, Paul
[Red rose speedway. *arr].* Red rose speedway / words and music by McCartney. — London : MPL : Music Sales, 1977. — 59p : ports ; 4to.
Fourteen songs for voice and piano.
ISBN 0-86001-478-9 : Unpriced

(B78-50135)

Mancini, Henry
[Songs. *Selections: arr].* Henry Mancini. — London : EMI, 1977. — 56p ; 4to.
Unpriced

(B78-50136)

Parissi, Robert
[Wild cherry. *arr].* Wild cherry : electrified funk / words and music by R. Parissi. — New York ; [London] : Chappell, 1977. — 47p ; 4to.
Contents: 1: Baby don't you know - 2: Electrified funk - 3: Hot to trot - 4: You are the closest thing to my mind - 5: Hole in the wall - 6: Dancing music band - 7: Are you boogie-ing around on your daddy - 8: Put yourself in my shoes.
Unpriced

(B78-50137)

Porter, Cole
[Songs. *Selections: arr].* The best of Cole Porter. — London : Chappell, 1977. — 160p ; 4to.
Unpriced

(B78-50138)

Reed, Les
[Songs. *Selections : arr].* The works of Les Reed / editor, Cecil Bolton. — London : EMI, 1978. — 64p ; 4to. — (Songsmiths)
Unpriced

(B78-50869)

Stephens, Geoff
Dear anyone ... : a musical story of the agony behind the agony column ... from the concept album / music by Geoff Stephens ; lyrics by Don Black. — London : Dick James : Music Sales (dist.), 1978. — 66p ; fol.
Unpriced

(B78-50870)

Stevens, Cat
[Izitso. *arr].* Izitso / [by] Cat Stevens ; arrangement, Laddie Chapman. — Hialeah : Columbia Pictures Publications ; [London] : [EMI], 1977. — 72p : ports ; 4to.
Ten songs for voice and piano. — 'Child for a day' with words and music by Paul Travis and David Gordon.
Unpriced

(B78-50139)

Stewart, Al
[Year of the cat. *arr].* Year of the cat / [by] Al Stewart. — London (71-75 New Oxford St., W.C.1) : Gwyneth Music, 1977. — 40p : ports ; 4to.
Songs for voice and piano. — Contents: 1: Broadway hotel - 2: Flying sorcery - 3: If it don't come naturally leave it - 4: Lord Grenville - 5: Midas shadow - 6: One stage before - 7: On the border - 8: Sand in your shoes - 9: Year of the cat.
Unpriced

(B78-50140)

Yancy, Marvin
Our love : a Marvin Yancy, Chuck Jackson songbook. — [New York] ; [London] : Chappell, 1978. — 88p ; 4to.
Words and music mainly by Marvin Yancy and Chuck Jackson.
Unpriced

(B78-50871)

Yes
Yes. — Paris ; [London] : Chappell, 1977. — 91p : ports ; 4to. — (Collection rock et folk Chappell)
Twelve songs composed by members of the group 'Yes'.
Unpriced

(B78-50141)

KDW/GB — Popular songs. Collections
Kennedy, Jimmy
[Songs. *Selections : arr].* The works of Jimmy Kennedy / editor, Cecil Bolton. — London : EMI, 1978. — 47p ; 4to.
Unpriced

(B78-50872)

Album, Mike Brant : 15 chansons. — Paris ; [London] : Chappell, 1977. — 44p ; 4to.
Unpriced

(B78-50142)

Andy Williams. — London : Wise : Music Sales, 1975. — 59p : port ; 4to. — (In words and music)
Twenty songs made popular by Andy Williams.
ISBN 0-86001-115-1 : £1.95

(B78-50143)

Berni Flint songbook. — London : Chappell, 1977. — 48p ; 4to.
Eleven songs made popular by Berni Flint, three of them composed by him.
Unpriced

(B78-50144)

The best of Bing. — London : EMI, 1977. — 32p : ports ; 4to.
Songs popularised by Bing Crosby.
Unpriced

(B78-50145)

The best of The Hollies. — London : Wise : Music Sales, 1977. — 50p ; 4to.
Fourteen songs made popular by The Hollies.
ISBN 0-86001-253-0 : Unpriced

(B78-50146)

Dick James Music presents 20 [per volume] greatest hits. — London : Dick James Music.
Vol.1. — 1976. — 71p ; 4to. — £2.50

(B78-50147)

Vol.2. — 1976. — 68p ; 4to. — Unpriced

(B78-50148)

Vol.3. — 1977. — 66p ; 4to. — Unpriced

(B78-50149)

Vol.4. — 1977. — 68p ; 4to. — Unpriced

(B78-50150)

Early Beatles. — London : Chappell, 1978. — 48p ; 4to.
Songs sung by the Beatles.
Unpriced

(B78-50151)

Édith Piaf / music compilation by Peter Foss. — London : Wise, 1976. — 119p : ill ; 4to.
The first part of this volume contains a biography of Edith Piaf - Twenty songs popularised by Edith Piaf.
ISBN 0-86001-112-7 : £3.95

(B78-50152)

Golden greats. — London : EMI Music, 1977. — 45p ; 4to.
Fifteen songs made popular by Cliff Richard.
Unpriced

(B78-50153)

How to dance : waltz, fox-trot, quick-step, tango, mambo, samba, cha-cha-cha, rumba, bossa-nova, jive ; plus! the music to 20 great dance numbers, plus! a detailed discography of dance records / [compild] by Donna M. Muir. — New York ; London : Omnibus Press : Books Sales, 1977. — 128p ; 4to.
ISBN 0-86001-380-4 : £3.50

(B78-50873)

La musique que j'aime : chansons. — Paris : Tanday Music :
Chappell ; [London] : [Chappell], 1978. — 200p ; 4to.
Sixty-one songs in the repertory of Johnny Hallyday, seven of them
composed by him and nine others by Chuck Berry.
Unpriced

(B78-50452)

The **Mathis** collection : 27 of my favorite songs. — London :
Chappell, 1977. — 84p ; 4to.
Songs made popular by Johnny Mathis.

(B78-50154)

Nat King Cole golden greats. — London : EMI, 1978. — 31p ; 4to.
Songs in the repertory of Nat King Cole.
Unpriced

(B78-50453)

Oh! it's a lovely war : songs, ballads and parodies of the Great
War / editor and collator, Cecil Bolton. — London : EMI, 1978.
— 119p ; 4to.
Unpriced

(B78-50874)

Our Gracie / editor and collator, Cecil Bolton. — London : EMI,
1978. — 3p ; 4to.
Songs in the repertory of Gracie Fields.
Unpriced

(B78-50875)

Pennies from heaven : a selection of popular songs of the thirties as
featured in the BBC TV series / editor, Cecil Bolton. — London :
EMI, 1978. — 31p ; 4to.
Unpriced

(B78-50454)

Pub favourites. — London : Campbell, Connelly and Connelly.
No.5. — 1978. — 32p ; 4to. —
Unpriced

(B78-50876)

Sinatra now. — London : Chappell, 1977. — 80p ; 4to.
Songs in the repertoire of Sinatra.
Unpriced

(B78-50877)

Sounds sensational : piano [or] vocal. — London : Chappell.
1. — 1977. — 152p ; 4to. —
Unpriced

(B78-50457)

2. — 1977. — 152p ; 4to. —
Unpriced

(B78-50456)

Tammy Wynette's greatest hits / editor, Cecil Bolton. — London :
EMI, 1978. — 87p ; 4to.
Twenty songs in the repertory of Tammy Wynette, five of them composed
by her.
Unpriced

(B78-50458)

The **'unforgettable'** Nat 'King' Cole. — London : Chappell, 1978.
— 96p ; 4to.
Songs in the repertory of Nat 'King' Cole.
Unpriced

(B78-50878)

KDW/GBS — Soul
Wonder, Stevie
[Phases, phases, phases, phases. *arr*]. Phases, phases, phases,
phases / [by] Stevie Wonder. — London : Jobete Music :
Chappell, 1977. — 88p ; 4to.
Music compiled by Tony Collier. — Twenty-one songs for voice and piano.
Unpriced

(B78-50155)

KDW/GC — Country songs
Williams, Hank
20 greatest hits / [by] Hank Williams. — London : Acuff-Rose :
Chappell, 1978. — 47p ; 4to.
Songs by Hank Williams with the exception of 'Take these chains from my
heart' and 'Settin' the woods on fire'.

(B78-50156)

KDW/GCG/AY — Bluegrass. Collections
The **best** bluegrass songbook - yet! / compiled and edited by Arthur
Bayas and Lipton Nemser. — Carlstadt : Lewis ; [London] :
[Phoenix], 1978. — 87p ; 4to.
Unpriced

(B78-50157)

KDW/HK/AY — Rock 'n' roll. Collections
"**Raised** on rock". — London : EMI Music, 1977. — 32p ; 4to.
Ten songs made popular by Elvis Presley.

(B78-50158)

KDW/HK/AY — Rock 'n' roll songs. Collections
A **tribute** to Elvis : 18 of his best loved songs. — London :
Chappell, 1977. — 56p ; 4to.
Unpriced

(B78-50159)

KDW/HKR — Rock
Bijou. — Paris ; [London] : Chappell, 1978. — 38p : ports ; 4to. —
(Collection rock et roll Chappell)
Songs by the group 'Bijou'.
Unpriced

(B78-50879)

Boston
[Boston. *arr*]. Boston. — Hialeah : Columbia Pictures
Publications ; [London] : [EMI], 1977. — ports ; 4to.
Songs composed by members of the group 'Boston'. — Contents: 1: More
than a feeling - 2: Foreplay 3: Peace of mind - 4: Long time - 5: Rock and
roll band - 6: Smokin' - 7: Hitch a ride - 8: Something about you - 9: let me
take you home tonight.
Unpriced

(B78-50075)

Browne, Jackson
The pretender / [by] Jackson Browne. — New York : Warner ;
[London] : Blossom, 1978. — 59p ; 4to.
Songs. — Contents: The pretender - The fuse - Here come those tears
again - Your bright baby blues - The only child - Daddy's tune.
Unpriced

(B78-50160)

Genesis
Genesis. — Paris ; [London] : Chappell, 1978. — 14p ; 4to. —
(Collection rock et folk Chappell)
Songs composed by the group 'Genesis'.
Unpriced

(B78-50459)

John, Elton
[Blue moves. *arr*]. Blue moves / [by Elton John] ; piano
transcriptions, Frank C. Harlow. — London : Big Pig Music :
Music Sales, 1975. — 92p : ports ; 4to.
Eighteen items. — Composed by Elton John with the exception of 'Your
starter for ...'. — Contents: 1: Medley (Yell help - Wednesday night - Ugly -
2: Dan Dare - 3: Island girl - 4: Grow some funk of your own 5: I feel like
a bullet - 6: Street kids - 7: Hard luck story - 8: Feed me - 9: Billy Bones
and the white bird.
£4.95

(B78-50161)

John, Elton
[Rock of the westies. *arr*]. Rock of the westies : songs from the
album / by Elton John and Bernie Taupin. — London : Big Pig
Music : Music Sales, 1975. — 47p : port ; 4to.
Composed by Elton John with the exception of 'Hard luck story' ; piano
transcriptions by Frank C. Harlow and Roy Green. Enclosed is a
photograph of the composer at Dodger Stadium, Los Angeles, 1975. —
Contents: 1: Medley (Yell help - Wednesday night - Ugly - 2: Dan Dare - 3:
Island girl - 4: Grow some funk of your own 5: I feel like a bullet - 6: Street
kids - 7: Hard luck story - 8: Feed me - 9: Billy Bones and the white bird.
£1.95

(B78-50162)

Moody Blues
The Moody Blues caught live + 5 / [by] The Moody Blues. —
New York : TRO : Essex Music International ; [London] : [Essex
Music], 1977. — 64p : ports ; 4to.
Eighteen songs composed by members of the group 'Moody Blues'.
Unpriced

(B78-50163)

Queen
[A day at the races. *arr*]. A day at the races / [by] Queen. —
Hollywood : Beechwood Music ; [London] : [EMI], 1977. — 64p :
ports ; 4to.
Ten songs composed by members of the group 'Queen'.
Unpriced

(B78-50164)

Steinman, Jim
bat out of hell / songs by Jim Steinman. — London : Dick James,
1978. — 80p ; 4to.
Unpriced

(B78-50880)

Stevens, Cat
Cat Stevens : hits / words and music by Cat Stevens. — Paris ;
[London] : Chappell, 1978. — 67p ; 4to. — (Collection rock et
folk Chappell)
Unpriced

(B78-50881)

Yes
[Going for the one. *arr*]. Going for the one / [by] Yes. — New
York : Warner ; [London] : [Blossom], 1978. — 55p ; 4to.
Composed by members of the group 'Yes'. — Contents: 1: Goin' for the
one - 2: Turn of the century - 3: Parallels - 4: Wondrous stories - 5:
Awaken.
Unpriced

(B78-50165)

KDW/JR — Films
Fox, Charles
[One on one. *Selections: arr*]. Songs from 'One on one' : a Warner
Bros. film / music by Charles Fox ; lyrics by Paul Williams. —
New York : Warner ; [London] : [Blossom], 1978. — 37p ; 4to.
Unpriced

(B78-50166)

KDW/JV — Music hall songs
Lauder, *Sir* Harry
The best of Sir Harry Lauder. — London : EMI, 1978. — 32p ;
4to.
Songs.
Unpriced

(B78-50460)

KDW/LC/AY — Spirituals. Collections
The **books** of American negro spirituals, including The book of
American negro spirituals and The second book of negro
spirituals / [compiled and edited by] James Weldon Johnson and
[musical arrangements by] Rosamund Johnson. — New York : Da
Capo Press ; [London] : [Robert Hale], 1977. — [376p] ; 8vo.
For voice and piano. — Reprint of the 1969 ed. published New York,
Viking Press, 1969. — Additional numbers arranged by Laurence Brown.
£6.50

(B78-50461)

KDW/LF — Songs, etc. Christmas
Pierpont, James S
Jingle bells / [by] E. Pierpont [or rather, J.S.] Pierpont ; arranged
by Cecil Bolton. — London : EMI, 1978. — 4p ; 4to.
Voice & piano.
Unpriced

(B78-50882)

**KE — VOCAL SOLOS WITH ACCOMPANIMENT OTHER
        THAN KEYBOARD**
KE/LDW/GB — With instruments. Popular songs
Malicorne
Recueil de vingt chansons et airs traditionnels / [par] Malicorne.
— Paris ; [London] : Chappell, 1977. — 59p ; ports ; 4to. —
(Collection rock et folk Chappell)
Twenty two songs and instrumental pieces composed or arranged by
members of the group 'Malicorne'.
Unpriced

(B78-50167)

KE/NYGDW — With strings, keyboard & percussion. Songs, etc
Wimberger, Gerhard
4 Songs nach Texten von Hans-Jurgen Heise, Heinz Piontek, Hans
Magnus Enzensberger und Ror Wolf für Singstimme, Klavier,
Kontrabass und Schlagzeug. — Kassel ; London : Bärenreiter,
1978. — [2],22p ; fol.
Duration 15 min. — Facsimile of composer's autograph.
£2.50

(B78-50883)

KE/SPDW — With violin & piano. Songs, etc
Ives, Charles
Sunrise : voice, violin and piano / [by] Charles Ives ; edited by
John Kirkpatrick. — New York ; London : Peters, 1977. — 6p ;
4to.
Duration 5 1/2 min.
Unpriced

(B78-50462)

KE/STPLTWDW — With viol & lute. Songs, etc
What is love? : songs for voice, lute and viola da gamba / edited
and transcribed by Carl Shavitz. — London : Chester Music,
1978. — [2],34p ; 4to.
Lute tablature & staff notation.
Unpriced

(B78-50884)

KE/TSDW — With guitar. Songs, etc
Moretti, Federico
Doce canciones = Twelve songs : with guitar accompaniment /
[by] Federico Moretti ; (London, c. 1812), with alternative piano
accompaniment by Manuel Rucker. / Complete facsimile ed. /
with an introduction and English translation of the Spanish texts
by Brian Jeffery. — london : Tecla, 1978. — xiv,56p ; 4to.
ISBN 0-8494-0140-2 : Unpriced
Also classified at KDW

(B78-50885)

KE/TSDW/AY — With guitar. Songs, etc. Collections
English! Sing it! : a structured presentation of spoken English
through the use of songs. — New York ; London : McGraw-Hill,
1976. — vii,56p ; 4to.
Songs compiled by Millie Greenough.
ISBN 0-07-024667-x : Unpriced

(B78-50168)

KE/TSDW/GB — With guitar. Popular songs
Berry, Chuck
[Songs. *Selections: arr*]. Chuck Berry : easy guitar. — London :
Jewel Music : Chappell, 1977. — 52p ; 4to.
Unpriced

(B78-50169)

Wishbone Ash
[Songs. *Selections*]. Classic Ash / [by] Wishbone Ash. —
London : EMI, 1977. — 20p : ports ; 4to.
Nine songs composed by members of the group 'Wishbone Ash'. —
Contents: 1: Blind eye - 2: Phoenix - 3: The pilgrim - 4: Blowin' free - 5:
The king will come - 6: Rock and roll widow - 7: Persephone - 8: Outward
bound - 9: Throw down the sword.
Unpriced

(B78-50170)

KE/TSDW/GB/AY — With guitar. Popular songs. Collections
The **Wurzels** song book. — London : EMI, 1977. — 28p : ports ;
4to.
Some of the songs are composed by members of the group 'The Wurzels'.
Unpriced

(B78-50171)

KE/TSDW/GC/AY — With guitar. Country songs. Collections
Great all-time country hits : melody, lyrics and guitar chords, 60 of
the greatest country songs ever written. — London : Southern
Music : Music Sales (dist.), 1978. — 67p ; 4to.
£1.95

(B78-50886)

KE/TSDW/HKR — With guitar. Rock
Queen
News of the world / [by] Queen. — London : EMI, 1977. —
44p : ill ; 4to.
Eleven songs composed by members of the group 'Queen'.
Unpriced

(B78-50173)

WHO
A decade of The Who : an authorised history in music, paintings,
words and photographs. — London : Fabulous Music : Music
Sales, 1977. — 239p : ill, ports ; 4to.
Forty-five songs composed by members of the group 'Who'. — Music edited
by Ray Steadman Allan and Bill Connor.
ISBN 0-8256-2670-6 : Unpriced

(B78-50172)

KE/TWDW/AY — With lute. Songs, etc. Collections
Mirror of love : lute songs of love and lust / edited and transcribed
by Carl Shavitz. — London : Chester Music, 1977. — [2],50p ;
4to.
For voice and the lute with gamba part.
Unpriced

(B78-50887)

KE/VTPDH — With oboe & piano. Motets, Anthems, Hymns, etc
Bach, Johann Sebastian
[Vocal music. *Collections : arr*]. Complete arias and sinfonias from
the cantatas, masses and oratorios, for solo voice, oboe d'amore,
oboe da caccia, basso continuo/piano in 31 volumes / by J.S.
Bach ; edited by John Madden and C.B. Naylor. — London :
Musica rara.
Score (523p.) & 3 parts. — Contents: 1: S.12: Movement 4 - 2: S.22:
Movement 2 - 3: S.44: Movement 3 - 4: S.48: Movement 4.
Vol.5. — 1977. — 4to.
Unpriced

(B78-50463)

Bach, Johann Sebastian
[Vocal music. *Collections : arr*]. Complete arias and sinfonias from
the cantatas, masses and oratorios, for solo voice, oboe, oboe
d'amore, oboe da caccia, basso continuo/piano in 31 volumes /
J.S. Bach ; edited by John Madden and C.B. Naylor. — London :
Musica rara.
Score (5-27p.) & 3 parts. — Contents: 1: S.176: Movement 5 - 2: S.185:
Movement 3 - 3: S.214: Movement 5 - 4: S.235: Movement 5.
Vol.7. — 1977. — 4to.
Unpriced

(B78-50464)

Bach, Johann Sebastian
[Vocal music. *Collections : arr*]. Complete arias and sinfonias from
the cantatas, masses and oratorios, for solo voice, oboe, oboe
d'amore, oboe da caccia, basso continuo/piano in 31 volumes / by
J.S. Bach ; edited by John Madden and C.B. Naylor. — London :
Musica rara.
Score(5-26p.) & 3 parts. — Contents: 1: S.79 Movement 2 - 2: S.102:
Movement 3 - 3: S.114: Movement 5 - 4: S.159: Movement 2.
Vol.6. — 1977. — 4to.
Unpriced

(B78-50465)

Bach, Johann Sebastian
[Vocal music. *Selections : arr*]. Complete arias and sinfonias from
cantatas, masses and oratorios : for solo voice, oboe, oboe
d'amore, oboe de caccia, basso continuo/piano / [by] J.S. Bach ;
edited by John Madden, notes by C.B. Naylor. — London :
Musica rara.

Vol.8 : Tenor, oboe, basso continuo/piano. — 1977. — 4to.
Unpriced
(B78-50888)

Vol.9 : Tenor, bass, oboe, basso continuo/piano. — 1978. — 4to.
Unpriced
(B78-50889)

Vol.10 : Bass, oboe, basso continuo/piano. — 1978. — 4to.
Unpriced
(B78-50891)

KE/VVPDW — With clarinet & piano. Songs, etc
Head, Michael
The world is mad : song, for voice, clarinet and piano / [by]
Michael Head ; [words] from 'The dark tower' ... by Louis
MacNeice. — Ampleforth : Emerson, 1977. — 4to.
Score (7p.) & part : the parts for clarinet and voice are printed.
Unpriced
(B78-50466)

KEZ — UNACCOMPANIED VOCAL SOLOS
KEZDW/G/AYD — Folk songs. Collections. England
The **ploughboy's** glory : a selection of hitherto unpublished folk
songs / collected by George Butterworth : edited from the
Butterworth manuscripts by Michael Dawney. — London :
English Folk Dance and Song Society, 1977. — 49p ; 8vo.
Unpriced
(B78-50467)

KEZDW/K/G/AYDM — Ballads. Collections. Ireland
Irish street ballads / collected and annotated by Colin O Lochlainn
and illustrated with woodcuts. — London : Pan Books, 1978. —
xvi,234p ; 8vo.
Originally published: Dublin : The Three Candles, 1939.
ISBN 0-330-25316-6 : £0.90
(B78-50468)

More Irish street ballads / collected and annotated by Colm O
Lochlainn and illustrated with woodcuts. — London : Pan Books,
1978. — xiv,269p ; 8vo.
Originally published: Dublin : The Three Candles, 1965.
ISBN 0-330-25317-4 : £0.90
(B78-50469)

KF — FEMALE VOICE, CHILD'S VOICE
KFDW — Songs, etc
Moroder, Giorgio
Zodiacs / words and music by Giorgio Moroder and Peter
Bellotte. — London : Hansa Productions : ATV Music : Music
Sales, 1977. — 4p ; 4to.
Unpriced
(B78-50174)

KFLDW/AY — Soprano voice. Songs, etc. Collections
Schirmer's singer's library : arias for soprano / compiled by Irving
Brown. — New York ; London : Schirmer.
Vol.1. — 1977. — [2],157p ; 4to.
Unpriced
(B78-50470)

KFLDX — Soprano voice. Secular cantatas
Egk, Werner
[Nachgefühl. *Vocal score*]. Nachgefühl : Kantate für Sopran und
Orchester nach Versen von Klabund / [von] Werner Egk. —
Mainz ; London : Schott, 1977. — 24p ; 4to.
Duration 12 min.
£4.80
(B78-50471)

KFLE/MDX — Soprano voice. With orchestra. Secular cantatas
Vaughan Williams, Ralph
[Symphony no.3, 'Pastoral']. Pastoral symphony / [by] R.
Vaughan Williams ... ; edited and corrected by Roy Douglas. —
London : Boosey and Hawkes, 1977. — 105p ; 8vo. — (Hawkes
pocket scores ; no.73)
Miniature score.
Unpriced
(B78-50175)

KFLE/NUPNPDX — Soprano voice. With woodwind, strings &
keyboard septet. Secular cantatas
Saxton, Robert
What does the song hope for? : for soprano, ensemble and tape /
[by] Robert Saxton ; [words by] W.H. Auden. — London :
Chester Music, 1977. — [2],26p ; 8vo.
Duration 10 min.
Unpriced
(B78-50892)

KFLE/NUVNTDW — Soprano voice. With clarinet, strings &
keyboard trio. Songs, etc
Knussen, Oliver
Rosary songs = Rosenkranzlieder : three poems of Georg Trakl,
for soprano, clarinet, viola and piano, Op.9 / [by] Oliver Knussen.
— London : Faber Music, 1978. — [4],20p ; obl.4to.
Text in German. — Duration 14 min.
Unpriced
(B78-50893)

KFLE/NVNNDX — Soprano voice. With wind & string octet.
Secular cantatas
Payne, Anthony
The world's winter : for soprano and instrumental ensemble / [by]
Anthony Payne ; [words by] Alfred, Lord Tennyson. — London :
Chester Music, 1978. — 27p ; 4to.
Duration 16 min.
Unpriced
(B78-50894)

KFLE/NYEP — Soprano voice. With woodwind, strings & percussion
Kelterborn, Rudolf
Consort-music, 1975 / [by] Rudolf Kelterborn. — Berlin : Bote
und Bock ; [London] : [Associated Music], 1977. — 23p ; 4to.
For flute, clarinet, percussion, soprano and four solo strings. — Text in
Spanish and English.
£5.75
(B78-50472)

KFLE/SQPLTSDW — Soprano voice. With viola & guitar. Songs,
etc
Williams, Graham
Japanese fragments : for soprano, viola and guitar / [by] Graham
Williams ; guitar part fingered by Michael Blake Watkins. —
London : Chester Music, 1978. — 13p ; obl.4to.
Performing score.
Unpriced
(B78-50895)

KFLE/VRDW — Soprano voice. With flute. Songs, etc
Musgrave, Thea
Primavera : for soprano and flute / [by] Thea Musgrave ; poem
by Amalia Elguera. — London : Chester Music, 1976. — 8p ; 4to.
Text in Spanish - Duration 3 min.
Unpriced
(B78-50896)

KFLE/VVNTDW — Soprano voice. With clarinet trio. Songs, etc
Knussen, Oliver
Trumpets : for soprano and three clarinets, op.12 / [by] Oliver
Knussen ; text by Georg Trakl. — London : Faber Music, 1978.
— [2],9p ; 4to.
Duration 4 min. — German text.
Unpriced
(B78-50897)

KFNDW/AY — Mezzo-soprano voice. Songs, etc. Collections
Schirmer's singer's library : arias for mezzo-soprano and alto /
compiled by Irving Brown. — New York ; London : Schirmer.
Vol.1. — 1977. — [2],140p ; 4to.
Unpriced
(B78-50473)

KFNE/NYDNQDX — Mezzo-soprano voice. With wind, string,
keyboard & percussion sextet. Secular cantatas
Hufschmidt, Wolfgang
Exercitien 3 'Das Prinzip Hoffnung' (nach Ernst Bloch) : für sechs
Ausführende (1974-1976) / [von] Wolfgang Hufschmidt. —
Kassel ; London : Bärenreiter, 1977. — 64p : obl.fol.
For voice, flute, violin, horn, percussion and piano.
£21.00
(B78-50898)

KFT — HIGH VOICE
KFTDH — Motets, Anthems, Hymns, etc
Herbst, Johannes
[Vocal music. *Selections : arr*]. Three sacred songs of Johannes
Herbert / edited and arranged by Karl Kroeger. — [New York] ;
[London] : Boosey and Hawkes, 1978. — 15p ; 4to. — (Moramus
edition)
Fo high voice and organ or piano. — Contents: 1: Abide in me = Bleibet in
mir - 2: See him, he is the Lamb of God = Siehe das ist Gottes Lamm - 3:
And thou shalt know it = Du Solst erfahren.
Unpriced
(B78-50899)

KFTDW — Songs, etc
Einem, Gottfried von
Leibes- und Abendlieder : für höhe Stimme und Klavier, Opus
48 : [von] Gottfried von Einem. — Berlin ; London : Bote und
Bock, 1977. — 13p ; 4to.
Contents: 1: Lass den Muno (Josef Weinheber) - 2: Mein kleiner weisser
Hund und ich (Silja Walter) - 3: An eine Geliebter (Josef Weinheber) - 4:
Sieh diesen Himmel (Max Bolliger).
£3.85
(B78-50474)

Klebe, Giselher
Drei Lieder nach Texten von Friedrich Hölderlin : für höhe
Stimme und Klavier, op.74 / [von] Giselher Klebe. — Kassel ;
London : Bärenreiter, 1977. — [2],13p ; fol.
Facsimile of the composer's autograph.
£3.90
(B78-50900)

Shield, William
[Rosina. *Selections : arr].* Four songs from 'Rosina' / [by] William
Shield ; arranged for high voice and piano by Leslie Russell. —
London : Boosey and Hawkes, 1978. — iii-4-11p ; fol.
Unpriced
(B78-50901)

KFTE/TQDW — With harp. Songs, etc
Britten, Benjamin, *Baron Britten*
A birthday hansel : for high voice and harp, op.92 / [by]
Benjamin Britten ; poems by Robert Burns, the harp part edited
by Osian Ellis. — London : Faber Music, 1978. — [4],30p ; 4to.
Unpriced
(B78-50475)

KFV — MIDDLE VOICE
KFVDE — Religious cantatas
Klebe, Giselher
'Beuge dich, du Menschenseele' : geistliche Szene für mittlere
Stimme und Orgel / [von] Giselher Klebe ; Text von Selma
Lagerlöf, Op.71. — Kassel ; London : Bärenreiter, 1977. — 16p ;
fol.
Facsimile of composer's autograph.
£5.60
(B78-50476)

KFVDW — Songs, etc
Berkeley, *Sir* **Lennox**
Five Chinese songs, op.78 : for medium voice and piano / [by]
Lennox Berkeley. — London : Chester Music, 1975. — 12p ; 4to.
Unpriced
(B78-50902)

Schubert, Franz
[Songs. *Selections].* Franz Schubert Lieder / Urtext der Neuen
Schubert-Ausgabe herausgegeben von Walther Dürr. — Kassel ;
London : Bärenreiter.
Heft 3 : Lieder nach Texten von Goethe, [für] mittlere Stimme. — 1978. —
80p ; 8vo.
£4.80
(B78-50903)

KFX — LOW VOICE
**KFXE/NWPNQDW — With woodwind & keyboard sextet. Songs,
etc**
Reutter, Hermann
Tre notturni : drei Gedichte von Friedrich Nietzsche, für tiefe
Männerstimme, Klavier und Bläser / [von] Hermann Reutter. —
Mainz ; [London] : Schott, 1977. — 4to.
Score & parts.
£6.00
(B78-50176)

KG — MALE VOICE
KGHDW — Tenor voice. Songs, etc
Holloway, Robin
This is just to say : for tenor and piano / [by] Robin Holloway ;
words by William Carlos Williams. — London : Boosey and
Hawkes, 1978. — iv,24p ; fol.
Duration 17 min.
Unpriced
(B78-50904)

KGHDW/AY — Tenor voice. Songs, etc. Collections
Schirmer's singer's library : arias for tenor / compiled by Irving
Brown. — New York ; London : Schirmer.
Vol.1. — 1977. — [2],122p ; 4to.
Unpriced
(B78-50477)

KGHE/TSDW — Tenor voice. With guitar. Songs, etc
Musgrave, Thea
Sir Patrick Spens : a ballad for tenor and guitar / [by] Thea
Musgrave. — London : Chester Music, 1976. — 10p ; 4to.
Duration 6 1/2 min.
Unpriced
(B78-50905)

**KGHE/VRPDH — Tenor voice. With flute. Motets, Anthems,
Hymns, etc**
Bach, Johann Sebastian
[Cantata no.113 : Herr Jesu Christ, du höchstes Gut. Jesus nimmt
die Sunder an]. Jesus nimmt die Sunder an : aria from cantata 113
for tenor, flute and continuo / [by] J.S. Bach ; edited by Samuel
Baron. — New York ; [London] : Oxford University Press, 1978.
— 4to.
Score (12p.) & 3 parts ; the parts for flute and tenor printed in score are in
duplicate.
Unpriced
(B78-50177)

KGNDW/AY — Baritone voice. Songs, etc. Collections
Schirmer's singer's library : arias for baritone / compiled by Irving
Brown. — New York ; London : Schirmer.
Vol.1. — 1977. — [2],139p ; 4to.
Unpriced
(B78-50478)

KGNE/MDW — Baritone voice. With orchestra. Songs, etc
Lutoslawski, Witold
Les espaces du sommeil : for baritone and orchestra / [by] Witold
Lutoslawski ; words by Robert Desnos. — London : Chester
Music, 1978. — ii,46p ; 4to.
Duration 15 min.
Unpriced
(B78-50906)

KGXDE — Bass voice. Religious cantatas
Brandmüller, Theo
Apokalyptische Vision : für Basstimme und Orgel / [von] Theo
Brandmüller ; Textauswahl nach der Offenbarung das Heiligen
Johannes in der Ubersetzung von Martin Luther. — Berlin : Bote
und Bock ; [London] : [Associated Music], 1977. — 22p ; 4to.
£4.80
(B78-50479)

KGXDW/AY — Bass voice. Songs, etc. Collections
Schirmer's singer's library : arias for bass / compiled by Irving
Brown. — New York ; London : Schirmer.
Vol.1. — 1977. — [2],141p ; 4to.
Unpriced
(B78-50480)

LN — ENSEMBLES
Davies, Peter Maxwell
[Taverner. Dances]. Points and dances ... : for instrumental
ensemble / [by] Peter Maxwell Davies. — London : Boosey and
Hawkes, 1978. — [4],40p ; 8vo. — (Hawkes pocket series ; 912)
Miniature score. — Duration 9 1/2 min.
Unpriced
(B78-50907)

Lanza, Alcides
Hip'nes 1 (1973 I) : versions a and b, for one or more
instrument / [by] Alcides Lanza. — New York ; [London] :
Boosey and Hawkes, 1977. — 7p ; obl.fol.
The 'e' in 'Hip'nes' is inverted - Duration 14 min.
£2.50
(B78-50481)

LNS — Quartets
Maschera, Florentio
[Libro primo de canzoni da sonare. *Selections].* Five canzonas for
four instruments SATB / [by] Fiorenzo Maschera ; [edited by]
Bernard Thomas. — London : London Pro Musica, 1977. — 4to.
— (Venetian instrumental music C.1600 ; vol.7)
With alternative tenore parts for viola (tenor viol), trombone or tenor
recorder.
Unpriced
(B78-50482)

LNSK/DU — Quartets. Arrangements. Madrigals
Josquin des Prés
[Selections]. Seven secular pieces : for four voices or instruments,
ATTB / [by] Josquin des Prés ; [edited by] Bernard Thomas. —
London : London Pro Musica, 1976. — [1],16p ; 4to. — (The art
of the Netherlanders, 1470-1530 ; vol.6)
Unpriced
Primary classification EZDU
(B78-50382)

Vento, Ivo de
[Newe teutsche Lieder, mit viern, fünff, und sechs Stimmen.
Selections]. Eight lieder, 1570 : for four voices or instruments,
ATTBB / [by] Ivo de Vento ; texts edited and translated by Alan
Robson. — London : London Pro Musica, 1977. — [1],24p ; 4to.
— (Anthologies of renaissance music ; vol.8)
With a 'turnover sheet', bearing a duplicate of pages 18, 19, 24 inserted.
Unpriced
Primary classification EZDU
(B78-50383)

LNSPW — Instruments (3) & keyboard

Frescobaldi, Girolamo
[Il primo libro delle canzoni a una, due, tre e quattro voci. *Selections*]. Three canzonas for two treble, one bass instrument and continuo / [by] Girolamo Frescobaldi ; [edited by] Bernard Thomas. — London : London Pro Musica Edition, 1977. — 4to. — (The ensemble canzonas of Frescobaldi ; vol.6)
Score ([1],20p.) & 3 parts.
Unpriced

(B78-50483)

LNU — Duets

Barratt, Carol
Chester's piano book / written by Carol Barratt, illustrated sies : for two instruments ; [by] Bernadino Luppacchino and Giovanni Tasso ; [edited by] Bernard Thomas. — London : London Pro Musica, 1977. — 19p ; 4to. — (Italian instrumental music of the renaissance ; vol.6)
Unpriced

(B78-50908)

Lupacchino, Bernadino
[Primo libro a due voci. *Selections*]. Nine fantasies : for two instruments / [by] Bernadino Luppacchino and Giovanni Tasso ; [edited by] Bernard Thomas. — London : London Pro Musica, 1977. — 19p ; 4to. — (Italian instrumental music of the renaissance ; vol.6)
Unpriced

(B78-50909)

LP — WORKS FOR UNSPECIFIED INSTRUMENT WITH PIANO

LXNUE/X — Bass instruments. Duets. Sonatas. Canons

Telemann, Georg Philipp
[Sonatas in canon. Op.5]. Sonatas in canon : for bass instruments / [by] Georg Philipp Telemann ; edited by Rodney Slatford. — London : Yorke.
Vol.3 : Sonata in B flat major, Sonata in B flat minor no.4. — 1978. — 6p ; 4to.
Unpriced

(B78-50910)

MJ — MISCELLANEOUS WORKS

Davies, Peter Maxwell
Five Klee pictures / [by] Peter Maxwell Davies. — London : Boosey and Hawkes, 1978. — 4to. — (Hawkes school series ; no.301)
For orchestra - Score (24p.) & 36 parts, with several copies of various parts.
Unpriced

(B78-50179)

Delius, Frederick
Sleigh ride = Schlittenfahrt / [by] Frederick Delius. — 1st ed. — London : Boosey and Hawkes, 1978. — 4to. — (Hawkes school series ; no.302)
For orchestra. — Score ([3],21p.) & 37 parts. — Duration 5 min.
Unpriced

(B78-50911)

Delius, Frederick
Sleigh ride = Schlittenfahrt / [by] Frederick Delius. — 1st ed. — London : Boosey and Hawkes, 1978. — 4to. — (Hawkes school series ; no.302)
For orchestra. — Score ([3],21p.) & 37 parts. — Duration 5 min.
Unpriced

(B78-50912)

Jenni, Donald
Elegy and dance : for small orchestra / [by] D. Jenni. — New York ; London : Associated Music, 1977. — [1],11p ; 4to.
£13.60

(B78-50484)

Platts, Kenneth
Sussex overture. Op.34 / [by] Kenneth Platts. — London : Edwin Ashdown, 1978. — 11p ; 4to.
Duration 3 1/2 min.
£2.00

(B78-50913)

Salaman, William
Class in concert : graded music for classroom orchestra. — London (7 Garrick St., W.C.2) : Middle Eight Music.
Score (16p.) & 26 parts, with several copies of various parts.
Grade A. — 1977. — 8vo.
Unpriced

(B78-50180)

Salaman, William
Class in concert : graded music for classroom orchestra. — London (7 Garrick St., W.C.2) : Middle Eight Music.
Score (16p.) & 26 parts, with several copies of various parts.
Grade B. — 1977. — 8vo.
Unpriced

(B78-50178)

Salaman, William
Class in concert : graded music for classroom orchestra / [by] William Salaman. — London (7 Garrick St., W.C.2) : Middle Eight Music.
Score (16p.) & 25 parts.
Grade C. — 1978. — 8vo.
Unpriced

(B78-50914)

Wade, Darrell
[Fanfare]. Fanfare, Lullaby, Cherokee war dance / by Darrell Wade. — Gnosall (16 Anchor Way, Danes Green, Gnosall) : Viking, 1977. — 8vo. — (The junior orchestra, series 1)
Score (14p.) & 10 parts.
Unpriced

(B78-50181)

MK — ARRANGEMENTS

MK/AGM — Arrangements. Marches

Grieg, Edvard
[Sigurd Jorsalfar. Op.56. Homage march. *arr*]. Homage march / [by] Edvard Grieg ; arranged by Anthony Carter. — London : Oxford University Press, 1978. — 20p ; 4to.
ISBN 0-19-363848-7 : Unpriced

(B78-50485)

MK/AH/AYU — Arrangements. Dances. Collections. Latin America

Latin-Americana : a selection of famous melodies and rhythms / arranged for school and amateur orchestra by Frank Naylor. — London : Bosworth and Co., 1977. — 43p ; 4to. — (Series for school and amateur orchestra)
£3.50

(B78-50182)

MK/AH/HM — Arrangements. Ballet music

Schubert, Franz
[Rosamunde. Ballet music. *arr*]. Rosamunde ballet music, no.2 / by Schubert ; arranged by David Stone. — London : Boosey and Hawkes, 1978. — 4to.
For orchestra - Score (24p.) & 30 parts, with several copies of various parts.
Unpriced

(B78-50183)

MK/AHW — Arrangements. Waltzes

Strauss, Johann, b.1825
[Erinnerung an Covent Garden. Op.329. *arr*]. Memories of Covent Garden = Erinnerung an Covent Garden : waltz, op.329, based on English music hall songs / [by] Johann Strauss ; arr. by Frank Naylor. — London : Bosworth & Co., 1978. — 36p ; 4to. — (Series for school and amateur orchestra)
Unpriced

(B78-50486)

MK/DM — Arrangements. Hymns

Bach, Johann Sebastian
[Chorales. *Selections : arr*]. Three chorales / harmonized by Bach, arranged by David Stone. — London : Boosey and Hawkes, 1978. — 4to. — (Hawkes school series ; no.201)
For orchestra. — Score ([2],26p.) & 30 parts, with several copies of various parts.
Unpriced

(B78-50184)

MK/DP/LF/AY — Arrangements. Carols. Christmas. Collections

A Christmas collection : for the junior school orchestra / by Darrell Wade. — Gnosall (16 Anchor Way, Danes Green) : Viking, 1978. — 8vo.
Score (12p.) & 5 parts.
Unpriced

(B78-50915)

MK/DW — Arrangements. Songs, etc

Frazer, Alan
Theme from Z Cars ('Johnny Todd') : traditional / arr. Alan Frazer. — London (7 Garrick St., W.C.2) : Middle Eight Music, 1977. — 4to. — (Music kit)
2 piano conductors (4p.) & 22 parts.
Unpriced

(B78-50916)

MM — WORKS FOR SYMPHONY ORCHESTRA

MM/HM — Ballet

Burgon, Geoffrey
Goldberg's dream / [by] Geoffrey Burgon. — London : Chester Music, 1977. — [2],36p ; 4to.
For orchestra. — Commissioned for the ballet 'Running Figures'. — Duration 20 min.
Unpriced

(B78-50917)

MME — Sonatas

Sutter, Robert
Sonata per orchestra in five parts / [by] Robert Sutter. — Kassel ; London : Bärenreiter, 1977. — 76p ; 4to.
Duration 18 1/2 min.
£11.20

(B78-50487)

MME — Symphonies
Davies, Peter Maxwell
Symphony / [by] Peter Maxwell Davies. — London : Boosey and
Hawkes, 1978. — [4],184p ; 8vo. — (Hawkes pocket scores ; 915)
Miniature score.
Unpriced
(B78-50185)

Einem, Gottfried von
Wiener Symphonie, Opus 49 / [von] Gottfried von Einem. —
Berlin : Bote und Bock ; [London] : [Schirmer], 1978. — [2],85p ;
fol.
Duration 33 min.
£14.40
(B78-50918)

Josephs, Wilfred
[Symphony no.3, op.59, 'Philadelphia']. Symphony no.3
(Philadelphia), op.59 / [by] Wilfred Josephs. — Sevenoaks :
Novello, 1974. — [5],104p ; 8vo.
£3.45
(B78-50488)

Rubbra, Edmund
[Symphony, no.10, op.145, 'Sinfonia da camera']. Sinfonia da
camera. Symphony no.10 in one movement, op.145 / [by] Edmund
Rubbra. — South Croydon : Lengnick, 1978. — [2],60p ; 4to.
Facsimile of the composer's autograph.
Unpriced
(B78-50919)

MMJ — Miscellaneous works
Argento, Dominick
A ring of time : preludes and pageants for orchestra and bells /
[by] Dominick Argento. — New York ; [London] : Boosey and
Hawkes, 1977. — 80p ; fol.
Duration 28 min.
Unpriced
(B78-50186)

Bazelon, Irwin
A quite piece for a violent time : orchestra / [by] Irwin Bazelon.
— New York ; London : Boosey and Hawkes, 1977. — [4],40p ;
fol.
Duration 10 min.
Unpriced
(B78-50187)

Bennett, Richard Rodney
Zodiac : orchestra / [by] Richard Rodney Bennett. — Sevenoaks :
Novello, 1977. — [6],50p ; 4to.
Duration 17 min. — Facsimile of composer's autograph.
£3.15
(B78-50188)

Berkeley, Sir Lennox
Voices of the night : for orchestra / [by] Lennox Berkeley. —
London : Chester Music, 1978. — [2],25p ; 8vo.
Miniature score. — Duration 10 min.
Unpriced
(B78-50920)

Bialas, Günter
Waldmusik : für Orchester und Soloinstrumente / [von] Günter
Bialas. — Kassel ; London : Bärenreiter, 1977. — 68p ; 4to.
With a corrigenda-slip inserted. — Contents: 1: Abschied (nach
Eichendorff) - 2: Jagdstück - 3: Vogelkonzert.
£8.40
(B78-50489)

Conyngham, Barry
Water ... footsteps ... time / [by] Barry Conyngham. — [Sydney] ;
[London] : Universal, 1977. — 34p ; 4to.
For orchestra. — Duration 20 min.
Unpriced
(B78-50921)

Fussell, Charles
Three processionals : for orchestra / [by] Charles Fussell. — New
York ; London : Schirmer, 1978. — 42p ; 8vo. — (Schirmer's
edition of study scores of orchestral works and chamber music ;
no.127)
Study score - Processional III quotes from Debussy's 'La mer'.
£5.45
(B78-50490)

Hartmann, Karl Amadeus
Miserae : symphonische Dichtung für Orchester, (1933-34) / [von]
Karl Amadeus Hartmann. — Mainz ; London : Schott, 1977. —
85p ; 4to.
Study score. — Duration 14 min.
£10.00
(B78-50189)

Hartmann, Karl Amadeus
Symphonische Ouverture für grosses Orchester (1942) / [von]
Karl Amadeus Hartmann. — Mainz ; London : Schott, 1977. —
110p ; 4to.
Preface by Andrew D. McCredie. — Duration 15 min.
£14.00
(B78-50190)

Jenner, Gustav
Serenade für Orchester / [von] Gustav Jenner. — Kassel ;
London : Bärenreiter, 1977. — 71p ; fol.
£22.40
(B78-50491)

Křenek, Ernst
Horizon circled = Horizont umkreist : for orchestra = für
Orchester, 1967 ; op.199 [by] Ernst Křenek. — Kassel ; London :
Bärenreiter, 1978. — [6],42p ; 4to.
Duration 20 min.
£10.50
(B78-50922)

Lees, Benjamin
Spectrum : for orchestra / [by] Benjamin Lees. — London :
Boosey and Hawkes, 1978. — 60p ; 8vo. — (Hawkes pocket
scores ; 942)
Unpriced
(B78-50923)

Mathias, William
Laudi : for orchestra / [by] William Mathias, Op.62. — London :
Oxford University Press, 1978. — [2],62p ; 8vo.
Facsimile of the composer's autograph. — Duration 14 min.
ISBN 0-19-365661-2 : Unpriced
(B78-50191)

Matthews, Colin
Night music : for orchestra / [by] Colin Matthews. — London :
Faber Music, 1978. — [2],57p ; 4to.
Facsimile of the composer's autograph.
Unpriced
(B78-50492)

Newton, Rodney Stephen
'The silmarillion' : a symphonic prelude after J.R.R. Tolkien ; for
orchestra / [by] Rodney Stephen Newton. — East Barnet (13
Chetwynd Ave., East Barnet, Herts.) : Composer Edition, 1977. —
[2],23p : col.
Facsimile of the composer's autograph.
Unpriced
(B78-50493)

Redel, Martin Christoph
Konfrontationen : für grosses Orchester, 1974 / [von] Martin
Christoph Redel. — Berlin : Bote und Bock ; [London] :
[Associated Music], 1977. — 44p ; 4to.
Duration 13 min.
£5.75
(B78-50494)

Washburn, Robert
Elegy : for orchestra / [by] Robert Washburn. — [New York] ;
[London] : Boosey and Hawkes, 1978. — 4to.
Duration 5 3/4 min. — Score (8p.) & 42 parts, with several copies of
various parts.
Unpriced
(B78-50924)

Zender, Hans
Zeitströme : für Orchester, 1974 / [von] Hans Zender. — Berlin :
Bote und Bock ; [London] : [Associated Music], 1976. — [2],31p ;
4to.
Study score.
£7.70
(B78-50495)

MP — WORKS FOR SOLO INSTRUMENT (S) & ORCHESTRA
MPQ — Piano & orchestra
Steffen, Wolfgang
Polychromie : für Klavier und 10 Instrumente, Opus 38 / [von]
Wolfgang Steffen. — Berlin : Bote und Bock ; [London] :
[Associated Music], 1976. — 26p ; 4to.
£5.75
(B78-50496)

MPQF — Piano & orchestra. Concertos
Mozart, Wolfgang Amadeus
[Concertos, piano, nos.17-22]. Piano concertos nos 17-22 in full
score / [by] Wolfgang Amadeus Mozart ; with Mozart's cadenzas
for nos 17-19. — New York : Dover Publications ; [London] :
[Constable], 1978. — [7],370p ; 4to.
Taken from portions (parts of Series 6 and 22) of the Breitkopf und Härtel
collected edition of Mozart's works.
ISBN 0-486-23599-8 : Unpriced
(B78-50925)

Mozart, Wolfgang Amadeus
[Concerto, piano, no.17, K.453, G major]. Piano concerto, G
major, K.453 / [by] Wolfgang Amadeus Mozart ; foreword by
Denis Matthews. — London : Eulenburg, 1974. — xiii,102p ; 8vo.
— (Edition Eulenburg ; no.760)
Miniature score.
£1.60

(B78-50497)

Sterkel, Franz Xaver
[Concerto, piano, no.1, op.20, C major. *arr*]. Erstes Konzert
C-Dur, Ut majeur, für Klavier mit 2 Oboen, 2 Hörnern und
Streichern, op.20 / [von] Franz Xaver Sterkel ; herausgegeben von
August Scharnagl. — Mainz ; London : Schott, 1977. — 59p ;
4to. — (Concertino ; 143)
£10.00

(B78-50192)

MPRE/AZ — Organ & orchestra. Sonatas. Collected works
Mozart, Wolfgang Amadeus
[Church sonatas. *Collections*]. Sämtliche Kirchensonaten =
Complete church sonatas / [von] Wolfgang Amadeus Mozart ;
herausgegeben von ... Minos E. Dounins. — Kassel ; London :
Bärenreiter.
III/IV : Zwei Sonaten in C für Orgel und Orchester, KV278 (271e), KV329
(317a) : Generalbassausetzung, Werner Bittinger. — 1977. — 23p ; 4to.
£2.80

(B78-50498)

MPRF — Organ & orchestra. Concertos
Handel, George Frideric
[Concerto, organ, op.4, no.1, G minor]. Organ concerto, G minor,
Op.4, no.1 / [by] George Frideric Handel ; edited by Peter
Williams. — London : Eulenburg, 1978. — xviii,35p ; 8vo. —
(Edition Eulenburg ; no.1801)
Miniature score.
Unpriced

(B78-50926)

Handel, George Frideric
[Concerto, organ, op.4, no.2, B flat major]. Organ concerto, B flat
major, Op.4, no.2 / [by] George Frideric Handel ; edited by Peter
Williams. — London : Eulenburg, 1978. — xviii,17p ; 8vo. —
(Edition Eulenburg ; no.1802)
Miniature score.
Unpriced

(B78-50927)

Handel, George Frideric
[Concerto, organ, op.4, no.3, G minor]. Organ concerto, G minor,
Op.4, no.3 / [by] George Frideric Handel ; edited by Peter
Williams. — London : Eulenburg, 1978. — xviii,19p ; 8vo. —
(Edition Eulenburg ; no.1803)
Miniature score.
Unpriced

(B78-50928)

Handel, George Frideric
[Concerto, organ, op.4, no.4, F major]. Organ concerto, F major,
Op.4, no.4 / [by] George Frideric Handel ; edited by Peter
Williams. — London : Eulenburg, 1978. — xviii,26p ; 8vo. —
(Edition Eulenburg ; no.1804)
Miniature score.
Unpriced

(B78-50929)

Handel, George Frideric
[Concerto, organ, op.4, no.5, F major]. Organ concerto, F major,
Op.4, no.5 / [by] George Frideric Handel ; edited by Peter
Williams. — London : Eulenburg, 1978. — xviii,11p ; 8vo. —
(Edition Eulenburg ; no.1805)
Miniaturee score.
Unpriced

(B78-50930)

Handel, George Frideric
[Concerto, organ, op.4, no.6, B flat major, 'Harp']. Organ
concerto, (Harp concerto), B flat major, Op.4, no.6 / [by] George
Frideric Handel ; edited by Peter Williams. — London :
Eulenburg, 1978. — xxi,14p ; 8vo. — (Edition Eulenburg ;
no.1806)
Miniature score.
Unpriced

(B78-50931)

MPSF — Violin & orchestra. Concerto's
Bennett, Richard Rodney
[Concerto, violin]. Concerto, violin & orchestra / [by] Richard
Rodney Bennett. — Sevenoaks : Novello, 1977. — [6],65p ; 4to.
Fascsimile of the composer's autograph. — Duration 22 min.
£4.20

(B78-50932)

Crosse, Gordon
[Concerto, violin, no.2, op.26]. Violin concerto 2 / [by] Gordon
Crosse. — London : Oxford University Press, 1978. — [4],119p ;
8vo.
Based on material from the opera 'The story of Vasco' and 'Ma maistresse'
by Okeghem - Duration 35 min.
ISBN 0-19-362479-6 : Unpriced

(B78-50193)

Wood, Hugh
[Concerto, violin, op.17]. Violin concerto, op.17 / [by] Hugh
Wood. — London : Chester Music, 1975. — 11p ; 4to.
Duration 29 min.
Unpriced

(B78-50933)

MPSRF — Cello & orchestra. Concertos
Delius, Frederick
[Concerto, cello]. Cello concerto / [by] Frederick Delius. —
London : Boosey and Hawkes, 1978. — 59p ; 8vo. — (Hawkes
pocket scores ; 910)
Miniature score. — A reprint in reduced format of the full score originally
published by Universal Edition, Vienna, 1882.
Unpriced

(B78-50934)

Pfitzner, Hans
[Concerto, cello, A minor, op. posth, (1888)]. Konzert für
Violoncello und Orchester (1888), Op. posth. / [von] Hans
Pfitzner ; Herausgabe und Klavierauszug von Wolfgang Osthoff.
— Mainz ; London : Schott, 1978. — 4to.
Score (37p.) & part.
£6.00

(B78-50935)

MPSSF — Double bass & orchestra. Concertos
Bennett, Richard Rodney
[Concerto, double bass & chamber orchestra. *arr*]. Concerto,
double bass & chamber orchestra / [by] Richard Rodney Bennett ;
facsimile double bass and piano score. — Sevenoaks : Novello,
1978. — 4to.
Duration 19 min. — Score ([2],30p.) & part.
£3.15

(B78-50936)

MPVRF — Flute & orchestra. Concertos
Yun, Isang
[Concerto, flute, (1977)]. Konzert für Flöte und kleiner Orchester
(1977) / von Isang Yun. — Berlin : Bote und Bock ; [London] :
[Schirmer], 1978. — 57p ; 4to.
£8.65

(B78-50937)

MPVTF — Oboe & orchestra. Concertos
Lebrun, Ludwig August
[Concerto, oboe, no.1, D minor]. Konzert No.1, d-Moll für Oboe
und Orchester / [von] Ludwig August Lebrun ; herausgegeben
von Hermann Tottcher. — Mainz ; London : Schott, 1977. —
55p ; 4to. — (Concertino ; 90)
£11.00

(B78-50194)

MPVTPLTQF — Oboe, harp & orchestra. Concertos
Yun, Isang
[Double concerto, oboe & harp]. Doppelkonzert für Oboe und
Harfe mit kleinem Orchester, 1977 / [von] Isang Yun. — Berlin :
Bote und Bock ; [London] : [Schirmer], 1978. — 82p ; fol.
Duration 34 min.
£14.40

(B78-50938)

MR — WORKS FOR CHAMBER ORCHESTRA
MRJ — Miscellaneous works
Antoniou, Theodore
Chorochronos 2 : für Bariton-Sprecher und Kammerochester =
for baritone-narrator and chamber orchestra ; 1973 / [von]
Theodore Antoniou. — Kassel ; London : Bärenreiter, 1978. —
[8],16p ; 4to.
£6.00

(B78-50939)

Croft, William
[Musicus apparatus academicas. Laurus cruentas. *Overture*].
Overture, Laurus cruentas / [by] William Croft ; edited by
Maurice Bevan. — London : Oxford University Press, 1977. —
8p ; 4to. — (Musica da camera ; 44)
ISBN 0-19-362424-9 : Unpriced

(B78-50195)

Davies, Peter Maxwell
A mirror of whitening light = Specolum luminis dealbensin : for
chamber orchestra / [by] Peter Maxwell Davies. — London :
Boosey and Hawkes, 1978. — [4],104p ; 8vo. — (Hawkes pocket
score ; 908)
Duration 22 min.
Unpriced

(B78-50940)

Harper, Edward
Ricercari, 'In memoriam Luigi Dallapiccola' : for 11 players / [by] Edward Harper. — London : Oxford University Press, 1978. — [3],44p ; 8vo.
ISBN 0-19-356888-8 : Unpriced

(B78-50941)

Lees, Benjamin
Collage : for string quartet, wind quintet and percussion / [by] Benjamin Lees. — New York ; [London] : Boosey and Hawkes, 1978. — [2],37p ; 8vo. — (Hawkes pocket scores ; 819)
Miniature score.
Unpriced

(B78-50942)

Newton, Rodney Stephen
'The path of the just' : poem, for chamber orchestra / [by] Rodney Stephen Newton. — East Barnet : Composer Edition, 1977. — [2],23p ; fol.
Facsimile of the composer's autograph.
Unpriced

(B78-50499)

Saxton, Robert
Reflections of Narziss and Goldmund : for two chamber groups, harp and piano [or] celesta / [by] Robert Saxton. — London : Chester Music, 1977. — 42p ; 8vo.
Duration 13 min.
Unpriced

(B78-50943)

MRK — Arrangements
Frescobaldi, Girolamo
[Recercari et canzoni francese. Libro primo. *Selections ; arr*]. Ricercar et canzoni / [by] Girolamo Frescobaldi ; transcribed and edited by Denis Stevens for oboes, bassoons and strings (without double basses). — Sevenoaks : Novello, 1977. — 12p ; 4to.
Duration 6 1/4 min.
£1.30

(B78-50196)

MV — WORKS FOR ORCHESTRAS INCLUDING TOY INSTRUMENTS
MVE — Symphonies
Horovitz, Joseph
Jubilee toy symphony / [by] Joseph Horovitz. — Sevenoaks : Novello, 1977. — [4],60p ; 4to.
Facsimile of the composer's autograph.
£3.45

(B78-50197)

NU — WIND, STRINGS & KEYBOARD
NURNT — Flute, strings & keyboard. Trios
Ludewig, Wolfgang
Reflexionen : fünf Psychogramme für Flöte (Alt-Flöte), Violoncello und Klavier, 1975 / [von] Wolfgang Ludewig. — Berlin : Bote und Bock ; [London] : [Associated Music], 1977. — 12p ; 4to.
£3.85

(B78-50500)

Weber, Carl Maria von, *Freiherr*
[Trio, flute, cello & piano, J. 259, G minor]. Trio for flute, cello and piano in G minor, J.259 / [by] Carl Maria von Weber ; edited by Roger Fiske ; foreword by John Warrack. — London : Eulenburg, 1977. — ix,36p ; 8vo. — (Edition Eulenburg ; no.400)
Miniature score.
Unpriced

(B78-50198)

NURNTE — Flute, strings & keyboard. Sonatas
Platti, Giovanni Benedetto
[Sonata, flute, violin & continuo, G major]. Triosonate, G-dur, G major, für Querflöte (Violine), Violine (Oboe) und B.C., for German flute (violin), violin (oboe) and b.c. / [von] Giovanni Benedetto Platti ; [herausgegeben von] Herbert Kölbel, Generalbassaussetzung, Ernst Meyerolbersleben. — Erstausgabe. — Wilhelmshaven : Heinrichshofen ; London : Peters, 1978. — 4to.
Score (16p.) & 4 parts.
Unpriced

(B78-50501)

NUXSNPE — Brass, strings & keyboard. Septets. Sonatas
Gabrielli, Domenico
[Sonata, trumpet, string quintet & continuo, D major]. Sonata, D. XI, 4 in D for trumpet, strings and basso continuo / [by] Domenico Gabrielli ; [ed.] R.P. Block. — London : Musica rara, 1978. — 4to. — (Italian 17th & 18th century sinfonias and sonatas for trumpets & strings ; 23)
Score ([1],12p.) & 8 parts, with alternative parts for trumpet in B flat and D.
Unpriced

(B78-50944)

NUXSNQE — Trumpets, strings & keyboard. Sextets. Sonatas
Gabrielli, Domenico
[Sonata, trumpet, string quartet & continuo, D major]. Sonata, D.XI, 5 in D for trumpet, strings and basso continuo / [by] Domenico Gabrielli ; [ed.] R.P. Block. — London : Musica rara, 1978. — 4to. — (Italian 17th & 18th century sinfonias and sonatas for trumpets and strings ; 23)
Score ([1],12p.) & 7 parts, with alternative parts for trumpet in B flat and D.
Unpriced

(B78-50945)

NV — WIND & STRINGS
NVP/AYD — Woodwind & strings. Collections. England
Musica Britannica : a national collection of music. — London : Stainer and Bell, for the Musica Britannica Trust.
Vol.40 : Music for mixed consort / edited and reconstructed by Warwick Edwards. — 1977. — xxv,163p ; fol.
ISBN 0-85249-436-x : Unpriced
Primary classification C/AYD

(B78-50001)

NVPNR — Woodwind & strings. Quintets
Blacher, Boris
[Quintet, woodwind & strings (1973/1974)]. Quintet für Flöte, Oboe, Violine, Viola und Violoncello (1973/74) / [von] Boris Blacher. — Berlin : Bote und Bock ; [London] : [Associated Music], 1976. — 28p ; 4to.
Duration 11 min.
£6.40

(B78-50502)

NVRNT — Flute & strings. Trios
Jolivet, André
[Alla rustica. *arr*]. Alla rustica : divertissement pour flûte et harpe ou deux flûtes et harpe / [par] André Jolivet. — London : Boosey and Hawkes, 1977. — 4to.
Score (16p.) & 2 parts ; the flute parts of the version for two flutes and harp are printed in score.
Unpriced
Primary classification VRPLTQ

(B78-50648)

Mathias, William
Zodiac trio, op.70 : for flute, viola, and harp / [by] William Mathias. — London : Oxford University Press, 1977. — [2],34p ; 8vo.
Duration 16 min. — Facsimile of the composer's autograph.
ISBN 0-19-335774-7 : Unpriced

(B78-50199)

Street, Tison
[Variations, flute, guitar & cello]. Variations for flute, guitar and cello / by Tison Street. — New York ; London : Schirmer, 1977. — 4to.
Score (14p.) & 3 parts.
Unpriced

(B78-50503)

NVSNS — Recorder & strings. Quartets
Hoffmeister, Franz Anton
[Quartet, recorder, viola d'amore, violin & cello, D major]. Quartetto in D for viola d'amore, recorder, violino con sordino and basso / [by] Franz Anton Hoffmeister ; edited by Ian White. — Kings Langley (Little Margaret, Penmans Green, Chipperfield, Kings Langley) : E.L. White, 1977. — 4pt ; fol.
Unpriced

(B78-50200)

NWNM — Nonets
Egk, Werner
Polonaise, Adagio und Finale : für vier Bläser und Streichquintett = for four wind instruments and string quintet / [von] Werner Egk. — Mainz ; [London] : Schott, 1978. — 9pt ; 4to.
A reissue of the 'Polonaise und Adagio' (1975) with a new finale.
Unpriced

(B78-50946)

Egk, Werner
Polonaise, Adagio und Finale : für vier Bläser (Oboe, Klarinette in B, Horn in F, Fagott) und Streichquintett (solistisch oder chorisch) = for four wind instruments (oboe, clarinet in B flat, horn in F, bassoon) and string quintet (solo or in chorus) / [von] Werner Egk. — Neufassung. — Mainz ; London : Schott, 1978. — 48p ; 4to.
A reissue of the 'Polonaise und Adagio' (1975) with a new finale. — Study score.
£12.00

(B78-50947)

NWNQF — Sextets. Concertos
McCabe, John
[Concerto, piano & wind quintet]. Concerto for piano and wind quintet / [by] John McCabe. — Sevenoaks : Novello, 1977. — 4to.
Score ([2],62p.) & 5 parts - Duration 21 min.
£6.25

(B78-50504)

NWPNT — Woodwind & keyboard. Trios
Head, Michael
Trio, oboe, bassoon and piano / [by] Michael Head. —
Ampleforth : Emerson, 1977. — 4to.
Score ([2],29p.) & 2 parts.
Unpriced
(B78-50201)

NWPNTK/LF — Woodwind & keyboard trio. Arrangements.
Concertos
Kalliwoda, Jan Vaclav
[Concertino, flute & oboe, F major. *arr*]. Concertino for flute,
oboe and orchestra / [by] Johann Wenzel Kalliwoda ; piano
reduction by R. Block, edited by H. Voxman. — London : Musica
rara, 1977. — 4to.
Score ([1],16p.) & 2 parts.
Unpriced
(B78-50202)

NX — STRINGS & KEYBOARD
Evans, Colin
Sounds for swinging strings : four pieces in popular style for
group music / by Colin Evans. — Sevenoaks : Paxton, 1977. —
22p ; 4to.
£1.32
(B78-50505)

NXNSE — Quartets. Sonatas
Handel, George Frideric
[Sonatas, violins (2) & continuo, Op.2, no.1-6]. Trio sonatas / [by]
George Frideric Handel ; edited by Basil Lam. — London :
Eulenburg. — (Edition Eulenburg ; no.1364)
Miniature score - Includes Dresden version of Op.2, no.1, in C minor -
Op.2, no.1 is for flute, strings & continuo.
Op.2, nos.1-3. — 1978. — xiv,54p ; 8vo.
Unpriced
(B78-50203)

Handel, George Frideric
[Sonatas, violins (2) & continuo, op.2, nos. 3, 8, 9]. Dresden trio
sonatas / [by] George Frideric Handel ; edited by Basil Lam. —
London : Eulenburg, 1978. — ix,46p ; 8vo.
Miniature score.
Unpriced
(B78-50204)

Handel, George Frideric
[Sonatas, violins (2) & continuo, op.2, nos.1-6]. Trio sonatas / [by]
George Frideric Handel ; edited by Basil Lam. — London :
Eulenburg. — (Edition Eulenburg, no.1365)
Miniature score - Op.2, no.4 is for flute, strings & continuo.
Op.2, no.4-6. — 1978. — xiii,43p ; 8vo.
Unpriced
(B78-50205)

Purcell, Henry
[Sonatas in 4 parts, Z.802-811]. Ten sonatas in four parts / [by]
Henry Purcell ; edited by Christopher Hogwood. — London :
Eulenburg. — (Edition Eulenburg ; no.1362)
Miniature score.
Nos. 1-6. — 1978. — xx,53p ; 8vo.
£2.00
(B78-50506)

Purcell, Henry
[Sonatas in 4 parts. Z.802-811]. Ten sonatas in four parts / [by]
Henry Purcell ; edited by Christopher Hogwood. — London :
Eulenburg. — (Edition Eulenburg ; no.1363)
Miniature score - With appendices.
Nos.7-10. — 1978. — xxi,53p ; 8vo.
£2.00
(B78-50507)

NXNT — Trios
Killmayer, Wilhelm
Brahms-Bildnis : für Violine, Violoncello und Klavier / [von]
Wilhelm Killmayer. — Mainz ; London : Schott, 1977. — 4to.
Score (17p.) & 2 parts.
£12.00
(B78-50948)

Michael, Frank
Yantra : für Klavier, Violine und Violoncello, Opus 41 (1974) /
[von] Frank Michael. — Berlin : Bote und Bock ; [London] :
[Schirmer], 1978. — fol.
Score ([2],21p.) & 2 parts ; the violin and cello parts are printed in score
with piano part.
£15.35
(B78-50949)

Stoker, Richard
[Trio, strings & piano, no.1, op.24]. Piano trio no.1, opus 24, for
violin, violoncello, and piano / [by] Richard Stoker. — London :
Peters, 1977. — 4to.
Score (20p.) & 2 parts.
Unpriced
(B78-50206)

NXNTG — Trios. Suites
Grabe
[Parthia, viola d'amore, gamba & harpsichord, C minor]. Parthia
in C minor for viola d'amore, gamba & harpsichord / by Grabe ;
figured bass by Peter Hollman, edited by Ian White. —
Chipperfield (Little Margaret, Penmans Green, Chipperfield) : Ian
White, 1978. — 4p ; fol.
Unpriced
(B78-50508)

NYD — WIND, STRINGS, KEYBOARD & PERCUSSION
NYDF — Concertos
Bazelon, Irwin
Churchill downs : chamber concerto no.2 / [by] Irwin Bazelon. —
New York ; [London] : Boosey and Hawkes, 1977. — [2],86p ;
fol.
Duration 15 min.
Unpriced
(B78-50207)

NYDPK/DP/LF — Woodwind, strings & keyboard ensemble.
Arrangements. Carols. Christmas
Boswell, Eric
[Little donkey. *arr*]. Little donkey / by Eric Boswell ; arranged by
Michael Burnett for school ensemble, recorders, melodicas,
glockenspiels, xylophone, percussion, piano, guitar. — London :
Chappell, 1977. — 4to. — (Pop into school)
Score (7p.) & 4 parts ; the percussion parts printed in score.
Unpriced
(B78-50950)

Davis, Katherine Kennicott
[Carol of the drum. *arr*]. The little drummer boy / by Harry
Simeone, Henry Onorati and [music by] Katherine Kennicott
Davis ; arranged by Michael Burnett for school ensemble,
recorders, melodicas, glockenspiels, xylophone, percussion, piano,
guitar. — London : Chappell, 1977. — 4to. — (Pop into school)
Score (7p.) & 4 parts ; the percussion parts printed in score.
Unpriced
(B78-50951)

NYDPNN — Woodwind, strings, keyboard & percussion. Octets
Steffen, Wolfgang
Music for piano and seven players = Musik für einen Pianisten
und sieben Spieler, Opus 44 / [by] Wolfgang Steffen. — Berlin :
Bote und Bock ; [London] : [Associated Music], 1977. — 22p ;
4to.
Duration 11 min.
£5.75
(B78-50509)

NYDPNP — Woodwind, strings, keyboard & percussion. Septets
Davies, Peter Maxwell
Versalii icones : for dancer, solo cello and instrumental ensemble /
[by] Peter Maxwell Davies. — London : Boosey and Hawkes,
1978. — 56p ; 4to.
Duration 40 min.
Unpriced
(B78-50510)

Redel, Martin Christoph
Interplay : für sieben Spieler, 1975 / [von] Martin Christoph
Redel. — Berlin : Bote und Bock ; [London] : [Associated Music],
1976. — 35p ; 4to.
£7.70
(B78-50511)

NYDPNR — Woodwind, keyboard & percussion. Quintets
Henze, Hans Werner
Amicizia! : Quintett für Klarinette in A, Posaune, Violoncello,
Schlagzeug und Klavier (1976) / [von] Hans Werner Henze. —
Mainz ; London : Schott, 1978. — 8vo.
(31p.) & 5 parts.
£8.00
(B78-50512)

NYDS — Recorders, strings, keyboard & percussion
Wade, Darrell
'Getting together' : a collection devised for the junior and middle
school / by Darrell Wade. — Gnosall (16 Anchor Way, Danes
Green, Gnosall) : Viking, 1977. — 8vo.
For recorders, violins, cellos, percussion & piano. — Contents: 1: Rumba -
2: Tango - 3: Cha cha - 4: Kumbaya.
Unpriced
(B78-50208)

NYE — WIND, STRINGS & PERCUSSION
NYEPNQ — Woodwind, strings & percussion. Sextets
Newton, Rodney Stephen
'Mountains in cloud' : 8 minatures [sic] after Chinese scrolls and
album leaves for chamber ensemble / [by] Rodney Stephen
Newton. — East Barnet (13 Chetwynd Ave., East Barnet,
Herts.) : Composer Edition, 1978. — [1],26p ; fol.
Facsimile of the composer's autograph.
Unpriced
(B78-50209)

NYF — WIND, KEYBOARD & PERCUSSION
NYFPK — Woodwind, keyboard & percussion. Arrangements
Bouwens, J
[Paloma blanca. *arr*]. Paloma blanca / by J. Bouwens ; arranged by Michael Burnett for school ensemble. — London : Chappell, 1977. — 4to. — (Pop into school)
Score (8p.) & 4 parts.
Unpriced

(B78-50513)

Trombey, Jack
[Eye level. *arr*]. Eye level / by Jack Trombey ; arranged by Michael Burnett for school ensemble. — London : Chappell, 1977. — 4to. — (Pop into school)
Score (6p.) & 4 parts.
Unpriced

(B78-50514)

NYFPK/DW — Woodwind, keyboard & percussion. Arrangements. Songs, etc
Lennon, John
[Yellow submarine. *arr*]. Yellow submarine / words and music by John Lennon and Paul McCartney : arranged by Michael Burnett for school ensemble. — London : Chappell, 1977. — 4to. — (Pop into school)
Score (6p.) & 4 parts.
Unpriced

(B78-50515)

Rodgers, Richard
[The sound of music. Do-re-mi. *arr*]. Do-re-mi / music by Richard Rodgers ; arranged by Michael Burnett for school ensemble. — London : Chappell, 1977. — 4to. — (Pop into school)
Score (6p.) & 4 parts.
Unpriced

(B78-50516)

NYFPK/DW/JR/LF — Woodwind, keyboard & percussion. Arrangements. Film songs. Christmas
Berlin, Irving
[Holiday inn. White Christmas. *arr*]. White Christmas / [by] Irving Berlin ; arr. Michael Burnett for school ensemble. — London : Chappell, 1978. — 4to.
Score (7p.) & 4 parts.
Unpriced

(B78-50952)

NYFPK/DW/LF — Woodwind, keyboard & percussion. Arrangements. Songs, etc. Christmas
Hairston, Jester
[Mary's boy child. *arr*]. Mary's boy child / [by] Jester Hairston ; arranged by Michael Burnett for school ensemble. — London : Chappell, 1977. — 4to. — (Pop into school)
Score (8p.) & 4 parts.
Unpriced

(B78-50953)

NYH — WIND & PERCUSSION
Feldman, Morton
Instruments 1 / [by] Morton Feldman. — Toronto ; [London] : Universal, 1977. — 24p ; 8vo.
For alto flute, oboe, trombone, celesta and percussion.
Unpriced

(B78-50954)

NYJ — STRINGS & PERCUSSION
NYJNQ — Sextets
Conyngham, Barry
Three / [by] Barry Conyngham. — [Sydney] ; [London] : Universal, 1977. — [4],43p ; 4to.
For string quartet and percussion. — Duration 21 min.

(B78-50955)

PWP — KEYBOARD SOLOS
PWPJ — Miscellaneous works
Howells, Herbert
Howell's clavichord : twenty pieces for clavichord or piano / by Herbert Howells. — Sevenoaks : Novello, [1978]. — 85p ; 4to.
Reissued in one volume.
£3.80

(B78-50517)

Q — PIANO
Q/AC — Tutors
Barratt, Carol
Chester's piano book / written by Carol Barratt ; illustrated by Wendy Hoile. — London : Chester Music.
With leaflets of accompaniments, (4p.).
Number 1. — 1977. — 36p ; 4to.
Unpriced

(B78-50956)

Number 4. — 1977. — 40p ; 4to. —
Unpriced

(B78-50957)

Barratt, Carol
Chester's piano book written by Carol Barratt, illustrated by Wendy Hoile. — London : Chester Music.
With leaflets of accompaniments (4p.).
Number 3. — 1977. — 36p ; 4to.
Unpriced

(B78-50958)

Childs, Lisa
Childs play for all / by Lisa Childs. — Sevenoaks : Novello, 1978. — [4],116p ; obl.4to.
Piano tutor.
£2.00

(B78-50959)

Enoch, Yvonne
Play the piano : a tutor for adults and late beginners / [by] Yvonne Enoch. — London : Faber Music, 1978. — 52p ; 4to.
Unpriced

(B78-50960)

Harrison, Sidney
The Sidney Harrison adult piano tutor. — London : Chappell, 1978. — 31p ; 4to.
Unpriced

(B78-50961)

Heilbut, Peter
Spass am Klavierspielen : Schule für Kinder aus Grund- un Früherziehungskursen / [von] Peter Heilbut. — Kassel ; London : Bärenreiter, 1977. — 164p ; obl.4to.
£4.20

(B78-50518)

Nikolaev, Aleksandr Aleksandrovich
The Russian school of piano playing / compiled by E. Kisell, V. Natanson, A. Nikolaev and N. Sretenskaya : general editor, A. Nikolaev and N. Sretenskaya, general editor A. Nikolaev, translated into English by Narineh Haratyanyan and Martin Hughes. — English ed. — London : Boosey and Hawkes.
[Vol.1]. — 1978. — 101p ; 4to.
Unpriced

(B78-50962)

Nikolaev, Aleksandr Aleksandrovich
The Russian school of piano playing / compiled by E. Kisell, V. Natanson, A. Nikolaev and N. Sretenskaya : general editor, A. Nikoleav and N. Sretenskaya, general editor, A. Nikolaev, translated into English by Narineh Harutyanyan and Martin Hughes. — English ed. — London : Boosey and Hawkes.
[Vol.2]. — 1978. — 84p ; 4to.
Unpriced

(B78-50963)

Owyang, Lily Siao
Creative piano : a modular approach for adult beginners / [by] Lily Siao Owyang and Linda Woodaman Ostrander. — Boston ; London : Houghton Mifflin, 1978. — xii,216p ; 4to.
ISBN 0-395-25569-4 : Unpriced

(B78-50964)

Q/AF — Exercises
Associated Board of the Royal Schools of Music
Pianoforte scales and arpeggios. — London : Associated Board of the Royal Schools of Music.
Grade 3. — 1978. — 7p ; 4to. —
Unpriced

(B78-50965)

Grade 4. — 1978. — 8p ; 4to. —
Unpriced

(B78-50966)

Grade 5. — 1978. — 11p ; 4to. —
Unpriced

(B78-50967)

Grade 6. — 1978. — 12p ; 4to. —
Unpriced

(B78-50968)

Grade 7. — 1978. — 19p ; 4to. —
Unpriced

(B78-50969)

Grade 8. — 1978. — 24p ; 4to. —
Unpriced

(B78-50970)

Associated Board of the Royal Schools of Music
Pianoforte scales and broken chords. — London : Associated Board of the Royal Schools of Music.
Grade 1. — 1978. — 4p ; 4to. —
Unpriced

(B78-50971)

Grade 2. — 1978. — 6p ; 4to. —
Unpriced

(B78-50972)

Q/AL — Examinations
Associated Board of the Royal Schools of Music
 Pianoforte examinations, 1979. — London : Associated Board of
 the Royal Schools of Music.
 Grade 1 : Lists A & B. — 1978. — 11p ; 4to. —
 £0.50
                                                              (B78-50973)

 Grade 2 : Lists A & B. — 1978. — 11p ; 4to. —
 £0.50
                                                              (B78-50975)

 Grade 3 : Lists A & B. — 1978. — 10p ; 4to. —
 £0.50
                                                              (B78-50976)

 Grade 4 : Lists A & B. — 1978. — 14p ; 4to. —
 £0.50
                                                              (B78-50977)

 Grade 5 : List A. — 1978. — 11p ; 4to. —
 £0.50
                                                              (B78-50978)

 Grade 5 : List B. — 1978. — 13p ; 4to. —
 £0.50
                                                              (B78-50979)

 Grade 6 : List A. — 1978. — 13p ; 4to. —
 £0.50
                                                              (B78-50980)

 Grade 6 : List B. — 1978. — 13p ; 4to. —
 £0.50
                                                              (B78-50981)

 Grade 7 : List A. — 1978. — 15p ; 4to. —
 £0.50
                                                              (B78-50982)

 Grade 7 : List B. — 1978. — 17p ; 4to. —
 £0.50
                                                              (B78-50983)

QNU — TWO PIANOS, 4 HANDS
Debussy, Claude
 En blanc et noir : three pieces for two pianos / [by] Claude
 Debussy ; edited by H. Swarsenski. — London : Peters, 1978. —
 50p ; 4to.
 Two copies.
 Unpriced
                                                              (B78-50984)

Ligeti, Gyorgy
 Monument, Selbstportrait, Bewegung : drei Stücke für zwei
 Klaviere ... (1976) / [von] Gyorgy Ligeti. — Mainz ; London :
 Schott, 1976. — 20ff ; fol.
 Facsimile of the composer's autograph. — Duration 16 min.
 £10.00
                                                              (B78-50210)

Smalley, Roger
 Accord : for two pianists (1974-5) / [by] Roger Smalley. —
 London : Faber Music, 1978. — [5],54p ; obl.fol.
 Duration 45 min.
 Unpriced
                                                              (B78-50985)

QNUE — Sonatas
Britten, Benjamin, *Baron Britten*
 [Sonata, pianos (2)]. Sonata for two pianos / by Antony Elton. —
 Durham (50 Middleham Rd, Durham) : Toad House Music, 1978.
 — 3 vols., 83p ; 4to.
 Duration 30 min. — Reproduced photographically from the composer's
 manuscript, the title-page bearing the composer's autograph signature.
 £9.00
                                                              (B78-50519)

QNUHKEF — Foxtrots
Martin, Frank
 Two pieces, overture and foxtrot : for two pianos, four hands /
 [by] Frank Martin. — New York ; London : Schirmer, 1976. —
 31p ; 4to.
 £3.65
                                                              (B78-50986)

QNUK/LF — Arrangements. Concertos
Sterkel, Johann Franz Xaver
 [Concerto, piano, no.1, op.20, C major. *arr*]. Erstes Konzert
 C-Dur, Ut majeur, C major, für Klavier mit 2 Oboen, 2 Hörnern
 und Streichern, Opus 20 / [von] Franz Xaver Sterkel ; Solostimme
 für den praktischen Gebrauch bearbeitet Kadenzen und
 Klavierauszug von Alexander Kaul. — Mainz ; London : Schott,
 1977. — 68p ; 4to.
 Two-piano score.
 £10.00
                                                              (B78-50211)

Surinach, Carlos
 [Concerto, piano. *arr*]. Concerto for piano and orchestra / [by]
 Carlos Surinach ; reduction by the composer. — New York ;
 London : Associated Music, 1977. — 2-70p ; 4to.
 £4.55
                                                              (B78-50520)

QNV — ONE PIANO, 4 HANDS
Wells, Elsie
 Sea pictures : fifteen easy piano duets in two sets. — London :
 Oxford University Press.
 Set 1. — 1977. — 21p ; 4to. —
 ISBN 0-19-373947-x : Unpriced
                                                              (B78-50212)

 Set 2. — 1977. — 17p ; 4to. —
 ISBN 0-19-373948-8 : Unpriced
                                                              (B78-50213)

QNVG — Suites
Fauré, Gabriel
 [Dolly suite, op.56]. Dolly. Op.36 [sic] : suite pour piano à 4
 mains / par Gabriel Fauré. — London : Cramer, 1978. — 47p ;
 4to.
 £2.75
                                                              (B78-50521)

QNVH — Dances
Mignone, Francisco
 [Caixinha de bringnedos. Dança compestre]. Dança campestre :
 piano a 4 mãos / de Francisco Mignone. — Rio de Janeiro :
 Arthur Napoleão ; [London] : [Essex Music], 1978. — 6p ; 4to.
 Unpriced
                                                              (B78-50522)

QNVHW — Waltzes
Berkeley, *Sir* **Lennox**
 Palm court waltz : for piano duet / [by] Lennox Berkeley. —
 London : Chester Music, 1976. — 12p ; 4to.
 Unpriced
                                                              (B78-50987)

QP — PIANO SOLOS
QP/AYT — Collections. United States
 Nineteenth-century American piano music / selected and introduced
 by John Gillespie. — New York : Dover Publications ; [London] :
 [Constable], 1978. — xxi,323p ; 4to.
 ISBN 0-486-23602-1 : Unpriced
                                                              (B78-50988)

QP/AYUR — Collections. Brazil
 Album comemorative do centenario do choro, no.1 : 20 choros para
 piano, 1877-1977. — São Paulo : Fermata do Brasil ; [London] :
 [Essex Music], 1977. — 56p ; 4to.
 Unpriced
                                                              (B78-50214)

QP/T — Variations
Finney, Ross Lee
 Variations on a theme by Alban Berg : piano solo / [by] Ross Lee
 Finney. — New York : Henmar Press : Peters ; London : Peters,
 1977. — [2],12p ; 4to.
 Duration 8 min.
 Unpriced
                                                              (B78-50215)

Webber, Andrew Lloyd
 Theme and variations 1-4 / by Andrew Lloyd Webber. — Ilford :
 Chappell, 1978. — 8p ; 4to.
 For piano - The theme taken from Paganini's Capricci, Op.1, No.24.
 Unpriced
                                                              (B78-50523)

QP/Y — Fugues
Bach, Johann Sebastian
 [Das wohltemperirte Clavier]. Well tempered clavier =
 Wohltemperiertes Clavier : forty-eight preludes and fugues, for the
 piano / [by] J.S. Bach ; edited by Carl Czerny, books 1 and 2
 complete combined in one volume. — Carlstadt : Ashley ;
 [London] : [Phoenix], 1978. — 249p ; 4to. — (World's favorite
 series ; no.106)
 An early edition of this work by Czerny reprinted.
 Unpriced
                                                              (B78-50989)

QPE — Sonatas
Beethoven, Ludwig van
[Sonatas, piano]. Sonaten für Klavier zu zwei Händen / [von]
Ludwig van Beethoven ; herausgegeben von Claudio Arrau,
musikwissenschaftliche Revision von Lothar Hoffmann-Erbrecht.
— Frankfurt : Litolff ; New York ; London : Peters.
Band 2 : [Nr.16-32]. — 1978. — [2],334p ; 4to.
Unpriced

(B78-50991)

Berkeley, *Sir* Lennox
[Sonata, piano]. Sonata for piano / [by] Lennox Berkeley. — 2nd
ed. embodying corrections to the first ed. — London : Chester
Music, 1974. — [1],30p ; 4to.
Unpriced

(B78-50992)

Blackford, Richard
[Sonata, piano, (1975)]. Sonata for piano (1975) / [by] Richard
Blackford. — New York ; London : Schirmer, 1977. — 22p ; 4to.
£3.05

(B78-50524)

Joubert, John
[Sonata, piano, no.2, op.71]. Sonata no.2 for piano, op.71 / [by]
John Joubert. — Sevenoaks : Novello, 1977. — 49p ; 4to.
Duration 20 min.
£2.50

(B78-50216)

Mozart, Wolfgang Amadeus
[Fantasia and sonata, piano, K.475, K.457, C minor]. Fantasia
and sonata in C minor, K.475 and 457 / [by] Mozart ; edited by
Stanley Sadie ; fingering and notes on performance by Denis
Matthews. — London : Associated Board of the Royal Schools of
Music, 1978. — 38p ; 4to.
Unpriced

(B78-50993)

Mozart, Wolfgang Amadeus
[Sonata, piano, no.2, K.280, F major]. Sonata in F. K.280 / [by]
Mozart ; edited by Stanley Sadie, fingering and notes on
performance by Denis Matthews. — London : Associated Board
of the Royal Schools of Music, 1978. — 15p ; 4to.
Unpriced

(B78-50994)

QPE — Symphonies
Jobim, Antonio Carlos
Sinfonia do Rio de Janeiro : piano / de Antonio Carlos Jobim &
Billy Blanco. — São Paulo : Arapua ; [London] : [Essex Music],
1978. — [1],17p ; fol.
Unpriced

(B78-50995)

QPE/AZ — Sonatas. Collected works of individual composers
Schubert, Franz
[Sonatas, piano]. Complete pianoforte sonatas, including the
unfinished works / [by] Franz Schubert ; edited, annotated and
fingered by Howard Ferguson. — London : Associated Board of
the Royal Schools of Music.
Vol.1. — 1978. — 207p ; 4to.
Unpriced

(B78-50996)

QPEM — Sonatinas
Dessau, Paul
[Sonatina, piano, no.2, (1975)]. Sonatine 2 für Klavier, 1975 /
[von] Paul Dessau. — Berlin : Bote und Bock ; [London] :
[Yorke], 1977. — 7p ; 4to.
£1.90

(B78-50997)

QPG — Suites
Baselli, Joss
Divertissement baroque en trois mouvements / de Joss Baselli et
André Astier. — Paris ; [London] : Chappell, 1978. — 10p ; fol.
For piano.
Unpriced

(B78-50998)

Binkerd, Gordon
[Suite, piano]. Suite for piano : five fantasias / [by] Gordon
Binkerd. — New York ; [London] : Boosey and Hawkes, 1978. —
33p ; 4to.
Nos 2,3 and 4 based on songs by Brahms.
Unpriced

(B78-50999)

Rorem, Ned
Eight études : for piano / [by] Ned Rorem. — [New York] ;
[London] : Boosey and Hawkes, 1977. — 35p ; 4to.
Duration 20 min.
£3.25

(B78-50217)

QPH/H — Dances for dancing
Higgins, Norman
Andantino / [by] N. Higgins. — London : Royal Academy of
Dancing, 1977. — 3p ; 4to. — (Children's dances series ; no.4)
For piano.
Unpriced

(B78-50218)

Higgins, Norman
Butterfly dance, and, Scherzo / [by] N. Higgins. — London :
Royal Academy of Dancing, 1976. — [2]p ; 4to. — (Children's
dances series ; no.3)
For piano.
Unpriced

(B78-50219)

Higgins, Norman
Two folk melodies / [by] N. Higgins. — London : Royal
Academy of Dancing, 1977. — [2]p ; 4to. — (Children's dances
series ; no.2)
For piano.
Unpriced

(B78-50220)

QPH/HM — Ballet
Tyrwhitt-Wilson, *Sir* Gerald Hugh, *14th Baron Berners*
[The triumph of Neptune. Suite. *arr*]. The triumph of Neptune :
suite for piano / [by] Lord Berners. — London : Chester Music,
1975. — 12p ; 4to.
Unpriced

(B78-51000)

QPHVHM — Polonaises
Dale, Mervyn
[6 pieces for the piano. Polonaise napolitana]. Polonaise
napolitana : piano solo / [by] Mervyn Dale. — London : Edwin
Ashdown, 1978. — 4to.
Unpriced

(B78-51001)

QPHW/H — Waltzes. Dances for dancing
Higgins, Norman
Waltz in E / [by] N. Higgins. — London : Royal Academy of
Dancing, 1976. — 2p ; 4to. — (Children's dances series ; no.1)
For piano.
Unpriced

(B78-50221)

QPHX — Jazz
Brubeck, Dave
[Piano music. *Selections*]. Originals / [by] Dave Brubeck ;
transcribed by Frank Metis. — London : EMI, 1978. — 50p ; 4to.
For piano. — Contents: 1: The Duke - 2: When I was young - 3: Walkin'
line - 4: In your own sweet way - 5: Swing bells - 6: Weep no more - 7: Two
part contention - 8: One moment worth years - 9: The waltz.
Unpriced

(B78-51002)

QPHXJ — Ragtime
EMI music book of piano rags / editor, Cecil Bolton. — London :
EMI, 1978. — 40p ; 4to.
Unpriced

(B78-50525)

Joplin, Scott
[Ragtime. *Selections*]. Easy winners : nine piano rags / by Scott
Joplin. — Sevenoaks : Paxton, 1978. — 35p ; 4to.
£1.25

(B78-50526)

QPJ — Miscellaneous works
Alt, Hansi
Where the palm trees grow : six pieces for the young pianist /
[by] Hansi Alt ; illustrations by Dawn Marie Guernsey. — New
York ; [London] : Oxford University Press, 1978. — 11p ; 4to.
Unpriced

(B78-51003)

Bailey, Freda O
Fun on the piano : for very young music makers to start learning
the happy way / by Freda O. Bailey. — Leeds : Regina Music.
Initial Book A. — 1978. — [1],8p ; 4to.
Unpriced

(B78-51004)

Barber, Samuel
Ballade, op.16 : for piano / [by] Samuel Barber. — New York ;
London : Schirmer, 1977. — [2],6p ; 4to.
Unpriced

(B78-51005)

Berkeley, *Sir* Lennox
Four piano studies / [by] Lennox Berkeley. — London : Chester
Music, 1976. — 15p ; 4to.
Unpriced

(B78-51006)

Blacher, Boris
24 préludes : für Klavier (1974) / [von] Boris Blacher. — Berlin :
Bote und Bock ; [London] : [Schirmer], 1978. — 32p ; fol.
£7.70

(B78-51007)

Blanco, Billy
Paulistana : piano / de Billy Blanco. — São Paulo : Arapua ;
[London] : [Essex Music], 1978. — 37p ; fol.
Unpriced

(B78-51008)

Brandmüller, Theo
5 Details : für Klavier (1975) / [von] Theo Brandmüller. —
Berlin : Bote und Bock ; London : Associated Music, 1977. —
8p ; 4to.
Unpriced

(B78-50527)

Centenario do choro : 20 choros para piano álbum. — São Paulo :
Fermata do Brasil ; [London] : [Essex Music].
No.3. — 1978. — [1],52p ; 4to. —
Unpriced

(B78-50528)

Copland, Aaron
Midsummer nocturne : piano solo / [by] Aaron Copland. — New
York ; [London] : Boosey and Hawkes, 1978. — 3p ; 4to.
Unpriced

(B78-50529)

Dale, Mervyn
[Clouds that veil the midnight moon]. Clouds that veil the
midnight moon [and] The straw hat : piano solo / [by] Mervyn
Dale. — London : Edwin Ashdown, 1978. — 7p ; 4to.
£0.40

(B78-51009)

Davies, Peter Maxwell
Stevie's ferry to Hoy : piano solo / [by] Peter Maxwell Davies. —
London : Boosey and Hawkes, 1978. — 4p ; 4to.
Unpriced

(B78-50222)

Garoto
15 choros / de Garoto. — São Paulo : Fermata do Brasil ;
[London] : [Essex Music], 1978. — 21p ; 4to.
For piano.
Unpriced

(B78-50530)

Griffes, Charles Tomlinson
De profundis : piano solo / [by] Charles T. Griffes ; edited by
Donna K. Anderson. — New York ; [London] : Peters, 1978. —
8p ; 4to.
Duration 6 min.
Unpriced

(B78-51010)

Gruber, Heinz Karl
6 Episoden aus einer unterbrochenen Chronik = 6 episodes from
a discontinued chronicle : Klavier = for piano : op.20 / [von]
H.K. Gruber. — London : Boosey and Hawkes, 1978. — 18p ;
4to.
Unpriced

(B78-51011)

Handel, George Frideric
[Suite, harpsichord, Craig Bell no.170, A major. Sarabande].
Sarabande and air : for keyboard / [by] G.F. Handel ; edited by
A.S. Craig. — York : Banks Music, 1978. — 3p ; 4to.
The Air appears in the Hallische Ausgabe, Ser. IV, Vol.6, page 58.
Unpriced

(B78-51012)

Helyer, Marjorie
Plum stones : for piano / [by] Marjorie Helyer. — Sevenoaks :
Novello, 1977. — 8p ; 4to.
Unpriced

(B78-50531)

Jobim, Antonio Carlos
Album para piano / de Antonio Carlos Jobim. — São Paulo :
Editôra Musical Arapuã ; [London] : [Essex Music], 1977. —
56p ; 4to.
Unpriced

(B78-50532)

Jubileu de guarânia, 1927-1977 : melhores guarânias de todos os
tempos. — São Paulo : Fermata do Brasil ; [London] : [Essex
Music], 1977. — 76p ; 4to.
Unpriced

(B78-50533)

Kabeláč, Miloslav
Eight preludes, op.30 : for piano / [by] Miloslav Kabeláč. —
Praha : Supraphon ; New York ; London : Schirmer, 1977. — [1],
50p ; 4to.
£3.65

(B78-50534)

Klebe, Giselher
Neun Klavierstücke für Sonja. Op.76 / [von] Giselher Klebe. —
Kassel ; London : Bärenreiter, 1977. — 22p ; fol.
Facsimile of the composer's autograph.
£5.04

(B78-50535)

Lambert, Sydney
[Premieres leçons de piano. *Selections*]. Six pieces in the early
grades / [by] Sydney Lambert ; [edited by] Paul Glass, for piano.
— New York ; London : Associated Music, 1977. — 11p ; 4to.
£1.20

(B78-50536)

Last, Joan
Alphabetically yours : 26 short fragments for piano / by Joan
Last. — London : Oxford University Press, 1978. — [2],14p ; 4to.
ISBN 0-19-373099-5 : Unpriced

(B78-51013)

Last, Joan
In changing mood : nine short easy piano pieces / [by] Joan Last.
— London : Oxford University Press, 1978. — 11p ; 4to.
ISBN 0-19-373122-3 : Unpriced

(B78-50223)

Last, Joan
Lyric pieces : for piano / by Joan Last. — London : Chappell.
Set 1. — 1978. — 5p ; 4to. —
Unpriced

(B78-50537)

Set 2. — 1978. — 5p ; 4to. —
Unpriced

(B78-50538)

Last, Joan
Two hand duos : nine pieces having equal interest for both
hands / by Joan Last. — London : Leonard, Gould and Bolttler,
1978. — 12p ; 4to.
Unpriced

(B78-50539)

Lazarof, Henri
[Textures. Cadence IV]. Cadence IV : for piano / [by] Henri
Lazarof. — New York ; London : Associated Music, 1977. — 9p ;
4to.
£1.50

(B78-50540)

Liszt, Franz
[Works]. Liszt Society publications. — London : Schott.
Vol.7 : Unfamiliar piano pieces. — 1978. — [9],74p ; 4to. —
£3.00
Primary classification C/AZ

(B78-50322)

Liszt, Franz
[Piano music. *Selections*]. Selected works : for piano solo /
compiled by Margaret Gresh. — New York ; London : Schirmer,
1977. — 159p ; 4to.
£3.60

(B78-50541)

Matthews, Colin
Toccata, nocturne and scherzo (1977) : for piano / [by] Colin
Matthews. — London : Faber Music, 1978. — 14p ; 4to.
Duration 12 min.
Unpriced

(B78-51014)

Mignone, Francisco
4 choros : piano / [de] Francisco Mignone. — Rio de Janeiro :
Arthur Napoleão ; [London] : [Essex Music], 1977. — 14p ; 4to.
Unpriced

(B78-50542)

Mignone, Francisco
Nazarethiana : 5 peças para piano / de Francisco Mignone. —
Rio de Janeiro : Arthur Napoleão ; [London] : [Essex Music],
1978. — 14p ; 4to.
Unpriced

(B78-50543)

Mozart, Wolfgang Amadeus
[Piano music. *Selections*]. Mozart : morçeaux choisis a l'usage des
mains petites de la 2e année de piano (assez facile) a la moyenne
difficulté / doigtes, annotés, commentés et interpretés par
Jacqueline Robin ... — Paris ; [London] : Chappell, 1978. — 40p ;
4to. — (Le petit concertiste ; no.2)
Imperfect, wanting the gramophone record.
Unpriced
(B78-51015)

Mozart, Wolfgang Amadeus
[Piano music. *Selections*]. Selected works : for piano solo /
compiled by Margaret Gresh. — New York ; London : Schirmer,
1977. — 160p ; 4to.
£3.60
(B78-50544)

Nazareth, Ernesto
[Piano music. *Selections*]. [Composicôes de Ernesto Nazareth]. —
Rio de Janeiro : Arthur Napoleäno ; [London] : [Essex Music].
Album 1 : 25 tangos brasileiros (choras) para piano / de Ernesto Nazareth.
— 1977. — 88p : ill, ports ; 4to. —
Unpriced
(B78-50545)

Nazareth, Ernesto
[Piano music. *Selections*]. [Composicôes de Ernesto Nazareth]. —
Rio de Janeiro : Arthur Napoleäo ; [London] : [Essex Music].
Album 2 : 26 Obras para piano. — 1977. — 88p : ill, ports ; 4to. —
Unpriced
(B78-50546)

Nazareth, Ernesto, b.1863
[Piano music. *Selections*]. 20 obras para piano / de Ernesto
Nazareth e 4 musicas de sens filhos Ernesto e Diniz. — Rio de
Janeiro : Arthur Napoleäo ; [London] : [Essex Music].
Album no.3. — 1978. — 77p ; fol.
Unpriced
(B78-51016)

Orton, Richard
Pièce de resistance / [by] Richard Orton ; piano solo. —
Birmingham : Arts Lab Music, 1978. — 4p ; 4to.
Unpriced
(B78-51017)

Parke, Dorothy
Ostinati : for piano solo / [by] Dorothy Parke. — York : Banks
Music, 1978. — [2]p ; 4to.
Unpriced
(B78-51018)

Parke, Dorothy
Prelude and burlesca : for piano solo / [by] Dorothy Parke. —
York : Banks, 1978. — 5p ; 4to.
Unpriced
(B78-51019)

Pert, Morris
Voyage in space : twenty pieces for solo piano / by Morris Pert.
— London : Weinberger, 1978. — [2],38p ; 4to.
Unpriced
(B78-50547)

Staempfli, Edward
Cinq préludes : pour piano / [par] Edward Staempfli. — Berlin :
Bote und Bock ; [London] : [Schirmer], 1978. — 11p ; fol.
£3.85
(B78-51020)

Villa-Lobos, Heitor
Prole do bebê no.1 : coleção completa, 8 peças para piano / [de]
Heitor Villa-Lobos. — Rio de Janeiro : Arthur Napoleäo ;
[London] : [Essex Music], 1978. — 41p ; 4to.
Unpriced
(B78-50548)

Wakeman, Rick
Rick Wakeman's criminal record / piano transcription, Jeff
Muston. — London : Rondor Music : Music Sales, 1978. — 92p ;
4to.
Unpriced
(B78-50224)

QPK — Arrangements
Bach, Johann Sebastian
[Selections. *arr*]. Three pieces for keyboard / by J.S. and W.F.
Bach ; edited and completed by Gwilym Beechey. — York :
Banks, 1978. — 5p ; 4to.
Pieces taken from the Wilhelm Friedemann Bach Clavierbuchlein.
Unpriced
(B78-50225)

Delius, Frederick
[Selections. *arr*]. Album of pianoforte solos / [by] Frederick
Delius. — London : Boosey and Hawkes, 1978. — 48p ; fol.
Also includes original piano solos.
Unpriced
(B78-51021)

Gomes, Antonio Carlos
[Il fucile ad ago. *arr*]. Il fucile ad ago : revista de 1866 / de A.
Scalvini ; transcrição para piano de Francisco Mignone. — Rio de
Janeiro : Arthur Napoleäo ; [London] : [Essex Music], 1968 [i.e.
1978]. — 3p ; 4to.
Unpriced
(B78-50549)

Gomes, Antonio Carlos
[Variaç ões. *arr*]. Variaç ês / música de Antonio Carlos Gomes ;
transcrição para piano de Francisco Mignone. — Rio de Janeiro :
Arthur Napoleäo ; [London] : [Essex Music], 1968 [i.e. 1978]. —
4p ; 4to.
Unpriced
(B78-50550)

Lorenzo-Fernandez, Oscar
[Noturno das folhas soltas. *arr*]. Noturno das folhas soltas / [de]
Lorenzo Fernandez ; transcrição para piano de Francisco
Mignone. — Rio de Janeiro : Arthur Napoleäo ; [London] :
[Essex Music], 1968 [i.e. 1978]. — [2]p ; 4to.
Unpriced
(B78-50551)

Mozart, Wolfgang Amadeus
[Ein musikalischen Spass. K.522. Presto. *arr*]. A musical joke :
theme from 'The horse of the year show' and other equestrian
events / [by] W.A. Mozart ; arranged by Stanley Jones. —
London : Fentone Music, 1978. — 4p ; 4to.
Unpriced
(B78-51022)

Villa-Lobos, Heitor
[Cantiga de roda. *arr*]. Cantiga de roda / de Heitor Villa-Lobos ;
transcrição para piano de Francisco Mignone. — Rio de Janeiro :
Arthur Napoleäo ; [London] : [Essex Music], 1968 [i.e. 1978]. —
[2]p ; 4to.
Unpriced
(B78-50552)

Villa-Lobos, Heitor
[Capricho, op.49. *arr*]. Capricho, Op.49 / [de] Heitor Villa-Lobos ;
transcrição para piano de Francisco Mignone. — Rio de Janeiro :
Arthur Napoleäo ; [London] : [Essex Music], 1968 [i.e. 1978]. —
4 ; 4to.
Unpriced
(B78-50553)

Villa-Lobos, Heitor
[As criancas. *arr*]. As criancas / de Heitor Villa-Lobos ;
transcrição para piano de Francisco Mignone. — Rio de Janeiro :
Arthur Napoleäo ; [London] : [Essex Music], 1968 [i.e. 1978]. —
[2]p ; 4to.
Unpriced
(B78-50554)

Villa-Lobos, Heitor
[Elegia. *arr*]. Elegia / de Heitor Villa-Lobos ; transcrição para
piano de Francisco Mignone. — Rio de Janeiro : Arthur
Napoleäo ; [London] : [Essex Music], 1968 [i.e. 1978]. — 5p ; 4to.
Unpriced
(B78-50555)

Villa-Lobos, Heitor
[Prelude, cello & piano, op.20, no.2, F minor. *arr*]. Prelúdio op.20,
no.2 em lá bemol / de Heitor Villa-Lobos ; transcrição para piano
de Francisco Mignone. — Rio de Janeiro : Arthur Napoleäo ;
[London] : [Essex Music], 1978. — 7p ; 4to.
Unpriced
(B78-50556)

Villa-Lobos, Heitor
[Sonhar. Op.14. *arr*]. Sonhar, Op.14 / de Heitor Villa-Lobos ;
transcrição para piano de Francisco Mignone. — Rio de Janeiro :
Arthur Napoleäo ; [London] : [Essex Music], 1978. — [2]p ; port ;
4to.
Unpriced
(B78-50557)

QPK/AAY — Arrangements. Collections
Chester's concert pieces / compiled and edited by Carol Barratt.
Vol.1. — London : Chester Music.
From Bach to blues for the younger pianist. — 1978. — [1],24p ; 4to.
Unpriced
(B78-51023)

QPK/AAYUR — Arrangements. Collections. Brazil
Centenário do choro : 20 choros para piano. — São Paulo :
Fermata do Brasil ; [London] : [Essex Music].
Mainly arranged by Hector Lagna Fietta.
Album no.1. — 1977. — 63p : ill ; 4to.
Unpriced
(B78-50558)

Centenário do choro : 20 choras para piano. — São Paulo :
Fermata do Brasil ; [London] : [Essex Music].
Mainly arranged by Hector Lagna Fietta.
Album no.2. — 1977. — 53p ; 4to.
Unpriced
(B78-50559)

QPK/AE/AY — Arrangements. Symphonies. Collections
Five greatest symphonies : for piano, two hands / compiled by
Robert Kail. — Carlstadt : Ashley ; [London] : [Phoenix], 1978.
— 160p ; 4to. — (World's favourite series ; no.96)
Includes symphonies by Schubert, Haydn, Mozart and Beethoven.
Unpriced
(B78-51024)

QPK/AH — Arrangements. Dances
Handel, George Frideric
[Alcina. *Selections : arr*]. Dances from 'Alcina' / [by] G.F.
Handel ; arranged by A. Craig Bell for piano solo. — York :
Banks, 1978. — 7p ; 4to.
Unpriced
(B78-51025)

QPK/AH/AYU — Arrangements. Dances. Latin America
Latin-Americana : a selection of famous melodies and rhythms for
piano / arranged by Frank Naylor. — London : Bosworth & Co.,
1978. — 19p ; 4to.
Unpriced
(B78-51026)

QPK/AHJN — Arrangements. Chaconnes
Bartók, Béla
[Sonata, violin. *Selections : arr*]. Tempo di ciaccona and fuga /
[by] Béla Bartók ; adapted for piano by György Sándor. —
London : Boosey and Hawkes, 1977. — 17p ; 4to.
Duration 12 1/2 min.
£3.00
(B78-50560)

QPK/AHVQT — Arrangements. Tambourins
Gossec, François Joseph
[Le camp de Grand-Pré. Tambourin. *arr*]. Tambourin / by
François Gossec ; piano solo, arranged by Thomas A. Johnson. —
London : Bosworth and Co., 1978. — 3p ; 4to.
Unpriced
(B78-51027)

QPK/AHXJ — Arrangements. Rag time
Joplin, Scott
[Maple leaf rag. *arr*]. Maple leaf rag / by Scott Joplin ; piano solo
arranged by Frank Naylor. — London : Bosworth and Co., 1978.
— 3p ; 4to.
Unpriced
(B78-51028)

QPK/DW/GB — Arrangements. Popular songs
McCartney, Paul
[Songs. *Selections : arr*]. The best of McCartney : for easy piano /
music arrangements by John Lane. — London : MPL
Communications ; Music Sales (Dist.), 1977. — 67p ; 4to.
Words and music mainly by Paul McCartney ; Denny Laine contributed to
two of the songs.
Unpriced
(B78-51029)

QPK/DW/GB/AY — Arrangements. Popular songs. Collections
Fun music : for piano / arranged by Bert Brewis. — London :
Chappell.
Vol.1. — 1976. — 23p ; 4to.
Unpriced
(B78-50226)

Vol.2. — 1976. — 27p ; 4to.
Unpriced
(B78-50227)

QPK/DW/GJ/AY — Children's songs. Collections. Arrangements
Children's songs and carols, including hymns and games : for easy
piano [or] organ / arranged by Jack Moore and Cecil Bolton. —
London : EMI, 1978. — 72p ; 4to.
Unpriced
(B78-51030)

QPK/DW/JR/AY — Arrangements. Film songs. Collections
Children's film favourites. — London : Chappell, 1978. — 32p ;
4to.
Arranged for piano. — All the songs from 'Hans Christian Andersen' by
Frank Loesser, 'Pinocchio', by Leigh Harline, and 'Snow White and the
seven dwarfs' by Frank Churchill.
Unpriced
(B78-51031)

QPK/DW/LF/AY — Arrangements. Christmas songs. Collections
The best of Christmas songs : piano [or] organ. — London : EMI,
1978. — 48p ; 4to.
Arranged for piano or organ by Cecil Bolton and Jack Moore.
Unpriced
Primary classification RK/DW/LF/AY

QPK/HM/AY — Arrangements. Ballet. Collections
Ballet / transcribed and simplified by Cyril C. Dalmaine. —
Manchester : Warren and Phillips, 1978. — 23p ; 4to.
Unpriced
(B78-51032)

QPK/JR — Films
Rota, Nino
[Death on the Nile. Love theme. *arr*]. Love theme from Death on
the Nile : piano solo / music composed by Nino Rota. — london :
EMI, 1978. — 4p ; 4to.
Unpriced
(B78-51033)

QPK/JS — Arrangements. Television
Bennett, Richard Rodney
[Eustace and Hilda. *arr*]. Eustace and Hilda : theme from the
award-winning BBV tv trilogy, for piano solo / [by] Richard
Rodney Bennett. — Sevenoaks : Novello, 1978. — 3p ; 4to.
Unpriced
(B78-51034)

Pearson, Johnny
[All creatures great and small. *arr*]. All creatures great and
small / by Johnny Pearson. — london : EMI, 1978. — 5p ; 4to.
Theme music of the television series for piano.
£0.50
(B78-51035)

Simpson, Dudley
[Blakes 7. *arr*]. Blakes 7 / [by] Dudley Simpson. — Ilford :
Chappell, 1978. — 4p ; 4to.
A piano transcription of theme music from a BBC TV series.
Unpriced
(B78-50228)

Webber, Andrew Lloyd
[Argentine melody. *arr*]. Argentine melody = Canción de
Argentina : official BBC tv World Cup theme / [by] Andrew
Lloyd Webber. — London : Chappell, 1978. — 4p ; 4to.
Unpriced
(B78-51036)

QRP — HARPSICHORD SOLOS
QRPE — Sonatas
Durante, Francesco
[Sei sonate divise in studii e divertimenti]. Sei sonate : (studii e
divertimenti), per cembalo / [von] Francesco Durante ;
herausgegeben von, edited by, Bernhard Paumgartner. — Kassel ;
London : Bärenreiter, 1978. — 36p ; 4to. — (Nagels
Musik-Archiv ; 241)
£4.80
(B78-51038)

QRPJ — Miscellaneous works
Maconchy, Elizabeth
Notebook for harpsichord / [by] Elizabeth Maconchy. —
London : Chester Music, 1977. — 16p ; 4to.
Unpriced
(B78-51039)

Zender, Hans
Chiffren : für Cembalo, (1976) / [von] Hans Zender. — Berlin :
Bote und Bock ; [London] : [Schirmer], 1978. — 4p ; fol.
£2.40
(B78-51040)

QRPK/AG — Arrangements. Suites
Telemann, Georg Phillip
[Overture, orchestra, E flat major. *arr*]. Overture in E flat / [by]
Georg Philipp Telemann ; from the Andreas-Bach-Buch ;
transcribed and edited by Igor Kipnis. — New York ; [London] :
Oxford University Press, 1978. — 23p ; 4to.
A contemporary arrangement for harpsichord of the orchestral work.
ISBN 0-19-385586-0 : Unpriced
(B78-51041)

58

THE BRITISH CATALOGUE OF MUSIC

R — ORGAN
R/AY — Collections
Anthologia organi : Orgelmusik aus acht Jahrhunderten / herausgegeben von Sándor Margittag. — Budapest : Edito Musica ; Mainz ; [London] : Schott.
Band 1 : Die Anfänge der Orgelmusik. — 1976. — 71p ; obl.4to.
£8.00

(B78-51042)

Band 2 : Die Niederlander und die Venezianische Schule. — 1976. — 58p ; obl.4to.
£8.00

(B78-51043)

Band 3 : Die Römische Schule und ihre Nachfolger. — 1976. — 55p ; obl.4to.
£8.00

(B78-51044)

R/LF/AY — Christmas. Collections
Classical Christmas music / compiled and edited for all organs by Richard Bradley. — Hialeah : Columbia Pictures ; [London] : [EMI], 1974. — 72p ; 4to.
Also contains a few arrangements from vocal works. — Title taken from cover.
Unpriced

(B78-51046)

RE — Sonatas
Jacob, Gordon
Fantasy sonata for organ / [by] Gordon Jacob. — London : Peters, 1978. — 21p ; obl.4to.
Unpriced

(B78-50561)

Pescetti, Giovanni Battista
[Sonata, organ, C minor]. Sonata in C minor for organ / [by] Giovanni Battista Pescetti ; edited by Peter Hurford. — London : Oxford University Press, 1977. — [1],7p ; 4to.
ISBN 0-19-375634-x : Unpriced

(B78-50229)

Wilson-Dickson, Andrew
[Sonata, organ, no.1]. Sonata no.1 for organ / [by] Andrew Wilson-Dickson. — York : Banks, 1978. — 15p ; 4to.
Unpriced

(B78-51047)

RG — Suites
Hurford, Peter
Bristol suite / [by] Peter Hurford. — Sevenoaks : Novello, 1977. — [3],12p ; obl. 4to. — (Novello modern organ repertory ; no.10)
Based on the hymn-tune 'Dickinson College' by Lee Hastings Bristol, Jr. — Duration 9 min.
£1.20

(B78-50562)

RJ — Miscellaneous works
Ferneyhough, Brian
Sieben Sterne : for organ / [by] Brian Ferneyhough. — London : Peters, 1978. — 11p ; obl. fol.
Unpriced

(B78-50230)

Inness, Peter
Six pieces : for organ / [by] Peter Inness. — Sevenoaks : Novello, 1978. — [2],30p ; 4to.
£2.40

(B78-51048)

Jenni, Donald
Musica dell'autumno : for organ / [by] D. Jenni. — New York ; London : Associated Music, 1977. — 1-20p ; obl. 4to.
£3.05

(B78-50563)

Kabeláč, Miloslav
[Fantasia, organ, op.32, no.1]. Fantasia, op.32, no.1, for organ / [by] Miloslav Kabeláč. — Praha : Supraphon ; New York ; London : Schirmer, 1976. — 14p ; 4to.
£2.10

(B78-50564)

Kelly, Bryan
Pastorale and paean / [by] Bryan Kelly. — Sevenoaks : Novello, 1977. — [3],16p ; obl. 4to. — (Novello modern organ repertory ; no.9)
Duration 11 min.
£1.45

(B78-50565)

Krol, Bernhard
Juba-mirum-Fantasia nach W.A. Mozart, K.V.626 : für Orgel, op.65 / [von] Bernhard Krol. — Berlin : Bote und Bock ; [London] : [Schirmer], 1977. — 32p ; obl.fol.
Duration 24 min.
£7.70

(B78-51049)

Krol, Bernhard
Orgelbüchlein für Vincenz : 10 festliche kleine Präludien, op.66 / [von] Bernhard Krol ; mit einem Vorwort von Gaston Litaize. — Berlin : Bote und Bock ; [London] : [Schirmer], 1977. — 16p ; obl.fol.
£3.85

(B78-51050)

MacDonald, Peter
Two plainsong preludes = Deux preludes de plain-chant = Zwei Choralmusik Vorspiele : for organ / [by] Peter MacDonald. — Holt (64 Pineheath Rd., High Kelling, Holt, Nflk.) : St Gregory, 1977. — [9]p ; 4to.
£1.25

(B78-50566)

Mathias, William
Fantasy for organ, Op.78 / [by] William Mathias. — London : Oxford University Press, 1978. — 24p ; fol.
Duration 10 min.
ISBN 0-19-375552-1 : Unpriced

(B78-51051)

Nieman, Alfred
Arie fantasie : for organ / [by] Alfred Nieman. — Sevenoaks : Novello, 1977. — 17p ; 4to.
£1.20

(B78-50567)

Reger, Max
Dreissig kleine Choral-vorspiele zu den gebrauchlichsten Choralen, für Orgel, Opus 135A / [von] Max Reger. — London : Peters, [1978]. — 27p ; obl.4to.
Contents listed alphabetically in German and English.
Unpriced

(B78-51052)

Thomson, Virgil
Prelude for organ / [by] Virgil Thomson. — New York ; London : Schirmer, 1977. — 7p ; 4to.
£1.50

(B78-50568)

Williamson, Malcolm
Vision of Christ-phoenix : for organ / [by] Malcolm Williamson. — Revised version. — London : Boosey and Hawkes, 1978. — iii, 20p ; obl.fol.
Duration 10 1/2 min.
Unpriced

(B78-51053)

Wills, Arthur
Scherzetto / [by] Arthur Wills. — London : Cramer, 1977. — [1], 8p ; obl. 4to.
For organ.
Unpriced

(B78-50231)

Yun, Isang
Fragment für Orgel, 1975 / [von] Isang Yun. — Berlin : Bote und Bock ; [London] : [Associated Music], 1977. — 7p ; obl. 4to.
£2.40

(B78-50569)

RK — Arrangements
Charpentier, Marc Antoine
[Te Deum, D major. Prelude. arr]. Trumpet tune / [by] Marc-Antoine Charpentier ; arranged by Bryan Hesford. — London : J.B. Cramer, 1978. — 4p ; 4to. — (St Martin's organ series ; no.21)
On page 1: 'St Martin's series, no.19'.
£0.45

(B78-51054)

Elgar, Sir Edward, bart
[Selections. arr]. Elgar organ album. — Sevenoaks : Novello.
Contents: 1: Cantique - 2: Adagio from the violoncello concerto - 3: Carillon - 4: Solemn prelude 'In memoriam' from 'For the fallen' - 5: Imperial march.
Book 1. — 1977. — [3],31p ; 4to.
£1.50

(B78-50232)

RK/AAY — Arrangements. Collections
Das klingende Orgelbuch : Bekanntes und Beliebtes aus Klassik Volks- und Unterhaltungsmusik, für elektronische Orgel (alle Modelle) / ausgewählt und bearbeitet von Willi Draths ; Ausgabe mit Akkordsymbolen, Fingersätzen, Registrieranweisungen, Registrierschema. — Mainz ; London : Schott.
Band 2. — 1977. — 100p ; 4to.
£7.20

(B78-50233)

Music for memorial and thanksgiving services for manuals / edited and arranged by C.H. Trevor. — Sevenoaks : Elkin, 1977. — [13], 20p ; 4to.
£1.30

(B78-51055)

World's favorite popular classics for organ and other favorites / arranged by Lawrence Grant. — Carlstadt : Ashley ; [London] : [Phoenix]. — (World's favorite series ; no.100)
Vol.1. — 1977. — 128p ; 4to.
Unpriced

(B78-50234)

World's favorite popular classics for organ and other favorites. — Carlstadt : Ashley ; [London] : [Phoenix]. — (World's favorite series ; no.101)
Vol.2 ; arranged by Lawrence Grant. — 1977. — 128p ; 4to.
Unpriced

(B78-50235)

RK/AAY — Collections
Bach, Johann Sebastian
[Selections. arr]. Transcriptions for organ / [by] Bach ; arranged by Bryan Hesford. — London : Cramer, 1978. — 39p ; obl.4to.
Unpriced

(B78-50570)

RK/DP/LF — Arrangements. Carols. Christmas
Gruber, Franz
[Stille Nacht, heilige Nacht. arr]. Silent night : all organ / by F. Gruber. — London : Chappell, 1977. — 3p ; 4to.
Arranged for organ.
Unpriced

(B78-50236)

RK/DR — Arrangements. Psalms
Marcello, Benedetto
[Estro poetico-armonico.　Salmo 18. arr]. 'The heavens devlare the glory of God' / [by] Benedetto Marcello ... ; arranged by Bryan Hesford. — London : Cramer, 1978. — 4p ; 4to. — (St Martin's organ series ; no.20)
'St Martin's organ series : no.18' printed at the top of page.
Unpriced

(B78-51056)

RK/DW/GB/AY — Arrangements. Popular songs. Collections
Fun music : for all organ / arranged by Bert Brewis. — London : Chappell.
Vol.1. — 1976. — 26p ; 4to.
Unpriced

(B78-50237)

Vol.2. — 1976. — 24p ; 4to.
Unpriced

(B78-50238)

RK/DW/LF/AY — Arrangements. Christmas songs. Collections
The best of Christmas songs : piano [or] organ. — London : EMI, 1978. — 48p ; 4to.
Arranged for piano or organ by Cecil Bolton and Jack Moore.
Unpriced
Also classified at QPK/DW/LF/AY

(B78-51057)

RPV — ELECTRIC ORGANS
RPV/AC — Electronic organ. Tutors
Delrieu, Jean Philippe
A vous de jouer : cours d'initiation rapide et progressive à l'orgue electronique / [par] Jean-Philippe Delrieu. — Paris ; [London] : Chappell.
Vol.1. — 1977. — 77p ; 4to. —
Unpriced

(B78-50571)

Draths, Willi
Orgelschule zum Selbstunterricht / [von] Willi Draths ; akkordprogrammierte Orgel. — Mainz ; London : Schott, 1977. — 47p ; obl. 8vo.
£4.00

(B78-50239)

RPVCK — Chord organ. Arrangements
Classic melodies / [arranged] by Cecil Bolton and Jack Moore. — London : EMI, 1978. — 48p ; 4to.
Unpriced

(B78-51058)

RPVCK/DW/GB/AY — Chord organ. Arrangements. Popular songs. Collections
Fun music : for chord organ / arranged by Bert Brewis. — London : Chappell.
Vol.1. — 1976. — 20p ; 4to.
Unpriced

(B78-50240)

Vol.2. — 1976. — 19p ; 4to.
Unpriced

(B78-50241)

RPVCK/DW/LF/AY — Arrangements. Christmas songs. Collections
The best of Christmas songs : chord organ. — London : EMI, 1978. — [1],37p ; 4to.
Arranged for chord organs by Cecil Bolton and Jack Moore.
Unpriced

(B78-51059)

RPVK/AAY — Arrangements. Collections
Fun organ : arrangements featuring automatic rhythm and accompaniment for all electronic and 'C' chord organs. — London : EMI.
Folio no.2 ; arranged by Jack Moore. — 1978. — 40p ; 4to. —
Unpriced

(B78-51060)

RPVK/DW — Arrangements. Songs, etc
Lehár, Franz
[Songs. Selections : arr]. Twelve melodies for organ : twelve favourite Lehár melodies / arranged for Hammond and all Tab organs by Bryan Rodwell. — London : Glocken Verlag, 1978. — 35p ; 4to.
Unpriced

(B78-51061)

More songs for chord organ / arranged by Dudley Bayford. — London : EMI Music, 1977. — 37p ; 4to.
Unpriced

(B78-50242)

RPVK/DW/G/AYE — Arrangements. Folk songs. Collections. Germany
Volkslieder in leichten Sätzen : elektronische Orgel / Arrangements mit Akkordbezifferung, Jürgen Sommer. — Kassel : Nagel ; [London] : [Bärenreiter], 1977. — 32p ; 4to.
£3.36

(B78-50572)

RPVK/DW/GB — Arrangements. Popular songs
Berlin, Irving
[Songs. Selections : arr]. 90 golden years of Irving Berlin / arranged by Bert Brewis, all organ. — London : Chappell, 1978. — 112p ; 4to.
Songs arranged for organ.
Unpriced

(B78-51062)

RPVK/DW/GB/AY — Arrangements. Popular songs. Collections
At home with Robin Richmond : twelve arrangements of favourite melodies for the home organ / [arranged by] Robin Richmond. — Sevenoaks : Paxton, 1978. — 47p ; 4to.
£1.80

(B78-51063)

Golden Latin : all organ / arranged by Bert Brewis. — London : Chappell, 1978. — 64p ; 4to.
Songs arranged.
Unpriced

(B78-51064)

RPVK/DW/GJ/AYE — Arrangements. Children's songs. Collections. Germany
Kinderlieder in leichten Sätzen : elektronische Orgel (1 Manual) / Arrangemsnts mit Akkordbezifferung, Jürgen Sommer. — Kassel : Nagel ; [London] : [Bärenreiter], 1977. — 32p ; 4to.
£3.36

(B78-50573)

RS — ACCORDION
RS/AC — Tutors
Abbott, Alain
Initiation a l'accordeon de concert = Initiation to the concert accordion = Einführung zum Konzertakkordeon / [par] Alain Abbott. — Paris ; [London] : Chappell, 1978. — 79p ; 4to.
Unpriced

(B78-50574)

RXM — STRING ORCHESTRA
RXM/AY — Collections
String music of the second Elizabeth : twelve original pieces for string orchestra / by Joseph Horovitz, Ernest Tomlinson, Malcolm Williamson, John Whitfield. — London : Belwin-Mills, 1977. — [1],33p ; 4to.
Condensed score.
Unpriced

(B78-50243)

RXM/JM — Incidental music
Locke, Matthew
[The tempest. Incidental music]. Incidental music [for] The
tempest : for strings and continuo / [by] Matthew Locke ; edited
by Peter Dennison. — London : Oxford University Press, 1977. —
[2],21p ; 4to. — (Musica da camera ; 41)
ISBN 0-19-365350-8 : Unpriced

(B78-50244)

RXME — Sonatas
Brown, Christopher
[Sonata, string orchestra, op.42]. Sonata for string orchestra,
op.42 / [by] Christopher Brown. — London : Chester Music,
1978. — [2],64p ; 4to.
Duration 20 min.
Unpriced

(B78-51065)

McCabe, John
Sonata on a motet / [by] John McCabe. — Sevenoaks : Novello,
1977. — [4],35p ; 8vo.
Duration 19 min. — Derived from Tallis's 40-part motet 'Spem in alium' -
For string orchestra.
£2.10

(B78-50575)

RXMF — Concertos
Humphries, John
[Concerto, string orchestra, op.3, no.10, D minor]. Concerto in D
minor, opus 3, no.10, for strings and continuo / [by] John
Humphries ; edited by Richard Platt. — London : Oxford
University Press, 1977. — [1],13p ; 4to. — (Musica da camera ;
36)
ISBN 0-19-364804-0 : Unpriced

(B78-50245)

RXMJ — Miscellaneous works
Baber, Joseph
Divertimento for string orchestra, Op.32, no.4 / [by] Joseph
Baber. — New York ; [London] : Oxford University Press, 1978.
— 12p ; 4to.
Duration 8 1/2 min.
Unpriced

(B78-50246)

Genzmer, Harald
Miniaturen : für Streicher / [von] Harald Genzmer. — Frankfurt :
Litolff ; London : Peters, 1976. — 26p ; 4to.
Unpriced

(B78-50576)

harbison, John
Incidental music for Shakespeare's 'The merchant of Venice' : for
string orchestra (or string quintet) / [by] John Harbison. — New
York ; London : Associated Music, 1977. — 27p ; 4to.
Duration 12 min.
Unpriced

(B78-51066)

Ives, Charles
[3 quarter-tone pieces. Quarter-tone chorale. arr]. Quarter-tone
chorale / [by] Charles Ives ; reconstructed for strings by Alan
Stout. — New York ; London : Peters, 1974. — [2],15p ; 4to.
A reconstruction of the original score for string orchestra.
Unpriced

(B78-51067)

Sculthorpe, Peter
Lament : for strings / [by] Peter Sculthorpe. — London : Faber
Music, 1978. — [2],10p ; 4to.
Duration 10 min.
Unpriced

(B78-51068)

Wade, Darrell
'11 minutes' : for the junior string orchestra / [by] Darrell Wade.
— Gnosall (16 Anchor Way, Danes Green) : Viking, 1978. —
16p ; 4to.
Unpriced

(B78-51069)

Wade, Darrell
'11 minutes' : for the junior string orchestra / [by] Darrell Wade.
— Gnosall (16 Anchor Way, Danes Green) : Viking, 1978. —
4pt ; 4to.
Unpriced

(B78-51070)

RXMK/AHW — Arrangements. Waltzes
Henze, Hans Werner
Amicizia! : Quintett für Klarinette in A, Posaune, Violoncello,
Schlagzeug und Klavier (1976) / [von] Hans Werner Henze. —
Mainz ; London : Schott, 1978. — 14p ; 4to. — (Concertino ;
183)
Score (31p.) & 5 parts.
£4.65

(B78-50247)

Schubert, Franz
[Valses nobles, D.969. Selections: arr]. Valses nobles, opus 77 /
[von] Franz Schubert ; für Streichorchester gesetzt von Wolfgang
Fortner. — Mainz ; London : Schott, 1978. — 14p ; 4to. —
(Concertino ; 183)
£4.65

(B78-50248)

RXMP — SOLO INSTRUMENT (S) & STRING ORCHESTRA
RXMPS — Violin & string orchestra
Conyngham, Barry
Ice carving / [by] Barry Conyngham. — [Sydney] ; [London] :
Universal, 1977. — [4],27p ; 4to.
For solo violin and four string orchestras.
Unpriced

(B78-51071)

RXMPSNUF — Violins (2) & string orchestra. Concertos
Telemann, Georg Philipp
[Concerto, violins (2) & string orchestra, G minor]. Concerto für
zwei Violinen, Streicher und Basso continuo G moll / [von]
George Philipp Telemann ; Generalbassaussetzung vom
Herausgeber. — Zum ersten Mal herausgegeben von Felix
Schroeder. — Frankfurt : Litolff ; London : Peters, 1977. — 22p ;
4to. — (Sinfonietta)
Unpriced

(B78-50577)

RXMPSQQF — Viola d'amore & string orchestra. Concertos
Vivaldi, Antonio
[Concerto, viola d'amore, Ryom 540, D minor]. Concerto con
viola d'amor [sic], e leuto [sic] e con tutti gl Isromti sordini / [di]
Antonio Vivaldi ; edited by Ian White. — Chipperfield (Little
Margaret, Penmans Green, Chipperfield) : Ian White, 1978. —
14p ; fol.
Unpriced

(B78-50578)

RXMPTSPLTXF — Guitar, mandolin & string orchestra. Concertos
Newton, Rodney Stephen
Concerto da camera no.1 for guitar, mandolin and strings / [by]
Rodney Stephen Newton. — East Barnet (13 Chetwynd Ave., East
Barnet, Herts.) : Composer Edition, 1977. — 18p ; fol.
Facsimile of the composer's autograph.
Unpriced

(B78-50249)

RXMPVNS/W — Woodwind quartet & string orchestra
Kodály, Zoltán
[Old Hungarian soldier songs]. Magyar rondo = Hungarian
rondo : vonószenekarra, két klarinéta és két fagottra = for string
orchestra, two clarinets and two bassoons / [zenéjét szerezte]
Kodály Zoltán. — Budapest : Editio musica ; [London] : [Boosey
and Hawkes], 1978. — 24p ; 8vo.
Unpriced

(B78-51072)

RXMPVR — Flute & string orchestra
Weinzweig, John
Divertimento 1 for flute and string orchestra / [by] John
Weinzweig. — London : Boosey and Hawkes, [1978]. — [2],29p ;
8vo. — (Hawkes pocket scores ; 913)
Miniature score.
Unpriced

(B78-51073)

RXMPVRF — Flute & string orchestra. Concertos
Newton, Rodney Stephen
Concerto da camera no.2 for flute and string orchestra / [by]
Rodney Stephen Newton. — East Barnet : Composer Edition,
1977. — 10p ; fol.
Facsimile of the composer's autograph.
Unpriced

(B78-50250)

RXMPVT — Oboe & string orchestra
Weinzweig, John
[Divertimento, oboe & string orchestra, no.2]. Divertimento 2 for
oboe and string orchestra / [by] John Weinzweig. — London :
Boosey and Hawkes, 1978. — [2],26p ; 8vo. — (Hawkes pocket
scores ; 914)
Duration 13 1/2 min. — Miniature score.
Unpriced

(B78-51074)

RXMPWSE — Trumpet & string orchestra. Symphonies
Torelli, Giuseppe
[Sinfonia, trumpet & string orchestra, G.9, D major]. Concerto
D-Dur per tromba con archi e continuo / [von] Giuseppe Torelli ;
herausgegeben von Heinz Zickler. — Mainz ; London : Schott,
1977. — 16p ; 4to. — (Concertino ; 156)
£4.00

(B78-50251)

RXMPWSF — Trumpet & string orchestra. Concertos
Humphries, John
[Concerto, trumpet & string orchestra, op.2, no.12, D major].
Concerto in D major, for trumpet (or horn), strings and
continuo / [by] John Humphries ; edited by Richard Platt. —
London : Oxford University Press, 1978. — 4to. — (Musica da
camera ; no.35)
Score ([2],18p.) & part.
ISBN 0-19-364797-4 : Unpriced

(B78-51075)

RXMPWSNUE — Trumpets (2) & string orchestra. Sonatas
Lazari, Ferdinando Antonio
[Sonata, trumpets (2) & string orchestra, D major]. Sonata à 6 for
trumpets, strings and continuo / [by] Ferd. Anto. Lazzari ; [edited
by] R.P. Block ; trumpet and piano reduction. — London :
Musica rara, 1978. — 4to. — (Italian 17th and 18th century
sinfonias and sonatas for trumpets and strings ; no.33)
Score (1-20p.) & 9 parts.
Unpriced

(B78-50579)

RXMPXF — Percussion & string orchestra. Concertos
Benker, Heinz
Mobile concertante : für Schlagwerk und Streicher / [von] Heinz
Benker. — Mainz ; London : Schott, 1977. — 44p ; 4to. —
(Concertino ; 181)
£14.00

(B78-50252)

RXNR — Quintets
Mozart, Wolfgang Amadeus
[Quintets, strings. *Collections*]. Complete string quartets with the
horn and clarinet quintets ... / [by] Wolfgang Amadeus Mozart.
— New York : Dover Publications ; [London] : [Constable], 1978.
— [7],181p ; 4to.
From series 13 of the Breitkopf und Härtel complete edition of 1883 ; omits
the 'Eine kleine Nachtmusik' published in that volume.
ISBN 0-486-23603-x : Unpriced

(B78-51076)

RXNS — Quartets
Alwyn, William
[Quartet, strings, no.2, 'Spring waters']. String quartet no.2 (Spring
waters) / [by] William Alwyn. — South Croydon : Lengnick,
1978. — [2],41p ; 8vo.
£1.50

(B78-51077)

Britten, Benjamin, *Baron Britten*
[Quartet, strings, no.3, op.94]. String quartet no.3, op.94 / [by]
Benjamin Britten. — London : Faber Music, 1977. — 8vo.
Score (37p.) & 4 parts.
Unpriced

(B78-50253)

Britten, Benjamin, *Baron Britten*
[Quartet, strings, no.3, op.94]. String quartet no.3, op.94 / [by]
Benjamin Britten. — London : Faber Music, 1978. — 4pt ; 4to.
Unpriced

(B78-50580)

Crosse, Gordon
Studies for string quartet. Op.34 / [by] Gordon Crosse. —
london : Oxford University Press.
Facsimile of the composer's autograph.
Set 2 : Fantasia, Aria (2) and Toccata. — 1978. — 17p ; obl.8vo.
ISBN 0-19-355974-9 : Unpriced

(B78-51078)

Einem, Gottfried von
[Quartet, strings, no.1, op.45]. Erstes Streichquartett, opus 45 /
[von] Gottfried von Einem. — London : Boosey and Hawkes,
1978. — 4pt ; 4to.
Unpriced

(B78-51079)

Einem, Gottfried von
[Quartet, strings, no.1, op.45]. Erstes Streichquartett, opus 45 /
[von] Gottfried von Einem. — London : Boosey and Hawkes,
1978. — [3],31p ; 8vo. — (Hawkes pocket scores ; 941)
Miniature score.
Unpriced

(B78-51080)

Henze, Hans Werner
[Quartet, strings, no.4]. 4. Streichquartett = 4th string quartet
(1976) / [von] Hans Werner Henze. — Mainz ; London : Schott,
1976. — 75p ; 8vo.
The last movement is printed in parts . The pagination is continuous.
£12.00

(B78-51081)

Henze, Hans Werner
[Quartet, strings, no.3]. 3. Streichquartett = 3rd string quartet /
[von] Hans Werner Henze. — Mainz ; London : Schott, 1976. —
8vo.
Study score - Score (43p.) & 4 parts.
£10.00

(B78-50581)

Henze, Hans Werner
[Quartet, strings, no.3]. 3. Streichquartett (1976) / [von] Hans
Werner Henze. — Mainz ; London : Schott, 1976. — 4pt ; 4to.
£12.80

(B78-50582)

Henze, Hans Werner
[Quartet, strings, no.5]. 5. Streichquartett (1976-77) / [von] Hans
Werner Henze. — Mainz ; London : Schott, 1977. — 64p ; 8vo.
Study score.
£12.00

(B78-50254)

Killmayer, Wilhelm
[Quartet, strings]. Quartett für Violinen, Viola abd Violoncello /
[von] Wilhelm Killmayer. — Mainz ; London : Schott, 1978. —
8p ; 4to.
£4.00

(B78-51082)

Sculthorpe, Peter
[Quartet, strings, no.8]. String quartet, no.8 / [by] Peter
Sculthorpe. — 2nd ed. — London : Faber Music, 1978. — [4],
19p ; 8vo.
£2.00

(B78-50255)

Sculthorpe, Peter
[Quartet, strings, no.9]. String quartet no.9 / [by] Peter
Sculthorpe. — London : Faber Music, 1978. — [3],15p ; 8vo.
£2.00

(B78-51083)

Sculthorpe, Peter
[Quartet, strings, no.9]. String quartet no.9 / [by] Peter
Sculthorpe. — London : Faber Music, 1978. — 4pt ; 4to.
£6.00

(B78-51084)

Stranz, Ulrich
[Quartet, strings, no.1]. 1. Streichquartett in vier Sätzen, 1976,
[von] Ulrich Stranz. — Kassel ; London : Bärenreiter, 1976. —
25p ; fol.
£7.00

(B78-50583)

Wood, Hugh
[Quartet, strings, no.2]. String quartet no.2 / [by] Hugh Wood. —
London : Chester Music, 1978. — 39p ; obl.8vo.
Unpriced

(B78-51085)

RXNT — Trios
Kodály, Zoltán
[Intermezzo, string trio]. Intermezzo per trio d'archi / [di] Zoltán
Kodály. — Budapest : Editio musica ; [London] : [Boosey and
Hawkes], 1976. — 4to.
Score (8p.) & 3 parts.
Unpriced

(B78-51086)

S — VIOLIN
S/AC — Tutors
Edwards, Aneurin J
Y ffidil = The violin : y camau cyntaf = the first steps / [gan]
Aneurin J. Edwards. — Abertawe = Swansea (4-5, Thomas Row,
Swansea) : Christopher Davies, 1976. — 52p ; 4to.
ISBN 0-7154-0299-4 : £1.25

(B78-51088)

S/AF — Exercises
Mazas, Jacques Féréol
[Études melodiques et progressives. Op.36]. Études speciales. Opus
36 : neu herausgegeben und bezeichnet von Walther Davisson. —
Neurevidierte Ausgabe. — Frankfurt ; London : Peters.
Hft.1. — [1978]. — 44p ; 4to.
Unpriced

(B78-51089)

Wade, Darrell
Twenty elementary studies for the young violinist / by Darrell
Wade. — Gnosall (16 Anchor Way, Danes Green, Gnosall) :
Viking, 1977. — 4p ; 4to.
Unpriced

(B78-50256)

Zukofsky, Paul
All-interval scale book, including a chart of harmonics for the
violin / [by] Paul Zukofsky. — New York ; London : Schirmer,
1977. — iv,47p ; 4to.
£3.65

(B78-50584)

S/AL — Examinations
Associated Board of the Royal Schools of Music
Violin examinations, 1979 and 1980. — London : Associated
Board of the Royal Schools of Music.
Score (13p.) & part.
Grade 1 : Lists A & B. — 1978. — 4to.
£1.00

(B78-51090)

Grade 2 : Lists A & B. — 1978. — 4to.
£1.00

(B78-51091)

Grade 3 : Lists A & B. — 1978. — 4to.
£1.00

(B78-51092)

Grade 4 : Lists A & B. — 1978. — 4to.
£1.00

(B78-51093)

Grade 5 : Lists A & B. — 1978. — 4to.
£1.00

(B78-51094)

Grade 6 : Lists A & B. — 1978. — 4to.
£1.00

(B78-51095)

Grade 7 : Lists A & B. — 1978. — 4to.
£1.00

(B78-51096)

SN — VIOLIN ENSEMBLE
SN/AC — Ensembles. Tutors
Wade, Darrell
Stringing along : a tutor for the second year school's violin class /
by Darrell Wade. — Gnosall (16 Anchor Way, Danes Green,
Gnosall, Staffs.) : Viking Publications, 1977. — 37p ; 4to.
Unpriced

(B78-50585)

SNTPWE — Violins (2) & keyboard. Sonatas
Leclair, Jean Marie
[Sonata, violins (2) & continuo, A major]. Sonata Opus 4 Nr.6
A-Dur für zwei Violinen und Basso continuo, A major for two
violins and basso continuo, La majeur pour deux Violons et basse
continue / [von] Jean Marie Leclair ; [herausgegeben von] Anne
Majewski. — Locarno : Ediziori Pegasus ; London : Peters, 1978.
— 4to.
Score (31p.) & 3 parts.
Unpriced

(B78-50586)

SNTQK/LF — Violins (2) & piano. Arrangements. Concertos
Telemann, Georg Philipp
[Concerto, violins (2) & string orchestra, G minor. arr]. Concerto
für zwei Violinen, Streicher, und Basso continuo G-moll / [von]
Georg Philipp Telemann. — Ausgabe für zwei Violinen und
Klavier von Herausgeber. Zum ersten Mal herausgegeben von
Felix Schroeder. — Frankfurt : Litolff ; London : Peters, 1977. —
4to.
Score (18p.) & 2 parts.
Unpriced

(B78-50587)

SP — VIOLIN & PIANO
SPE — Sonatas
Beyer, Frank Michael
[Sonata, violin & piano, (1977)]. Sonate für Violine und Klavier
(1977) / [von] Frank Michael Beyer. — Berlin : Bote und Bock ;
[London] : [Schirmer], 1978. — fol.
Score (16p.) & parts.
£7.70

(B78-51097)

Hoddinott, Alan
[Sonata, violin & piano, no.4]. Sonata no.4 for violin and piano /
[by] Alan Hoddinott. — london : Oxford University Press, 1978.
— 4to.
Score (32p.) & part.
ISBN 0-19-357166-8 : Unpriced

(B78-51098)

Newton, Rodney Stephen
[Sonata, violin & piano]. Sonata for violin and piano / [by]
Rodney Stephen Newton. — East Barnet (13 Chetwynd Ave., East
Barnet, Herts.) : Composer Edition, 1978. — 11p ; fol.
Facsimile of the composer's autograph.
Unpriced

(B78-50257)

Stanley, John
Six solos, Op.4 : for flute or violin and continuo / [by] John
Stanley ; edited and realised by George Pratt. — London : Chester
Music, 1975. — 4to.
Score ([4],44p.) & 2 parts.
Unpriced
Primary classification VRPE

SPEM — Sonatinas
Weiner, Stanley
[Sonatina, violin & piano, op.69]. Sonatina for violin and piano,
op.69 / [by] Stanley Weiner. — Berlin : Bote und Bock ;
[London] : [Associated Music], 1977. — 4to.
Score ([1],26p.) & part.
£7.70

(B78-50588)

SPH — Dances
Nieman, Alfred
Mountain dance : for violin and piano / [by] Alfred Nieman. —
Wendover : Roberton, 1978. — 4to.
Score (10p.) & part.
£0.60

(B78-50258)

SPHM — Gavottes
Nieman, Alfred
Gavotte for a Latin lady : for violin and piano / [by] Alfred
Nieman. — Wendover : Roberton, 1978. — 4to.
Score (6p.) & part.
£0.50

(B78-50259)

SPJ — Miscellaneous works
Britten, Benjamin, *Baron Britten of Aldeburgh*
[Suite, violin & piano, op.6. *Selections*]. Three pieces for violin and
piano from the suite, op.6 / [by] Benjamin Britten. — London :
Boosey and Hawkes, 1977. — 4to.
Score ([1],20p.) & part.
Unpriced

(B78-50260)

Crumb, George
Four nocturnes. (Night Music II) : violin and piano / [by] George
Crumb. — New York ; London : Peters, [1978]. — 11p ; obl.fol.
Facsimile printing from the manuscript by the composer. — Duration 9
min.
Unpriced

(B78-51099)

Dvořák, Antonín
[Romantic pieces. Op.75]. Four romantic pieces : for violin and
piano / [by] Antonín Dvořák ; violin part edited by Rok Klopčič.
— New York ; London : Schirmer, 1977. — 4to. — (Schirmer's
library of musical classics ; vol.1913)
£2.10

(B78-50589)

Lombardi, Luca
Elegy for violin and piano / [by] Luca Lombardi. — New York ;
London : Schirmer, 1977. — 4to.
Score ([1],11p.) & part.
£2.40

(B78-51100)

SPK/LFL — Arrangements. Concertinos
Léhar, Franz
[Concertino, violin, B minor. arr]. Concertino for violin and
orchestra, für Violine und Orchester / [by] Franz Léhar ;
reduction for violin and piano. — London : Glocken Verlag, 1978.
— 4to.
Score ([2],23p.) & part - Duration 14 min.
Unpriced

(B78-50590)

SPLSS — VIOLIN & DOUBLE BASS
SPLSSEM — Sonatinas
Vogt, Hans
[Sonata, violin & double bass, (1976)]. Sonatina per violino &
contrabasso (1976) / [von] Hans Vogt. — Berlin : Bote und
Bock ; Loindon : Yorke, 1978. — 15p ; fol.
Unpriced

(B78-51101)

SPLTS — VIOLIN & GUITAR
Brindle, Reginald Smith
Five sketches : for guitar and violin / [by] Reginald Smith
Brindle. — London : Schott, 1978. — 15p ; 4to.
£0.70

(B78-51102)

SPM — UNACCOMPANIED VIOLIN
SPM/T — Variations
Mignone, Francisco
Variaç ões para violão sobro o tema 'Luar do sertão' de Catullo
da Paixão Cearense / de Francisco Mignone. — Rio de Janeiro :
Arthur Napoleão ; [London] : [Essex Music], 1978. — 4p ; 4to.
Unpriced

(B78-50591)

Yun, Isang
Königliches Thema : für Violine solo, 1976 / [von] Isang Yun. —
Berlin : Bote und Bock ; [London] : [Associated Music], 1977. —
5p ; 4to.
Variation on the theme of Bach's 'Musikalische Opfer'.
£2.40

(B78-50592)

SPME — Sonatas
Einem, Gottfried von
[Sonata, violin, op.47]. Sonata für Solo-Violine, Opus 47 / [von]
Gottfried von Einem ; bezeichnet von Christiane Edinger. —
Berlin : Bote und Bock ; [London] : [Schirmer], 1977. — 19p ; fol.
Duration 21 min.
£5.75

(B78-51103)

Jones, Kenneth
Sonata for solo violin / [by] Kenneth Jones. — London : Chester
Music, 1978. — 7p ; 8vo.
Unpriced

(B78-51104)

SPMHW — Waltzes
Mignone, Francisco
Valsa de esquina : para violão / de Francisco Mignone. — Rio de
Janeiro : Arthur Napoleão ; [London] : [Essex Music], 1976 [i.e.
1978]. — 3p ; 4to.
Unpriced

(B78-50593)

SPMJ — Miscellaneous works
Dagg, Archie
The Congnetdale garland : a collection of tunes for fiddle and
small-pipes / composed by Archie Dagg. — Morpeth (Swinden,
Sharperton, Morpeth) : Archie Dagg, 1978. — [18]p ; 8vo.
Unpriced
Also classified at VYSPMJ

(B78-51105)

Dale, Gordon
Twelve tunes for violin : for groups of mixed ability / [by]
Gordon Dale. — London : EMI Music, 1978. — 8p ; 4to.
Unpriced

(B78-51106)

Vishnick, Martin
Four pieces for solo violin / [by] Martin Vishnick. — London :
Edwin Ashdown, 1978. — [4]p ; 4to.
Unpriced

(B78-51107)

SPMK — Arrangements
Cearense, Catallo da Paixão
[Luar do sertão. arr]. Luar do sertão / de Catallo da Paixão
Cearense ; transcrição para violão solo (guitar solo) de Isais Sávio.
— Rio de Janeiro : Arthur Napoleão ; [London] : [Essex Music],
1968 [i.e. 1978]. — [2]p ; 4to.
Unpriced
Also classified at TSPMK

(B78-50594)

SQN — VIOLA ENSEMBLE
SQNUK — Duets. Arrangements
Rubbra, Edmund
[Meditations on a Byzantine hymn. Op.117a. arr]. Meditations on
a Byzantine hymn 'O quando in croce', op.117a / [by] Edmund
Rubbra ; arranged for two violas by the composer. — South
Croydon : Lengnick, 1978. — 12p ; 4to.
Unpriced

(B78-51108)

SQP — VIOLA & PIANO
SQPGM/X — Marches. Canons
Anderson, Muriel Bradford
Prelude and march in canon : for viola and piano / [by] M.
Bradford Anderson. — London : Boosey and Hawkes, 1977. —
4to.
Score (8p.) & part.
Unpriced

(B78-50261)

SQPK/LF — Arrangements. Concertos
Jacob, Gordon
[Concerto, viola, new version. arr]. Concerto for viola and
orchestra : für viola und Orchester / [by] Gordon Jacob ; viola
and piano [reduction]. — London ; Hamburg : Simrock, 1978. —
4to.
Duration 16 min.
Unpriced

(B78-50595)

Reicha, Joseph
[Concerto, viola, op.2, no.1, E flat major. arr]. Konzert Es-dur für
Viola und Orchester = Concerto E-flat major for viola and
orchestra / [von] Joseph Reicha ; herausgegeben und bearbeitet
von Michael Goldstein, Klavierauszug und Solostimme. —
Hamburg ; London : Simrock, 1978. — 4to.
Score (44p.) & part.
£5.50

(B78-50596)

SQPM — UNACCOMPANIED VIOLA
SQPMEM — Sonatinas
Weiner, Stanley
[Sonatinas, viola, op.70, nos 1-3]. 3 Sonatinen für Viola solo,
op.70. — Berlin : Bote und Bock ; [London] : [Associated Music],
1977. — 16p ; 4to.
£4.80

(B78-50597)

SQPMJ — Miscellaneous works
Schonthal, Ruth
Four epiphanies : for unaccompanied viola / [by] Ruth
Schonthal ; edited and fingered by Paul Doktor. — New York ;
[London] : Oxford University Press, 1977. — 7p ; 4to.
Unpriced

(B78-50262)

SQQ — VIOLA D'AMORE
SQQPE — Sonatas
Rust, Friedrich Wilhelm
[Sonata, viola d'amore & keyboard, Czach 87, D major]. Sonata
for viola d'amore and harpsichord / by Friedrich Wilhelm Rust ;
edited by Ian White. — Chipperfield (Little Margaret, Penmans
Green, Chipperfield) : Ian White, 1978. — fol.
Score (11p.) & part.
Unpriced

(B78-50598)

SQQPLSR/T — Viola d'amore & cello. Variations
Rust, Friedrich Wilhelm
[Aria and variations, viola d'amore & cello, Czach 90, D major].
Aria and VII variations : for viola d'amore and cello / [by]
Friedrich Wilhelm Rust ; [edited by] Ian White. — Chipperfield
(Little Margaret, Penmans Green, Chipperfield) : Ian White, 1978.
— 4p ; fol.
Unpriced

(B78-50599)

SR — CELLO
Ferneyhough, Brian
Time and motion study 2 : for solo 'cello and electronics' / [by]
Brian Ferneyhough. — London : Peters, 1978. — [9]ff ; obl.fol.
Facsimile of the composer's autograph.
Unpriced

(B78-51109)

SR/EG — Sight reading
Smith, Doreen
A cello sight-reading book : eighty studies / by Doreen Smith. —
London : Oxford University Press.
Part 1. — 1978. — 8p ; 4to.
ISBN 0-19-358845-5 : Unpriced

(B78-51110)

Part 2. — 1978. — 8p ; 4to. —
ISBN 0-19-358846-3 : Unpriced

(B78-51111)

SRN — CELLO ENSEMBLE
SRN/AC — Tutors
Mish, Violet
'Stringing along' : a tutor for the first year schools' cello class /
by Violet Mish. — Gnosall ((16 Anchor Way, Danes Green,
Gnosall)) : Viking, 1977. — 36p ; 4to.
Unpriced

(B78-50263)

SRNSK/AAY — Quartets. Arrangements. Collections
Four pieces for four cellos : Byrd, Tchaikovsky, Berlioz, Mozart /
arranged by Doreen Smith. — London : Oxford University Press,
1978. — 4to.
Score (9p.) & 2 parts.
ISBN 0-19-358850-1 : Unpriced

(B78-51112)

SRNT — Trios
Zender, Hans
Litanei : für 3 Violoncello (1976) / [von] Hans Zender. — Berlin :
Bote und Bock ; [London] : [Schirmer], 1978. — 14p ; obl.fol.
£5.75

(B78-51113)

SRNU/AY — Duets. Collections
Sammlung kleiner Stücke für Violoncello = Collection of small
pieces for violoncello : duets and solos from the 18th century /
[compiled by] Erich Doflein. — Mainz ; London : Schott.
Vol.2 : 1st to 4th position. — 1977. — 32p ; 4to.
£4.00

(B78-50264)

SRNUK/AAY — Duets. Arrangements, Collections
Tortelier cello book one : twelve classical and folk pieces / arranged
for cello in first position with accompaniment for second cello
arranged by Paul Tortelier. — London : Chester Music, 1975. —
19p ; 4to.
Score (30p.) & part.
Unpriced

(B78-51114)

SRP — CELLO & PIANO
SRP/T — Variations
Blacher, Boris
[Variations on a theme of Tchaikovsky]. Variationer über ein
Thema von Tschaikowsky. (Rokoko Variationen) : für Violoncello
und Klavier (1974) / [von] Boris Blacher. — Berlin : Bote und
Bock ; [London] : [Associated Music], 1977. — 4to.
Score (19p.) & part.
£6.40

(B78-50600)

Webber, Andrew Lloyd
[Variations, cello & piano]. Variations / [by] Andrew Lloyd
Webber. — Ilford : Chappell, 1978. — The theme is Caprice
no.24 in A minor by Paganini.
The theme is Caprice no.24 in A minor by Pagamini.
Unpriced

(B78-51115)

SRPE — Sonatas
Routh, Francis
[Sonata, cello & piano, op.31]. Sonata for violoncello and piano /
[by] Francis Routh ; edited by Christopher Bunting. — London
(Arlington Park House, W.4) : Redcliffe Edition, 1976. — 4to.
Score (23p.) & part.
Unpriced

(B78-51116)

SRPJ — Miscellaneous works
Heiden, Bernhard
Siena : for cello and piano / [by] Bernhard Heiden. — New
York ; London : Associated Music, 1977. — 4to.
Score (17p.) & part.
£3.05

(B78-50601)

Newton, Rodney Stephen
Canzonietta [sic] : for cello and piano / [by] Rodney Stephen
Newton. — East Barnet : Composer Edition, 1978. — 3p ; fol.
Facsimile of the composer's autograph.
Unpriced

(B78-50265)

SRPK — Arrangements
Saint-Saëns, Camille
[Le carnaval des animaux. Le cygne. arr]. The swan ... / [by] C.
Saint-Saëns : violoncello and piano ; edited by Peter J. Maxwell.
— London : Leonard, Gould and Bolttler, 1978. — 4to.
Score (3p.) & part.
£0.50

(B78-50266)

SRPK/AAY — Arrangements. Collections
Tortelier cello book two : twelve classical and folk pieces /
arranged for cello in first position with accompaniment for piano
arranged by Paul Tortelier. — London : Chester Music, 1975. —
4to.
Unpriced

(B78-51117)

SRPK/LF — Arrangements. Concertos
Hindemith, Paul
[Concerto, cello, op.3, E flat major. arr]. Konzert für Violoncello
und Orchester in Es-Dur, Opus 3 (1915) / [von] Paul Hindmith
... ; Klavierauszug von Willy Giefer. — Mainz ; London : Schott,
1977. — 4to.
Score (63p.) & part.
£20.00

(B78-51118)

SRPLTS — CELLO & GUITAR
Brindle, Reginald Smith
Ten-string music : for cello and guitar / [by] Reginald Smith
Brindle. — London : Schott, 1978. — 7p ; 4to.
Unpriced

(B78-51119)

SRPM — UNACCOMPANIED CELLO
SRPMJ — Miscellaneous works
Schlumpf, Martin
Monolog 1 : für Violoncello solo (1976) / [von] Martin Schlumpf.
— Berlin : Bote und Bock ; [London] : [Schirmer], 1978. — 22p ;
fol.
£5.75

(B78-51120)

SS — DOUBLE BASS
SS/AZ — Collected works of individual composers
Bottesini, Giovanni
Complete Bottesini / [edited by] Rodney Slatford. — London :
Yorke.
Score (iv,55p.) & part.
Vol.1 : For two double basses and piano. — 1978. — 4to.
Unpriced
Also classified at SSNU

(B78-51121)

SSN — DOUBLE BASS ENSEMBLE
SSNS — Quartets
Lancen, Serge
Cavatine : for four double basses / [by] Serge Lancen. —
London : Yorke, 1978. — fol.
Score (4p.) & part.
Unpriced

(B78-51122)

SSNSG — Quartets. Suites
Runswick, Daryl
'Suite and low' : for double basses / [by] Daryl Runswick ; [edited
by] Rodney Slatford. — London : Yorke, 1978. — fol.
Score (20p.) & 4 parts.
Unpriced

(B78-51123)

SSNSK — Quartets. Arrangements
Fitzenhagen, Wilhelm Carl Friedrich
[Ave Maria. Op.42. arr]. Ave Maria : for four double basses / [by]
William Fitzenhagen ; tr. Jorma Harkonen. — London : Yorke,
1978. — 4to.
Score (4p.) & 4 parts.
Unpriced

(B78-51124)

SSNU — Duets
Acker, Dieter
Equale 1 : Szene für drei Kontrabasse = Scene for three basses,
1974 / [von] Dieter Acker. — Berlin : Bote und Bock ;
[London] : [Yorke], 1976. — 14p ; obl.4to.
Facsimile of the composer's manuscript.
Unpriced

(B78-51125)

Bottesini, Giovanni
Complete Bottesini / [edited by] Rodney Slatford. — London :
Yorke.
Score (iv,55p.) & part.
Vol.1 : For two double basses and piano. — 1978. — 4to.
Unpriced
Primary classification SS/AZ

Bottesini, Giovanni
[Duet no.2]. Gran duetto 2 : for double basses / [by] Giovanni
Bottesini ; edited by Rodney Slatford. — London : Yorke, 1978.
— [1],31p ; 4to.
Foreword in English and German.
Unpriced

(B78-51126)

SSP — DOUBLE BASS & PIANO
SSPJ — Miscellaneous works
Lancen, Serge
Croquis : for double bass and piano / [by] Serge Lancen. —
London : Yorke, 1978. — 20p ; 4to.
Score (20p.) & part.
Unpriced

(B78-51127)

SSPM — UNACCOMPANIED DOUBLE BASS
SSPME — Sonatas
Ellis, David
[Sonata, double bass, op.42]. Sonata for unaccompanied double
bass / [by] David Ellis ; [edited by] Rodney Slatford. — London :
Yorke, 1978. — [4]p ; fol.
Unpriced

(B78-51128)

SSPMJ — Miscellaneous works
Acker, Dieter
Orakel : für Kontrabass solo, 1974 / [von] Dieter Acker. — Berlin : Bote und Bock ; London : Yorke, 1978. — 8p ; fol.
Facsimile of the composer's autograph. — Duration 7 min.
Unpriced
(B78-51129)

Klebe, Giselher
Sechs Stücke : für Kontrabass solo, Op.68 / [von] Giselher Klebe. — Kassel ; London : Bärenreiter, 1977. — 6p ; fol.
Facsimile of the composer's autograph.
£2.70
(B78-51130)

Ridout, Alan
Little sad sound : a melodrama for double bass and narrator / [by] Alan Ridout and [words by] David Delve. — London : Yorke, 1978. — 11p ; 4to.
Unpriced
(B78-51131)

STN — VIOL CONSORT
Jenkins, John
Consort music : for viols in four parts / [by] John Jenkins ; edited by Andrew Ashbee. — London : Faber Music, 1978. — 4to.
The title page is headed 'The Viola da Gamba Society of Great Britain'. — Score (xxvi,102p.) & 5 parts, including part for organ.
Unpriced
(B78-51132)

TPMK/DW/G/AYT — Arrangements. Folk songs. Collections. United States
World's favorite folk explosion : for all fretted instruments, guitar, banjo, ukulele, mandolin, tenor banjo, tenor guitar, baritone uke / compiled and edited by Lipton Nemser and Arthur Bayas. — Carlstadt [N.J.] : Ashley ; [London] : [Phoenix], 1978. — 117p ; 4to. — (World's favorite series ; no.103)
Folksongs arranged.
Unpriced
(B78-50267)

TQPM — UNACCOMPANIED HARP
TQPME — Sonatas
Rossini, Gioacchino Antonio
[Sonata, harp]. Sonata, für Harfe, for harp / [von] Gioacchino Rossini ; herausgegeben von Marcelo Kozikova ; edited by Lucile Johnson. — Mainz ; London : Schott, 1978. — 7p ; 4to.
£2.40
(B78-51133)

TQPMJ — Miscellaneous works
Arnold, Malcolm
[Fantasy, harp, op.117]. Fantasy for harp, Op.117 / [by] Malcolm Arnold ; edited by Osian Ellis. — London : Faber Music, 1978. — 15p ; 4to.
Unpriced
(B78-51134)

Burgon, Geoffrey
Three nocturnes for harp / [by] Geoffrey Burgon ; pedalling by David Watkins. — London : Chester Music, 1978. — 7p ; 4to.
Unpriced
(B78-51135)

Grundman, Clare
Nocturne for harp and wind ensemble / [by] Clare Grundman ; transcribed for non-pedal harp by Marilyn S. Marzuki. — [New York] ; [London] : Boosey and Hawkes, 1978. — 5p ; 4to.
Duration 6 min.
Unpriced
(B78-51136)

Kelkel, Manfred
Melancolia und Mirabilis : zwei Stücke für Harfe solo = deux morceaux pour pour harpe seule = two pieces for solo harp : opus 23 / [von] Manfred Kelkel. — Berlin : Bote und Bock ; [London] : [Schirmer], 1978. — 7p ; fol.
£2.90
(B78-51137)

Klebe, Giselher
Alborada : per arpa sola, op.77 / [von] Giselher Klebe. — Kassel ; London : Bärenreiter, 1977. — 20p ; fol.
£4.50
(B78-51138)

TQR/AC — Irish harp. Tutors
Cuthbert, Sheila Larchet
The Irish harp book : a tutor and companion / [by] Sheila Larchet Cuthbert ; including works by the harper-composers, 17-19th century Irish composers [and] contemporary Irish composers. — Dublin : Mercier Press, 1977. — 245p ; 4to.
ISBN 0-85342-279-6 : Unpriced
(B78-51139)

TS — GUITAR
TS/AC — Tutors
Bolton, Cecil
An introduction to the guitar / by Cecil Bolton and Jack Moore ; including full basic instruction for playing the guitar, with songs to play and sing. — London : EMI Music, 1977. — 49p ; 4to.
Unpriced
(B78-51140)

Fanen, Pierre
Rock and roll-blues guitare / méthode de Pierre Fanen. — Paris ; [London] : Chappell, 1976. — 72p ; ill ; 4to.
with a 33 1/3 r p m gramophone record.
Unpriced
(B78-50268)

Skiera, Ehrenhard
Sass im Wald ein Ungetier : Kinderschule für Gitarre / [von] Ehrenhard Skiera. — Kassel ; London : Bärenreiter.
With a leaflet 'Noten-und Griffe-Lernspiel' inserted.
Band 1 : Ein Lehr- und Spielbuch, für Kinder abs Jahven im Einzel-oder Gruppenunterricht. — 1978. — 48p ; 4to.
£4.20
(B78-51141)

TS/AF — Exercises
Associated Board of the Royal Schools of Music
Guitar scales and arpeggios. — London : Associated Board of the Royal Schools of Music.
Grade 3-8. — 1978. — 22p ; 4to. —
Unpriced
(B78-51142)

Lester, Bryan
Essential guitar skill = Tecnica essenziale per la chitarra = Grundlagen der Fertigkeit im Gittarenspiel / [by] Bryan Lester. — Chesham : Ricordi.
[Book 1]. — 1977. — 21p ; 4to. —
Unpriced
(B78-50603)

[Book 2]. — 1977. — 21p ; 4to. —
Unpriced
(B78-50602)

Wright, Francis
Scales and arpeggios (and how they are played) : for the guitar / compiled by Francis Wright. — Leicester : Charnwood Music, 1978. — 15p ; 4to. — (Techni-music series for the guitarist)
With a chart of the guitar neck inserted.
Unpriced
(B78-50604)

TS/AY — Collections
A tune a day : for classical guitar / [compiled by] S. George Urwin. — Boston [Mass.] : Boston Music ; London : Chappell.
Book 1. — 1978. — 24p ; 4to.
Unpriced
(B78-51143)

TS/ED — Accompaniment
Goran, Ulf
Accompniment guide for guitar / [by] Ulf Goran. — London : Oxford University Press, 1978. — 32p ; 8vo.
ISBN 0-19-322213-2 : Unpriced
(B78-51144)

TS/PFT/AF — Transposition. Exercises
Wright, Francis
The capodastro and its use / [by] Francis Wright. — Leicester : Charnwood Music, 1978. — 15p ; 8vo. — (Techni-music series for the guitarist)
Unpriced
(B78-50605)

TSN — GUITAR ENSEMBLE
TSNSHW — Quartets. Waltzes
Biberian, Gilbert
Eight valses for four guitars / by Gilbert Biberian. — Melville [Croydon] : Belwin Mills, 1976. — 46p ; 4to. — (Guitar ensemble series)
Unpriced
(B78-50606)

TSNSK — Quartets. Arrangements
Merulo, Claudio
Canzona in 4 parts / [by] Claudio Merulo ; transcribed and edited for four guitars by Reginald Smith Brindle from a lute duo [arranged] by G.A. Terzi (1593). — London : Schott, 1977. — 11p ; obl.4to.
Unpriced
(B78-50607)

Terzi, Giovanni Antonio
[Intavolatura di liutto, lib.2. Canzona a 8. *arr]*. Canzona in 8 parts / by G.A. Terzi ; transcribed and edited for four guitars by Reginald Smith Brindle. — London : Schott, 1977. — 11p ; 4to. £0.70

(B78-50608)

TSNT — Trios
Regan, Michael
[Trio, guitars]. Trio for three guitars / by Michael Regan. — London : Schott, 1978. — 16p ; obl.4to.
Unpriced

(B78-51145)

TSNU — Duets
Dodgson, Stephen
Take two = A due = Für zwei : five guitar duets / by Stephen Dodgson and Hector Quine. — Chesham : Ricordi, 1977. — 11p ; 4to.
In fact, composed by Stephen Dodgson and edited by Hector Quine.
Unpriced

(B78-50609)

Weiss, Sylvius Leopold
[Duet, lute. *arr]*. Duett für Gitarren = Duet for guitars / [von] Sylvius Leopold Weiss ; aus der Lautentabulatur übertragen und für Gitarre bearbeitet von Dieter Kreidler = transcribed from the lute tablature and arranged for guitar by Dieter Kreidler. — Mainz ; London : Schott, 1978. — 7p ; 4to. — (Gitarren-Archiv ; 454)
£2.00

(B78-51146)

TSNUG — Duets. Suites
Holland, B J C
[Suite, guitars (2)]. Suite for two guitars / [by] B.J.C. Holland. — London : Schott, 1977. — [2],9p ; 4to.
£0.50

(B78-50269)

TSNUK — Duets. Arrangements
Haydn, Joseph
[Duet, barytones (2), Hob XII/4, G major. *arr]*. Duett in G nach dem Original für 2 Barytone, Hob XII, 4 / [von] Joseph Haydn ; eingerichtet von Dieter Kriedler für 2 Gitarren. — Mainz ; London : Schott, 1978. — 15p ; 4to. — (Gitarren-Archiv ; 449)
£4.00

(B78-50270)

TSP — GUITAR & PIANO
TSPJ — Miscellaneous works
Kelly, Bryan
Basque suite : for guitar and harpsichord (or piano) / [by] Bryan Kelly ; guitar part fingered by Hector Quine. — London : Oxford University Press, 1978. — 4to.
Score (24p.) & part.
ISBN 0-19-357423-3 : Unpriced

(B78-50610)

TSPM — UNACCOMPANIED GUITAR
TSPM/T — Variations
Giuliani, Mauro
Six airs irlandois nationales variées, [Op.125] / [by] Mauro Giuliani ... ; arranged and edited by Timothy Walker. — Croydon : Belwin Mills Music, 1977. — [1],24p ; 4to. — (Belwin Mills solo series for guitar)
For guitar.
£1.50

(B78-51147)

Puma, Joe
Carry me Bach : themes and variations on original classical and jazz themes for guitar solo / [by] Joe Puma. — New York ; London : Associated Music, 1977. — 64p ; 4to.
£2.40

(B78-50611)

TSPME — Sonatas
Giuliani, Mauro
[Sonata, guitar, op.15, C major]. Sonata in C major, opus 15 / [by] Mauro Giuliani ; edited and fingered by Frederick Noad. — London : Ariel : [Music Sales], 1977. — [38]p ; 4to. — (Noad guitar library : performance series)
ISBN 0-86001-377-4 : £1.95

(B78-51148)

TSPMF — Concertos
Camilleri, Charles
Fantasia concertante no.5 : for solo guitar / by Charles Camilleri ; edited by Alan Torok. — Wendover : Basil Ramsey : Roberton, 1978. — 12p ; 4to.
£2.00

(B78-51149)

TSPMG — Suites
Law, Leslie
A space age suite : six easy guitar pieces for the young beginner / by Leslie Law. — Leicester : Charnwood Music, 1977. — 7p ; 4to.
Unpriced

(B78-50612)

Walker, Timothy
African light suite / by Timothy Walker. — Croydon : Belwin Mills, 1976. — 2-14p ; 4to. — (Belwin Mills solo series for guitar)
Unpriced

(B78-50613)

TSPMH — Dances
Tarrega, Francisco
Zwei spanische Stücke = Two Spanish pieces = Deux pièces espagnoles : für Gitarre ... / von Francisco Tarrega. — Revidierte Neuausgabe / von Robert Brojer. — Mainz ; London : Schott, 1978. — 10p ; 4to. — (Gitarren-Archiv ; 451)
Contents: 1: Danza mora - 2: Capricho arabe.
£3.20

(B78-50271)

TSPMHVG — Pavanes
Wills, Arthur
Pavane and galliard for solo guitar / [by] Arthur Wills ; edited by Hector Quine. — Chesham : Ricordi, 1977. — 5p ; 4to.
Unpriced

(B78-50614)

TSPMHW — Waltzes
Branson, David
Waltz-impromptu : for guitar / [by] David Branson. — [Hastings] : Helicon, 1978. — 7p ; 4to.
Unpriced

(B78-51150)

TSPMHX — Jazz
Reinhardt, Django
Django Reinhardt. — London : EMI, 1978. — 63p ; 4to. — (The music makers)
Guitar pieces by Django Reinhardt and others.
Unpriced

(B78-51151)

TSPMJ — Miscellaneous works
Branson, David
Saudade : for guitar / [by] David Branson ; transcription by the composer. — Hastings : Helicon, 1978. — 4p ; 4to.
Unpriced

(B78-51152)

Brindle, Reginald Smith
Four poems of García Lorca : for solo guitar / by Reginald Smith Brindle. — London : Schott, 1977. — 11p ; 4to.
Unpriced

(B78-50615)

Corbetta, Francesco
[La guitarre royale. *Selections]*. Suite in A minor ... : guitar solo / [by] Francesco Corbetta. — [Sydney] ; [London] : Universal, 1978. — 12p ; 4to.
Arranged by John W. Duarte. — Edited and fingered by Konrad Ragossnig. — Preface in English, German, French and Spanish.
Unpriced

(B78-51153)

Garcia, Gerald
First guitar pieces / written and arranged by Gerald Garcia and John Whitworth. — Oxford : Holley Music, 1978. — 7p ; 4to.
Unpriced

(B78-51154)

Giuliani, Mauro
[Overture, guitar, op.61]. Grande ouverture for solo guitar, op.61 / [by] Mauro Giuliani ; edited and revised by Julian Bream. — London : Faber Music, 1978. — [4],12p ; 4to.
Slightly revised and shortened.
£2.00

(B78-51155)

Giuliani, Mauro
Twenty-five etudes / [by] Mauro Giuliani ... ; edited and fingered by Frederick Noad. — London : Ariel : [Music Sales], 1977. — [47]p ; 4to. — (Noad guitar library : study series)
ISBN 0-86001-372-3 : £1.95

(B78-51156)

Guitar masters of the 19th century : Italian masters, 19 original easy pieces, collected, edited and arranged in progressive order by June Yakeley. — Chesham : Ricordi, 1977. — [1],12p ; 4to.
Works by Carolli, Carcossi, Giuliani.
Unpriced

(B78-50616)

Kolb, Barbara
Looking for Claudio : solo and tape / [by] Barbara Kolb ; edited
by David Starobin. — Oceanside ; [London] : Boosey and
Hawkes, 1978. — [4],19p ; 4to.
Facsimile of the composer's autograph.
Unpriced
(B78-51157)

Regan, Michael
Four shanties : for guitar / [by] Michael Regan. — London :
Schott, 1978. — 7p ; 4to.
£0.70
(B78-51158)

Royal, Timothy
Blues 1, 2 & 3 : for classical guitar / by Timothy Royal. —
Bristol (16 Oldfield Place, Hotwells, Bristol 8) : Shed Music, 1978.
— 7p ; 4to.
£0.75
(B78-50272)

Smith, Isabel
Out and about : 8 descriptive pieces for guitar / [by] Isabel Smith.
— Chesham : Ricordi, 1978. — 8p ; 4to.
Unpriced
(B78-50617)

Smith, Isabel
Up the High Street with my guitar : 8 pieces for beginners. —
Chesham : Ricordi, 1978. — 8p ; 4to.
Unpriced
(B78-50618)

Sor, Fernando
[Sonata, guitar, op.22, C major. *Selections*]. Menuett und Rondo :
für Gitarre / [von] Fernando Sor. — Revidierte Neuausgabe / von
Robert Brojer. — Mainz ; London : Schott, 1978. — 10p ; 4to. —
(Gitarren-Archiv ; 450)
Duration 8 1/2 min.
£3.20
(B78-50273)

Walker, Timothy
Etude / [by] Timothy Walker. — Croydon : Belwin Mills, 1977.
— 3p ; 4to. — (Belwin Mills solo series for guitar)
£0.50
(B78-50619)

Walker, Timothy
Fantasia celestina / [by] Timothy Walker. — Croydon : Belwin
Mills Music, 1977. — [1],5p ; 4to. — (Belwin Mills solo series for
guitar)
For guitar.
£0.80
(B78-51159)

Walker, Timothy
[Prelude, guitar]. Prelude / [by] Timothy Walker. — Croydon :
Belwin Mills Music, 1977. — 4p ; 4to. — (Belwin Mills solo series
for guitar)
For guitar.
£0.50
(B78-51160)

Walters, Gareth
Invocation and toccata : guitar / [by] Gareth Walters. —
London : Oxford University Press, 1978. — 11p ; 4to.
ISBN 0-19-359380-7 : Unpriced
(B78-50274)

TSPMK — Arrangements
Capirola, Vincenzo
Capirola lute book : seven pieces, guitar solo. — [Sydney] ;
[London] : Universal, 1978. — 16p ; 4to.
Edited by John W. Duarte. — Preface in English, German, French and
Spnish. — Contents: Padoana alla francese II - Padoana - Che farala, che
dirala - Stavasi amor dormendo - Balleto - La villanella - Ricercar VIII.
Unpriced
(B78-51161)

Cearense, Catallo da Paixão
[Luar do sertão. *arr*]. Luar do sertão / de Catallo da Paixão
Cearense ; transcrição para violão solo (guitar solo) de Isais Sávio.
— Rio de Janeiro : Arthur Napoleão ; [London] : [Essex Music],
1968 [i.e. 1978]. — [2]p ; 4to.
Unpriced
Primary classification SPMK
(B78-50594)

Dowland, John
[Lute music. *Selections : arr*]. Selected works for one and two
lutes with original lute tablature and transcription for the guitar /
[by] John Dowland ; edited and fingered by Frederick Noad. —
London : Ariel : [Music Sales], 1977. — 41p ; 4to. — (Noad
guitar library : performance series)
ISBN 0-86001-294-8 : £1.95
Also classified at TWPMJ
(B78-51162)

Handel, George Frideric
[Instrumental music. *Selections : arr*]. Selected solos and duets /
[by] G.F. Handel ; transcribed for the guitar by Frederick Noad.
— London : Ariel : [Music Sales], 1977. — 16p ; 4to. — (Noad
guitar library : performance series)
ISBN 0-86001-378-2 : £1.50
(B78-51163)

Mendelssohn, Felix
[Lieder ohne Worte. *Selections: arr*]. 6 Lieder ohne Worte / [von]
Felix Mendelssohn Bartholdy ; für Gitarre solo ... bearbeitet von
... Anton Stingl. — Mainz ; London : Schott, 1978. — 20p ; 4to.
— (Gitarren-Archiv ; 453)
£4.80
(B78-50275)

Purcell, Henry
[Harpsichord music. *arr*]. Purcell for the guitar : five pieces ... /
transcribed for solo guitar by Michael Grayson. — London :
Oxford University Press, 1978. — 7p ; 4to.
Works comprise Z.T697, Z.D219/1, Z.2677, Z.T 694, and Z.D221.
ISBN 0-19-358356-9 : Unpriced
(B78-51164)

Reusner, Esaias
[Neuen Lautenfrüchte. *Selections*]. Two pieces ... : guitar solo /
[by] Esaias Reusner. — [Sydney] ; [London] : Universal, 1978. —
8p ; 4to.
Edited by John W. Duarte. — Preface in English, German, French and
Spanish.
Unpriced
(B78-51165)

TSPMK/AAY — Arrangements. Collections
Ausgewählte Stücke alter und neuer Meister : für Gitarre / [von]
Siegfried Behrend. Heft 2. — Wilhemshaven : Heinrichshofen ;
[London] : [Peters], 1978. — 16p ; 4to.
Unpriced
(B78-50620)

Play a piece : easy solos in two books, guitar solo / [compiled by]
Ulf Goran. — London : Oxford University Press.
Book 1. — 1978. — 16p ; 4to.
ISBN 0-19-356796-2 : Unpriced
(B78-50621)

Book 2. — 1978. — 16p ; 4to.
ISBN 0-19-356797-0 : Unpriced
(B78-50622)

Six anonymous lute solos / transcribed for guitar by Anthony
Rooley. — Sevenoaks : Novello, 1977. — 6p ; 4to.
£0.72
(B78-50623)

World's favorite selected masterpieces : for classic guitar. —
Carlstadt : Ashley ; [London] : [Phoenix]. — (World's favorite
series ; no.108)
Vol.3 : compiled and edited by Frantz Cassens. — 1978. — 109p ; 4to.
Unpriced
(B78-50276)

TSPMK/AHR — Arrangments. Minuets
Weiss, Sylvias Leopold
[Minuets, lute. *arr*]. Zwei Menuette = Two minuets / [von]
Sylvius Leopold ; aus der Lautentabulatur übertragen und für
Gitarre bearbeitet von Pieter Kreidler = transcribed from the lute
tablature and arranged for guitar by Dieter Kreidler. — Mainz ;
London : Schott, 1978. — 7p ; 4to. — (Gitarren-Archiv ; 452)
£2.00
(B78-51166)

TSPMK/AHXJ — Arrangements. Ragtime
Joplin, Scott
[Piano music. *Selections : arr*]. Rags for guitar / by Scott Joplin
and Tom Turpin ; arranged by Michael Karp. — New York ;
London : Schirmer, 1977. — 28p ; 4to.
£1.50
(B78-51167)

TSPMK/AYK — Arrangements. Collections. Spain
Drei spanische Solostücke = Three Spanish solo pieces = Trois
morceaux espagnoles : for guitar / edited by Dieter Kreidler. —
Mainz ; London : Schott, 1977. — 6p ; 4to. — (Gitarren-Archiv ;
448)
Contents: Spanische Romanze (anon) - Lagrima by Francisco Tarrega -
Etude by Francisco Tarrega.
£2.40
(B78-50277)

TSPMK/DP/LF/AY — Arrangements. Carols. Christmas. Collections
Christmas carols for guitar / arranged by Jerry Mayes. —
Leicester : Charnwood Music, 1978. — 11p ; 4to.
With a separate leaf of chord diagrams inserted.
Unpriced
(B78-51168)

TSPMK/DW/GJ/AY — Arrangements. Children's songs. Collections
Children's songs and carols, including hymns and games : for easy
guitar [or] recorder / arranged by Jack Moore and Cecil Bolton.
— London : EMI, 1978. — 40p ; 4to.
Unpriced
Also classified at VSPMK/DW/GJ

(B78-51169)

TSPMK/DW/LF/AY — Arrangements. Christmas songs. Collections
The **best** of Christmas songs : guitar [or] recorder. — London :
EMI, 1978. — 40p ; 4to.
ASrranged for guitar or recorder by Cecil Bolton and Jack Moore.
Unpriced
Also classified at VSPMK/DW/LF/AY

(B78-51170)

TTPM — UNACCOMPANIED BANJO
TTPMJ — Miscellaneous works
Familiar music for 5 string banjo / arranged by Walter Kage Bauer.
— Carlstadt : Lewis Music ; [London] : [Phoenix], 1977. — [1],
33p ; 4to.
Unpriced

(B78-50624)

TVPM — UNACCOMPANIED VIHUELA
TVPMJ — Unaccompanied vihuela. Miscellaneous works
Fuenllana, Miguel de
[Libro de musica para vihuela, intitulado Orphenica lyra].
Orphenica lyra (Seville 1554) / [by] Miguel de Fuenllana ; edited
by Charles Jacobs. — Oxford : Clarendon Press, 1978. — 997p ;
4to.
£30.00

(B78-50625)

TW — LUTE
TW/AZ — Collected works of individual composers
Dowland, John
[Lute music. *Collections*]. The collected lute music of John
Dowland / transcribed and edited by Diana Poulton and Basil
Lam. — 2nd ed. [with 3 more pieces]. — London : Faber Music,
1978. — xvi,339p ; fol.
ISBN 0-571-10024-4 : Unpriced

(B78-51171)

TWPM — UNACCOMPANIED LUTE
TWPMJ — Miscellaneous works
Dowland, John
[Lute music. *Selections : arr*]. Selected works for one and two
lutes with original lute tablature and transcription for the guitar /
[by] John Dowland ; edited and fingered by Frederick Noad. —
London : Ariel : [Music Sales], 1977. — 41p ; 4to. — (Noad
guitar library : performance series)
ISBN 0-86001-294-8 : £1.95
Primary classification TSPMK

TXN — MANDOLIN ENSEMBLE
TXNS — Quartets
Henze, Hans Werner
4. Streichquartett = 4th string quartet : (1976) / [von] Hans
Werner Henze. — Mainz ; London : Schott, 1976. — 4pt ; 4to.
£26.00

(B78-51172)

UM — WIND BAND
UMJ — Miscellaneous works
Burgon, Geoffrey
Gending / [by] Geoffrey Burgon. — London : Chester Music,
1977. — [2],83p ; 4to.
For wind band and percussion. — Facsimile of the composer's autograph -
Duration 20 min.
Unpriced

(B78-51173)

Françaix, Jean
Quasi improvvisando : pour ensemble à vent = für
Bläserenseble / [par] Jean Françaix. — Mainz ; London : Schott,
1978. — 11p ; 4to.
Among works quoted are excerpts from Für elise by Beethoven, a fugue
from 'Das Wohltemprierte Klavier', i.e. S.871, Aufforderung zum Tänz by
Weber, Polonaise in A flat by Chopin, etc.
£6.00

(B78-51174)

Wimberger, Gerhard
Short stories : für elf Bläser / [von] Gerhard Wimberger. —
Kassel ; London : Bärenreiter, 1977. — 24p ; 4to.
Facsimile of composer's autograph.
£4.20

(B78-51175)

UMM — MILITARY BAND
UMMG — Suites
Newton, Rodney Stephen
'Constantine suite' : a Byzantine suite in seven movements for
symphonic wind ensemble / [by] Rodney Stephen Newton. —
East Barnet (13 Chetwynd Ave., East Barnet, Herts.) : Composer
Edition, 1977. — 55p ; fol.
Facsimile of the composer's autograph.
Unpriced

(B78-50278)

Schneider, Willy
Ein Sommertag : Suite für Bläsorchester / [von] Willy Schneider.
— Mainz ; London : Schott, 1978. — 4to. — (Der Blaserkreis,
Reihe C ; no.208)
Conductor (16p.) & 41 parts, with several copies of various parts.
£20.00

(B78-51176)

UMMGM — Marches
Stephan, Wilhelm
Fahnengruss / [von] Wilhelm Stephan. — Berlin : Bote und
Bock ; [London] : [Associated Music], 1977. — 3p ; 4to.
For military band.
£1.60

(B78-50626)

Stephan, Wilhelm
Panzergrenadiermarsch / [von] Wilhelm Stephan. — Berlin : Bote
und Bock ; [London] : [Associated Music], 1977. — 7p ; 4to.
For military band.
£3.20

(B78-50627)

Walters, Harold L
The third century : concert march / [by] Harold L. Walters. —
Miami : Rubank ; [Sevenoaks] : [Novello], 1977. — 4to. —
(Rubank symphonic band library ; no.152)
For military band - Conductor (8p.) & 43 parts, with several copies of
various parts.
Unpriced

(B78-50279)

UMMGM/KH — Regimental marches
Carson, D
Regimental quick march of The Ulster Defence Regiment, 'The
sprig of Shillelagh' 'Garry owen' / arranged by D. Carson. —
London : Boosey and Hawkes, 1978. — 27pt : obl.8vo.
With several copies of various parts.
Unpriced

(B78-50280)

UMMJ — Miscellaneous works
Balent, Andrew
Strange encounters / by Andrew Balent. — New York : Warner ;
[London] : [Blossom], 1978. — 4to. — (Supersound series for
young bands)
For military band. — Score (7p.) & 48 parts, with several copies of various
parts.
Unpriced

(B78-51177)

Brunelli, Louis Jean
Chronicles / [by] Louis Jean Brunelli. — New York ; [London] :
Boosey and Hawkes, 1978. — 4to. — (Q.M.B. edition ; 398)
For military band. — Score (46p.) & 71 parts, with several copies of various
parts.
Unpriced

(B78-50629)

Grundman, Clare
Overture on a short theme / [by] Clare Grundman. — New
York ; [London] : Boosey and Hawkes, 1978. — 4to. — (Q.M.B.
edition ; 407)
Score (27p.) & 73 parts, with several copies of various parts. — Duration 4
1/4 min.
Unpriced

(B78-51178)

Jacob, Gordon
Tribute to Canterbury / [by] Gordon Jacob. — London : Boosey
and Hawkes, 1977. — 4to. — (Q.M.B. Edition ; no.285)
For military band. — Score (70p.) & 75 parts, with several copies of various
parts.
Unpriced

(B78-50281)

Littell, Barbara
March for a free spirit / by Barbara Littell. — New York :
Warner ; [London] : [Blossom], 1978. — 4to. — (Supersound
series for young bands)
Unpriced

(B78-51180)

Littell, Barbara
Slightly lightly Latin / by Barbara Littell. — New York :
Warner ; [London] : [Blossom], 1978. — 4to. — (Supersound
series for young bands)
For military band. — Score (9p.) & 49 parts, with several copies of various
parts.
Unpriced

(B78-51181)

Schaefer, Will
Fanfare and processional : for concert band / [by] Will Schaefer.
— New York ; London : Schirmer, 1978. — 10p ; 4to.
Conductor.
£18.20

(B78-51182)

Sparke, Philip
Gaudium : concert piece for wind symphony orchestra / [by]
Philip Sparke. — London : Boosey and Hawkes, 1978. — 4to. —
(Q.M.B. edition ; no.287)
Score ([1],42p.) & 52 parts, with several copies of various parts.
Unpriced

(B78-51183)

Tull, Fisher
Cryptic essay : for symphonic band / [by] Fisher Tull. — New
York ; [London] : Boosey and Hawkes, 1978. — 4to. — (Q.M.B.
Edition ; 404)
Score (50p.) & 72 parts, with several copies of various parts.
Unpriced

(B78-50282)

Washburn, Robert
Trigon / [by] Robert Washburn. — New York ; [London] :
Boosey and Hawkes, 1978. — 4to. — (Q.M.B. Edition ; 408)
For military band. — Score (40p.) & 70 parts, with several copies of various
parts.
£21.00

(B78-51184)

Williams, Clifton
Songs of heritage : symphonic band / [by] Clifton Williams ;
[edited by] Francis McBeth and Harold Watters. — Miami :
Rubank ; [Sevenoaks] : [Novello], 1978. — 4to. — (Rubank
symphonic band library ; no.154)
Conductor & 63 parts, with several copies of various parts.
Unpriced

(B78-51185)

UMMK — Arrangements
Bernstein, Leonard
[Slana!. arr]. Slava! : a concert overture / [by] Leonard Bernstein ;
transcribed for symphonic band by Clare Grundman. — New
York : Amberson : Boosey and Hawkes ; [London] : [Boosey and
Hawkes], 1978. — 4to. — (Q.M.B. Edition ; 406)
Score (27p.) & part, with several copies of various parts.
Unpriced

(B78-51186)

Britten, Benjamin, *Baron Britten*
[The building of the house. arr]. The building of the house : for
concert band / by Benjamin Britten ; transcribed by Thad
Marciniak. — London : Faber Music, 1977. — [1],39p ; 4to.
Duration 5 1/2 min.
Unpriced

(B78-50628)

Farnaby, Giles
[Selections. arr]. Giles Farnaby suite / arranged for band by Bram
Wiggins. — New York ; [London] : Oxford University Press,
1978. — 4to.
For military band. — Score (20p.) & 55 parts. — Contents: 1: A toye - 2:
Giles Farnaby's dream - 3: His rest - 4: Giles Farnaby's conceit - 5: His
humour.
Unpriced

(B78-50283)

Josephs, Wilfred
[Rail. Op.57. arr]. Rail / [by] Wilfred Josephs ; arranged for
concert band by Lawrence Odom. — New York : Galaxy ;
[London] : [Stainer and Bell], 1977. — 4to.
Score (54p.) & 70 parts.
Unpriced

(B78-50630)

Mancini, Henry
[Baby elephant walk. arr]. Baby elephant walk / by Henry
Mancini ; arranged by Johnnie Vinson. — New York : Warner ;
[London] : [Blossom], 1978. — 8vo & obl. 8vo. — (WB easy
marching bands series)
Scores (7p.) & 68 parts, with several copies of various parts.
Unpriced

(B78-50631)

Mancini, Henry
[Baby elephant walk. arr]. Baby elephant walk / by Henry
Mancini ; arranged by John Stuart. — New York : Warner ;
[London] : [Blossom], 1978. — 4to. — (Supersound series for
young bands)
Score (8p.) & 49 parts, with several copies of various parts.
Unpriced

(B78-51187)

UMMK/AHT — Arrangements. Passacagalias
Handel, George Frideric
[Suite de pièces, 1st collection. Passacaille. arr]. Passacaglia in G
minor / [by] G.F. Handel ; transcribed by Ivan C. Phillips. —
New York ; [London] : Oxford University Press, 1978. — 4to.
For military band. — Score (15p.) & 70 parts.
Unpriced

(B78-50632)

UMMK/DW — Arrangements. Songs, etc
Hartford, John
[Gentle on my mind. arr]. Gentle on my mind / by John
Hartford ; arranged by Milton Bush. — New York : Warner ;
[London] : [Blossom], 1978. — 8vo & obl. 8vo. — (WB easy
marching bands series)
For military band. — Score (9p.) & 68 parts, with several copies of various
parts.
Unpriced

(B78-50634)

Rogers, Richard
[Love me tonight, Mimi. arr]. Mimi / music by Richard Rogers ;
words by Lorenz Hart, arranged by Joel Leach. — New York :
Warner ; [London] : [Blossom], 1978. — 8vo.
For military band. — Score (7p.) & 68 parts, with several copies of various
parts.
Unpriced

(B78-50635)

UMMK/DW/JR — Arrangements. Songs, etc. Films
Lerner, Sammy
[Popeye the sailor. I'm Popeye the sailor man. arr]. I'm Popeye
the sailor man / by Sammy Lerner ; arranged by Kelly Love. —
New York : Warner ; [London] : [Blossom], 1978. — 8vo &
obl.8vo. — (WB easy marching bands series)
For military band. — Score (7p.) & 72 parts, with several copies of various
parts.
Unpriced

(B78-50636)

Livingston, Jay
[The paleface. Buttons and bows. arr]. Buttons and bows / by Jay
Livingston and Ray Evans ; arranged by Leonard Rush. — New
York : Warner ; [London] : [Blossom], 1978. — 4to. —
(Supersound series for young bands)
Score (7p.) & 50 parts, with several copies of various parts. — Arranger
given as Andrew Balent on cover and title page : entry taken from page 2.
Unpriced

(B78-51188)

Livingston, Jay
[The paleface. Buttons and bows. arr]. Buttons and bows / by Jay
Livingston and Ray Evans ; arranged by Kelly Love. — New
York : Warner ; [London] : [Blossom], 1978. — 8vo & obl. 8vo.
— (WB easy marching bands series)
Score (7p.) & 70 parts, with several copies of various parts.
Unpriced

(B78-50637)

UMMK/DW/JS — Arrangements. Songs, etc. Television
Fox, Charles
[Happy days. arr]. Happy days : from the Paramount TV series
'Happy days' / by Charles Fox ; arranged by Charlie Hill. —
New York : Warner ; [London] : [Blossom], 1978. — 8vo & obl.
8vo. — (WB easy marching bands series)
For military band. — Score (9p.) & 68 parts, with several copies of various
parts.
Unpriced

(B78-50638)

UMMK/JR — Arrangements. Films
Rota, Nino
[The godfather. Selections : arr]. Themes from The godfather and
The godfather, part II / by Nino Rota ; arranged by Milton Bush.
— New York : Warner ; [London] : Blossom, 1978. — 8vo & obl.
8vo. — (WB easy marching bands series)
For military band. — Score (8p.) & 68 parts, with several copies of various
parts.
Unpriced

(B78-50639)

UMMK/JS — Arrangements. Television
Roddenberry, Gene
[Star trek. *Selections : arr*]. Theme from 'Star Trek' / by Gene
Roddenberry and Alexander Courage ; arranged by Albert
Ahronheim. — New York : Warner ; [London] : [Blossom], 1978.
— 8vo & obl.8vo. — (WB easy marching bands series)
For military band. — Score (11p.) & 69 parts, with several copies of various
parts.
Unpriced

(B78-50640)

Roddenberry, Gene
[Star trek. Theme. *arr*]. Theme from Star trek / by Gene
Roddenberry and Alexander Courage ; arranged by Leonard
Rush. — New York : Warner ; [London] : [Blossom], 1978. —
4to. — (Supersound series for young bands)
Score (8p.) & 50 parts, with several copies of various parts. — Arranger
given as Andrew Balent on page 2.
Unpriced

(B78-51189)

UMP — SOLO INSTRUMENT (S) & WIND BAND
UMPQ — Piano & wind band
Globokar, Vinko
Vendre le vent : für einen Pianisten, einen Schlagzeuger und neun
Bläser / [von] Vinko Globokar. — Frankfurt : Litolff ; London :
Peters, 1978. — 64p ; fol.
Reproduction of the composer's manuscript. — Study score. — Duration 30
min.
Unpriced

(B78-51190)

Reynolds, Roger
Only now, and again : winds, piano and percussion (3) / [by]
Roger Reynolds. — New York ; London : Peters, 1978. — [2],
26p ; fol.
Unpriced

(B78-51191)

UN — WIND ENSEMBLE
UNN — Octets
Bialas, Günter
Romanza, e danza : für Bläser - Oktett (nach J. Meyerbeer) /
[von] Günter Bialas. — Kassel ; London : Bärenreiter, 1977. —
24p ; 4to.
After L'Africaine.
£3.92

(B78-50641)

Haydn, Joseph
[Divertimento, woodwind quartet, Hob.II, no.7, C major].
Feld-Parthie in C for wind ensemble / [by] Joseph Haydn ; edited
by Peter Wastall. — London : Boosey and Hawkes, 1978. — 4to.
— (Exploring music series. Ensemble series)
Score (8p.) & 8 parts.
Unpriced

(B78-50284)

UNNHG — Octets. Dance suites
Lowe, Thomas
Suite of dances : wind ensemble / [by] Thomas Lowe. —
Ampleforth : Emerson, 1977. — 4to.
Score ([1],15p.) & parts.
£3.50

(B78-50285)

UNNK/AH — Octets. Arrangements. Dances
Dvořák, Antonín
[Slavonic dance, no.8, op.46, no.8, G minor. *arr*]. Slavonic dance,
no.8 / [by] Antonín Dvořák. — London : Boosey and Hawkes,
1978. — 4to. — (Exploring music series ; Ensemble series)
Duration 5 min. — Score (13p.) & 9 parts.
Unpriced

(B78-50642)

Dvořák, Antonín
[Slavonic dance, no.9, op.72, no.1. *arr*]. Slavonic dance no.9 / [by]
Antonin Dvorak ; arranged for wind ensemble by Patrick
Clements. — London : Boosey and Hawkes, 1978. — 4to. —
(Exploring music series ; Ensemble series)
Duration 3 1/2 min. — Score (16p.) & 9 parts.
Unpriced

(B78-50643)

Dvořák, Antonín
[Slavonic dance, no.15, op.72, no.7, C major. *arr*]. Slavonic dance,
no.15 / [by] Antonin Dvorak ; arranged for wind ensemble by
Patrick Clements. — London : Boosey and Hawkes, 1978. — 4to.
— (Exploring music series ; Ensemble series)
Duration 3 min. — Score (16p.) & 10 parts.
Unpriced

(B78-50644)

UNPK/LF — Septets. Concertos
Vivaldi, Antonio
[Concerto, trumpets (2), Ryom 537, C major. *arr*]. Concerto in C,
op.46, no.1, for two B flat trumpets and clarinet choir / [by]
Antonio Vivaldi ; transcribed by Charles P. yates. — london :
Associated Music, 1978. — 4to.
Score (35p.) & 7 parts. — Duration 7 min.
Score, £10.25, Parts, unpriced

(B78-51192)

UNQ — Sextets
Haydn, Joseph
[Divertimento, wind sextet, Hob.II/23, F major]. Feld-Parthie in
F, for wind ensemble / [by] Joseph Haydn ; edited by Peter
Wastall. — London : Boosey and Hawkes, 1978. — 4to. —
(Exploring music series : Ensemble series)
The fourth movement is omitted. — Score ([2],5p.) & 7 parts ; alternative
clarinet parts are printed on the back of the parts provided.
Unpriced

(B78-51193)

Mozart, Wolfgang Amadeus
[Serenade, wind sextet, no.11, K.375, E flat major. Adagio].
Adagio ... for wind ensemble / [by] Wolfgang Amadeus Mozart ;
edited by Peter Wastall. — London : Boosey and Hawkes, 1978.
— 4to. — (Exploring music series : Ensemble series)
Original scoring. — Score ([1],8p.) & 7 parts.
Unpriced

(B78-51194)

UNR — Quintets
Einem, Gottfried von
[Quintet, wind instruments, op.46]. Bläserquintett. Op.46 / [von]
Gottfried von Einem. — London : Boosey and Hawkes, 1978. —
50p ; fol.
Unpriced

(B78-51195)

Einem, Gottfried von
[Quintet, wind instruments, op.46]. Bläserquintett. Opus 46 /
[von] Gottfried von Einem. — London : Boosey and Hawkes,
1978. — [2],38p ; 8vo. — (Hawkes pocket scores ; 920)
Miniature score.
Unpriced

(B78-51196)

Nordenstrom, Gladys
[Quintet, wind instruments]. Wind quintet = Bläser Quintett /
[by] Gladys Nordenstrom. — Kassel ; London : Bärenreiter, 1977.
— fol.
Score ([2],17p.) & 5 parts.
£13.50

(B78-51197)

UNRHJKS — Quintets. Bossa novas
Greaves, Terence
Beethoven's fifth bossa nova : wind quintet / [by] Terence
Greaves. — Ampleforth : Emerson, 1977. — 4to.
A dance based on themes from Beethoven's Fifth Symphony in C minor.
Unpriced

(B78-50286)

VN — WOODWIND ENSEMBLE
VNSK/AH — Quartets. Arrangements. Dances
Schubert, Franz
[Dances. *Selections : arr*]. 3 Schubert dances / arranged by Alan
Frazer. — London (7 Garrick St., W.C.2) : Middle Eight Music,
1977. — 4to. — (Opticus 4 woodwind ; fol.1)
Score (6p.) & 8 parts, including alternative parts for flutes, oboes, clarinets,
horn and bassoon. — Contents: 1: Ländler, D.790, no.1 - 2: Minuet and
trio, D.41, no.12 - 3: Ecossaise.
Unpriced

(B78-50287)

**VNSK/DW/GMC/AY — Quartets. Arrangements. Sea shanties.
Collections**
Haul away! : 3 movements based on a sea shanties / arranged by
Tony Mason, edited by Alan Cave. — London (7 Garrick St.,
W.C.2) : Middle Eight Music, 1974. — 4to. — (Option 4
woodwind ; fol.2)
Score (6p.) & 8 parts, with alternative parts for flutes, oboes, clarinets, horn
and bassoon.
Unpriced

(B78-50288)

VNT — Trios
Devienne, François
[Trio, flute, clarinet & bassoon, op.61, no.3, A minor]. Trio für
Flöte, Klarinette (Violine) und Fagott (Violoncello), Opus 61,
Nr.3 / [von] François Devienne ; herausgegeben von George
Meerwein. — Frankfurt : Litolff ; London : Peters, 1977. — 3 pt ;
4to.
Unpriced
(B78-50646)

Holst, Gustav
Terzetto (1925) : for flute, oboe and viola (or clarinet) / [by]
Gustav Holst ; (revised)– Imogen Holst. — 2nd revised ed. —
London : Chester Music, 1978. — 4to. — (Chester woodwind
series)
Score ([2],10p.) & 4 parts. — Clarinet adapted from the viola part by R.
James Whipple.
Unpriced
(B78-51198)

Redel, Martin Christoph
Mobile : für Oboe (Oboe d'amore ad lib.), Klarinette und Fagott,
1976 / [von] Martin Christoph Redel. — Berlin : Bote und Bock ;
[London] : [Schirmer], 1977. — obl.fol.
Score (15p.) & 3 parts.
£4.80
(B78-51199)

VNTF — Trios. Concertos
Cambini, Giuseppe
[Trio concertans, flute, oboe & bassoon, op.45, no.6]. Trio op.45,
no.6 for flute, oboe and bassoon / [by] Giuseppe Cambini ; edited
by H. Voxman. — London : Musica rara, 1978. — 4to.
Score ([1],6p.) & 3 parts.
Unpriced
(B78-51200)

VNU — Duets
Schweizer, Klaus
Klappentexte : für Flöte [oder] Piccolo und Oboe [oder] English
Horn, 1976 / [von] Klaus Schweizer. — Kassel ; London :
Bärenreiter, 1977. — 11p ; obl.fol.
Duration 5 min.
£8.96
(B78-50647)

VRN — FLUTE ENSEMBLE
Tull, Fisher
Cyclorama 1 : flute ensemble / [by] Fisher Tull. — [New York] ;
[London] : Boosey and Hawkes, 1978. — 4to.
Duration 13 min. — Score (32p.) & 11 parts.
Unpriced
(B78-51201)

VRNTQK/DW — Flutes (2) & piano. Arrangements. Songs, etc
Bach, Johann Sebastian
[Cantata no.208 : Was mir behagt. Schafe können sicher weiden.
arr]. Sheep may safely graze / [by] J.S. Bach ; arranged for two
flutes or treble recorders and piano by Sidney Lawton. —
London : Oxford University Press, 1978. — 4to.
Score (4p.) & part ; the parts for two flutes are printed in score.
ISBN 0-19-355280-9 : Unpriced
(B78-50289)

VRNTQK/LF — Flutes (2) & piano. Arrangements. Concertos
Telemann, Georg Philipp
[Concerto, flutes (2), E minor. arr]. Concerto in E minor for two
flutes and piano / [by] Georg Philipp Telemann ; edited and with
piano reduction by Louis Moyse. — New York ; London :
Schirmer, 1978. — 4to. — (Louis Moyse flute collection)
Score ([1],32p.) & part.
£2.75
(B78-51202)

VRNU — Duets
Flute duets / editor, Trevor Wye. — London : Chester Music. —
(Chester woodwind series)
Vol.1 : Thirty duets by Devienne, Berbiguier, Boismortier, Loeillet, Naudot,
Tulou, Kohler and Mozart. — 1978. — [2],29p ; 4to.
Unpriced
(B78-51205)

Vol.2. — 1978. — [2],26p ; 4to.
Unpriced
(B78-51204)

Vol.3 : Six easy duos for two flutes / [by] Eugene Walkiers (opus 55A(2)).
— 1978. — 35p ; 4to.
Unpriced
(B78-51203)

VRP — FLUTE & PIANO
VRP/AY — Collections
Associated Board of the Royal Schools of Music
New pieces for flute : with piano accompaniment. — London :
Associated Board of the Royal Schools of Music. — (Graded
wind music series)
Score (24p.) & part.
Book 1 : Grades 3 & 4. — 1978. — 4to.
Unpriced
(B78-51206)

New pieces for flute : with piano accompaniment. — London :
Associated Board of the Royal Schools of Music.
Score (3p.) & part.
Book 2 : Grades 5 and 6. — 1978. — 4to.
Unpriced
(B78-51207)

Three original pieces, composed for the sight-reading examinations
at the Paris Conservatoire : for flute and piano / foreword by
John Solum. — New York ; [London] : Oxford University Press,
1978. — 4to.
Works published for the first time. — Score (12p.) & part. — Contents: 1:
Morceau (Concours de flute, 1876), by Delibes - 2: Morceau (Concours de
flute, 1881), by Massenet - 3: Morceau (Concours de flute, 1887), by
Massenet.
Unpriced
(B78-50290)

VRP/AY — Miscellaneous works
Classical and romantic pieces / arranged for flute and piano by
Watson Forbes. — London : Oxford University Press.
Score (20p.) & part.
Book 1. — 1978. — 4to.
ISBN 0-19-356538-2 : Unpriced
(B78-51208)

Classical and romantic pieces / arranged for flute and piano by
watson Forbes. — London : Oxford University Press.
Score (24p.) & part.
Book 2. — 1978. — 4to.
ISBN 0-19-356539-0 : Unpriced
(B78-51209)

VRP/T — Vriations
Genin, P A
[Le carnival de Venice. Op.14]. Carnival of Venice : for flute and
piano / [by] P.A. Genin ; editor Trevor Wye. — London :
Chester Music, 1978. — 4to. — (Chester woodwind series)
Score (22p.) & part.
Unpriced
(B78-51210)

VRPE — Sonatas
Blacher, Boris
[Sonata, flute & piano, (1940)]. Sonate für Flöte und Klavier
(1940) / [von] Boris Blacher. — Berlin : Bote und Bock ;
[London] : [Schirmer], 1978. — 4to.
Score (16p.) & part.
£5.75
(B78-51211)

Cervetto, Giacobbe, b.1682
[Sonata, flute & continuo, op.3, no.6, D minor]. Sonate, d-moll für
Querflöte C (oder Violine) und Basso continuo = Sonata in D
minor for transverse flute (or violin and basso continuo) / [von]
Giacomo Cervetto ; herausgegeben von, edited by Marcello
Castellani. — Kassel ; London : Bärenreiter, 1978. — 4to. —
(Hortus musicus ; 229)
Score (15p.) & 2 parts. — Continuo realization by Annaberta Conti.
£3.00
(B78-51212)

Moyse, Louis
[Sonata, flute & piano, no.1 (1975)]. First sonata (1975) for flute
and piano / [by] Louis Moyse. — New York ; London : Schirmer,
1978. — 4to. — (Louis Moyse flute collection)
Score (44p.) & part.
£3.95
(B78-51213)

Stanley, John
Six solos, Op.4 : for flute or violin and continuo / [by] John
Stanley ; edited and realised by George Pratt. — London : Chester
Music, 1975. — 4to.
Score ([4],44p.) & 2 parts.
Unpriced
Also classified at SPE
(B78-51214)

VRPJ — Miscellaneous works
Doppler, Franz
[Fantaisie pastorale hongroise. Op.26]. Hungarian pastoral
fantasy : for flute and piano / [by] Franz Doppler ; editor, Trevor
Wye. — London : Chester Music, 1978. — 4to. — (Chester
woodwind series)
Score ([2],13p.) & part.
Unpriced
(B78-51215)

Fauré, Gabriel
[Fantasie, flute & piano, op.79]. Fantasie for flute and piano,
op.79 / [by] Gabriel Fauré ; editor, Trevor Wye. — London :
Chester Music, 1978. — 4to. — (Chester woodwind series)
Score (17p.) & part.
Unpriced

(B78-51216)

Feld, Jindřich
Three pieces : for oboe (or flute or clarinet) and piano / [by]
Jindřich Feld. — Prague : Supraphon ; New York ; London :
Schirmer, [1978]. — 4to.
Score (11p.) & 3 parts.
Unpriced
Primary classification VTPJ

Ferneyhough, Brian
Four miniatures : flute and piano / [by] Brian Ferneyhough. —
London : Peters, 1978. — 7p ; obl. fol.
Printed on one side of the leaf only.
Unpriced

(B78-50291)

Godard, Benjamin
Suite de trois morçeaux : for flute and piano, op.116 / [by]
Benjmin Godard ; editor, Trevor Wye. — London : Chester
Music, 1978. — 4to. — (Chester woodwind series)
Score (20p.) & part. — Contents: 1: Allegretto - 2: Idylle - 3: Valse.
Unpriced

(B78-51217)

Redel, Martin Christoph
Szenen : für Flöte und Klavier, Opus 26 (1977) / [von] Martin
Christoph Redel. — Berlin : Bote und Bock ; [London] :
[Schirmer], 1978. — 15p ; fol.
Duration 13 min.
£4.80

(B78-51218)

VRPK — Arrangements
Busoni, Ferruccio
[Drei Albumblätter, no.1]. Albumblatt / [by] Busoni ; arranged by
Millicent Silver ; edited by John Francis. — South Croydon :
Lengnick, 1978. — 4to.
Score (1],5p.) & part.
£0.60

(B78-51219)

Delius, Frederick
[Koanga. La calinda. arr]. La calinda, and, Air and dance / [by]
Frederick Delius ; arranged for flute and piano by Eric Fenby. —
London : Boosey and Hawkes, 1978. — 4to.
Unpriced

(B78-50292)

VRPK/AAY — Arrangements. Collections
Flute solos with piano accompaniment / editor, Trevor Wye. —
London : Chester Music. — (Chester woodwind series)
Score ([2],32p.) & part.
Vol.3. — 1977. — 4to.
Unpriced

(B78-51220)

VRPK/AHVQ/JM — Arrangements. Sicilianos. Incidental music
Fauré, Gabriel
[Pelléas et Melisande. Op.80. Sicilienne. arr]. Sicilienne from
Pelléas et Melisande : for flute and piano / [by] Gabriel Fauré ;
edited and arranged by Robert Bigio. — London : Chester Music,
1978. — 4to. — (Chester woodwind series)
Score (8p.) & part.
Unpriced

(B78-51221)

VRPK/AHVQT — Arrangements. Tambourins
Hasse, Johann Adolf
[Piramo e Tisbe. Tambourin. arr]. Tambourin / [by] Hasse ;
arranged for flute and piano by John Francis and Millicent Silver.
— South Croydon : Lengnick, 1978. — 4to.
Score ([2],5p.) & part.
£0.60

(B78-51222)

VRPK/DP/LF/AY — Arrangements. Carols. Christmas. Collections
Christmas time / arranged by Alan Laken. — London : Chappell,
1978. — 24p ; 4to.
For flute and piano. — Score (24p.) & part.
Unpriced

(B78-51223)

VRPK/DW — Arrangements. Songs, etc
Mozart, Wolfgang Amadeus
[Don Giovanni. Deh vieni alla finestra. arr]. Canzonetta / [by]
Mozart ; arranged for flute and piano by John Francis and
Millicent Silver. — South Croydon : Lengnick, 1978. — 4to.
Score ([1],5p.) & part.
£0.60

(B78-51224)

Mozart, Wolfgang Amadeus
[Die Zauberflöte. Wie stark ist nicht dein Zauberton. arr].
Andante / [by] Mozart ; arranged for flute and piano by John
Francis and Millicent Silver. — South Croydon : Lengnick, 1978.
— 4to.
Score ([2],4p.) & part.
Unpriced

(B78-51225)

VRPK/LF — Arrangements. Concertos
Arnold, Malcolm
[Concerto, flute, no.2, op.111. arr]. Flute concerto no.2, op.111 /
[by] Malcolm Arnold ; flute and piano reduction. — London :
Faber Music, 1978. — 4to.
Score ([2],24p.) & part.
Unpriced

(B78-51226)

Mozart, Wolfgang Amadeus
[Concerto, flute & harp, K.299, C major. arr]. Concerto in C
major (K.299) for flute, harp and orchestra / [by] Wolfgang
Amadeus Mozart ; arranged for flute and piano by Louis Moyse.
— New York ; London : Schirmer, 1978. — 4to. — (Louis Moyse
flute collection)
Score ([1],48p.) & part.
£2.75

(B78-51227)

VRPLR — FLUTE & ORGAN
Wahren, Karl Heinz
Entrerue : für Flöte und Orgel, 1976, 1977 / [von] Karl Heinz
Wahren. — Berlin : Bote und Bock ; [London] : [Schirmer], 1978.
— obl.fol.
Score (11p.) & part.
£4.30

(B78-51228)

VRPLSQ — FLUTE & VIOLA
Neubaur, Franz
Four pieces for flute and viola ... op.10 / [by] Franz Neubaur ;
transcribed and adapted by Louis Moyse. — New York ;
London : Schirmer, 1978. — 4to. — (Louis Moyse flute
collection)
£2.50

(B78-51229)

VRPLTQ — FLUTE & HARP
Dodgson, Stephen
[Duet, flute & harp]. Duo for flute and harp in four movements /
[by] Stephen Dodgson ; harp part edited by Susan Drake. —
London : Oxford University Press, 1978. — 4to.
Score (16p.) & part for flute. — Duration 9 1/2 min.
ISBN 0-19-356269-3 : Unpriced

(B78-51230)

Jolivet, André
[Alla rustica. arr]. Alla rustica : divertissement pour flûte et harpe
ou deux flûtes et harpe / [par] André Jolivet. — London : Boosey
and Hawkes, 1977. — 4to.
Score (16p.) & 2 parts ; the flute parts of the version for two flutes and harp
are printed in score.
Unpriced
Also classified at NVRNT

(B78-50648)

Rorem, Ned
Book of hours : eight pieces for flute and harp / [by] Ned Rorem.
— New York ; [London] : Boosey and Hawkes, 1978. — 4to.
Score (24p.) & part. — Duration 20 min.
Unpriced

(B78-51231)

VRPLTS — FLUTE & GUITAR
Carulli, Ferdinando
[Fantasia, flute & guitar, op.337]. Fantasie, op.337, für Flöte und
Gitarre / [von] Ferdinando Carulli ; nach zwei Motiven aus der
Oper 'Il pirata' von Vincenzo Bellini, revidiert und herausgegeben
von Spiro Thomatos. — Wilhelmshaven : Heinrichshofen ;
London : Peters, 1978. — 4to.
Score (16p.) & part.
Unpriced

(B78-50649)

Zehm, Friedrich
Serenade für Flöte und Gitarre / [von] Friedrich Zehm ;
Gitarrenbezeichnung, Anton Stingl. — Mainz ; London : Schott,
1977. — 4to. — (Gitarren-Archiv ; 443)
Score (11p.) & part.
£6.00

(B78-50293)

VRPLTSF — Flute & guitar. Concertos
Giuliani, Mauro
[Duetto concertante, flute & guitar, op.52]. Gran duetto
concertante, op.52 : für Flöte (Violine) und Gitarre / [von] Mauro
Giuliani ; herausgegeben von Frank Nagel. — Mainz ; London :
Schott, 1977. — 2pt ; 4to. — (Il flauto traverso ; 104)
£4.80
(B78-50294)

VRPLTSK — Arrangements
Wolf-Ferrari, Ermanno
[Operas. *Selections ; arr*]. Italian intermezzo : six pieces / by
Ermanno Wolf-Ferrari ; arranged for flute and guitar by Mary
Criswick. — London : Weinberger, 1978. — 4to.
Six items in six separate scores in a folder. — Contents: 1. Romance from
'Susanna's secret' - 2. Prelude from 'The school for fathers' - 3. Intermezzo
from 'The school for fathers - 4. Intermezzo no.1 from 'The jewels of the
Madonna' - 5. Intermezzo no.2 from 'The jewels of the Madonna' - 6.
Dance of the Camorrists from 'The jewels of the Madonna'.
Unpriced
(B78-50650)

VRPLVV — FLUTE & CLARINET
Becker, John
Sound piece no.6 : flute and clarinet / [by] John Becker. — New
York ; London : Peters, 1978. — 16p ; 4to.
Unpriced
(B78-51232)

VRPM — UNACCOMPANIED FLUTE
VRPMJ — Miscellaneous works
Aquino Carrilho, Altamiro
Album de chôros / [de] Altamiro Carrilho. — 16p ; 4to.
Unpriced
(B78-50651)

Debussy, Claude
Syrinx : for solo flute / [by] Claude Debussy ; general editor,
Trevor Wye. — London : Chester Music, 1978. — 2p ; 4to. —
(Chester woodwind series)
Unpriced
(B78-51233)

Steffen, Wolfgang
Tetraphonie : für Flöten (1 Spieler), (Altflöte, Grosse Flöte,
Bassflöte ad libitum, Piccolo mit 2 Lotusflöten, Opus 42 / [von]
Wolfgang Steffen. — Berlin : Bote und Bock ; [London] :
[Schirmer], 1977. — 9p ; fol.
£3.85
(B78-51234)

Yun, Isang
[Der weise Mann. Salomo]. Salomo : Solo für Alt-Flöte oder
Grosse Flöte aus der Cantate "Der weise Mann" (1977-1978) /
[von] Isang Yun. — Berlin : Bote und Bock ; [London] :
[Schirmer], 1978. — 3p ; fol.
£1.90
(B78-51235)

VRSPLSRE — Alto flute & cello. Sonatas
Johnson, Robert Sherlaw
[Sonata, flute (alto) & cello]. Sonata for alto flute and cello / [by]
Robert Sherlaw Johnson. — London : Oxford University Press,
1978. — 4to.
Score (11p.) & part.
ISBN 0-19-357337-7 : Unpriced
(B78-51236)

VS — RECORDER
VS/AC — Tutors
Playtime : Longman first recorder course. — London : Longman.
Stage 5. — 1978. — [1],49p ; obl.8vo. —
ISBN 0-582-18526-2 : Unpriced
(B78-51237)

Rosenberg, Steve
Recorder playing / [by] Steve Rosenberg. — Wellington : Prince
Milburn Music ; London : Boosey and Hawkes, 1978. — [1],31p ;
4to.
Unpriced
(B78-51238)

VSN — RECORDER ENSEMBLE
Neri, Massimiliano
[Sonate e canzone a quatro]. Canzone del terzo tuono : for
recorder concert / [by] Massimiliano Neri. — Haslemere :
Dolmetsch ; London : Chappell, 1978. — 4to. — (Dolmetsch
library)
Score (8p.) & 4 parts.
Unpriced
(B78-51239)

VSNG — Ensembles. Suites
Harvey, Raymond
[Suite, recorder ensemble, no.1]. Suite no.1 for recorder ensemble,
for descant, treble, 2 tenor and bass recorders / [by] Raymond
Harvey. — London : Chester Music, 1975. — 4to. — (Chester
recorder series ; no.12)
Score ([1],14p.) & 5 parts.
Unpriced
(B78-51240)

VSNK/DW/AYX — Arrangements. Songs, etc. Collections. Australia
Four Australian songs / arranged for descant and treble recorders
(3 and 4) by Colin J. Jenkins. — London : Schott, 1976. — [1],
8p ; obl.8vo.
Contents: 1: Click go the shears - 2: Waltzing Matilda - 3: Ten thousand
miles away - 4: Moreton Bay.
Unpriced
(B78-51241)

VSNQK/DJ — Sextets. Arrangements. Motets
Hartmann, Heinrich
[Erster Theil confortativae sacrae symphoniacae. Wenn der Herr
die Gefangnen Zion erlösen wird. *arr*]. Motet, Wenn der Herr die
Gefangnen Zion erlösen wird / by Heinrich Hartmann ; arranged
for recorder sextet, (descant, 2 trebles, 2 tenors, bass), by Roy
Touchin. — Bury : Tomus, 1978. — 8vo.
Score (11p.) & 6 parts.
Unpriced
(B78-51242)

VSNR — Quintets
Le Jeune, Henri
Fantasia a cinque : for recorder quintet / by Henri Le Jeune. —
Haslemere : Dolmetsch ; London : Chappell, 1978. — 4to. —
(Dolmetsch library)
Taken from Mersenne's Harmonie universelle. — Edited by Arnold
Dolmetsch.
Unpriced
(B78-51243)

VSNRK/DJ — Arrangements. Motets
Morley, Thomas
[A plaine and easy introduction to practicall musicke. O amica
mea. *arr*]. O amica mea / [by] Thomas Morley ; transcribed from
'A plaine and easy introduction to practicall musicke'. [With]
Deus omnipotens, [by] John Bull ; transcribed from the
common-placebook of John Baldwin ... for recorder quintet
(SSATB) ... [edited by] C.F. Simkins. — Locarno : Edizioni
Pegasus ; [London] : [Peters], 1977. — obl.8vo. — (Windsor series
of old music for recorders)
Score (16p.) & 5 parts.
Unpriced
(B78-50652)

VSNS — Quartets
Mozart, Wolfgang Amadeus
[Selections. *arr*]. A Mozart suite / arranged for recorder quartet
by Christopher Gordon. — London : Janus Music, 1978. — 4pt ;
4to.
Unpriced
(B78-51244)

VSNSK/AAY — Quartets. Arrangements. Collections
Nine recorder quartets / arranged from the Fitzwilliam Virginal
Book for two descants, treble, and tenor by Nicholas Marshall. —
London : Oxford University Press, 1977. — 23p ; 4to.
ISBN 0-19-357749-6 : Unpriced
(B78-50295)

VSNSK/AH — Quartets. Arrangements. Dances
Grieg, Edvard
[Holberg suite, op.40. *Selections : arr*]. Sarabande and gavotte ... /
[by] Edvard Grieg ; arranged for recorders (descant, treble, tenor
& bass) by Herbert Hersom. — York : Banks Music, 1978. —
5p ; 4to.
Unpriced
(B78-50296)

Haydn, Joseph
[Quartet, strings, no.3].
[Dances. *Selections: arr*]. Klassische Tanze von Joseph Haydn
[und] Wolfgang Amadeus Mozart : für Blockflöten - Ensemble ...
Sopran, Alt, Tenor, Bass ... / bearbeitet von ... Karl Stockert. —
Mainz ; London : Schott, 1978. — 23p ; obl. 8vo.
Works by Haydn comprise Hob. IX/10, nos. 1, 3, Hob. IX/29, nos. 1, 2, 4,
Hob. IX/28, no.1. Works by Mozart comprise K.600, nos. 2, 3 and 5,
K.602, nos. 1, 3 and K.605, no.3.
£3.20

(B78-50298)

VSNSK/DW/AYDM — Quartets. Arrangements. Songs, etc.
Collections. Ireland
Four Irish folksongs : for 2 descant, treble and tenor recorders /
arranged by Douglas Gunn. — London : Chester Music, 1975. —
7p ; 4to. — (Chester recorder series ; no.9)
Unpriced

(B78-51245)

VSNTG — Trios. Suites
Smith, Peter Melville
Willowbrook suite : for descant, treble and tenor recorders / [by]
Peter Melville Smith ; general editor, Pamela Morgan. —
Sevenoaks : Lengnick, 1978. — 7p ; 4to.
£0.55

(B78-51246)

VSNTK — Trios. Arrangements
Byrd, Morley, Tallis : three-part vocal compositions / arranged for
recorders ... by Aaron Williams. — Chesham : Ricordi, 1978. —
16p ; 4to. — (Polyphonic music of the golden age)
Unpriced

(B78-51247)

Greene, Maurice
[Voluntary, organ, no.6, B flat major. *arr*]. Voluntary in C major,
for descant, treble and tenor recorders / [by] Maurice Greene ;
arranged by Roger S. Jarvis. — London : Chester Music, 1975. —
4to. — (Chester recorder series ; no.11)
Score ([1],4p.) & 3 parts.
Unpriced

(B78-51248)

Scarlatti, Alessandro
[Il tigrane. *Selections : arr*]. Suite ... for 2 descant, treble (or
tenor) recorders / [by] Alessandro Scarlatti ; arranged by Janet E.
Beat. — London : Chester Music, 1978. — 11p ; 4to. — (Chester
recorder series ; no.10)
Unpriced

(B78-51249)

VSNTK/DU/AYH — Trios. Arrangements. Madrigals. Collections.
France
Thirty chansons, 1529 : for three instruments or voices / [edited by]
Bernard Thomas. — London : London Pro Musica, 1977. — [1],
40p ; 4to. — (Parisian chanson ; vol.10)
Taken from Attaingnant's collection 'Quarante et deux chansons musicales.
— Includes a separate appendix of six chansons for voice and lute, 1529.
Unpriced
Primary classification EZDU/AYH

(B78-50384)

VSNTQ — Recorders (2) & piano
Drewar, Della
Mingled jingles : for recorders and piano / [by] Della Drewar. —
Gnosall (16 Anchor Way, Danes Green) : Viking, 1978. — 4to &
obl.8vo.
Score (8p.) & 2 parts.
Unpriced

(B78-51250)

VSNTQHVKS — Recorders (2) & piano. Sambas
Bonsor, Brian
Simple samba : for descant 1, descant 2, and, or, treble recorder
and piano / [by] Brian Bonsor. — London : Schott, 1978. — c̄
4to.
Score ([3],10p.) & 3 parts.
Unpriced

(B78-51251)

VSNUK/AYF — Duets. Arrangements. Czechoslovakia
Aus dem alten tschechischen Sammlungen : zweistimmige Sätze, für
Sopran-und Altblockflöte / herausgegeben von Pavel Klapil. —
Kassel ; London : Bärenreiter, 1977. — 18p ; obl.8vo.
£1.40

(B78-50653)

VSPLTS — RECORDER & GUITAR
VSPLTSK — Recorder & guitar. Arrangements
Popular Elizabethan tunes : for recorder and guitar / arrangments
by Frederick Noad. — London : Ariel : Music Sales, 1977. —
24p ; 4to. — (Noad guitar library : ensemble series)
ISBN 0-86001-371-5 : Unpriced

(B78-51252)

VSPM — UNACCOMPANIED RECORDER
VSPMK/DW/GB/AY — Arrangements. Popular songs. Collections
Pop goes the recorder : 20 great tunes with chord symbols for
guitar / arranged by Bert Brewis. — London : Chappell.
Book 1. — 1977. — 24p ; 4to.
Unpriced

(B78-50299)

Book 2. — 1977. — 26p ; 4to.
Unpriced

(B78-50300)

VSPMK/DW/GJ — Arrangements. Children's songs. Collections
Children's songs and carols, including hymns and games : for easy
guitar [or] recorder / arranged by Jack Moore and Cecil Bolton.
— London : EMI, 1978. — 40p ; 4to.
Unpriced
Primary classification TSPMK/DW/GJ/AY

VSPMK/DW/LF/AY — Arrangements. Christmas songs. Collections
The best of Christmas songs : guitar [or] recorder. — London :
EMI, 1978. — 40p ; 4to.
ASrranged for guitar or recorder by Cecil Bolton and Jack Moore.
Unpriced
Primary classification TSPMK/DW/LF/AY

VSQ — SOPRANINO RECORDER
VSQW — Whistle. Tutors
Vallely, Eithne
Making music. The tin whistle / [by] Eithne Vallely and John
Vallely. — 2nd ed. — Belfast (6 Dublin Rd, Belfast) : Appletree
Press, 1977. — 31p ; 8vo.
With a 'Quick reference card' inserted.
ISBN 0-904651-19-3 : Unpriced

(B78-50301)

VSR — DESCANT RECORDER
VSR/AC — Tutors
Galloway, Malcolm
Recorder tutor : for descant recorders / [by] Malcolm Galloway.
— Leeds : Regina Music, 1978. — 32p ; 4to.
Unpriced

(B78-51254)

VSRNTPWE — Descant recorders (2) & keyboard. Sonatas
Bononcini, Giovanni Maria
[Church sonata, violins (2), op.6, no.9, D minor]. Sonata a tre,
d-mòll, d minor, op.VI, no.9, für zwei Sopranblockflöten und
Basso continuo, for two soprano [i.e. descant] recorders and basso
continuo / [von] Giovanni Maria Bononcini ; [herausgegeben von]
Klaus Rennicke. — Wilhemshaven : Noetzel ; London : Peters,
1977. — 4to.
Score (7p.) & 3 parts.
Unpriced

(B78-50654)

VSRNTPWF — Descant recorders (2) & keyboard. Concertos
Mouret, Jean Joseph
[Concert de chambre, liv.1, no.1]. Premier concert de chambre :
for two descant recorders and keyboard / [by] Jean Joseph
Mouret ; [edirted by] Jeanne Dolmetsch. — Haslemere :
Dolmetsch, 1978. — 4to. — (Dolmetsch library)
Score (12p.) & 4 parts, with alternative parts for viola da gamba or
violoncello or bassoon, and bass recorder. — Arnold Dolmetsch realised the
keyboard accompaniment.
Unpriced

(B78-51255)

VSRPK/AG — Descant recorder & piano. Arrangements. Suites
Caix D'Hervelois, Louis de
[Suite, flute & continuo, op.6, no.4, C major. *arr*]. Suite no.4, for
descant recorder and keyboard / Louise de Caix D'Hervelois ;
[edited by] Jeanne Dolmetsch. — Haslemere : Dolmetsch ;
London : Chappell, 1978. — 4to. — (Dolmetsch library)
Score (12p.) & part.
Unpriced

(B78-51256)

VSRPMK/AAY — Arrangements. Collections
The school recorder assembly book for pupils / [by] B.W. Appleby
[and] F. Fowler. — Leeds : E.J. Arnold, 1978. — [1],40p ; obl.
8vo.
With optional treble recorders.
ISBN 0-560-00379-x : Unpriced

(B78-51257)

Recorder playing : for descant recorders / [compiled by] Brian
Davey ; illustrated by Gordon Davey. — London : Chappell.
Junior book 2. — 1978. — 32p ; 4to.
Unpriced

(B78-51258)

VSS — TREBLE RECORDER
VSSPE — Treble recorder & piano. Sonatas
Schickhard, Johann Christian
 L'alphabet de la musique, Op.30 : 24 sonatas in all the keys for
 treble recorder and basso continuo in 6 volumes / [by] Johann
 Christian Schickhardt ; edited and realized by Paul J. Everett. —
 London : Musica rara.
 Score (536p.) & 2 parts.
 Vol.1 : Nos 1-4. — 1977. — 4to.
 Unpriced
 (B78-50655)

Schickhard, Johann Christian
 L'alphabet de la musique. Op.30 : 24 sonatas in all the keys for
 treble recorder and basso continuo in 6 volumes / [by] Johann
 Christian Schickhardt ; edited and realised by Paul G. Everett. —
 London : Musica rara.
 Score ([7],46p.) & 2 parts.
 Vol.2 : Sonatas 5-8. — 1978. — 4to.
 £6.50
 (B78-51259)

Schickhard, Johann Christian
 [Sonatas, treble recorder & continuo, op.17, nos 5,9]. Sonatas
 op.17, nos 5 and 9 for treble recorder and basso continuo / by
 J.C. Schickhardt ; ed. Paul J. Everett. — London : Musica rara,
 1978. — 4to.
 ([2],18p.) & 2 parts.
 Unpriced
 (B78-50656)

Schickhard, Johann Christian
 [Sonatas, treble recorder & continuo, op.17, nos 10,11]. Sonatas
 op.17, nos 10 and 11 for treble recorder and basso continuo / [by]
 J.C. Schickhardt ; ed. Paul J. Everett. — London : Musica rara,
 1978. — 4to.
 Score ([2],18p.) & 2 parts.
 Unpriced
 (B78-50657)

Schickhard, Johann Christian
 [Sonatas, treble recorder & continuo, op.17, nos.1-2]. Sonatas
 op.17, nos 1 and 2, for treble recorder and basso continuo / [by]
 J.C. Schickhardt ; ed. Paul J. Everett. — London : Musica rara,
 1978. — 4to.
 Score ([2],20p.) & 2 parts.
 Unpriced
 (B78-50658)

Telemann, Georg Philipp
 [Neue Sonatinen, nos.2,5]. Two new sonatinas, for treble recorder
 and basso continuo / [by] George Philipp Telemann ; continuo
 part and harpsichord realization by Claus E. Maynfrank. — 1st
 ed. — London : Musica rara, 1978. — 4to.
 Score ([1],29p.) & 3 parts.
 Unpriced
 (B78-51260)

VSSPK/AAY — Arrangements. Collections
 First book of treble recorder solos / edited for treble (alto) recorder
 and piano by Walter Dergmann. — London : Faber Music, 1978.
 — 4to.
 Score ([4]p,28p.) & part.
 Unpriced
 (B78-51261)

VSX — PIPES
VSX/AC — Tutors
Meiklem, Colin L
 Starter's whistle, or, How to play the penny whistle / by Colin L.
 Meiklem. — London : Feldman, 1978. — 44p ; 4to.
 An amplified edition of that published in 1970.
 Unpriced
 (B78-51262)

VTN — OBOE ENSEMBLE
VTNUK/AAY — Duets. Arrangements. Collections
 Oboe duets / editor, James Brown. — London : Chester Music. —
 (Chester woodwind series)
 Vol.1. — 1978. — [2],23p ; 4to.
 Unpriced
 (B78-51263)

VTP — OBOE & PIANO
VTP/AY — Collections
 Associated Board of the Royal Schools of Music
 New pieces for oboe : with piano accompaniment. — London :
 Associated Board of the Royal Schools of Music. — (Graded
 wind music series)
 Score (27p.) & part.
 Book 1 : Grades 3 & 4. — 1978. — 4to.
 Unpriced
 (B78-51264)

New pieces for oboe : with piano accompaniment. — London :
 Associated Board of the Royal Schools of Music.
 Score (29p.) & part.
 Book 2 : Grades 5 and 6. — 1978. — 4to.
 Unpriced
 (B78-51265)

VTPE — Sonatas
Tessarini, Carlo
 [Sonata, oboe & continuo, op.2, no.1, F major]. Sonata no.1 in F
 for oboe and piano / [by] Carlo Tessarini ; edited by Evelyn
 Rothwell and Valda Aveling. — London : Chester Music, 1978.
 — 4to. — (Chester woodwind series)
 Score (11p.) & part.
 Unpriced
 (B78-51266)

VTPJ — Miscellaneous works
Feld, Jindřich
 Three pieces : for oboe (or flute or clarinet) and piano / [by]
 Jindřich Feld. — Prague : Supraphon ; New York ; London :
 Schirmer, [1978]. — 4to.
 Score (11p.) & 3 parts.
 Unpriced
 Also classified at VRPJ; VVPJ
 (B78-51267)

VTPK — Arrangements
Krol, Bernhard
 Capricetten : für Oboe und Streichorchester, op.49 / [von]
 Bernhard Krol ; Oboe und Klavier. — Berlin : Bote und Bock ;
 [London] : [Schirmer], 1978. — fol.
 Score (22p.) & part.
 £7.70
 (B78-51268)

VTPK/LE — Arrangements. Symphonies
Berkeley, Sir Lennox
 [Sinfonia concertante, oboe & chamber orchestra, op.84. *arr*].
 Sinfonia concertante for oboe and chamber orchestra / [by]
 Lennox Berkeley ; piano reduction by the composer. — London :
 Chester Music, 1978. — 4to.
 Score (36p.) & part.
 Unpriced
 (B78-51269)

VTPK/LF — Arrangements. Concertos
Lebrun, Ludwig August
 [Concerto, oboe, no.1, D minor. *arr*]. Konzert No.1, d-moll, für
 Oboe und Orchester / [von] Ludwig August Lebrun ;
 herausgegeben von Hermann Tottcher, Kadenz von Lothar Koch,
 Klavierauszug von Helmut May. — Mainz ; London : Schott,
 1977. — 4to. — (Oboe Bibliothek ; 13)
 Score (36p.) & part with a separate leaf containing the cadenzas inserted.
 £9.60
 (B78-50302)

VTWN/AY — Crumhorn. Ensembles. Collections
 Crumhorn consort anthology. — London : Musica rara.
 Score ([1],24p.) & 4 parts.
 Vol.2 ; [edited by Pater Nothnagle and R.P. Block]. — 1977. — č 4to.
 Unpriced
 (B78-51270)
 Vol.3 ; [edited by Peter Nothnagle and R.P. Block]. — 1977. — 4to.
 Unpriced
 (B78-51271)

VUN — SAXOPHONE ENSEMBLE
VUNSK/AAY — Quartets. Arrangements. Collections
 Saxophone quartets / editor, Paul Harvey. — London : Chester
 Music.
 Score ([2],20p.) & 4 parts.
 Vol.1. — 1978. — 4to.
 Unpriced
 (B78-51272)

VUP — SAXOPHONE & PIANO
VUPEM — Sonatinas
Mathias, William
 [Sonatina, clarinet & piano, op.3]. Sonatina for clarinet in B flat
 and piano, Op.3 / [by] William Mathias. — London : Oxford
 University Press, 1978. — 4to.
 Score (16p.) & part.
 ISBN 0-19-357777-1 : Unpriced
 (B78-51273)

VV — CLARINET
VV/AC — Tutors
Dingle, Patrick
 An introduction to the clarinet / by Patrick Dingle and Frank
 Holdsworth. — London : EMI.
 Book 1. — 1978. — [1],52p ; 4to.
 Unpriced
 (B78-50659)

VV/AF — Exercises
Galper, Avrahm
Clarinet scales and arpeggios / annotated by Avrahm Galper. — Willowdale ; [London] : Boosey and Hawkes, 1978. — [1],40p ; 4to.
Unpriced

(B78-51274)

VVN — CLARINET ENSEMBLE
VVNK/X/AY — Arrangements. Canons. Collections
Chalumeau canons for clarinets / [compiled and arranged by] John Robert Brown. — London : Chappell, 1977. — 11p ; 4to.
Unpriced

(B78-50660)

VVNS — Quartets
Newton, Rodney Stephen
Byzantine sketches : for clarinet quartet / by Rodney Stephen Newton. — East Barnet : Composer Edition, 1978. — 20p ; fol.
Facsimile of the composer's autograph.
Unpriced

(B78-50661)

Parfrey, Raymond
Three tunes for four clarinets / by Raymond Parfrey. — London : EMI, 1978. — 4to.
Score (5p.) & 4 parts. — Contents: 1: Whistling tune - 2: Chorale - 3: Tunes from out of town.
Unpriced

(B78-51275)

VVNSK — Quartets. Arrangements
Schumann, Robert
[Clavierstücke für die Jugend. Op.68. *Selections : arr*]. A Schumann suite : seven pieces from 'Album for the young'. opus 68 / arranged for four equal clarinets by Philip G. Wilkinson. — Sevenoaks : Novello, 1978. — [1],16p ; 8vo.
Duration 13 min.
Unpriced

(B78-51276)

VVNTK/B/FJ — Trios. Arrangements. Automata
Haydn, Joseph
[Werke für das Laufwerk. *Selections : arr*]. Four clock pieces / [by] Joseph Haydn ; arranged for three equal clarinets by Wadham Sutton. — Sevenoaks : Novello, 1978. — 4p ; 8vo.
Nos 7,17,11 and 18.
Unpriced

(B78-51277)

VVNU — Duets
Kolb, Barbara
Rebuttal : two clarinets / [by] Barbara Kolb. — New York : Henmar Press : Peters ; [London] : [Peters], 1975. — [1],7p ; 4to.
Unpriced

(B78-51278)

VVP — CLARINET & PIANO
VVP/AY — Collections
Associated Board of the Royal Schools of Music
New pieces for clarinet : with piano accompaniment. — London : Associated Board of the Royal Schools of Music. — (Graded wind music series)
Score (20p.) & part.
Book 1 : Grades 3 & 4. — 1978. — 4to.
Unpriced

(B78-51279)

Book 1 : Grades 3 & 4. — 1978. — 4to.
Unpriced

(B78-51280)

Book 1 : Grades 5 & 6. — 1978. — 4to.
Unpriced

(B78-51281)

Contemporary music for clarinet, including music by Copland, Goldman, Holloway, Reizenstein, Soproni / edited by Peter Wastall. — London : Boosey and Hawkes, 1978. — 4to.
Unpriced
Also classified at VVPM/AY

(B78-51282)

VVPE — Sonatas
Poulenc, Francis
[Sonata, clarinet & piano]. Sonata for clarinet in B flat and piano / [by] Francis Poulenc. — 5th ed. [embodying corrections to the first ed.], edited by Thea King and Georgina Dobree. — London : Chester Music, 1976. — 4to.
Score (24p.) & part.
Unpriced

(B78-51283)

VVPJ — Miscellaneous works
Feld, Jindřich
Three pieces : for oboe (or flute or clarinet) and piano / [by] Jindřich Feld. — Prague : Supraphon ; New York ; London : Schirmer, [1978]. — 4to.
Score (11p.) & 3 parts.
Unpriced
Primary classification VTPJ

Garland, Neil
Five times of day : clarinet and piano / [by] Neil Garland. — Ampleforth : Emerson, 1977. — 4to.
Score ([1],8p.) & part.
£1.50

(B78-50662)

Kelly, Bryan
Zodiac : twelve pieces for clarinet in B flat and piano, in two sets. — London : Oxford University Press.
Score (16p.) & part.
Set 1. — 1978. — 4to.
ISBN 0-19-357442-x : Unpriced

(B78-51284)

Set 2. — 1978. — 4to.
ISBN 0-19-357443-8 : Unpriced

(B78-51285)

VVPK/AAY — Arrangements. Collections
Baroque music for clarinet : including music by Couperin, Handel, Molter, Pokorny, Stamitz / edited and annotated by Peter Wastall ; continuo realisations by Peter Wastall ; clarinet and piano. — London : Boosey and Hawkes, 1978. — 4to. — (Exploring music series)
Score (13p.) & part.
Unpriced

(B78-51286)

Classical music for clarinet, including music by Beethoven, Grétry, Haydn, Mozart, Stamitz / edited and annotated by Peter Wastall. — London : Boosey and Hawkes, 1978. — 4to.
([1],13p.) & part.
Unpriced

(B78-50303)

Romantic music for clarinet, including music by Baerman, Bruch, Gade, Spohr, Weber / edited and annotated by Peter Wastall. — London : Boosey and Hawkes, 1978. — 4to.
Score & part.
Unpriced

(B78-50304)

VVPK/AE — Arrangements. Sonatas
Mozart, Wolfgang Amadeus
[Church sonatas. *Selections : arr*]. Four church sonatas / [by] W.A. Mozart ; arranged for B flat clarinet and piano by Yona Ettlinger. — London : Boosey and Hawkes, 1978. — 4to.
Score ([4],20p.) & part.
£2.25

(B78-50305)

VVPK/LF — Arrangements. Concertos
Beer, Joseph
[Concerto, clarinet, op.1, B flat major. *arr*]. Concerto no.1 for clarinet and orchestra, op.1 / [by] Joseph Beer ; clarinet and piano reduction [edited by] John Madden. — London : Musica rara, 1978. — 4to.
Score (48p.) & part.
Unpriced

(B78-50663)

VVPLX — CLARINET & PERCUSSION
Davies, Peter Maxwell
Stedman doubles : for clarinet and percussion / by Peter Maxwell Davies ; (1956 rev. 1968). — London : Boosey and Hawkes, 1978. — 18p ; 4to.
Duration 30 min. — Notes by Alan Hacker.
Unpriced

(B78-50664)

VVPM — UNACCOMPANIED CLARINET
VVPM/AY — Collections
Contemporary music for clarinet, including music by Copland, Goldman, Holloway, Reizenstein, Soproni / edited by Peter Wastall. — London : Boosey and Hawkes, 1978. — 4to.
Unpriced
Primary classification VVP/AY

VVPMJ — Miscellaneous works
Clifford, Keith
Momentella : for clarinet in B flat / [by] Keith Gifford. — Birmingham : Arts Lab Music, 1978. — 8ff ; obl.4to.
Printed on one side of the leaf only.
Unpriced

(B78-51287)

**VVPMK/DW/AYE — Arrangements. Songs, etc. Collections.
Germany**
Mein Heimatland : die schönsten Volks- , Wander- , Trink- und
Scherzlieder / herausgegeben von Ludwig Andersen. — Neu-
Ausgabe mit vollstandigem Text, Trompete [oder] Klarinette in
B / von W. Draths mit übergelegtem Text. — Mainz ; London :
Schott, 1977. — 88p ; 4to.
£7.20
Primary classification WSPMK/DW/AYE

(B78-50314)

VVPMK/DW/LF/AY — Arrangements. Christmas songs. Collections
The **best** of Christmas songs : clarinet. — London : EMI, 1978. —
33p ; 4to.
Arranged for clarinet by Cecil Bolton and Jack Moore.
Unpriced

(B78-51288)

**VVU — BASS CLARINET
VVUPMJ — Unaccompanied bass clarinet. Miscellaneous works**
Ferneyhough, Brian
Time and motion study I : solo bass clarinet / [by] Brian
Ferneyhough. — London : Peters, 1977. — 8ff : obl.fol.
Facsimile of the composer's manuscript - Printed on one side of the leaf
only.
Unpriced

(B78-50306)

**VWP — BASSOON & PIANO
VWP/AY — Collections**
New pieces for bassoon : with piano accompaniment. — London :
Associated Board of the Royal Schools of Music.
Score (28p.) & part.
Book 1 : Grades 3 and 4. — 1978. — 4to.
Unpriced

(B78-51289)

Book 2 : Grades 5 and 6. — 1978. — 4to.
Unpriced

(B78-51290)

VWPJ — Miscellaneous works
Walker, James
A la russe : for bassoon & piano, based on a theme by
Moscheles / by James Walker. — London : Weinberger, 1978. —
4to.
The Moscheles theme is taken from 'Variations. Op.23 - Score (7p.) & part.
Unpriced

(B78-50665)

VWPK/LF — Arrangements. Concertos
Fasch, Johann Friedrich
[Concerto, bassoon & string orchestra, C major. *arr*]. Concerto
C-dur für Fagott, Streicher und Basso continuo / [von] Johann
Friedrich Fasch ; [Generalbassaussetzung von Renée La Roche].
— Ausgabe für Fagott und Klavier / von Walter Hermann
Sallager. — Wilhemshaven : Noetzel ; [London] : [Peters], 1978.
— 4to.
Score (15p.) & part.
Unpriced

(B78-50666)

Hertel, Johann Wilhelm
[Concerto, bassoon & string orchestra, B flat major. *arr*]. Concerto
in B flat for bassoon, strings and basso continuo / [by] Johann
Wilhelm Hertel ... ; edited by H. Voxman, piano reduction by
R.P. Block. — London : Musica rara, 1978. — 4to.
Score ([1],24p.) & part.
Unpriced

(B78-51291)

Joubert, John
[Concerto, bassoon & chamber orchestra, Op.77. *arr*]. Concerto
for bassoon and chamber orchestra, Opus 77 / [by] John Joubert ;
bassoon and piano score. — Sevenoaks : Novello, 1977. — 4to.
Score (4-36p.) & part. — Duration 17 min.
£3.15

(B78-50667)

Kozeluch, Johann Anton
[Concerto, bassoon, C major. *arr*]. Concerto in C for bassoon and
orchestra / [by] Johann Anton Kozeluch ; bassoon and piano
reduction, [editor] H. Voxman. — London : Musica rara, 1978. —
4to.
Score ([1],32p.) & part.
Unpriced

(B78-51292)

VWPK/W — Arrangements. Rondos
Kalliwoda, Jan Václav
[Introduction & rondo, orchestra, op.51. *arr*]. Introduction and
rondo, op.51, for horn and orchestra / [by] J.W. Kalliwoda ;
edited with a piano reduction by John Madden. — London :
Musica rara, 1978. — 4to.
Score ([1],26p.) & part.
Unpriced

(B78-51293)

**VXR — MELODICA
VXR/AC — Melodica. Tutors**
Slack, Roy
An introduction to the melodica : a beginner's guide to the
melodica with well known tunes to play and sing / by Roy Slack.
— London : EMI, 1978. — [1],32p ; 4to.
Unpriced

(B78-51294)

**VY — BAGPIPES
VYQ/AC — Northumbrian pipes. Tutors**
Butler, Richard
A basic tutor for the Northumbrian small pipe / [by] Richard
Butler. — Cramlington (22 Newlyn Drive, Parkside Dale,
Cramlington, Northumberland) : Richard Butler, 1976. — 56p ;
4to.
ISBN 0-9505591-0-5 : Unpriced

(B78-50308)

VYSPMJ — Northumbrian small-pipes
Dagg, Archie
The Congnetdale garland : a collection of tunes for fiddle and
small-pipes / composed by Archie Dagg. — Morpeth (Swinden,
Sharperton, Morpeth) : Archie Dagg, 1978. — [18]p ; 8vo.
Unpriced
Primary classification SPMJ

**W — BRASS WIND INSTRUMENTS
W/AC — Tutors**
Ridgeon, John
Brass for beginners : treble clef piston - valved brass instruments /
[by] John Ridgeon. — London : Boosey and Hawkes, 1977. — vi,
54p ; 4to.
£2.20

(B78-50309)

**WM — BRASS BAND
WM/AY — Collections**
Bandkraft / consultant and musical adviser, Harry Mortimer, series
editor, Ifor James, editorial assistant, John Golland ; foreword by
Gordon Jacob. — Manchester : Forsyth.
Score (40p.) & 17 parts. — Contents: Bandkraft, by John Golland -
Saraband, by Gordon Jacob - La Donna e mobile, by Verdi, arr. Roy
Newsome - Spike's rag, by Michael Ball - National anthem, arr. John
Golland.
1. — 1978. — 4to & obl.4to.
Unpriced

(B78-51295)

2. — 1978. — 4to & obl.4to.
Unpriced

(B78-51296)

3. — 1978. — 4to & obl.4to.
Unpriced

(B78-51297)

Intermediate band book. — Watford : R. Smith.
Book 1 : Sandwell festival march, by Stuart Johnson [and arrangements of
songs, hymns, and carols]. — 1977. — 52p ; 4to.
Unpriced

(B78-50669)

The **Salvation** Army Brass Band Journal (Festival series). —
London : Salvationist Publishing and Supplies.
Nos 388-391 : Saints of God : song arrangements, by James Curnew. Balm
in Gilead : spiritual : by Donald Osgood. Through the Blood of the Lamb :
rhapsody by Kenneth Downie. Selection from 'Spirit' arr. Ray
Steadman-Allen. — 1978. — [1],65p ; obl.8vo. —
Unpriced

(B78-51298)

Salvation Army Brass Band Journal (General series). — London :
Salvationist Publishing and Supplies.
Nos 1697-1700 : Here at the cross : meditation, by Roy Steadman-Allen.
Camp Akatarawa, by Dean Goffin. The call of Christ : cornet solo by
Norman Bearcroft, [and] Aria from concerto grosso. no.12 by Handel, arr.
Michael Kenyon. In his hands : selection, by Erik Silfverberg. — 1977. —
[1],53p ; obl.4to. —
Unpriced

(B78-50670)

Nos 1705-1708 : St John's Citadel : march, by Eric O. Abbott. Christmas
comes but once a year, by Brian Bowen. Prelude on 'Govaars', by Ray
Steadman-Allen, melody by Gerrit Govaars. A joy untold : euphonium solo,
by Terry Camsey. — 1978. — [1],45p ; obl.4to. —
Unpriced

(B78-51299)

Nos.1701-1704 : Spirit divine : meditation by Leslie Condon. Selection from 'Glory', by Ray Steadman-Allen, (melodies, John Larsson), Stephanus : hymn-tune arrangement by J. Paul Green. Joyous proclamation : cornet quartet, by Norman Bearcroft. — 1978. — [1],57p ; obl.8vo. — Unpriced

(B78-51300)

Salvation Army Brass Band Journal (Triumph series). — London : Salvationist Publishing and Supplies.
Score ([1],45p.) & 14 parts.
Nos. 813-816 : Joyful service : march by Edgar Grinsted. A little Mozart suite, by Ken Griffin. Whiter than snow : meditation by Terry Camsey. Thetford march : by Charles Craig. — 1977. — 8vo.
Unpriced

(B78-50310)

Nos 821-824 : Sing to God ; selection by Ralph Pearce. Kum ba yah ; spiritual by Ray Steadman-Allen. Listowel : march, by Dirk Krommenhoek. Forward to victory, by E.A. Smith. — 1978. — [1],45p ; obl.8vo. — Unpriced

(B78-51301)

Nos.817-820 : When the glory gets into your soul, by John Larsson, arr. Ray Steadman-Allen. Variations on 'Duke Street', by Michael Kenyon. Our Father God : selection, by Derek Jordan. A song of fight : euphonium solo, by Erik Silferberg. — 1978. — [1],57p ; obl.8vo. — Unpriced

(B78-51302)

WM/T — Variations
Broadbent, Derek
The battle hymn of the Republic / arranged by Derek Broadbent. — London : Polyphonic Reproductions : Studio Music, 1977. — 8vo.
Variations for brass band on W. Steffe's theme. — Conductor & 25 parts ; various parts are in duplicate.
Unpriced

(B78-50671)

WMG — Suites
Catelinet, Philip
The Isle of Avalon : suite for brass band / [by] Philip Catelinet. — Watford : R. Smith, 1978. — [1],26p ; obl.4to.
Duration 10 min.
Unpriced

(B78-51303)

Mathias, William
Vivat regina : suite for brass band / [by] William Mathias. — London : Oxford University Press, 1978. — 22pt ; 4to.
Unpriced

(B78-50672)

Mathias, William
Vivat regina : suite for brass band, op.75 / [by] William Mathias. — London : Oxford University Press, 1978. — 55p ; 4to.
Duration 10 min. — Facsimile of the composer's manuscript.
ISBN 0-19-365694-9 : Unpriced

(B78-50673)

WMGM — Marches
Howarth, Elgar
Berne patrol : for brass band / a traditional Swiss tune arranged by Elgar Howarth. — London : Chester Music, 1977. — 4to. — (Just brass ; no.9BB)
Piano conductor (8p.) & 24 parts, with several copies of various parts.
Unpriced

(B78-51304)

Johnson, Stuart
A march overture / [by] Stuart Johnson. — Watford : R. Smith, 1977. — 18p ; obl.4to.
For brass band.
Unpriced

(B78-50674)

Siebert, Edrich
The queen's trumpeters : concert march / by Edrich Siebert. — London : Harmer Music, 1977. — 8vo.
For brass band. — Cornet conductor & 24 parts.
Unpriced

(B78-50675)

WMGN — Fanfares
Howarth, Elgar
Two processional fanfares / [by] Elgar Howarth. — London : Chester Music, 1975. — 4to. — (Just brass ; no.6)
Score ([2],3p.) & 11 parts.
Unpriced

(B78-51305)

WMH — Dances
Kelly, Bryan
Edinburgh dances / [by] Bryan Kelly. — London : Novello, 1978. — [2],50p ; obl.4to. — (Novello Brass Band Series)
For brass band. — Edited by Bram Gay. — Duration 14 min.
£4.50

(B78-51306)

Siebert, Edrich
Gipsy wedding / [by] Edrich Siebert. — London : Harmer Music : Studio Music, 1977. — 8vo.
For brass band. — B flat cornet donductor & 24 parts, with several copies of various parts.
Unpriced

(B78-50676)

WMJ — Miscellaneous works
Broadbent, Derek
Cornets a-go-go / [by] Derek Broadbent. — London : Polyphonic Reproductions : Studio Music, 1978. — 8vo.
For brass band. — Conductor & 27 parts, with several copies of various parts.
Unpriced

(B78-50677)

Butterworth, Arthur
Nightflight : symphonic study for brass band / [by] Arthur Butterworth. — London : Chester Music, 1978. — 55p ; 4to. — (Just brass ; no.13BB)
Facsimile of the composer's autograph.
Unpriced

(B78-51307)

Butterworth, Arthur
Nightflight : symphonic study for brass band / [by] Arthur Butterworth. — London : Chester Music, 1978. — 27pt ; 4to. — (Just brass ; no.13BB)
With several copies of various parts.
Unpriced

(B78-51308)

Calvert, Morley
Introduction, elegy and caprice / [by] Morley Calvert. — Watford : R. Smith, 1978. — [1],33p ; obl.4to.
For brass band.
Unpriced

(B78-51309)

Crookes, Brian
Way out west / [by] Brian Crookes. — London (50 Ladbroke Grove, W.11) : Midland Music, 1976. — 8vo.
For brass band - Conductor & 25 parts.
Unpriced

(B78-50311)

Huber, Paul
Caprice / [by] Paul Huber. — Watford : R. Smith, 1978. — 26p ; obl.4to.
For brass band.
Unpriced

(B78-51310)

Hughes, Eric
Overture to youth / by Eric Hughes. — London : Studio Music, 1977. — 25pt ; 8vo.
For brass band.
Unpriced

(B78-51311)

Lear, W Hogarth
Cops and robbers : for brass band / [by] W. Hogarth Lear. — London : Paxton, 1978. — 8vo.
Duration 4 min. — Conductor & 26 parts, with several copies of various parts.
Unpriced

(B78-51312)

Newsome, Roy
Hat trick / [by] Roy Newsome. — London : Midland Music, 1976. — 8vo.
For brass band. — Conductor & 26 parts, with several copies of various parts.
Unpriced

(B78-50312)

Siebert, Edrich
Bees-a-buzzin' / by Edrich Siebert. — London : Harmar : Studio Music, 1978. — 8vo.
For brass band. — Conductor & 25 parts, with several copies of various parts.
Unpriced

(B78-50678)

Siebert, Edrich
Drummer's delight : drum feature / by Edrich Siebert. — London : Studio Music, 1978. — 8vo.
For brass band. — Conductor & 23 parts, with several copies of various parts.
Unpriced

(B78-51313)

Siebert, Edrich
Sunday morning / by Edrich Siebert. — London : Harmer :
Studio Music, 1977. — 8vo.
For brass band. — Cornet conductor & 24 parts, with several copies of
various parts.
Unpriced

(B78-50679)

Wood, Gareth
Introduction and allegro / [by] Gareth Wood. — Watford : R.
Smith, 1978. — 37p ; obl. 4to.
For brass band.
Unpriced

(B78-50680)

Woods, Stanley
Cornet cosmology : for brass band / [by] Stanley Woods. —
London : Chester Music, 1978. — 4to. — (Just brass ; no.12BB)
Piano conductor (8p.) & 26 parts, with several copies of various parts.
Unpriced

(B78-51314)

WMK — Arrangements
Fauré, Gabriel
[Dolly. Op.56, no.1. Berceuse. *arr*]. Berceuse. ('Listen with
Mother' theme) ... / [by] Fauré ; arr. Philip Sparke. — London :
R. Smith, 1978. — 8vo.
Conductor & 25 parts.
Unpriced

(B78-51315)

WMK/AAY — Arrangements. Collections
Hinrichsen second band book : four original compositions and four
arrangements of classical works / by Stuart Johnson. — London :
Peters in conjunction with the National School Brass Band
Association, 1978. — 27pt ; obl.8vo.
Includes music by Schubert, Diabelli and Schumann.
Unpriced

(B78-51316)

Hinrichsen second band book : four original compositions and four
arrangements of classical works / by Stuart Johnson. — London :
Peters in conjunction with the National School Brass Band
Association, 1978. — [2],43p ; obl.4to.
Includes music by Schubert, Diabelli and Schumann.
Unpriced

(B78-51317)

Hinrichsen third band book : a miscellany of 6 popular pieces /
selected and arranged by Stuart Johnson. — London : Peters in
conjunction with the National School Brass Band Association,
1978. — 27pt ; 8vo.
Includes music by Haydn, Beethoven, Purcell and Bizet.
Unpriced

(B78-51318)

Hinrichsen third band book : a miscellany of 6 popular pieces /
selected and arranged by Stuart Johnson. — London : Peters in
conjunction with the National School Brass Band Association,
1978. — [2],45p ; obl.4to.
Includes music by Haydn, Beethoven, Purcell and Bizet.
Unpriced

(B78-51319)

WMK/AE — Arrangements. Symphonies
Bach, Johann Christian
[Symphony, wind instruments, no.6, B flat major. *arr*].
Bläser-Sinfonie für Blechbläser / [von] Johann Christian Bach ;
bearbeitet von Johannes H.E. Koch. — Kassel ; [London] :
Bärenreiter, 1977. — 15p ; 8vo.
The third and second movements of the fourth wind symphony substituted
for the third movement.
Unpriced

(B78-50681)

WMK/AGM — Arrangements. Marches
Byrd, William
[The battell. The marche before the battell. *arr*]. The Earle of
Oxford's march / [by] William Byrd ; arranged by Elgar Howarth
for brass ensemble. — London : Chester Music, 1978. — 4to. —
(Just brass ; no.26)
Score ([2],10p.) & 9 parts.
Unpriced

(B78-51320)

WMK/AH — Arrangements. Dances
Susato, Thielman
[Het derde musyck boexken. *Selections : arr*]. Six Susato dances :
for brass band ... / arranged by John Iveson. — London : Chester
Music, 1978. — to. — (Just brass ; no.11BB)
Piano conductor (10p.) & 21 parts with several copies of various parts.
Unpriced

(B78-51321)

WMK/AHXJ — Arrangements. Ragtime
Joplin, Scott
Gladiolus rag / by Scott Joplin ; arranged from brass band by
Michael Brand. — Watford : R. Smith, 1978. — 8vo.
Conductor & 25 parts, with several copies of various parts.
Unpriced

(B78-51322)

WMK/DW — Arrangements. Songs, etc
Brand, Michael
Portsmouth : traditional / arr. Michael Brand. — Watford : R.
Smith, 1978. — 8vo.
For brass band. — Conductor & 25 parts with several copies of various
parts.
Unpriced

(B78-51323)

Broadbent, Derek
The Lincolnshire poacher / arranged by Derek Broadbent. —
London : Logo Music : Studio Music (dist.), 1978. — 8vo.
For brass band. — Conductor & 24 parts, with several copies of various
parts.
Unpriced

(B78-51324)

Broadbent, Derek
Strawberry fair / arranged by Derek Broadbent. — London :
Logo Music : Studio Music, 1978. — 8vo.
For brass band. — Conductor & 25 parts.
Unpriced

(B78-51325)

French, Percy
[Phil the fluter's ball. *arr*]. Phil the fluter's ball / [by] Percy
French ; arranged by Derek Broadbent. — London : Polyphonic
Reproductions : Studio Music, 1977. — 8vo.
For brass band. — Conductor & 25 parts ; various parts in duplicate.
Unpriced

(B78-50682)

Howarth, Elgar
Greensleeves / arranged by Elgar Howarth for brass ensemble. —
London : Chester Music, 1978. — 4to. — (Just brass ; no.28)
Score ([2],6p.) & 10 parts.
Unpriced

(B78-51326)

Howarth, Elgar
Greensleeves : for brass band / arranged by Elgar Howarth. —
London : Chester Music, 1977. — 4to. — (Just brass ; no.10BB)
Piano conductor (6p.) & 23 parts, with several copies of various parts.
Unpriced

(B78-51327)

WMK/HM — Arrangements. Ballet
Bliss, Sir Arthur
[Checkmate. *Selections : arr*]. Four dances from the ballet ... /
[by] Arthur Bliss ; arranged for brass band by Eric Ball. —
Sevenoaks : Novello, 1978. — [2],61p ; obl.4to. — (Novello brass
band series)
Duration 14 min.
£4.85

(B78-51328)

WMP — SOLO INSTRUMENT (S) & BRASS BAND
WMPWR — Cornet & brass band
Bellstedt, Herman
Napoli : cornet solo / [by] Herman Bellstedt. — Watford : R.
Smith, 1978. — 8vo.
Conductor & 26 parts, with several copies of various parts, some of which
are intended to be split in half.
Unpriced

(B78-50683)

WMPWRK/AHVQT — Cornet & brass band. Arrangements.
Tambourins
Gossec, François Joseph
[Le camp de Grand-Pré. Tambourin. *arr*]. Tambourin : solo for B
flat cornet / [by] François Joseph Gossec ; arranged by Edrich
Siebert. — London : Studio Music, 1978. — 8vo.
Conductor & 25 parts.
Unpriced

(B78-51329)

WMPWRNTHVH — Cornets (3) & brass band. Polkas
Siebert, Edrich
Warriors three : trio for B flat cornets [and brass band] / [by]
Edrich Siebert. — London : Harmer : Studio Music, 1977. — 8vo.
Conductor & 25 parts ; various parts in duplicate.
Unpriced

(B78-50684)

WMPWTR — Post horn & brass band
Bryce, Frank
 Colin's fancy : for post horn solo and brass band / [by] Frank
 Bryce. — Sevenoaks : Novello, 1978. — 8vo.
 Duration 3 min. — Conductor (8p.) & 27 parts with several copies of
 various parts.
 Unpriced
(B78-51330)

WMPWU — Tuba & brass band
Brand, Michael
 Tuba tapestry : E flat bass solo / [by] Michael Brand. —
 Watford : R. Smith, 1978. — 8vo.
 Conductor & 26 parts.
 Unpriced
(B78-50685)

WMPWX — Bass tuba & brass band
Siebert, Edrich
 The bombastic bombardon : solo for E flat bass [and brass
 band] / [by] Edrich Siebert. — London : Harmer Music : Studio
 Music, 1977. — 8vo.
 Conductor & 24 parts, with several copies of various parts.
 Unpriced
(B78-50686)

WN — BRASS ENSEMBLE
WN/AY — Collections
 Neue Musik für Bläser. — Kassel ; London : Bärenreiter.
 Heft 4 : Werke von Herbert Gadsch, Eberhard Wenzel, Theodor Hlouschek,
 Rolf Schweizer, Hans Friedrich Micheelsen. — 1977. — 29p ; 4to.
 £4.20
(B78-51331)

WN/T — Variations
Heiden, Bernhard
 [Variations, tuba & horns (9)]. Variations for solo tuba and nine
 horns / [by] Bernhard Heiden. — New York ; London :
 Associated Music, 1977. — 4to.
 Score (25p.) & 10 parts.
 £9.05
(B78-50687)

WNK/AH — Arrangements. Dances
Susato, Thielman
 [Dances. Selections : arr]. A suite of dances / by Tylman Susato
 (early 16th century) ; for brass ensemble. edited and arranged by
 John Iveson. — London : Chester Music, 1975. — 4to. — (Just
 brass ; no.7)
 Score ([2],12p.) & 12 parts.
 Unpriced
(B78-51332)

WNK/DW/LC — Arrangements. Spirituals
 Spirituals für Blechbläser : bearbeitet von Rolf Schweizer. —
 Kassel ; [London] : Bärenreiter, 1977. — [1],32p ; 8vo.
 £2.80
(B78-50688)

WNNE — Octets. Sonatas
Gabrieli, Giovanni
 [Sacrae symphoniae. Bk.1. Sonata pian'e forte]. Sonata pian'e
 forte : for brass octet / [by] Giovanni Gabrieli ; edited by Philip
 Jones. — London : Chester Music, 1978. — 4to. — (Just brass ;
 no.30)
 Score (8p.) & 13 parts, with alternative parts for horns, trombones
 euphonium or tuba or E flat bass.
 Unpriced
(B78-51333)

WNQ — Sextets
Haan, Stefan de
 [Suite, brass sextet]. Suite for brass sextet / [by] Stefan de Haan.
 — London : Chester Music, 1977. — [2],12p ; 4to.
 Unpriced
(B78-51334)

WNQG — Sextets. Suites
Feld, Jindřich
 Partita canonica / [von] Jindřich Feld ; herausgegeben von
 Wilhelm Ehmann. — Kassel ; London : Bärenreiter, 1977. —
 19p ; 8vo. — (Neue Musik für Bläser ; Hft.5)
 For 3 trumpets in C and 3 trombones.
 £3.60
(B78-51335)

WNR — Quintets
Bishop, Jeffrey
 Moshe Timloch : fantasy for brass quintet / [by] Jeffrey Bishop.
 — Sevenoaks : Novello, 1978. — [1],18p ; 8vo.
 Duration 15 min.
 £1.30
(B78-51336)

Carter, Elliott
 A fantasy about Purcell's 'Fantasia upon one note' : for brass
 quintet / [by] Elliott Carter. — New York ; London : Associated
 Music, 1977. — 4to.
 Score (8p.) & 5 parts.
 £5.75
(B78-50689)

Pearson, Leslie
 Hiplips . (Philip's) : for brass quintet / [by] Leslie Pearson. —
 London : Chester Music, 1978. — 4to. — (Just brass ; no.31)
 Score (8p.) & 6 parts, with alternative part for horn or trombone.
 Unpriced
(B78-51337)

WNRK/AHXJ — Quintets. Arrangements. Ragtime
Joplin, Scott
 [Ragtime. Selections : arr]. Three rags for five / [by] Scott Joplin ;
 arranged by John Iveson for brass quintet. — London : Chester
 Music, 1978. — 4to. — (Just brass ; no.25)
 Score ([2]p.) & 8 parts, with alternative parts for horns in F and E flat,
 trombones, treble clef and bass clef and tuba or E flat bass. — Contents: 1:
 The entertainer - 2: Ragtime dance - 3: Gladiolus rag.
 Unpriced
(B78-51338)

WNS — Quartets
Watters, Cyril
 Pastoral theme : for 2 B flat cornets, E flat horn and euphonium /
 by Cyril Watters. — London : Studio Music, 1977. — 8vo.
 Score (8p.) & 4 parts.
 Unpriced
(B78-50690)

WNSK — Quartets. Arrangements
Banchieri, Adriano
 [Fantasie overo canzoni alla francese. Fantasie no.6. arr]. Echo
 fantasia : for brass quartet / [by] Adriano Banchieri ; edited and
 arranged by Philip Jones. — London : Chester Music, 1975. —
 4to. — (Just brass ; no.9)
 Score ([3],2p.) & 12 parts including two sets of parts, with alternative parts
 for 2nd trumpet or horn and horn or trombone.
 Unpriced
(B78-51339)

WNSK/AH — Quartets. Arrangements. Dances
Peuerl, Paul
 [Newe Padouan, Intrada, Täntz unnd Galliarda. Selections]. Four
 dances (1611) / [by] Paul Peuerl ; arranged by Peter Reeve, for
 brass quartet with optional percussion. — London : Chester
 Music, 1978. — 4to. — (Just brass ; no.27)
 The couranta is in fact, from 'Musicalische Tafelfrendt' by I. Pósch. —
 Score '8p.) & 11 parts, with altrnative parts for horn in F or E flat or
 trombone treble or bass clef, and trombone, treble or bass clef, or E flat bass
 or tuba.
 Unpriced
(B78-51340)

WNT — Trios
Schmitt, Meinrad
 [Trio, trumpet, bassoon & tuba]. Trio für Trompete, Posaune und
 Tuba / [von] Meinrad Schmitt. — Berlin : Bote und Bock ;
 [London] : [Associated Music], 1977. — 3pt ; 4to.
 £3.85
(B78-50691)

WRP — CORNET & PIANO
WRPK — Arrangements
Bellstedt, Herman
 [Napoli. arr]. Napoli : cornet solo / [by] Herman Bellstedt. —
 Watford : R. Smith, 1978. — 9p ; obl. 4to.
 Unpriced
(B78-50692)

WRPK/AAY — Arrangements. Collections
 Harry Mortimer souvenir album : a unique collection of famous
 cornet solos / selected and edited by Harry Mortimer, with piano
 accompaniment. — London : Boosey and Hawkes, 1978. — 4to.
 Unpriced
(B78-51341)

WSN — TRUMPET ENSEMBLE
WSNS — Quartets
Scheidt, Samuel
 [Paduana, galliarda .... Cantus 18]. Canzon cornetto : for four
 trumpets / [by] Samuel Scheidt ; edited by Philip Jones. —
 London : Chester Music, 1975. — 4to. — (Just brass ; no.10)
 Score ([2],6p.) & 4 parts.
 Unpriced
(B78-51342)

WSNTQK/AE — Trumpets (2) & piano. Arrangements. Sonatas
Lazari, Ferdinando Antonio
[Sonata, trumpets (2) & string orchestra, D major. *arr*]. Sonata à 6, for 2 trumpets, strings and continuo / [by] Ferd. Anto. Lazzari ; [edited by] R.P. Block ; trumpet and piano reduction. — London : Musica rara, 1978. — 4to. — (Italian 17th and 18th century sinfonias and sonatas for trumpets and strings ; no.33)
Score ([1],12p.) & 3 parts.
Unpriced

(B78-50693)

WSNTR — Trumpets (2) & organ
Gardner, John
Sonata da chiesa sopra un tema di Claudio Monteverdi / [by] John Gardner ; for 2 trumpets and organ ; Op.136. — London : Oxford University Press, 1978. — 4to.
Based on the toccata from 'Orfeo'. — Score (32p.) & 2 parts.
ISBN 0-19-356713-x : Unpriced

(B78-51343)

WSP — TRUMPET & PIANO
WSP/T — Variations
Stone, David
[Variations, trumpet & piano]. Variations for trumpet (or trombone) and piano / [by] David Stone. — London : Boosey and Hawkes, 1978. — fol.
Score (8p.) & parts for trumpet and trombone.
Unpriced
Also classified at WUP/T

(B78-51344)

WSPK/AE — Arrangements. Sonatas
Gabrielli, Domenico
[Sonata, trumpet, string quartet & continuo, D major. *arr*]. Sonata D. XI.5 in D for trumpet, strings and basso continuo / [by] Domenico Gabrielli ; [ed.] R.P. Block. — London : Musica rara, 1978. — 4to. — (Italian 17th & 18th century sinfonias and sonatas for trumpets and strings ; 23)
Score ([1],6p.) & part, with alternative parts for trumpet in B flat and D.
Unpriced

(B78-51345)

Gabrielli, Domenico
[Sonata, trumpet, string quintet & continuo, D major. *arr*]. Sonata D, XI, 4 in D for trumpet, strings and basso continuo / [by] Domenico Gabrielli ; [ed.] R.P. Block. — London : Musica rara, 1978. — 4to. — (Italian 17th & 18th century sinfonias and sonatas for trumpets & strings ; 23)
Score ([1],7p.) & part.
Unpriced

(B78-51346)

WSPK/LE — Arrangements. Symphonies
Torelli, Giuseppe
[Sinfonia, trumpet & string orchestra, G.9, D major. *arr*]. Concerto D-Dur per tromba con archi e continuo / [von] Giuseppe Torelli ; herausgegeben von Heinz Zickler, Klavierauszug von Friedrich Zehm. — Mainz ; London : Schott, 1977. — 4to. — (La tromba ; 7)
Score (11p.) & 2 parts, with alternative parts for trumpets in C or D.
£3.20

(B78-50313)

WSPLX — TRUMPET & PERCUSSION
Bazelon, Irwin
Double crossings : duo for trumpet and percussion / [by] Irwin Bazelon. — London : Boosey and Hawkes, 1978. — 4to.
Score ([3],21p.) & part. — Duration 10 min.
£4.50

(B78-51347)

WSPM — UNACCOMPANIED TRUMPET
WSPMK/DW/AYE — Arrangements. Songs, etc. Collections.
Germany
Mein Heimatland : die schönsten Volks- , Wander- , Trink- und Scherzlieder / herausgegeben von Ludwig Andersen. — Neu-Ausgabe mit vollstandigem Text, Trompete [oder] Klarinette in B / von W. Draths mit übergelegtem Text. — Mainz ; London : Schott, 1977. — 88p ; 4to.
£7.20
Also classified at VVPMK/DW/AYE

(B78-50314)

WSPMK/DW/LF/AY — Arrangements. Christmas songs. Collections
The best of Christmas songs : trumpet. — london : EMI, 1978. — 33p ; 4to.
Arranged for trumpet by Cecil Bolton and Jack Moore.
Unpriced

(B78-51348)

WT — HORN
WT/AC — Tutors
Tuckwell, Barry
Playing the horn : a practical guide / [by] Barry Tuckwell. — London : Oxford University Press, 1978. — 45p ; 4to.
Unpriced

(B78-51349)

WT/AF — Exercises
Tuckwell, Barry
Fifty first exercises for horn / [by] Barry Tuckwell. — London : Oxford University Press, 1978. — [3],44p ; 4to.
ISBN 0-19-359150-2 : Unpriced

(B78-51350)

WTP — HORN & PIANO
WTPGM/X — Marches. Canons
Anderson, Muriel Bradford
Prelude and march in canon : for French horn and piano / [by] M. Bradford Anderson. — London : Boosey and Hawkes, 1977. — 4to.
Originally published separately. — Score (8p.) & part.
Unpriced

(B78-50315)

WTPJ — Miscellaneous works
Krol, Bernhard
Figaro-Metamorphosen 'Voi che sapete' : für Horn (F) und Klavier, Opus 61 / [von] Bernhard Krol. — Berlin : Bote und Bock ; [London] : [Associated Music], 1977. — 4to.
Score (39p.) & part.
£7.70

(B78-50694)

McCabe, John
[The goddess triology. 1 : The castle of Arianrhod]. The castle of Arianrhod : for horn and piano / [by] John McCabe. — Sevenoaks : Novello, 1978. — 4to.
Score ([6],34p.) & part.
£2.75

(B78-51352)

McCabe, John
[The goddess triology. 2 : Floraison]. Floraison : for horn and piano / [by] John McCabe. — Sevenoaks : Novello, 1978. — 4to.
Score ([3],16p.) & part. — Duration 9 min. — Facsimile of composer's autograph.
£1.65

(B78-51353)

McCabe, John
[The goddess trilogy. 3 : Shapeshifter]. Shapeshifter : for horn and piano / [by] John McCabe. — Sevenoaks : Novello, 1978. — 4to.
Score ([5],18p.) & part. — Duration 8 min. — Facsimile of composer's autograph.
£1.80

(B78-51351)

WTPK/AH — Arrangements. Dances
Marais, Marin
[Pièces de violes, liv 4. Le Basque. *arr*]. Le Basque : old French dance / after Martin Marais ; arr. horn & piano. — London (116 Long Acre, W.C.2) : Paxman, 1978. — 4to.
Score (3p.) & part.
Unpriced

(B78-50316)

WTPK/LW — Arrangements. Rondos
Mozart, Wolfgang Amadeus
[Concerto, horn, no.3, K.447, E flat major. Rondo. *arr*]. Rondo from horn concerto no.3, K.447 / [by] Mozart ; arranged for solo E flat horn with piano accompaniment by Roy Newsome. — London (50 Ladbroke Grove, W.11) : Midland Music, 1976. — 4to.
Unpriced

(B78-50317)

WUN — TROMBONE ENSEMBLE
WUNS — Quartets
Beethoven, Ludwig van
[Equali, trombones(4), nos.1-3]. Three equali for four trombones / [by] Ludwig van Beethoven ; edited by Philip Jones. — London : Chester Music, 1975. — 4to. — (Just brass ; no.8)
Score ([4],4p.) & 4 parts.
Unpriced

(B78-51354)

WUP — TROMBONE & PIANO
WUPLRK/DM/AYE — Trombone & organ. Arrangements. Hymns. Collections. Germany
Zehn Chorale alter Meister für Posaune und Orgel / bearbeitet von Wolfgang Stockmeier. — Kassel ; London : Bärenreiter, 1977. — 4to.
Score ([1],24p.) & part.
£4.80

(B78-51355)

WUU — BASS TROMBONE
Orton, Richard H
Ambierce : for bass trombone and tape / [by] Richard H. Orton. — Birmingham : Arts Lab Music, 1977. — 3ff ; obl.fol.
Unpriced

(B78-51356)

WUUPLX — Bass trombone & percussion
  Anderson, Thomas Jefferson
    Minstrel man : for bass trombone, bass drum and hi-hat cymbals
    (1977) / [by] T.J. Anderson. — Berlin : Bote und Bock ;
    [London] : [Schirmer], 1978. — 7p ; fol.
    For one player.
    £2.40

(B78-51357)

WV — TUBA
  Soaster, Timothy
    Heavy reductions : for tuba and tape, 1977 / [by] Timothy
    Soaster. — Birmingham : Arts Lab Music, 1978. — 17ff ; obl.4to.
    Based on the Vorspiel to 'Das Rheingold', by Wagner. — Printed on one
    side of the leaf only.
    Unpriced

(B78-51358)

WVP — TUBA & PIANO
WVPK/LF — Arrangements. Concertos
  Gregson, Edward
    [Concerto, tuba. *arr*]. Tuba concerto / [by] Edward Gregson ;
    arranged for tuba and piano by the composer. — Sevenoaks :
    Novello, 1978. — 4to.
    Score (29p.) & part.
    £2.85

(B78-50695)

WVPM — UNACCOMPANIED TUBA
WVPM/T — Variations
  Emmerson, Simon
    [Variations, tuba]. Variations for tuba / [by] Simon Emmerson. —
    Birmingham : Arts Lab Music, 1977. — 1p ; 4to.
    Unpriced

(B78-51359)

WVPMJ — Miscellaneous works
  Cresswell, Lyell Richard
    Drones 4 : for tuba, 1977 / [by] Lyell Richard Cresswell. —
    Birmingham : Arts Lab Music, 1977. — 4ff ; fol.
    Printed on one side of the leaf only.
    Unpriced

(B78-51360)

  Poore, Melvyn
    Vox superios : for solo tuba, 1976 / [by] Melvyn Poore. —
    Birmingham : Arts Lab Music, 1977. — 5p ; 4to.
    Unpriced

(B78-51361)

X — PERCUSSION INSTRUMENTS
X/AC — Tutors
  Keune, Eckehardt
    Schlaginstrumente = Percussion instruments : a method of
    instruction / [von] Eckehardt Keune. — Kassel ; London :
    Bärenreiter.
    Teil 2 : Pauken = Timpani. — 1977. — 155p ; 4to. —
    £7.00

(B78-50696)

X/AF — Exercises
  Keetman, Gunild
    Musik für Kinder. — Mainz ; London : Schott. —
    (Orff-Schulwerk)
    7 : Rhythmische Übung. — 1970. — 23p ; obl. 8vo. —
    Unpriced

(B78-50318)

XN — PERCUSSION ENSEMBLE
XNPF — Septets. Concertos
  Bazelon, Irwin
    Propulsions : concerts for percussion / [by] Irwin Bazelon. —
    New York ; [London] : Boosey and Hawkes, 1978. — [6],54p ;
    4to.
    Duration 18 min. — Musicians occasionally shout vocal accents.
    £12.50

(B78-51362)

XQ — DRUM
XQ/AF — Studies
  Fink, Siegfried
    Studien für Drum Set = Studies for drum set / von Siegfried
    Fink ; unter Mitarbeit von, with the assistance by, Bernd
    Kremling. — Hamburg : Simrock. — (Percussion Studio)
    Heft 2 = Vol.2 : Mittelstufe = Intermediate. — 1978. — 32p ; 4to. —
    Unpriced

(B78-51363)

Composer and Title Index

Amicizia! : Quintett für Klarinette in A, Posaune, Violoncello, Schlagzeug und Klavier (1976). (Henze, Hans Werner). *Schott. £8.00* NYDPNR (B78-50512)

Andantino. (Higgins, Norman). *Royal Academy of Dancing. Unpriced* QPH/H (B78-50218)

Andersen, Ludwig. Mein Heimatland : die schönsten Volks-, Wander- , Trink- und Scherzlieder. Neu- Ausgabe mit vollstandigem Text, Trompete oder Klarinette in B. *Schott. £7.20* WSPMK/DW/AYE (B78-50314)

Anderson, Ian, *b.1946.* Rock record collectors guide. *77 New Bond St., W.1 : MRP Books. £2.99* A/HKR/FD(WT) (B78-02937) ISBN 0-905590-04-x

Anderson, Muriel Bradford.

Prelude and march in canon : for French horn and piano. *Boosey and Hawkes. Unpriced* WTPGM/X (B78-50315)

Prelude and march in canon : for viola and piano. *Boosey and Hawkes. Unpriced* SQPGM/X (B78-50261)

Anderson, Thomas Jefferson.

Minstrel man : for bass trombone, bass drum and hi-hat cymbals (1977). *Bote und Bock : Schirmer. £2.40* WUUPLX (B78-51357)

Andrews, Frank. A catalogue of 'Clarion' & 'Ebonoid' records. (Carter, Sydney Horace). *19 Glendale Rd, Bournemouth BH6 4JA : 'Talking machine review'. £2.00* A/FD(QB/WT) (B78-20766) ISBN 0-902338-29-3

Ange. 'Par les fils de Mandrin'. *arr.* 'Par les fils de Mandrin'. *Chappell. Unpriced* KDW/GB (B78-50123)

Anglican hymn book : Robin Sheldon, musical editor Revised ed., with supplement. *Wine Office Court, E.C.4 : Vine Books. £4.85* DM/LSD/AY (B78-50736)

Annand, James King. Carmina Burana. Selections. Songs from 'Carmina Burana'. *Edgefield Rd, Loanhead, Midlothian : Macdonald Publishers. Unpriced* ADW(XCH101) (B78-30833) ISBN 0-904265-20-x

Annual index to popular music record reviews

1976. *Scarecrow Press : Distributed by Bailey and Swinfen. £17.00* A/GB/FD(T) (B78-20767) ISBN 0-8108-1070-0

Another spring. Op.93 : three songs to poems by Walter de la Mare. (Berkeley, *Sir* Lennox). *Chester Music. Unpriced* KDW (B78-50859)

Anthologia organi : Orgelmusik aus acht Jahrhunderten

Band 1: Die Anfänge der Orgelmusik. *Edito Musica : Schott. £8.00* R/AY (B78-51042)

Band 2: Die Niederlander und die Venezianische Schule. *Edito Musica : Schott. £8.00* R/AY (B78-51043)

Band 3: Die Römische Schule und ihre Nachfolger. *Edito Musica : Schott. £8.00* R/AY (B78-51044)

Band 4: Englische Orgelmusik bis Purcell. *Edito Musica : Schott. £8.00* R/AY (B78-51045)

Anthologies of renaissance music. Vento, Ivo de. Newe teutsche Lieder, mit viern, fünff, und sechs Stimmen. *Selections.* Eight lieder, 1570 : for four voices or instruments, ATTBB. *London Pro Musica. Unpriced* EZDU (B78-50383)

Anthony, James R. French baroque music : from Beaujoyeulx to Rameau. Revised ed. *Batsford. £12.50* A(YH/XDZA153) (B78-26886) ISBN 0-7134-1076-0

Antiphon : S.A.T.B. (Walton, *Sir* William). *Oxford University Press. Unpriced* DH (B78-50021) ISBN 0-19-350366-2

Antiphon : S.A.T.B. (unacc.). (Howells, Herbert). *Oxford University Press. Unpriced* EZDH (B78-50044) ISBN 0-19-350365-4

Antoniou, Theodore. Chorochronos 2 : für Bariton-Sprecher und Kammerochester = for baritone-narrator and chamber orchestra ; 1973. *Bärenreiter. £6.00* MRJ (B78-50939)

Antony Duddyngton, organ maker : the Duddyngton manuscripts at All Hallows-by-the-Tower, London. (Blewett, P R W). *22 Edgar Rd, Sanderstead, South Croydon CR2 0NG : Rev. P. Blewett. £0.50* AR/BC(P) (B78-33169) ISBN 0-906257-00-x

Apokalyptische Vision : für Basstimme und Orgel. (Brandmüller, Theo). *Bote und Bock : Associated Music. £4.80* KGXDE (B78-50479)

Appleby, Benjamin William. The school recorder assembly book for pupils. *E.J. Arnold. Unpriced* VSRPMK/AAY (B78-51257) ISBN 0-560-00379-x

Aquino Carrilho, Altamiro. Album de chôros. *Unpriced* VRPMJ (B78-50651)

Arabesque = Eine Arabeske : for baritone solo, mixed chorus and orchestra = für Bariton-Solo, gemischter Chor und Orchester. (Delius, Frederick). *Boosey and Hawkes. Unpriced* EMDX (B78-50751)

Arbeitskreis für Schlessisches Lied und Schlessische Musik. Meilensteine eines Komponistenlebens : kleine Festschrift zum 70. Geburtstag von Günter Bialas. *32 Gt Titchfield St., W1P 7AD : Bärenreiter. £10.08* BBNO(D) (B78-19399)

Argentine melody = Canción de Argentina : official BBC tv World Cup theme. (Webber, Andrew Lloyd). *Chappell. Unpriced* QPK/JS (B78-51036)

Argentine melody. *arr.* Argentine melody = Canción de Argentina : official BBC tv World Cup theme. (Webber, Andrew Lloyd). *Chappell. Unpriced* QPK/JS (B78-51036)

Argento, Dominick.

The masque of angels. Sanctus. *arr.* Sanctus : double chorus and piano or organ from the opera 'The masque of angels'. *Boosey and Hawkes. Unpriced* DGE (B78-50721)

A ring of time : preludes and pageants for orchestra and bells. *Boosey and Hawkes. Unpriced* MMJ (B78-50186)

Aria and variations, viola d'amore & cello, Czach 90, D major. Aria and VII variations : for viola d'amore and cello. (Rust, Friedrich Wilhelm). *Little Margaret, Penmans Green, Chipperfield : Ian White. Unpriced* SQQPLSR/T (B78-50599)

Aria and VII variations : for viola d'amore and cello. (Rust, Friedrich Wilhelm). *Little Margaret, Penmans Green, Chipperfield : Ian White. Unpriced* SQQPLSR/T (B78-50599)

Ariadne auf Naxos : Oper in einem Akt nebst einem Vorspiel. (Hofmannsthal, Hugo von). *Boosey and Hawkes. £0.85* BSUAC

Arie fantasie : for organ. (Nieman, Alfred). *Novello. £1.20* RJ (B78-50567)

Arien, Szenen, Ensembles

Textbuch italienisch-deutsch. *32 Gt Titchfield St., W1P 7AD : Bärenreiter. £1.68* BMSADW (B78-26890)

Arise, shine, for your light has come : S.A.T.B. (Mathias, William). *Oxford University Press. Unpriced* DK (B78-50732) ISBN 0-19-350367-0

Aristophanes. Chorus of the frogs : for four-part chorus of mixed voices with piano accompaniment. (Turok, Paul). *Schirmer. £0.45* DW (B78-50353)

Arne, Thomas Augustine.

Thomas and Sally : dramatic pastoral in two acts. *Eulenburg. Unpriced* CQC (B78-50329)

Thomas and Sally. *Vocal score.* Thomas and Sally : a dramatic pastoral in two acts. *Schott. Unpriced* CC (B78-50323)

Arnold, Malcolm.

Concerto, flute, no.2, op.111. *arr.* Flute concerto no.2, op.111. *Faber Music. Unpriced* VRPK/LF (B78-51226)

Fantasy, harp, op.117. Fantasy for harp, Op.117. *Faber Music. Unpriced* TQPMJ (B78-51134)

Arnold, Matthew. The sea of faith, Dover Beach. (Hemingway, Roger). *Novello. £0.45* DH (B78-50726)

Arrau, Claudio. Sonaten für Klavier zu zwei Händen

Band 2: Nr.16-32. (Beethoven, Ludwig van). *Litolff : Peters. Unpriced* QPE (B78-50991)

Art of the conductor. Robinson, Paul. Stokowski. *Macdonald and Jane's. £4.95* A/EC(P) (B78-01681) ISBN 0-354-04232-7

Art of the Netherlands, 1470-1530. Josquin des Prés. Seven secular pieces : for four voices or instruments, ATTB. *London Pro Musica. Unpriced* EZDU (B78-50382)

As I crossed a bridge of dreams : for unaccompanied chorus (12 or more singers divided into 3 SATB groups). (Boyd, Anne). *Faber Music. Unpriced* EZDW (B78-50385)

As serious as your life : the story of the new jazz. (Wilmer, Valerie). *Quartet Books. £2.95* AMT(M/YTLD) (B78-05410) ISBN 0-7043-3164-0

As serious as your life : the story of the new jazz. (Wilmer, Valerie). *Allison and Busby. £6.50* AMT(M/XQ18) (B78-11201) ISBN 0-85031-224-8

Ascendo ad Patrem meum. (Handl, Jacob). *Cathedral Music. Unpriced* GEZDJ/LM (B78-50422)

Ashbee, Andrew. Consort music : for viols in four parts. (Jenkins, John). *Faber Music. Unpriced* STN (B78-51132)

Ashburnham, George. The 2nd pocket organ tutor. *22 Effingham Close, Sutton, Surrey SM2 6AG : Ashburnham School of Music. £9.14* AR/E (B78-36280)

Ashburnham School of Music. The 2nd pocket organ tutor. (Ashburnham, George). *22 Effingham Close, Sutton, Surrey SM2 6AG : Ashburnham School of Music. £9.14* AR/E (B78-36280)

Ashdown unison songs. Potter, Archibald James. Lovelie Jemmie. *Ashdown. Unpriced* JFDW (B78-50092)

Ashdown vocal duets.

Dexter, Harry. Mary and Martha : negro spiritual. *Edwin Ashdown. £0.20* FDW/LC (B78-50818)

Dexter, Harry. Wake up, Jacob : negro spiritual. *Edwin Ashdown. £0.20* FDW/LC (B78-50819)

Hudson, Hazel. The Daniel quodlibet (based on three negro spirituals) : for two female, two male or one female and one male voices. *Edwin Ashdown. Unpriced* FDW/LC (B78-50394)

Hudson, Hazel. Feed my sheep : a quodlibet based on negro spirituals. *Ashdown. Unpriced* FDW/LC (B78-50065)

Ashfield, Robert. Responses for A.T.B. *Cathedral Music. Unpriced* GEZDGMM (B78-50412)

Ashland, Ulf Goran. *See* Goran, Ulf.

Ashlund, Ulf Goran. Play a piece : easy solos in two books, guitar solo

Book 1. *Oxford University Press. Unpriced* TSPMK/AAY (B78-50621) ISBN 0-19-356796-2

Aslanian, Vahe. Liber primus qui missas ... aliaque cumplectitut, 1576. Nigra sum. Nigra sum de beata virgine : for six-part chorus of mixed voices unaccompanied. (Victoria, Tomás Luis de). *Roberton. £0.20* EZDJ (B78-50779)

Asprey, Jonathan.

The celebration song. *57 Dorchester Rd, Lychett Minster, Poole : Celebration Services. Unpriced* FDM (B78-50059)

Jubilate Deo : psalm 100. *Celebration Services. Unpriced* JDGNT (B78-50077)

Associated Board of the Royal School of Music.

Pianoforte examinations, 1979

Grade 1: Lists A & B. *Associated Board of the Royal Schools of Music. £0.50* Q/AL (B78-50973)

Grade 2: Lists A & B. *Associated Board of the Royal School of Music. £0.50* Q/AL (B78-50974)

Associated Board of the Royal Schools of Music.

Guitar scales and arpeggios

Grade 3-8. *Associated Board of the Royal Schools of Music. Unpriced* TS/AF (B78-51142)

New pieces for clarinet : with piano accompaniment

Book 1: Grades 3 & 4. *Associated Board of the Royal Schools of Music. Unpriced* VVP/AY (B78-51279)

Book 1: Grades 3 & 4. *Associated Board of the Royal Schools of Music. Unpriced* VVP/AY (B78-51280)

Book 1: Grades 5 & 6. *Associated Board of the Royal Schools of Music. Unpriced* VVP/AY (B78-51281)

New pieces for flute : with piano accompaniment

Book 1: Grades 3 & 4. *Associated Board of the Royal Schools of Music. Unpriced* VRP/AY (B78-51206)

New pieces for oboe : with piano accompaniment

Book 1: Grades 3 & 4. *Associated Board of the Royal Schools of Music. Unpriced* VTP/AY (B78-51264)

Pianoforte examinations, 1979

Grade 2: Lists A & B. *Associated Board of the Royal Schools of Music. £0.50* Q/AL (B78-50975)

Grade 3: Lists A & B. *Associated Board of the Royal Schools of Music. £0.50* Q/AL (B78-50976)

Grade 4: Lists A & B. *Associated Board of the Royal Schools of Music. £0.50* Q/AL (B78-50977)

Grade 5: List A. *Associated Board of the Royal Schools of Music. £0.50* Q/AL (B78-50978)

Grade 5: List B. *Associated Board of the Royal Schools of Music. £0.50* Q/AL (B78-50979)

Grade 6: List A. *Associated Board of the Royal Schools of Music. £0.50* Q/AL (B78-50980)

Grade 6: List B. *Associated Board of the Royal Schools of Music. £0.50* Q/AL (B78-50981)

Grade 7: List A. *Associated Board of the Royal Schools of Music. £0.50* Q/AL (B78-50982)

Grade 7: List B. *Associated Board of the Royal Schools of Music. £0.50* Q/AL (B78-50983)

Pianoforte scales and arpeggios

Grade 3. *Associated Board of the Royal Schools of Music. Unpriced* Q/AF (B78-50965)

Grade 4. *Associated Board of the Royal Schools of Music. Unpriced* Q/AF (B78-50966)

Grade 5. *Associated Board of the Royal Schools of Music. Unpriced* Q/AF (B78-50967)

Grade 6. *Associated Board of the Royal Schools of Music. Unpriced* Q/AF (B78-50968)

Grade 7. *Associated Board of the Royal Schools of Music. Unpriced* Q/AF (B78-50969)

Grade 8. *Associated Board of the Royal Schools of Music. Unpriced* Q/AF (B78-50970)

Pianoforte scales and broken chords

Grade 1. *Associated Board of the Royal Schools of Music. Unpriced* Q/AF (B78-50971)

Grade 2. *Associated Board of the Royal Schools of Music. Unpriced* Q/AF (B78-50972)

Violin examinations, 1979 and 1980

Grade 1: Lists A & B. *Associated Board of the Royal Schools of Music. £1.00* S/AL (B78-51090)

Grade 2: Lists A & B. *Associated Board of the Royal Schools of Music. £1.00* S/AL (B78-51091)

Grade 3: Lists A & B. *Associated Board of the Royal Schools of Music. £1.00* S/AL (B78-51092)

Grade 4: Lists A & B. *Associated Board of the Royal Schools of Music. £1.00* S/AL (B78-51093)

Grade 5: Lists A & B. *Associated Board of the Royal Schools of Music. £1.00* S/AL (B78-51094)

Grade 6: Lists A & B. *Associated Board of the Royal Schools of Music. £1.00* S/AL (B78-51095)

Grade 7: Lists A & B. *Associated Board of the Royal Schools of Music. £1.00* S/AL (B78-51096)

Association of English Singers and Speakers.

A heritage of 20th century British song

Vol.1. *Boosey and Hawkes. Unpriced* KDW/AYD (B78-50119)

Vol.2. *Boosey and Hawkes. Unpriced* KDW/AYC (B78-50118)

Astier, André. Divertissement baroque en trois mouvements. (Baselli, Joss). *Chappell. Unpriced* QPG (B78-50998)

At home with Robin Richmond : twelve arrangements of favourite melodies for the home organ. *Paxton. £1.80* RPVK/DW/GB/AY (B78-51063)

At the round earth's imagined corners : cantata for tenor solo, SATB and string orchestra. (Kelly, Bryan). *Novello. Unpriced* DE (B78-50015)

At the round earth's imagined corners : for unaccompanied voices S.M. S.A.T.B. (Routh, Francis). *Radcliffe. Unpriced* EZDH (B78-50774)

At the round earth's imagined corners. *Vocal score.* At the round earth's imagined corners : cantata for tenor solo, SATB and string orchestra. (Kelly, Bryan). *Novello. Unpriced* DE (B78-50015)

Atkins, Harold. Beecham stories : anecdotes, sayings and impressions of Sir Thomas Beecham. *Robson. £3.50 : CIP rev.* A/EC(P/E) (B78-26892) ISBN 0-86051-044-1

Atthill, Catherine. Maria Callas : a tribute. (Rémy, Pierre Jean). *Macdonald and Jane's. £6.95* AKFL/E(P) (B78-35471) ISBN 0-354-04315-3

Attwood, Tony. Pop workbook. *Edward Arnold. £1.75 : CIP rev.* A/GB (B77-28559) ISBN 0-7131-0155-5

Aubade, op.17 : for mixed chorus. (Brown, Christopher). *Chester Music. Unpriced* EZDW (B78-50795)

Audel, Stéphane. My friends and myself : conversations with Francis Poulenc. *Dobson. £4.95* BPO(N) (B78-39780) ISBN 0-234-77251-4

Auden, Wystan Hugh. Lands : two settings for unaccompanied mixed voice choir of poems by W.H. Auden, music by Antonin Tučapský. (Tučapský, Antonin). *Roberton. £0.32* EZDW (B78-50055)

Auden, Wysten Hugh. What does the song hope for? : for soprano, ensemble and tape. (Saxton, Robert). *Chester Music. Unpriced* KFLE/NUPNPDX (B78-50892)

Auerbach, Lore. Musikalische Grundausbildung in der Musikschule

Lehrerhandbuch. Teil 1 : Didaktik und Methodik. *Schott.*

£9.50 A(VF) (B78-33930)

Augustine : an opera in one or two acts for children. (Boyle, Rory). *Chester Music. Unpriced* CN (B78-50704)

Augustine : an opera in one or two acts for children. (Boyle, Rory). *Chester Music. Unpriced* DACN (B78-50714)

Augustine. *Choral score.* Augustine : an opera in one or two acts for children. (Boyle, Rory). *Chester Music. Unpriced* DACN (B78-50714)

Augustine. *Vocal score.* Augustine : an opera in one or two acts for children. (Boyle, Rory). *Chester Music. Unpriced* CN (B78-50704)

Aus dem alten tschechischen Sammlungen : zweistimmige Sätze, für Sopran-und Altblockflöte. *Bärenreiter. £1.40* VSNUK/AYF (B78-50653)

Ausgewählte Stücke alter und neuer Meister : für Gitarre. *Heinrichshofen : Peters. Unpriced* TSPMK/AAY (B78-50620)

Authentic Gilbert & Sullivan songbook : 92 unabridged selections from all 14 operas reproduced from early vocal scores. (Sullivan, *Sir* Arthur Seymour). *Dover Constable. £5.35* DW (B78-50028) ISBN 0-486-23482-7

Ave Maria. In Annuntiationis B. Maria Virginis,. (Victoria, Tomás Luis de). *36 Ranelagh Gdns. W.6 : Cathedral Music. Unpriced* EZDJ (B78-50377)

Ave Maria. Op.42. *arr.* Ave Maria : for four double basses. (Fitzenhagen, Wilhelm Carl Friedrich). *Yorke. Unpriced* SSNSK (B78-51124)

Ave verum corpus : for male voice choir unaccompanied. (Byrd, William). *Roberton. £0.20* GEZDJ (B78-50826)

Aveling, Valda. Sonata, oboe & continuo, op.2, no.1, F major. Sonata no.1 in F for oboe and piano. (Tessarini, Carlo). *Chester Music. Unpriced* VTPE (B78-51266)

Averre, Dick. That's entertainment. That's entertainment. *arr.* That's entertainment : S.S.A. with piano. (Schwartz, Arthur). *Chappell. Unpriced* FDW/JR (B78-50817)

Ayres and dialogues. Dialogue on a kiss. A dialogue on a kiss : for two solo voices and continuo. (Lawes, Henry). *Oxford University Press. Unpriced* JNEDW (B78-50858) ISBN 0-19-345494-7

B. Schott *(Firm.) See* Schott (B.) *Firm.*

Baber, Joseph. Divertimento for string orchestra, Op.32, no.4. *Oxford University Press. Unpriced* RXMJ (B78-50246)

Baby elephant walk. *arr.* Baby elephant walk. (Mancini, Henry). *Warner : Blossom. Unpriced* UMMK (B78-50631)

Baby elephant walk. *arr.* Baby elephant walk. (Mancini, Henry). *Warner : Blossom. Unpriced* UMMK (B78-51187)

Bach, Jan. Hair today : for mixed chorus (SAATBB) a cappella. *New Galaxy Music : Stainer and Bell. Unpriced* EZDW (B78-50049)

Bach, Johann Christian. Symphony, wind instruments, no.6, B flat major. *arr.* Bläser-Sinfonie für Blechbläser. *Bärenreiter. Unpriced* WMK/AE (B78-50681)

Bach, Johann Sebastian.

Cantata no.113 : Herr Jesu Christ, du höchstes Gut. Jesus nimmt die Sunder an. Jesus nimmt die Sunder an : aria from cantata 113 for tenor, flute and continuo. *Oxford University Press. Unpriced* KGHE/VRPDH (B78-50177)

Cantata no.208 : Was mir behagt. Schafe können sicher weiden. *arr.* Sheep may safely graze. *Oxford University Press. Unpriced* VRNTQK/DW (B78-50289) ISBN 0-19-355280-9

Complete arias and sinfonias from cantatas, masses and oratorios : for solo voice, oboe, oboe d'amore, oboe de caccia, basso continuo/piano

Vol.8: Tenor, oboe, basso continuo/piano. *Musica rara. Unpriced* KE/VTNDH (B78-50888)

Vol.9: Tenor, bass, oboe, basso continuo/piano. *Musica rara. Unpriced* KE/VTNDH (B78-50889)

Vol.10: Bass, oboe, basso continuo/piano. *Musica rara. Unpriced* KE/VTNDH (B78-50891)

Complete arias and sinfonias from the cantatas, masses and oratorios, for solo voice, oboe d'amore, oboe da caccia, basso continuo/piano in 31 volumes

Vol.5. *Musica rara. Unpriced* KE/VTPDH (B78-50463)

Complete arias and sinfonias from the cantatas, masses and oratorios, for solo voice, oboe, oboe d'amore, oboe da caccia, basso continuo/piano in 31 volumes

Vol.6. *Musica rara. Unpriced* KE/VTPDH (B78-50465)

Vol.7. *Musica rara. Unpriced* KE/VTPDH (B78-50464)

Three chorales. *Boosey and Hawkes. Unpriced* MK/DM (B78-50184)

Three pieces for keyboard. *Banks. Unpriced* QPK (B78-50225)

Transcriptions for organ. *Cramer. Unpriced* RK/AAY (B78-50570)

Das wohltemperirte Clavier. Well tempered clavier = Wohltemperiertes Clavier : forty-eight preludes and fugues, for the piano. *Ashley : Phoenix. Unpriced* QP/Y (B78-50989)

Bach, Wilhelm Friedemann. Three pieces for keyboard. (Bach, Johann Sebastian). *Banks. Unpriced* QPK (B78-50225)

Baggett, Ed. We really want to thank you, Lord. *Yeldall Manor, Hare Hatch, Reading : Celebration Services. Unpriced* JFDM (B78-50087)

Bagly, Thomas H. The misletoe bough, p.61 : traditional carol for SSATBB and piano woodwork or string orchestra and percussion. (Blyton, Carey). *Roberton. £0.20* EZDW (B78-50050)

Bailey, Freda O. Fun on the piano : for very young music makers to start learning the happy way

Initial Book A. *Regina Music. Unpriced* QPJ (B78-51004)

Baines, Anthony. Catalogue of musical instruments in the Victoria and Albert Museum

Vol.2: Non-keyboard instruments. (Victoria and Albert Museum). 2nd ed. *H.M.S.O. £8.75* AL/B(WJ) (B78-36278) ISBN 0-11-290263-4

Baker, David N. The black composer speaks. *Scarecrow Press : Distributed by Bailey and Swinfen. £17.00* A/D(YTLD/M) (B78-22844) ISBN 0-8108-1045-X

Baker, Nicholas. Songs to sing in the bath : waterproof cartoons. *Allison and Busby. £0.75* AKDW (B78-08476) ISBN 0-85031-190-x

Baker, Richard, *b.1925.* The magic of music. *Sphere. £1.25* A(X) (B78-33932) ISBN 0-7221-1422-2

Balent, Andrew. Strange encounters. *Warner : Blossom. Unpriced* UMMJ (B78-51177)

Ball, Eric. Checkmate. *Selections : arr.* Four dances from the ballet ... (Bliss, *Sir* Arthur). *Novello. £4.85* WMK/HM (B78-51328)

Ballade, op.16 : for piano. (Barber, Samuel). *Schirmer. Unpriced* QPJ (B78-51005)

Ballads and songs of Lancashire

Part 2: Modern. 3rd ed. *EP Publishing. £5.25* AKDW/K/G(YDJD) (B78-02615) ISBN 0-7158-1182-7

Ballads from the pubs of Ireland. 3rd ed. *25 Lower Abbey St., Dublin 1 : Mercier Press. £1.50* AKDW/K/G(YDM) (B78-37866)

Ballet. *Warren and Phillips. Unpriced* QPK/HM/AY (B78-51032)

Balthes, Heinz. Monsieur Choufleuri restera chez lui de. *Vocal score.* Salon Blumenkohl/Monsieur Choufleuri restera chez lui de ... : Buffo-Operette in einem Akt deutsch nach Karl Fr. Wiltmann von Heinz Balthes und Paul Vasil, opéra bouffe en un acte de St. Rémy, E. L'Epine, Hector Crémieux et Ludovic Halévy, musikalische Revision, neue Instrumentation und praktische Bearbeitung von Caspar Richter. (Offenbach, Jacques). *Bote und Bock : Associated music. £11.50* CF (B78-50703)

Banchieri, Adriano. Fantasie overo canzoni alla francese. Fantasie no.6. *arr.* Echo fantasia : for brass quartet. *Chester Music. Unpriced* WNSK (B78-51339)

Band on the run. (McCartney, Paul). *MPL : Music Sales. Unpriced* KDW/GB (B78-50134) ISBN 0-86001-479-7

Band on the run. *arr.* Band on the run. (McCartney, Paul). *MPL : Music Sales. Unpriced* KDW/GB (B78-50134) ISBN 0-86001-479-7

Bandkraft

1. *Forsyth. Unpriced* WM/AY (B78-51295)
2. *Forsyth. Unpriced* WM/AY (B78-51296)
3. *Forsyth. Unpriced* WM/AY (B78-51297)

Barber, Samuel. Ballade, op.16 : for piano. *Schirmer. Unpriced* QPJ (B78-51005)

Barbier, Jules. Faust. Ah! je ris. *arr.* Jewel song ... (Gounod, Charles). *Leonard, Gould and Bolttler. Unpriced* KDW (B78-50115)

Barford, Philip. Bruckner symphonies. *British Broadcasting Corporation. £1.00* BBUEAMME (B78-33165) ISBN 0-563-12767-8

Barnes, R.

Cantiones, 1575. Derelinquat impius. Derelinquat impius. (Tallis, Thomas). *Cathedral Music. Unpriced* EZDJ (B78-50376)

Motettorum ... portim quinis ... vocibus ... liber primus. O magnum mysterium. O magnum mysterium. (Palestrina, Giovanni Pierluigi da). *36 Ranelagh Gdns., W.6 : Cathedral Music. Unpriced* EZDGKH/LF (B78-50367)

Secundus tomus musici operis. Ascendo ad Patrem meum. *arr.* Ascendo ad Patrem meum. (Handl, Jacob). *Cathedral Music. Unpriced* GEZDJ/LM (B78-50422)

Barnes, Richard. The story of 'Tommy'. *The Boathouse, Ranelagh Drive, Twickenham, Middx TW1 1QZ : Eel Pie Publishing Ltd. £6.95* AKDW/HKR/E(P) (B78-18545) ISBN 0-906008-02-6

Baron, Samuel. Cantata no.113 : Herr Jesu Christ, du höchstes Gut. Jesus nimmt die Sunder an. Jesus nimmt die Sunder an : aria from cantata 113 for tenor, flute and continuo. (Bach, Johann Sebastian). *Oxford University Press. Unpriced* KGHE/VRPDH (B78-50177)

Baroque concerto. (Hutchings, Arthur). 3rd revised ed. *Faber. £3.95 : CIP rev.* ALF(XFQ31) (B78-30835) ISBN 0-571-10865-2

Baroque music for clarinet : including music by Couperin, Handel, Molter, Pokorny, Stamitz. *Boosey and Hawkes. Unpriced* VVPK/AAY (B78-51286)

Barratt, Carol.

Chester's piano book : for two instruments. *London Pro Musica. Unpriced* LNU (B78-50908)

Chester's piano book

Number 1. *Chester Music. Unpriced* Q/AC (B78-50956)

Number 4. *Chester Music. Unpriced* Q/AC (B78-50957)

Chester's piano book written by Carol Barratt, illustrated by Wendy Hoile

Number 3. *Chester Music. Unpriced* Q/AC (B78-50958)

Barrett, Carol. Chester's concert pieces

From Bach to blues for the younger pianist. *Chester Music. Unpriced* QPK/AAY (B78-51023)

Bartered bride : a comic opera in three acts. (Smetana, Bedřich). Revised English libretto. *Boosey and Hawkes. Unpriced* CC (B78-50702)

Bartered bride. *Vocal score.* The bartered bride : a comic opera in three acts. (Smetana, Bedřich). Revised English libretto. *Boosey and Hawkes. Unpriced* CC (B78-50702)

Bartlett, Ken W. The ice break. *Vocal score.* The ice break : an opera in three acts. (Tippett, *Sir* Michael). *Schott. £13.00* CC (B78-50009)

Barto, A. Three children's songs for three equal voices (SSA). (Lutoslawski, Witold). *Chester Music. Unpriced* FDW/GJ (B78-50816)

Bartók, Béla. Sonata, violin. *Selections : arr.* Tempo di ciaccona and fuga. *Boosey and Hawkes. £3.00* QPK/AHJN (B78-50560)

Baselli, Joss. Divertissement baroque en trois mouvements. *Chappell. Unpriced* QPG (B78-50998)

Basic tutor for the Northumbrian small pipe. (Butler, Richard). *22 Newlyn Drive, Parkside Dale, Cramlington, Northumberland : Richard Butler. Unpriced* VYQ/AC (B78-50308) ISBN 0-9505591-0-5

Basin Street to Harlem : jazz masters and masterpieces, 1917-1930. (Lyttleton, Humphrey). *Robson. £5.25 : CIP rev.* AMT(M/XMS14) (B78-27526) ISBN 0-903895-91-9

Basque : old French dance. (Marais, Marin). *116 Long Acre, W.C.2 : Paxman. Unpriced* WTPK/AH (B78-50316)

Basque suite : for guitar and harpsichord (or piano). (Kelly, Bryan). *Oxford University Press. Unpriced* TSPJ (B78-50610) ISBN 0-19-357423-3

Bassin, Ethel. The old songs of Skye : Frances Tolmie and her circle. *Routledge and Kegan Paul. £5.95* ADW/G(YDLZS/P) (B78-03578) ISBN 0-7100-8546-x

Bate, Philip. The trumpet and trombone : an outline of their history, development and construction. 2nd ed. *E. Ben etc.. £8.50* AWS/B (B78-09121) ISBN 0-510-36412-8

Battell. The marche before the battell. *arr.* The Earle of Oxford's march. (Byrd, William). *Chester Music. Unpriced* WMK/AGM (B78-51320)

Batten, Adrian.

Holy, holy, holy. Holy, Lord God almighty : verse anthem for Trinity Sunday. *36 Ranelagh Gdns., W.6 : Cathedral Music. Unpriced* DK/LNB (B78-50344)

Short service for men. Benedicite. Benedicite ... *36 Ranelagh Gdns., W.6 : Cathedral Music. Unpriced* GEZDGNR (B78-50415)

Battle hymn of the Republic. (Broadbent, Derek). *Polyphonic Reproductions : Studio Music. Unpriced* WM/T (B78-50671)

Bauer, Walter Kage. Familiar music for 5 string banjo. *Lewis Music : Phoenix. Unpriced* TTPMJ (B78-50624)

Bavicchi, John. Three American choruses. *Vocal score.* Three American choruses : for SATB voices, piano and optional brasses. *Oxford University Press. Unpriced* DW (B78-50027)

Bayas, Arthur.

The best bluegrass songbook - yet! *Lewis : Phoenix. Unpriced* KDW/GCG/AY (B78-50157)

World's favorite folk explosion : for all fretted instruments, guitar, banjo, ukulele, mandolin, tenor banjo, tenor guitar, baritone uke. *Ashley : Phoenix. Unpriced* TPMK/DW/G/AYT (B78-50267)

Bayford, Dudley Escott. More songs for chord organ. *EMI Music. Unpriced* RPVK/DW (B78-50242)

Bayly, Ernest. A catalogue of 'Clarion' & 'Ebonoid' records. (Carter, Sydney Horace). *19 Glendale Rd, Bournemouth BH6 4JA : 'Talking machine review'. £2.00* A/FD(QB/WT) (B78-20766) ISBN 0-902338-29-3

Bayly, Ernie. A catalogue of 'Clarion' & 'Ebonoid' records. (Carter, Sydney Horace). *19 Glendale Rd, Bournemouth BH6 4JA : 'Talking machine review'. £2.00* A/FD(QB/WT) (B78-20766) ISBN 0-902338-29-3

Bazelon, Irwin.

Churchill downs : chamber concerto no.2. *Boosey and Hawkes. Unpriced* NYDF (B78-50207)

Double crossings : duo for trumpet and percussion. *Boosey and Hawkes. £4.50* WSPLX (B78-51347)

Propulsions : concerts for percussion. *Boosey and Hawkes. £12.50* XNPF (B78-51362)

A quite piece for a violent time : orchestra. *Boosey and Hawkes. Unpriced* MMJ (B78-50187)

BBC. *See* British Broadcasting Corporation.

BBC music guides. *See* British Broadcasting Corporation. BBC music guides.

Be known to us : a collection of general anthems for mixed voices. *57 Dorchester Rd, Lytchett Minster : Celebration Publishing. Unpriced* DH/AY (B78-50727) ISBN 0-906309-03-4

Beat, Janet E. Il tigrane. *Selections : arr.* Suite ... for 2 descant, treble (or tenor) recorders. (Scarlatti, Alessandro). *Chester Music. Unpriced* VSNTK (B78-51249)

Beatles. *See* Lennon, John.

Beatles album no.2. (Lennon, John). *Chappell. Unpriced* KDW/GB (B78-50451)

Beatles : the authorized biography. (Davies, Hunter). New ed.. *Mayflower. £1.25* AKDW/GB/E(P) (B78-26244) ISBN 0-583-11530-6

Beatles : the singles collections, 1962-1970. (Lennon, John). *Wise : Music Sales. Unpriced* KDW/GB (B78-50133) ISBN 0-86001-274-3

Beatles, yesterday, today, tomorrow. (Larkin, Rochelle). *161 Fulham Rd, S.W.3 : Scholastic Book Services. Unpriced* AKDW/GB/E(P) (B78-06261)

Beaumont, Francis. Jillian of Berry : four part song for male voices T.T.B.B. (Pasfield, William Reginald). *Edwin Ashdown. £0.20* GEZDW (B78-50829)

Beauty on a back street. (Hall, Daryl). *Chappell. Unpriced* KDW/GB (B78-50131)

Beauty on a back street. *arr.* Beauty on a back street. (Hall, Daryl). *Chappell. Unpriced* KDW/GB (B78-50131)

Becker, John. Sound piece no.6 : flute and clarinet. *Peters. Unpriced* VRPLVV (B78-51232)

Beckett, Samuel. That time. (Fortner, Wolfgang). *Schott. £12.00* JNDE/NXNT (B78-50109)

Bede, *Saint.* A maiden most gentle : (a Christmas carol) ; S.A.T.B., French tune. (Carter, Andrew). *Oxford University Press. Unpriced* DP/LF (B78-50737) ISBN 0-19-343067-3

Bee Gees. Main course. *arr.* Main course : songs. *Wise :*

Music Sales. Unpriced KDW/GB (B78-50124)
ISBN 0-86001-254-9
Beecham, *Sir* Thomas, *bart.* Sea drift. (Delius, Frederick). *Boosey and Hawkes. Unpriced* EMDX (B78-50032)
Beecham stories : anecdotes, sayings and impressions of Sir Thomas Beecham. *Robson. £3.50 : CIP rev.* A/EC(P/E) (B78-26892) ISBN 0-86051-044-1
Beechey, Gwilym. Three pieces for keyboard. (Bach, Johann Sebastian). *Banks. Unpriced* QPK (B78-50225)
Beer, Joseph. Concerto, clarinet, op.1, B flat major. *arr.* Concerto no.1 for clarinet and orchestra, op.1. *Musica rara. Unpriced* VVPK/LF (B78-50663)
Bees-a-buzzin'. (Siebert, Edrich). *Harmar : Studio Music. Unpriced* WMJ (B78-50678)
Beethoven, Ludwig van.
Equali, trombones(4), nos.1-3. Three equali for four trombones. *Chester Music. Unpriced* WUNS (B78-51354)
Sonaten für Klavier zu zwei Händen
Band 2: Nr.16-32. *Litolff : Peters. Unpriced* QPE (B78-50991)
Beethoven quartets. (Kerman, Joseph). *Oxford University Press. £3.95* BBJARXNS (B78-37869)
ISBN 0-19-315145-6
Beethoven studies
2. *Oxford University Press. £9.50 : CIP rev.* BBJ(D) (B77-28782) ISBN 0-19-315315-7
Beethoven's fifth bossa nova : wind quintet. (Greaves, Terence). *Emerson. Unpriced* UNRHJKS (B78-50286)
Beethoven's string quartets. (Radcliffe, Philip). 2nd ed. *Cambridge University Press. £6.95* BBJARXNS (B78-29840) ISBN 0-521-21963-9
Beginning crafts. Tolley, Bryan. Musical instruments. *Wayland. £1.75* AL/BC (B78-31598)
ISBN 0-85340-529-8
Behind the Beatles songs. (Cowan, Philip). *159 Wardour St., W.1 : Polytantric Press. £2.50* AKDW/GB/E(P) (B78-28699) ISBN 0-905150-09-0
Behrend, Siegfried. Ausgewählte Stücke alter und neuer Meister : für Gitarre. *Heinrichshofen : Peters. Unpriced* TSPMK/AAY (B78-50620)
Bel and the dragon. Op.120. *Chorus score.* Bel and the dragon, opus 120. (Gardner, John). *Oxford University Press. Unpriced* FACN (B78-50804)
ISBN 0-19-336205-8
Bel and the dragon. Op.120. *Vocal score.* Bel and the dragon : an opera for children. (Gardner, John). *Oxford University Press. Unpriced* CN (B78-50709)
ISBN 0-19-336202-3
Bel and the dragon, opus 120. (Gardner, John). *Oxford University Press. Unpriced* FACN (B78-50804)
ISBN 0-19-336205-8

Bell, Arnold Craig.
Alcina. *Selections : arr.* Dances from 'Alcina'. (Handel, George Frideric). *Banks. Unpriced* QPK/AH (B78-51025)
Suite, harpsichord, Craig Bell no.170, A major. Sarabande. Sarabande and air : for keyboard. (Handel, George Frideric). *Banks Music. Unpriced* QPJ (B78-51012)
Bell ringing, minimus : three and four bell methods. (Lewis, Harold). *36 Great Clarendon St., Oxford : J. Hannon and Co. £1.50* AXSR/E (B78-17617)
Bellotte, Pete. Zodiacs. (Moroder, Giorgio). *Hansa Productions : ATV Music : Music Sales. Unpriced* KFDW (B78-50174)
Bellstedt, Herman.
Napoli. *arr.* Napoli : cornet solo. *R. Smith. Unpriced* WRPK (B78-50692)
Napoli : cornet solo. *R. Smith. Unpriced* WMPWR (B78-50683)
Beloved Scotch & Irish songs & ballads. *Ashley : Phoenix. Unpriced* KDW/AYDM (B78-50120)
Belt, Lida M. The black composer speaks. *Scarecrow Press : Distributed by Bailey and Swinfen. £17.00* A/D(YTLD/M) (B78-22844) ISBN 0-8108-1045-X
Belt and Braces Roadshow Company. England expects : a musical entertainment for all those sick with sacrifice. (Richards, Gavin). *97 Ferme Park Rd, Crouch End, N8 9SA : Journeyman Press : Belt and Braces Roadshow Co. £1.20* BFKSACM (B78-01675) ISBN 0-904526-25-9
Belwin Mills solo series for guitar.
Giuliani, Mauro. Six airs irlandois nationales variées Op.125. *Belwin Mills Music. £1.50* TSPM/T (B78-51147)
Walker, Timothy. African light suite. *Belwin Mills. Unpriced* TSPMG (B78-50613)
Walker, Timothy. Étude. *Belwin Mills. £0.50* TSPMJ (B78-50619)
Walker, Timothy. Fantasia celestina. *Belwin Mills Music. £0.80* TSPMJ (B78-51159)
Walker, Timothy. Prelude, guitar. Prelude. *Belwin Mills Music. £0.50* TSPMJ (B78-51160)
Benham, Hugh.
Latin church music in England, c.1460-1575. *Barrie and Jenkins. £10.00* ADFF(YD/XCT116) (B78-26889)
ISBN 0-214-20059-0
Six-part masses. (Taverner, John). *Stainer and Bell. Unpriced* EZDG (B78-50769) ISBN 0-85249-477-7
Benker, Heinz. Mobile concertante : für Schlagwerk und Streicher. *Schott. £14.00* RXMPXF (B78-50252)
Benn studies : music. Morley-Pegge, Reginald. The French horn : some notes on the evolution of the instrument and of its technique. 2nd ed. *E. Benn etc.. £7.50* AWT/B
Bennett, Richard Rodney.
Concerto, double bass & chamber orchestra. *arr.* Concerto, double bass & chamber orchestra. *Novello. £3.15* MPSSF (B78-50936)
Concerto, violin. Concerto, violin & orchestra. *Novello. £4.20* MPSF (B78-50932)
Eustace and Hilda. *arr.* Eustace and Hilda : theme from the award-winning BBV tv trilogy, for piano solo. *Novello. Unpriced* QPK/JS (B78-51034)
Zodiac : orchestra. *Novello. £3.15* MMJ (B78-50188)
Bennett, Roy. Enjoying music
Book 2. *Longman. £0.95* A/C(VF) (B78-37863)
ISBN 0-582-22180-3
Bent, Margaret. Two 14th-century motets in praise of music. *Newton Abbot. Unpriced* EZDW (B78-50793)
Benyon, Tony. How t'make it as a rockstar. *IPC Magazines. £0.40* AKDW/HKR/E(MN)
Berceuse. ('Listen with Mother' theme) ... (Fauré, Gabriel). *R. Smith. Unpriced* WMK (B78-51315)
Berendt, Joachim. The story of jazz : from New Orleans to Rock Jazz. *Barrie and Jenkins etc.. £5.50* AMT(X) (B78-09118) ISBN 0-214-20379-4
Bergmann, Walter. First book of treble recorder solos. *Faber Music. Unpriced* VSSPK/AAY (B78-51261)
Berke, Dietrich. Voce et tuba : gesammelte Reden und Aufsätze, 1934-1974. (Ehmann, Wilhelm). *32 Great Titchfield St., W.1 : Bärenreiter Kassel. Unpriced* A(D) (B78-03573)
Berkeley, *Sir* Lennox.
Another spring. Op.93 : three songs to poems by Walter de la Mare. *Chester Music. Unpriced* KDW (B78-50859)
Five Chinese songs, op.78 : for medium voice and piano. *Chester Music. Unpriced* KFVDW (B78-50902)
Four piano studies. *Chester Music. Unpriced* QPJ (B78-51006)
The hill of the graces : for unaccompanied chorus, SSAATTBB. *Chester Music. Unpriced* EZDW (B78-50794)
Judica me. Op.96 : for unaccompanied chorus, SSATBB. *Chester Music. Unpriced* EZDJ (B78-50776)
Palm court waltz : for piano duet. *Chester Music. Unpriced* QNVHW (B78-50987)
Sinfonia concertante, oboe & chamber orchestra, op.84. *arr.* Sinfonia concertante for oboe and chamber orchestra. *Chester Music. Unpriced* VTPK/LE (B78-51269)
Sonata, piano. Sonata for piano. 2nd ed. embodying corrections to the first ed. *Chester Music. Unpriced* QPE (B78-50992)
Voices of the night : for orchestra. *Chester Music. Unpriced* MMJ (B78-50920)
Berlin, Irving.
90 golden years of Irving Berlin. *Chappell. Unpriced* RPVK/DW/GB (B78-51062)
Holiday inn. White Christmas. *arr.* White Christmas. *Chappell. Unpriced* NYFPK/DW/JR/LF (B78-50952)
Berlioz, Hector. New edition of the complete works
Vol.9: Grande messe des morts ; edited by Jürgen Kindermann. *Bärenreiter. Unpriced* C/AZ (B78-50698)
Bernard of Clairvaux, *Saint.* Jesu dulcis memoria. Jusu! the very thought is sweet : for 4-part female choir unaccompanied. (Victoria, Tomás Luis de). *Roberton. £0.15* FEZDJ (B78-50824)
Berne patrol : for brass band. (Howarth, Elgar). *Chester Music. Unpriced* WMGM (B78-51304)
Berners, *Lord. See* Tyrwhitt-Wilson, Gerald Hugh, 14th Baron Berners.
Berni Flint songbook. *Chappell. Unpriced* KDW/GB/AY (B78-50144)
Bernsdorff-Engelbrecht, Christiane. Voce et tuba : gesammelte Reden und Aufsätze, 1934-1974. (Ehmann, Wilhelm). *32 Great Titchfield St., W.1 : Bärenreiter Kassel. Unpriced* A(D) (B78-03573)
Bernstein, Leonard.
Haiku souvenirs : for voice and piano. (Gottlieb, Jack). *Amberson : Boosey and Hawkes : Boosey and Hawkes. Unpriced* KDW (B78-50861)
Slana!. *arr.* Slava! : a concert overture. *Amberson : Boosey and Hawkes : Boosey and Hawkes. Unpriced* UMMK (B78-51186)
Berry, Chuck. Chuck Berry : easy guitar. *Jewel Music : Chappell. Unpriced* KE/TSDW/GB (B78-50169)
Best bluegrass songbook - yet! *Lewis : Phoenix. Unpriced* KDW/GCG/AY (B78-50157)
Best of Bing. *EMI. Unpriced* KDW/GB/AY (B78-50145)
Best of Christmas songs : chord organ. *EMI. Unpriced* RPVCK/DW/LF/AY (B78-51059)
Best of Christmas songs : clarinet. *EMI. Unpriced* VVPMK/DW/LF/AY (B78-51288)
Best of Christmas songs : guitar or recorder. *EMI. Unpriced* TSPMK/DW/LF/AY (B78-51170)
Best of Christmas songs : piano or organ. *EMI. Unpriced* RK/DW/LF/AY (B78-51057)
Best of Christmas songs : trumpet. *EMI. Unpriced* WSPMK/DW/LF/AY (B78-51348)
Best of Daryl Hall and John Oates. (Hall, Daryl). *Chappell. Unpriced* KDW/GB (B78-50130)
Best of jazz. Lyttleton, Humphrey. Basin Street to Harlem : jazz masters and masterpieces, 1917-1930. *Robson. £5.25 : CIP rev.* AMT(M/XMS14) (B78-27526)
ISBN 0-903895-91-9
Best of McCartney. (McCartney, Paul). *MPL Communications : Music Sales. Unpriced* KDW/GB (B78-50867)
Best of McCartney : for easy piano. (McCartney, Paul). *MPL Communications : Music Sales (Dist.). Unpriced* QPK/DW/GB (B78-51029)
Best of Sir Harry Lauder. (Lauder, *Sir* Harry). *EMI. Unpriced* KDW/JV (B78-50460)
Best of The Hollies. *Wise : Music Sales. Unpriced* KDW/GB/AY (B78-50146) ISBN 0-86001-253-0
Bethell, Tom. George Lewis : a jazzman from New Orleans. *University of California Press. £8.75* AMT(P)
'Beuge dich, du Menschenseele' : geistliche Szene für mittlere Stimme und Orgel. (Klebe, Giselher). *Bärenreiter. £5.60* KFVDE (B78-50476)
Bevan, Maurice.
Evening service for men's voices 'in three parts'. (Mundy, William). *Cathedral Music. Unpriced* GEZDGPP (B78-50418)
Holy, holy, holy. Holy, Lord God almighty : verse anthem for Trinity Sunday. (Batten, Adrian). *36 Ranelagh Gdns., W.6 : Cathedral Music. Unpriced* DK/LNB (B78-50344)
Magnificat & Nunc dimittis, op.69, nos.3, 1. Magnificat and Nunc dimittis. (Mendelssohn, Felix). *36 Ralelagh Gdns., W.6 : Cathedral Music. Unpriced* DGPP (B78-50338)
Musicus apparatus academicas. Laurus cruentas. *Overture.* Overture, Laurus cruentas. (Croft, William). *Oxford University Press. Unpriced* MRJ (B78-50195)
ISBN 0-19-362424-9
Short service for men. Benedicite. Benedicite ... (Batten, Adrian). *36 Ranelagh Gdns., W.6 : Cathedral Music. Unpriced* GEZDGNR (B78-50415)
Beyer, Frank Michael.
Canticum Mose et Agni : für Doppelchor a cappella (1976). *Bote und Bock. £4.80* EZDE (B78-50364)
Sonata, violin & piano, (1977). Sonate für Violine und Klavier (1977). *Bote und Bock : Schirmer. £7.70* SPE (B78-51097)
Beyond Schenkerism : the need for alternatives in music analysis. (Narmour, Eugene). *University of Chicago Press. £14.00* A/AM(P) (B78-03570)
ISBN 0-226-56847-4
Bialas, Günter.
Meilensteine eines Komponistenlebens : kleine Festschrift zum 70. Geburtstag von Günter Bialas. *32 Gt Titchfield St., W1P 7AD : Bärenreiter. £10.08* BBNO(D) (B78-19399)
Romanza, e danza : für Bläser - Oktett (nach J. Meyerbeer). *Bärenreiter. £3.92* UNN (B78-50641)
Waldmusik : für Orchester und Soloinstrumente. *Bärenreiter. £8.40* MMJ (B78-50489)
Biberian, Gilbert. Eight valses for four guitars. *Belwin Mills. Unpriced* TSNSHW (B78-50606)
Bible. Old Testament. Esther. *Adaptations.* Turnabout : a musical version of the Book of Esther. (Easton, Ken) French's acting ed.. *French. £1.65* BSGNHACM (B78-20438) ISBN 0-573-62527-1
Bibliography of discographies
Vol.1: Classical music, 1925-1975. (Gray, Michael H). *Bowker. £15.00* A/FD(WT/T) (B78-09309)
ISBN 0-8352-1023-5
Bickerstaffe, Isaac.
Thomas and Sally : dramatic pastoral in two acts. (Arne, Thomas Augustine). *Eulenburg. Unpriced* CQC (B78-50329)
Thomas and Sally. *Vocal score.* Thomas and Sally : a dramatic pastoral in two acts. (Arne, Thomas Augustine). *Schott. Unpriced* CC (B78-50323)
Biesenthal, Linda.
Annual index to popular music record reviews
1976. *Scarecrow Press : Distributed by Bailey and Swinfen. £17.00* A/GB/FD(T) (B78-20767)
ISBN 0-8108-1070-0
Popular music periodicals index
1976. *Scarecrow Press : Distributed by Bailey and Swinfen. £8.50* A/GB(DD/B/T) (B78-50320)
ISBN 0-8108-1079-4
Big bands. The observer's book of big bands. (White, Mark). *F. Warne. £1.25* AMT(M) (B78-37101)
ISBN 0-7232-1589-8
Big red songbook. *Unit 10, Specner Court, Chalcot Rd, N.W.1 : Plato Press. £1.00* JEZDW/AY (B78-50835)
ISBN 0-904383-12-1
Bigio, Robert. Pelléas et Melisande. Op.80. Sicilienne. *arr.* Sicilienne from Pelléas et Melisande : for flute and piano. (Fauré, Gabriel). *Chester Music. Unpriced* VRPK/AHVQ/JM (B78-51221)
Bijou. *Chappell. Unpriced* KDW/HKR (B78-50879)
Bimonte, Richard. Yankee ingenuity : a musical. French's acting ed. *French. £1.65* BWNTSACM (B78-12987)
ISBN 0-573-68082-5
Bing. The complete Crosby. (Thompson, Charles). Revised and augmented ed. *W.H. Allen. £5.95* AKDW/GB/E(P) (B78-20440) ISBN 0-491-02335-9
Bing : the authorised biography. (Thompson, Charles). Large print ed.. *Magna Print Books. £4.75* AKDW/GB/E(P) (B78-04324) ISBN 0-86009-048-5
Binkerd, Gordon.
Intermezzo, piano, op.117, no.1, E flat major. *arr.* Wiegenlied : for mixed chorus and piano four hands. (Brahms, Johannes). *Boosey and Hawkes. Unpriced* DW (B78-50349)
Song under the silver umbrella : for children's voices and accompaniment
1: The Christ-Child : (S.A. and piano or harp). *Boosey and Hawkes. Unpriced* FDP/LF (B78-50809)
2: Song of innocence : (three-part children's chorus). *Boosey and Hawkes. Unpriced* FEZDH (B78-50823)
3: An evening falls : (unison children's voices and piano). *Boosey and Hawkes. Unpriced* JFDW (B78-50841)
4: The merry man of Paris : (unison children's voices and piano). *Boosey and Hawkes. Unpriced* JFDW (B78-50842)
5: Child's song : (three-part children's chorus and piano). *Boosey and Hawkes. Unpriced* FDW (B78-50812)
6: White fields : (S.A. and piano). *Boosey and Hawkes. Unpriced* FDW (B78-50813)
Suite, piano. Suite for piano : five fantasias. *Boosey and Hawkes. Unpriced* QPG (B78-50999)
Binney, Malcolm. The authentic Gilbert & Sullivan

songbook : 92 unabridged selections from all 14 operas reproduced from early vocal scores. (Sullivan, *Sir* Arthur Seymour). *Dover : Constable. £5.35* DW (B78-50028) ISBN 0-486-23482-7

BIOS. *See* British Institute of Organ Studies.

BIOS journal
Vol.1 : 1977. (British Institute of Organ Studies). *130 Southfield Rd, Oxford OX4 1PA : Positif Press. Unpriced* AR(B) (B78-20443) ISBN 0-9503892-8-5

Birkbeck College. Foundation orations. Goehr, Alexander. Musical ideas and ideas about music. *Birkbeck College. £0.25* A (B78-32354)

Birthday hansel : for high voice and harp, op.92. (Britten, Benjamin, *Baron Britten*). *Faber Music. Unpriced* KFTE/TQDW (B78-50475)

Bishop, Cecil Henry. The Folkestone fiery serpent, and other Kentish poems : a selection. *Springfield, Maidstone, Kent : Kent County Library. £0.50* AKDW/G(YDCM) (B78-11199) ISBN 0-905155-13-0

Bishop, Ian Courtney. The Gibson guitar from 1950. *20 Denmark St., WC2H 8NE : Musical New Services Ltd. Unpriced* ATS/B

Bishop, Jeffrey. Moshe Timloch : fantasy for brass quintet. *Novello. £1.30* WNR (B78-51336)

Bishop Thorpe. *arr.* By cool Siloam's shady rill. (Clarke, Jeremiah). *Galaxy : Stainer and Bell. Unpriced* EZDM (B78-50380)

Bittinger, Werner. Church sonatas. *Collections.* Sämtliche Kirchensonaten = Complete church sonatas
III/IV: Zwei Sonaten in C für Orgel und Orchester, KV278 (271e), KV329 (317a) : Generalbassausetzung, Werner Bittinger. (Mozart, Wolfgang Amadeus). *Bärenreiter. £2.80* MPRE/AZ (B78-50498)

Bizet, Georges. Valse avec choeur. *Vocal score.* Valse avec choeur = Walzermit Chor : pour choeur mixte et petit orchestra = für gemischten Chor und kleines Orchester. *Schott. £8.00* DW (B78-50744)

Blacher, Boris.
24 préludes : für Klavier (1974). *Bote und Bock Schirmer. £7.70* QPJ (B78-51007)
Kabale und liebe. Op.44. *Vocal score.* Kabale und Liebe : Oper in 2 teilen (9 Bildern) nach Friedrich von Schiller. (Einem, Gottfried von). *Boosey and Hawkes. Unpriced* CC (B78-50006)
Kabale und Liebe : Opera in 2 Teilen (9 Bildern) nach Friedrich von Schiller. (Einem, Gottfried von). *Boosey and Hawkes. Unpriced* CC (B78-50005)
Quintet, woodwind & strings (1973/1974). Quintet für Flöte, Oboe, Violine, Viola und Violoncello (1973/74). *Bote und Bock : Associated Music. £6.40* NVPNR (B78-50502)
Sonata, flute & piano, (1940). Sonate für Flöte und Klavier (1940). *Bote und Bock : Schirmer. £5.75* VRPE (B78-51211)
Variations on a theme of Tchaikovsky. Variationer über ein Thema von Tschaikowsky. (Rokoko Variationen) : für Violoncello und Klavier (1974). *Bote und Bock Associated Music. £6.40* SRP/T (B78-50600)

Blacher, Lotte. Kabale und Liebe : Oper in 2 Teilen (9 Bildern) nach Friedrich von Schiller. (Einem, Gottfried von). *Boosey and Hawkes. Unpriced* CQC (B78-50710)

Black, Don. Dear anyone ... : a musical story of the agony behind the agony column ... from the concept album. (Stephens, Geoff). *Dick James : Music Sales (dist.). Unpriced* KDW/GB (B78-50870)

Black composer speaks. *Scarecrow Press : Distributed by Bailey and Swinfen. £17.00* A/D(YTLD/M) (B78-22844) ISBN 0-8108-1045-X

Black music. *For later issues of this periodical see* Black music & jazz review.

Black music & jazz review. *For earlier issues of this periodical see* Black music.

Black music & jazz review
Vol.1, issue 1- ; Apr. 1978-. *IPC Specialist and Professional Press. £0.40* AMT(YTLD/B) (B78-26878)

Blackford, Richard. Sonata, piano, (1975). Sonata for piano (1975). *Schirmer. £3.05* QPE (B78-50524)

Blackwood, Alan, *b.1932.* The pageant of music : an introduction to the history of music. *Barrie and Jenkins. £3.95* A(X) (B78-04318) ISBN 0-214-20423-5

Blades, James. Ready to play : stories with percussion sounds. *British Broadcasting Corporation. £1.50* AX/GR(VE) (B78-38609) ISBN 0-563-17610-5

Blake, David, *b.1936.* Toussaint, or, The aristocracy of the skin : opera in 3 acts and 22 scenes. (Ward, Anthony). *Novello. £1.70* BBPLAC (B78-06260)

Blake, Howard. The new national song book. *Vocal score.* The new national song book. *Lengnick. £1.95* CP (B78-50013)

Blake, William. Song under the silver umbrella : for children's voices and accompaniment
2: Song of innocence : (three-part children's chorus). (Binkerd, Gordon). *Boosey and Hawkes. Unpriced* FEZDH (B78-50823)

Blakes 7. (Simpson, Dudley). *Chappell. Unpriced* QPK/JS (B78-50228)

Blakes 7. *arr.* Blakes 7. (Simpson, Dudley). *Chappell. Unpriced* QPK/JS (B78-50228)

Blanco, Billy.
Paulistana : piano. *Arapua : Essex Music. Unpriced* QPJ (B78-51008)
Sinfonia do Rio de Janeiro : piano. (Jobim, Antonio Carlos). *Arapua : Essex Music. Unpriced* QPE (B78-50995)

Blaserkreis, Reihe C. Schneider, Willy. Ein Sommertag : Suite für Bläsorchester. *Schott. £20.00* UMMG (B78-51176)

Bleiler, Ellen H. The making of an opera : 'Don Giovanni' at Glyndebourne. (Higgins, John, *b.1934*). *Secker and Warburg. £7.95* BMSAC/E (B78-33162) ISBN 0-436-19595-x

Bletschacher, Richard.
Milchzahnlieder. *Choral score.* Milchzahnlieder = Milktooth songs. (Eröd, Iván). *Boosey and Hawkes. Unpriced* JFADW (B78-50836)
Milchzahnlieder. *Vocal score.* Milchzahnlieder = Milktooth songs : für Gesang oder Kinderchor, mit Klavier oder Kammerorchester = for solo voice, or children's chorus with piano or chamber orchestra. (Eröd, Iván). *Boosey and Hawkes. Unpriced* KDW (B78-50860)

Blewett, P R W. Antony Duddyngton, organ maker : the Duddyngton manuscripts at All Hallows-by-the-Tower, London. *22 Edgar Rd, Sanderstead, South Croydon CR2 0NG : Rev. P. Blewett. £0.50* AR/BC(P) (B78-33169) ISBN 0-906257-00-x

Bliss, *Sir* Arthur. Checkmate. *Selections : arr.* Four dances from the ballet ... *Novello. £4.85* WMK/HM (B78-51328)

Block, Robert Paul.
Concertino, flute & oboe, F major. *arr.* Concertino for flute, oboe and orchestra. (Kalliwoda, Jan Vaclav). *Musica rara. Unpriced* NWPNTK/LF (B78-50202)
Concerto, bassoon & string orchestra, B flat major. *arr.* Concerto in B flat for bassoon, strings and basso continuo. (Hertel, Johann Wilhelm). *Musica rara. Unpriced* VWPK/LF (B78-51291)
Crumhorn consort anthology
Vol.2 ; edited by Pater Nothnagle and R.P. Block. *Musica rara. Unpriced* VTWN/AY (B78-51270)
Vol.3 ; edited by Peter Nothnagle and R.P. Block. *Musica rara. Unpriced* VTWN/AY (B78-51271)
Sonata, trumpet, string quartet & continuo, D major. Sonata, D.XI, 5 in D for trumpet, strings and basso continuo. (Gabrielli, Domenico). *Musica rara. Unpriced* NUXSNQE (B78-50945)
Sonata, trumpet, string quartet & continuo, D major. *arr.* Sonata D. XI.5 in D for trumpet, strings and basso continuo. (Gabrielli, Domenico). *Musica rara. Unpriced* WSPK/AE (B78-51345)
Sonata, trumpet, string quintet & continuo, D major. Sonata, D. XI, 4 in D for trumpet, strings and basso continuo. (Gabrielli, Domenico). *Musica rara. Unpriced* NUXSNPE (B78-50944)
Sonata, trumpet, string quintet & continuo, D major. *arr.* Sonata D, XI, 4 in D for trumpet, strings and basso continuo. (Gabrielli, Domenico). *Musica rara. Unpriced* WSPK/AE (B78-51346)
Sonata, trumpets (2) & string orchestra, D major. Sonata à 6 for trumpets, strings and continuo. (Lazari, Ferdinando Antonio). *Musica rara. Unpriced* RXMPWSNUE (B78-50579)
Sonata, trumpets (2) & string orchestra, D major. *arr.* Sonata à 6, for 2 trumpets, strings and continuo. (Lazari, Ferdinando Antonio). *Musica rara. Unpriced* WSNTQK/AE (B78-50693)

Blow, John. Paratum cor meum Deus. *36 Ranelagh Gdns. W.6 : Cathedral Music. Unpriced* FLDJ (B78-50404)

Blue moves. (John, Elton). *Big Pig Music : Music Sales. £4.95* KDW/HKR (B78-50161)

Blue moves. *arr.* Blue moves. (John, Elton). *Big Pig Music : Music Sales. £4.95* KDW/HKR (B78-50161)

Blues 1, 2 & 3 : for classical guitar. (Royal, Timothy). *16 Oldfield Place, Hotwells, Bristol 8 : Shed Music. £0.75* TSPMJ (B78-50272)

Blues & the poetic spirit. (Garon, Paul). *Eddison Press. £3.50* AKDW/HHW (B78-30829) ISBN 0-85649-018-0

Blum, David. Casals and the art of interpretation. *Heinemann Educational. £8.50* ASR/E(P) (B78-06993) ISBN 0-435-81150-9

Blyton, Carey. The misletoe bough, p.61 : traditional carol for SSATBB and piano woodwork or string orchestra and percussion. *Roberton. £0.20* EZDW (B78-50050)

Bob Dylan starring in Rolling Thunder logbook. Rolling Thunder logbook. (Shepard, Sam). *Penguin. £1.75* AKDW/HKR/E(P/YT/XQQ) (B78-20439) ISBN 0-14-004750-6

Bobri, Vladimir. The Segovia technique. *Collier Books : Collier Macmillan. £4.50* ATS/CY (B78-01056) ISBN 0-02-079240-9

Bolton, Cecil.
An introduction to the guitar. *EMI Music. Unpriced* TS/AC (B78-51140)
The best of Christmas songs : chord organ. *EMI. Unpriced* RPVCK/DW/LF/AY (B78-51059)
The best of Christmas songs : clarinet. *EMI. Unpriced* VVPMK/DW/LF/AY (B78-51288)
The best of Christmas songs : guitar or recorder. *EMI. Unpriced* TSPMK/DW/LF/AY (B78-51170)
The best of Christmas songs : piano or organ. *EMI. Unpriced* RK/DW/LF/AY (B78-51057)
The best of Christmas songs : trumpet. *EMI. Unpriced* WSPMK/DW/LF/AY (B78-51348)
Children's songs and carols, including hymns and games : for easy guitar or recorder. *EMI. Unpriced* TSPMK/DW/GJ/AY (B78-51169)
Children's songs and carols, including hymns and games : for easy piano or organ. *EMI. Unpriced* QPK/DW/GJ/AY (B78-51030)
Classic melodies. *EMI. Unpriced* RPVCK (B78-51058)
EMI music book of piano rags. *EMI. Unpriced* QPHXJ (B78-50525)
Jingle bells. (Pierpont, James S). *EMI. Unpriced* KDW/LF (B78-50882)
Oh! it's a lovely war : songs, ballads and parodies of the Great War. *EMI. Unpriced* KDW/GB/AY (B78-50874)
Our Gracie. *EMI. Unpriced* KDW/GB/AY (B78-50875)
Pennies from heaven : a selection of popular songs of the thirties as featured in the BBC TV series. *EMI. Unpriced* KDW/GB/AY (B78-50454)
Tammy Wynette's greatest hits. *EMI. Unpriced* KDW/GB/AY (B78-50458)
The works of Jimmy Kennedy. (Kennedy, Jimmy). *EMI. Unpriced* KDW/GB (B78-50872)
The works of Les Reed. (Reed, Les). *EMI. Unpriced* KDW/GB (B78-50869)

Bombastic bombardon : solo for E flat bass and brass band. (Siebert, Edrich). *Harmer Music : Studio Music. Unpriced* WMPWX (B78-50686)

Bononcini, Giovanni Maria. Church sonata, violins (2), op.6, no.9, D minor. Sonata a tre, d-moll, d minor, op.VI, no.9, für zwei Sopranblockflöten und Basso continuo, for two soprano i.e. descant recorders and basso continuo. *Noetzel : Peters. Unpriced* VSRNTPWE (B78-50654)

Bonsor, Brian. Simple samba : for descant 1, descant 2, and, or, treble recorder and piano. *Schott. Unpriced* VSNTQHVKS (B78-51251)

Book of hours : eight pieces for flute and harp. (Rorem, Ned). *Boosey and Hawkes. Unpriced* VRPLTQ (B78-51231)

Book of musicals : from 'Show Boat' to 'A Chorus Line'. (Jackson, Arthur). *Mitchell Beazley. £7.95* ACM(XKF112) (B78-16385) ISBN 0-85533-116-x

Books of American negro spirituals, including The book of American negro spirituals and The second book of negro spirituals. *Da Capo Press : Robert Hale. £6.50* KDW/LC/AY (B78-50461)

Boon, Brindley. Sing the happy song! : (a history of Salvation Army vocal music). *Salvationist Publishing and Supplies. Unpriced* AD/LSK(X) (B78-34738) ISBN 0-85412-321-0

Booth, Victor. We piano teachers. Revised ed.. *Hutchinson. £2.95* AQ/E(VC) (B78-40354) ISBN 0-09-106191-1

Boston. Boston. *arr.* Boston. *Columbia Pictures Publications : EMI. Unpriced* KDW/HKR (B78-50075)

Boston. *arr.* Boston. (Boston). *Columbia Pictures Publications : EMI. Unpriced* KDW/HKR (B78-50075)

Boswell, Eric. Little donkey. *arr.* Little donkey. *Chappell. Unpriced* NYDPK/DP/LF (B78-50950)

Bottesini, Giovanni.
Complete Bottesini
Vol.1: For two double basses and piano. *Yorke. Unpriced* SS/AZ (B78-51121)
Duet no.2. Gran duetto 2 : for double basses. *Yorke. Unpriced* SSNU (B78-51126)

Boulez, Pierre. Pierre Boulez, conversations with Célestin Deliège. *48 Great Marlborough St., W1V 2BN : Eulenburg Books. £3.00* BBRO (B78-11192) ISBN 0-903873-21-4

Bourne series. Ridout, Alan. That virgin's child : for S.A.T.B. unacc. *Williams School of Church Music. Unpriced* EZDP/LF (B78-50047)

Boustead, Alan. Saint Martha and the dragon. *Vocal score.* Saint Martha and the dragon : a dramatic legend set to music, for narrator, soprano and tenor soloists, chorus, children's chorus (with percussion) and chamber orchestra. (Tate, Phyllis). *Oxford University Press. Unpriced* DE (B78-50718) ISBN 0-19-338397-7

Bouwens, J. Paloma blanca. *arr.* Paloma blanca. *Chappell. Unpriced* NYFPK (B78-50513)

Box and fiddle
No.1- ; Oct. 1977-. *c/o The editor, 50 Mount Vernon Rd, Stranraer : National Association of Accordion and Fiddle Clubs. £0.10* ARS(B) (B78-03581)

Boyce, Max.
Max Boyce songbook
Vol.1. *EMI. Unpriced* KDW/GB (B78-50125)
Vol.2. *EMI. Unpriced* KDW/GB (B78-50126)

Boyd, Anne. As I crossed a bridge of dreams : for unaccompanied chorus (12 or more singers divided into 3 SATB groups). *Faber Music. Unpriced* EZDW (B78-50385)

Boyd, Jack. Credo. Crucifixus. *arr.* Crucifixus = (He was crucified) : for two-part chorus of women's voices with keyboard accompaniment. (Suidell, Padre). *Roberton. £0.15* FDJ (B78-50808)

Boyd, Malcolm, *b.1932.* William Mathias. *University of Wales Press for the Welsh Arts Council. Unpriced* BMGH (B78-15753) ISBN 0-7083-0672-1

Boyle, Rory.
Augustine. *Choral score.* Augustine : an opera in one or two acts for children. *Chester Music. Unpriced* DACN (B78-50714)
Augustine. *Vocal score.* Augustine : an opera in one or two acts for children. *Chester Music. Unpriced* CN (B78-50704)

Boys' Brigade. *Glasgow Battalion.* Company section song book. *168 Bath St., G.2 : Boys' Brigade, Glasgow Battalion. Unpriced* JFVBDW/AY (B78-50856)

Brace, Geoffrey. Listen! music and civilization. *Cambridge University Press. £2.25* A/KD(X) (B78-22160) ISBN 0-521-21153-0

Bradley, Ernest. The gift of December : for four-part chorus of men's voices and baritone solo with piano accompaniment. (Gump, Richard). *Schirmer. Unpriced* GDH/LF (B78-50069)

Bradley, Richard. Classical Christmas music. *Columbia Pictures : EMI. Unpriced* R/LF/AY (B78-51046)

Brahms, Johannes. Intermezzo, piano, op.117, no.1, E flat major. *arr.* Wiegenlied : for mixed chorus and piano four hands. *Boosey and Hawkes. Unpriced* DW (B78-50349)

Brahms-Bildnis : für Violine, Violoncello und Klavier. (Killmayer, Wilhelm). *Schott. £12.00* NXNT (B78-50948)

Brahms piano music. (Matthews, Denis). *British*

Broadcasting Corporation. £1.00 BBTAQ (B78-28703)
ISBN 0-563-12981-6

Brand, Geoffrey.
Napoli. *arr.* Napoli : cornet solo. (Bellstedt, Herman). *R. Smith. Unpriced* WRPK (B78-50692)
Napoli : cornet solo. (Bellstedt, Herman). *R. Smith. Unpriced* WMPWR (B78-50683)

Brand, Michael.
Gladiolus rag. (Joplin, Scott). *R. Smith. Unpriced* WMK/AHXJ (B78-51322)
Portsmouth : traditional. *R. Smith. Unpriced* WMK/DW (B78-51323)
Tuba tapestry : E flat bass solo. *R. Smith. Unpriced* WMPWU (B78-50685)

Brandmüller, Theo.
5 Details : für Klavier (1975). *Bote und Bock : Associated Music. Unpriced* QPJ (B78-50527)
Apokalyptische Vision : für Basstimme und Orgel. *Bote und Bock : Associated Music.* £4.80 KGXDE (B78-50479)

Brandreth, Gyles. The funniest man on earth : the story of Dan Leno. *Hamilton.* £4.50 AKDW/JV/E(P) (B78-01692)
ISBN 0-241-89810-2

Branson, David.
Saudade : for guitar. *Helicon. Unpriced* TSPMJ (B78-51152)
Waltz-impromptu : for guitar. *Helicon. Unpriced* TSPMHW (B78-51150)

Brass for beginners : treble clef piston - valved brass instruments. (Ridgeon, John). *Boosey and Hawkes.* £2.20 W/AC (B78-50309)

Breakaway. (Gallagher, Benny). *Wise : Music Sales. Unpriced* KDW/GB (B78-50129) ISBN 0-86001-278-6

Breakaway. *arr.* Breakaway. (Gallagher, Benny). *Wise : Music Sales. Unpriced* KDW/GB (B78-50129)
ISBN 0-86001-278-6

Breathnach, Breandán. Folk music and dances in Ireland. Revised ed. *25 Lower Abbey St., Dublin 1 : Mercier Press Ltd.* £2.10 A/G(YDM) (B78-34736)
ISBN 0-85342-509-4

Breese, Pamela.
Workers' carol. *arr.* The workers' carol. (Petrokino, Paul). *Roberton. Unpriced* DP/LF (B78-50026)
Workers' carol. *arr.* The workers' carol. (Petrokino, Paul). *Roberton.* £0.12 JE/VSPDP/LF (B78-50426)

Brett, Philip. The music of William Byrd.
Vol.3: The consort and keyboard music of William Byrd. (Kerman, Joseph). *Faber.* £15.00 : CIP rev. BBX (B78-19401) ISBN 0-571-10566-1

Brewis, Bert.
90 golden years of Irving Berlin. (Berlin, Irving). *Chappell. Unpriced* RPVK/DW/GB (B78-51062)
Fun music : for all organ
Vol.1. *Chappell. Unpriced* RK/DW/GB/AY (B78-50237)

Vol.2. *Chappell. Unpriced* RK/DW/GB/AY (B78-50238)

Fun music : for chord organ
Vol.1. *Chappell. Unpriced* RPVCK/DW/GB/AY (B78-50240)
Vol.2. *Chappell. Unpriced* RPVCK/DW/GB/AY (B78-50241)
Fun music : for piano
Vol.1. *Chappell. Unpriced* QPK/DW/GB/AY (B78-50226)
Vol.2. *Chappell. Unpriced* QPK/DW/GB/AY (B78-50227)
Golden Latin : all organ. *Chappell. Unpriced* RPVK/DW/GB/AY (B78-51064)
Pop goes the recorder : 20 great tunes with chord symbols for guitar
Book 1. *Chappell. Unpriced* VSPMK/DW/GB/AY (B78-50299)
Book 2. *Chappell. Unpriced* VSPMK/DW/GB/AY (B78-50300)

Bricusse, Leslie. The travelling music show. *Selections : arr.* Leslie Bricusse and Anthony Newley's The travelling music show. *Tro-Essex. Unpriced* KDW (B78-50441)

Bridges, Robert. Seven part-songs for female voices and strings. (Holst, Gustav). Revised ed. 1973. *Novello. Unpriced* FE/RXNRDW (B78-50821)

Brief history of the Middlesex Yeomanry (Duke of Cambridge's Hussars) Association Military Band. (Thrower, Arthur Harry). *44 South Easling Rd, W.5 : The author. Unpriced* AUMM(QB/X) (B78-30834)

Briegel, Wolfgang Carl. Evangelischer Blumengarten.
Machet die Töre weit. Machet die Töre weit : Du König der Ehren, wir danken Dir : für vierstimmigen gemischten Chor. *Bärenreiter.* £0.84 EZDH (B78-50370)

Brindle, Reginald Smith.
Five sketches : for guitar and violin. *Schott.* £0.70 SPLTS (B78-51102)
Four poems of García Lorca : for solo guitar. *Schott. Unpriced* TSPMJ (B78-50615)
Intavolatura di liutto, lib.2. Canzona a 8. *arr.* Canzona in 8 parts. (Terzi, Giovanni Antonio). *Schott.* £0.70 TSNSK (B78-50608)
Ten-string music : for cello and guitar. *Schott. Unpriced* SRPLTS (B78-51119)
Bristol suite. (Hurford, Peter). *Novello.* £1.20 RG (B78-50562)

British Broadcasting Corporation. BBC music guides.
Barford, Philip. Bruckner symphonies. *British Broadcasting Corporation.* £1.00 BBUEAMME (B78-33165)
ISBN 0-563-12767-8
King, Alexander Hyatt. Mozart wind and string concertos. *British Broadcasting Corporation.* £1.00 BMSAMPSF (B78-28702)
ISBN 0-563-12770-8

Layton, Robert. Dvořák symphonies and concertos. *British Broadcasting Corporation.* £1.00 BDXAMME (B78-29839) ISBN 0-563-12676-0
Matthews, Denis. Brahms piano music. *British Broadcasting Corporation.* £1.00 BBTAQ (B78-28703)
ISBN 0-563-12981-6
Ottaway, Hugh. Shostakovich symphonies. *British Broadcasting Corporation.* £1.00 BSGRAMME (B78-28701) ISBN 0-563-12772-4
Radcliffe, Philip. Mozart piano concertos. *British Broadcasting Corporation.* £1.00 BMSAMPQF (B78-33168) ISBN 0-563-12771-6

British Broadcasting Corporation.
Catalogue of music broadcast on Radio 3 and Radio 4 1974. *B.B.C.* £4.00 A/JT(WT) (B78-20763)
ISBN 0-563-17369-6
Ready to play : stories with percussion sounds. (Blades, James). *British Broadcasting Corporation.* £1.50 AX/GR(VE) (B78-38609) ISBN 0-563-17610-5

British catalogue of music
1977. *British Library, Bibliographic Services Division.* £11.00 A(TC) (B78-24790) ISBN 0-900220-68-6

British Country Music Association. Yearbook
1978. *PO Box 2, Newton Abbot, Devon TQ12 4HT : The Association. Unpriced* AKDW/GCW(BC) (B78-21397)

British Federation of Brass Bands. Directory of British brass bands : associations, societies, contests
Vol.2 : 1978-79. *28 Marigold St., Rochdale OL11 1RJ : British Federation of Brass Bands.* £1.00 AWM(QB/YC/BC) (B78-27525)

British Federation of Music Festivals. Year book
1978. *106 Gloucester Place, W1H 3DB : The Federation.* £1.50 A(YC/WE/Q) (B78-17612)

British Institute of Organ Studies. BIOS journal
Vol.1 : 1977. *130 Southfield Rd, Oxford OX4 1PA : Positif Press. Unpriced* AR(B) (B78-20443)
ISBN 0-9503892-8-5

British Library. Bibliographic Services Division. British catalogue of music
1977. *British Library, Bibliographic Services Division.* £11.00 A(TC) (B78-24790) ISBN 0-900220-68-6

British records charts, 1955-1978. Revised and updated ed.. *Macdonald and Jane's.* £4.95 AKDW/GB/FD(XPQ24) (B78-37424) ISBN 0-354-08523-9

British Society for Music Therapy. Music therapy in the community : papers read at the conference held in London on the 16th October 1976. *48 Lanchester Rd, N6 4TA : British Society for Music Therapy. Unpriced* A(ZD) (B78-12810)

British traditional ballad in North America. (Coffin, Tristram Potter). Revised ed. reprinted. *University of Texas Press.* £11.25 ADW/G(YT/TC) (B78-01317)
ISBN 0-292-70719-3

Britt, Stan. The illustrated encyclopedia of jazz. (Case, Brian). *27 Old Gloucester St., WC1N 3AF : Salamander Books.* £6.95 AMT(C) (B78-22169)
ISBN 0-86101-013-2

Britten, Benjamin, *Baron Britten.*
A birthday hansel : for high voice and harp, op.92. *Faber Music. Unpriced* KFTE/TQDW (B78-50475)
The building of the house. *arr.* The building of the house : for concert band. *Faber Music. Unpriced* UMMK (B78-50628)
The little sweep ... (Crozier, Eric). *Boosey and Hawkes. Unpriced* BBUAC (B78-28697)
Sonata, pianos (2). Sonata for two pianos. *50 Middleham Rd, Durham : Toad House Music.* £9.00 QNUE (B78-50519)

Britten, Benjamin, *Baron Britten*
Quartet, strings, no.3, op.94. String quartet no.3, op.94. *Faber Music. Unpriced* RXNS (B78-50253)
Quartet, strings, no.3, op.94. String quartet no.3, op.94. *Faber Music. Unpriced* RXNS (B78-50580)
Suite, violin & piano, op.6. *Selections.* Three pieces for violin and piano from the suite, op.6. *Boosey and Hawkes. Unpriced* SPJ (B78-50260)

Broadbent, Derek.
The battle hymn of the Republic. *Polyphonic Reproductions : Studio Music. Unpriced* WM/T (B78-50671)
Cornets a-go-go. *Polyphonic Reproductions : Studio Music. Unpriced* WMJ (B78-50677)
The Lincolnshire poacher. *Logo Music : Studio Music (dist.) Unpriced* WMK/DW (B78-51324)
Phil the fluter's ball. *arr.* Phil the fluter's ball. (French, Percy). *Polyphonic Reproductions : Studio Music. Unpriced* WMK/DW (B78-50682)
Strawberry fair. *Logo Music : Studio Music. Unpriced* WMK/DW (B78-51325)

Broadway's greatest musicals. (Laufe, Abe). *David and Charles.* £9.50 ACM/E(YT/X) (B78-37865)
ISBN 0-7153-7712-4

Brojer, Robert.
Sonata, guitar, op.22, C major. *Selections.* Menuett und Rondo : für Gitarre. (Sor, Fernando). Revidierte Neuausgabe. *Schott.* £3.20 TSPMJ (B78-50273)
Zwei spanische Stücke = Two Spanish pieces = Deux pièces espagnoles : für Gitarre ... (Tarrega, Francisco). Revidierte Neuausgabe. *Schott.* £3.20 TSPMH (B78-50271)

Brontë, Emily. A little Whitsuntide cantata : for unaccompanied chorus SATB. (Payne, Anthony). *Chester Music. Unpriced* EZDE/LN (B78-50767)

Brown, Christopher.
Aubade, op.17 : for mixed chorus. *Chester Music. Unpriced* EZDW (B78-50795)
Hodie salvator apparuit : a sequence for Christmas, op.28. *Chester Music. Unpriced* EZDE/LF (B78-50765)
Sonata, string orchestra, op.42. Sonata for string orchestra,

op.42. *Chester Music. Unpriced* RXME (B78-51065)

Brown, Daniel. Celebration hymnal. Vocal/guitar ed. with supplement. *Mayhew-McCrimmon. Unpriced* JE/TSDM/LSB/AY (B78-50832) ISBN 0-85597-263-7

Brown, Irving.
Schirmer's singer's library : arias for baritone
Vol.1. *Schirmer. Unpriced* KGNDW/AY (B78-50478)
Schirmer's singer's library : arias for bass
Vol.1. *Schirmer. Unpriced* KGXDW/AY (B78-50480)
Schirmer's singer's library : arias for mezzo-soprano and alto
Vol.1. *Schirmer. Unpriced* KFNDW/AY (B78-50473)
Schirmer's singer's library : arias for soprano
Vol.1. *Schirmer. Unpriced* KFLDW/AY (B78-50470)
Schirmer's singer's library : arias for tenor
Vol.1. *Schirmer. Unpriced* KGHDW/AY (B78-50477)

Brown, James. Oboe duets
Vol.1. *Chester Music. Unpriced* VTNUK/AAY (B78-51263)

Brown, John Robert. Chalumeau canons for clarinets. *Chappell. Unpriced* VVNK/X/AY (B78-50660)

Brown, Lawrence. The books of American negro spirituals, including The book of American negro spirituals and The second book of negro spirituals. *Da Capo Press : Robert Hale.* £6.50 KDW/LC/AY (B78-50461)

Brown, Marcia. I believe in God : a sacred song. (Geiger, George). *Lewis Music : Phoenix. Unpriced* KDH (B78-50111)

Brown university choral series.
Nelson, Ron. Four pieces after the seasons : S.A.T.B. with instrumental accompaniment
1: Early May. *Boosey and Hawkes.* £0.50 ENYLDW (B78-50035)
Nelson, Ron. Four pieces after the seasons : S.A.T.B. with instrumental accompaniment
2: Wonder and wild honey. *Boosey and Hawkes.* £0.40 ENYLDW (B78-50036)
Nelson, Ron. Four pieces after the seasons : S.A.T.B. with instrumental accompaniment
3: Late September. *Boosey and Hawkes.* £0.40 ENYLDW (B78-50037)
Nelson, Ron. Four pieces after the seasons : S.A.T.B. with instrumental accompaniment
4: Winter journeyings. *Boosey and Hawkes.* £0.40 ENYLDW (B78-50038)

Browne, Jackson. The pretender. *Warner : Blossom. Unpriced* KDW/HKR (B78-50160)

Brubeck, Dave. Originals. *EMI. Unpriced* QPHX (B78-51002)

Bruckner, Anton. Mass, no.2, E minor, (1896). *Vocal score.* Mass no.2, E minor, for eight part choir and wind instruments (1896 version). Revised version of the edition of Kurt Soldan by James Erber. *Peters. Unpriced* DG (B78-50720)

Bruckner symphonies. (Barford, Philip). *British Broadcasting Corporation.* £1.00 BBUEAMME (B78-33165)
ISBN 0-563-12767-8

Brunelli, Louis Jean. Chronicles. *Boosey and Hawkes. Unpriced* UMMJ (B78-50629)

Bryce, Frank. Colin's fancy : for post horn solo and brass band. *Novello. Unpriced* WMPWTR (B78-51330)

Budden, Julian. The operas of Verdi
2: From 'Il trovatore' to 'La forza del destina'. *Cassell.* £17.50 BVEAC (B78-39231) ISBN 0-304-30056-x

Building of the house. *arr.* The building of the house : for concert band. (Britten, Benjamin, *Baron Britten*). *Faber Music. Unpriced* UMMK (B78-50628)

Building of the house : for concert band. (Britten, Benjamin, *Baron Britten*). *Faber Music. Unpriced* UMMK (B78-50628)

Bull, John. A plaine and easy introduction to practicall musicke. O amica mea. *arr.* O amica mea. (Morley, Thomas). *Edizioni Pegasus : Peters. Unpriced* VSNRK/DJ (B78-50652)

Buller, John. The mime of Mick, Nick and the Maggies : on part 2 of 'Finnegans Wake'. *Schirmer.* £17.50 EMDX (B78-50355)

Bullock, Peter. The funny family : songs, rhymes and games for children. *Ward Lock.* £3.95 JFDW/GJ/AY (B78-50847) ISBN 0-7062-3719-6

Bullock-Davies, Constance. Menestrellorum multitudo : minstrels at a royal feast. *University of Wales Press.* £7.50 AL/E(YD/XCKF) (B78-12983)
ISBN 0-7083-0656-x

Bülow, Cosima von. *See* Wagner, Cosima.

Bunnett, Rex. London musical shows on record, 1897-1976. (Rust, Brian Arthur Lovell). *177 Kenton Rd, Harrow, Middx HA3 0HA : General Gramophone Publications Ltd.* £11.00 ACM/FD(XL596) (B78-02935)
ISBN 0-902470-07-8

Bunting, Christopher. Sonata, cello & piano, op.31. Sonata for violoncello and piano. (Routh, Francis). *Arlington Park House, W.4 : Redcliffe Edition. Unpriced* SRPE (B78-51116)

Burgon, Geoffrey.
Gending. *Chester Music. Unpriced* UMJ (B78-51173)
Goldberg's dream. *Chester Music. Unpriced* MM/HM (B78-50917)
Three nocturnes for harp. *Chester Music. Unpriced* TQPMJ (B78-51135)

Burnett, Michael.
Carol of the drum. *arr.* The little drummer boy. (Davis, Katherine Kennicott). *Chappell. Unpriced* NYDPK/DP/LF (B78-50951)
Eye level. *arr.* Eye level. (Trombey, Jack). *Chappell. Unpriced* NYFPK (B78-50514)
Holiday inn. White Christmas. *arr.* White Christmas. (Berlin, Irving). *Chappell. Unpriced* NYFPK/DW/JR/LF (B78-50952)

Mary's boy child. *arr.* Mary's boy child. (Hairston, Jester). *Chappell. Unpriced* NYFPK/DW/LF (B78-50953)
Music education review : a handbook for music teachers
Vol.1 : 1977. *Chappell. £5.95* A(VC)
Paloma blanca. *arr.* Paloma blanca. (Bouwens, J). *Chappell. Unpriced* NYFPK (B78-50513)
The sound of music. Do-re-mi. *arr.* Do-re-mi. (Rodgers, Richard). *Chappell. Unpriced* NYFPK/DW (B78-50516)

Yellow submarine. *arr.* Yellow submarine. (Lennon, John). *Chappell. Unpriced* NYFPK/DW (B78-50515)
Burns, Robert. A birthday hansel : for high voice and harp, op.92. (Britten, Benjamin, *Baron Britten*). *Faber Music. Unpriced* KFTE/TQDW (B78-50475)
Burtch, Mervyn. Songs of London town. *Selections.* Highgate and The tower. *Roberton. £0.18* JFDW (B78-50090)
Burton, Ian, *b.1942.* Listen! music and civilization. (Brace, Geoffrey). *Cambridge University Press. £2.25* A/KD(X) (B78-22160) ISBN 0-521-21153-0
Burton, Peter. Rod Stewart : a life on the town. *New English Library. £3.50* AKDW/HKR/E(P) (B78-06262) ISBN 0-450-03429-1
Busenello, Francesco. L'incoronazione di Poppea. Vocal score. L'incoronazione di Poppea = The coronation of Poppea : opera in two acts and prologue. (Monteverdi, Claudio). New ed. *Faber Music. Unpriced* CC (B78-50007)
Bush, Geoffrey. Invitation to the partsong
3: Shakespeare settings by Bishop, Cooke, Hatton, MacFarren, Stevens, Webbe ; a selection of four- and five-part works newly transcribed and edited by Geoffrey Bush and Michael Hurd. *Stainer and Bell. £1.25* EZDW/AY (B78-50056) ISBN 0-85249-491-2
Bush, Milton.
Gentle on my mind. *arr.* Gentle on my mind. (Hartford, John). *Warner : Blossom. Unpriced* UMMK/DW (B78-50634)
The godfather. *Selections : arr.* Themes from The godfather and The godfather, part II. (Rota, Nino). *Warner : Blossom. Unpriced* UMMK/JR (B78-50639)
Busoni, Ferruccio. Drei Albumblätter, no.1. Albumblatt. *Lengnick. £0.60* VRPK (B78-51219)
Butler, Richard. A basic tutor for the Northumbrian small pipe. *22 Newlyn Drive, Parkside Dale, Cramlington, Northumberland : Richard Butler. Unpriced* VYQ/AC (B78-50308) ISBN 0-9505591-0-5
Butterfly dance, and, Scherzo. (Higgins, Norman). *Royal Academy of Dancing. Unpriced* QPH/H (B78-50219)
Butterworth, Arthur.
Nightflight : symphonic study for brass band. *Chester Music. Unpriced* WMJ (B78-51307)
Nightflight : symphonic study for brass band. *Chester Music. Unpriced* WMJ (B78-51308)
Butterworth, George. The ploughboy's glory : a selection of hitherto unpublished folk songs. *English Folk Dance and Song Society. Unpriced* KEZDW/G/AYD (B78-50467)
Buttons and bows. (Livingston, Jay). *Warner : Blossom. Unpriced* UMMK/DW/JR (B78-50637)
Buttons and bows. (Livingston, Jay). *Warner : Blossom. Unpriced* UMMK/DW/JR (B78-51188)
By cool Siloam's shady rill. (Clarke, Jeremiah). *Galaxy Stainer and Bell. Unpriced* EZDM (B78-50380)
Byrd, William.
The battell. The marche before the battell. *arr.* The Earle of Oxford's march. *Chester Music. Unpriced* WMK/AGM (B78-51320)
Gradualia, lib.1. Ave verum corpus. *arr.* Ave verum corpus : for male voice choir unaccompanied. *Roberton. £0.20* GEZDJ (B78-50826)
Pavane, 'Earl of Salisbury', virginals. *arr.* The 'Earl of Salisbury' carol, adapted from 'The Earl of Salisbury's Pavane', two-part. *Banks. Unpriced* FDP/LF (B78-50810)
Byrd, Morley, Tallis : three-part vocal compositions. *Ricordi. Unpriced* VSNTK (B78-51247)
Cable, Michael. The pop industry inside out. *W.H. Allen. £4.95* A/GB/FD(XPQ22) (B78-03111) ISBN 0-491-02381-2
Cadence IV : for piano. (Lazarof, Henri). *Associated Music. £1.50* QPJ (B78-50540)
Caix D'Hervelois, Louis de. Suite, flute & continuo, op.6, no.4, C major. *arr.* Suite no.4, for descant recorder and keyboard. *Dolmetsch : Chappell. Unpriced* VSRPK/AG (B78-51256)
Caixinha de bringnedos. Dança compestre. Dança campestre : piano a 4 mãos. (Mignone, Francisco). *Arthur Napoleão : Essex Music. Unpriced* QNVH (B78-50522)
Caldwell, John, *b.1938.* Medieval music. *Hutchinson. £12.50* A(XCE601) (B78-17613) ISBN 0-09-120900-5
Calico pie and other nonsense rhymes : songs and rounds for children. (Maw, Nicholas). *Boosey and Hawkes. £2.60* FDW (B78-50392)
Calinda, and, Air and dance. (Delius, Frederick). *Boosey and Hawkes. Unpriced* VRPK (B78-50292)
Calo, José Lopez-. *See* Lopez-Calo, José.
Calouste Gulbenkian Foundation. *United Kingdom and British Commonwealth Branch.* Training musicians : a report to the Calouste Gulbenkian Foundation on the training of professional musicians. (Committee of Enquiry into the Training of Musicians). *98 Portland Place, W1N 4ET : The Foundation, UK and Commonwealth Branch. £1.50* A(VQ) (B78-18539) ISBN 0-903319-11-x
Calvert, Morley. Introduction, elegy and caprice. *R. Smith. Unpriced* WMJ (B78-51309)
Cambini, Giuseppe. Trio concertans, flute, oboe & bassoon, op.45, no.6. Trio op.45, no.6 for flute, oboe and bassoon. *Musica rara. Unpriced* VNTF (B78-51200)
Camilleri, Charles. Fantasia concertante no.5 : for solo guitar. *Basil Ramsey : Roberton. £2.00* TSPMF (B78-51149)
Camner, James. The great opera stars in historic photographs : 343 portraits from the 1850s to the 1940s. *Dover Publications etc. : Constable. £4.35* AC/E(M/XJK100/EM) (B78-31599) ISBN 0-486-23575-0

Camp, Leonard van. *See* Van Camp, Leonard.
Camp de Grand-Pré. Tambourin. *arr.* Tambourin. (Gossec, François Joseph). *Bosworth and Co. Unpriced* QPK/AHVQT (B78-51027)
Camp de Grand-Pré. Tambourin. *arr.* Tambourin : solo for B flat cornet. (Gossec, François Joseph). *Studio Music. Unpriced* WMPWRK/AHVQT (B78-51329)
Cantata no.113 : Herr Jesu Christ, du höchstes Gut. Jesus nimmt die Sunder an. Jesus nimmt die Sunder an : aria from cantata 113 for tenor, flute and continuo. (Bach, Johann Sebastian). *Oxford University Press. Unpriced* KGHE/VRPDH (B78-50177)
Cantata no.208 : Was mir behagt. Schafe können sicher weiden. *arr.* Sheep may safely graze. (Bach, Johann Sebastian). *Oxford University Press. Unpriced* VRNTQK/DW (B78-50289) ISBN 0-19-355280-9
Cantatas of Johann Sebastian Bach : sacred and secular
Vol.1. (Whittaker, William Gillies). *Oxford University Press. £6.95(set of 2 vols)* BBCADE (B78-39233) ISBN 0-19-315238-x
Cantica : for soprano and tenos soloists, chorus and orchestra. (Chapple, Brian). *Chester Music. Unpriced* DE (B78-50715)
Cantica sacra senis vocibus. Quem vidistis pastores? Quem vidistis pastores? : Motet for Christmas for six voices. (Dering, Richard). *Chester Music. Unpriced* DJ/LF (B78-50731)
Cantica. *Vocal score.* Cantica : for soprano and tenos soloists, chorus and orchestra. (Chapple, Brian). *Chester Music. Unpriced* DE (B78-50715)
Canticle of the Mother of God. (Tavener, John). *Chester Music. Unpriced* EZDE (B78-50764)
Canticum canticorum Salomonis. Liberprimus : for 16-part vocal ensemble and orchestra. (Penderecki, Krzysztof). *Schott. £30.00* EMDE (B78-50030)
Canticum Mose et Agni : für Doppelchor a cappella (1976). (Beyer, Frank Michael). *Bote und Bock. £4.80* EZDE (B78-50364)
Cantiga de roda. (Villa-Lobos, Heitor). *Arthur Napoleão Essex Music. Unpriced* QPK (B78-50552)
Cantiga de roda. *arr.* Cantiga de roda. (Villa-Lobos, Heitor). *Arthur Napoleão : Essex Music. Unpriced* QPK (B78-50552)
Cantiones, 1575. Derelinquat impius. Derelinquat impius. (Tallis, Thomas). *Cathedral Music. Unpriced* EZDJ (B78-50376)
Canzon cornetto : for four trumpets. (Scheidt, Samuel). *Chester Music. Unpriced* WSNS (B78-51342)
Canzona in 4 parts. (Merulo, Claudio). *Schott. Unpriced* TSNSK (B78-50607)
Canzona in 8 parts. (Terzi, Giovanni Antonio). *Schott. £0.70* TSNSK (B78-50608)
Canzone del terzo tuono : for recorder concert. (Neri, Massimiliano). *Dolmetsch : Chappell. Unpriced* VSN (B78-51239)
Canzonetta. (Mozart, Wolfgang Amadeus). *Lengnick. £0.60* VRPK/DW (B78-51224)
Canzonietta sic : for cello and piano. (Newton, Rodney Stephen). *Composer Edition. Unpriced* SRPJ (B78-50265)
Capirola, Vincenzo. Capirola lute book : seven pieces, guitar solo. *Universal. Unpriced* TSPMK (B78-51161)
Capirola lute book : seven pieces, guitar solo. (Capirola, Vincenzo). *Universal. Unpriced* TSPMK (B78-51161)
Capodastro and its use. (Wright, Francis). *Charnwood Music. Unpriced* TS/PFT/AF (B78-50605)
Capon, Frank. Musical instruments. (Tolley, Bryan). *Wayland. £1.75* AL/BC (B78-31598) ISBN 0-85340-529-8
Caprice. (Huber, Paul). *R. Smith. Unpriced* WMJ (B78-51310)
Capricetten, op.47. *arr.* Capricetten : für Oboe und Streichorchester, op.49. (Krol, Bernhard). *Bote und Bock : Schirmer. £7.70* VTPK (B78-51268)
Capricho, op.49. *arr.* Capricho, Op.49. (Villa-Lobos, Heitor). *Arthur Napoleão : Essex Music. Unpriced* QPK (B78-50553)
Cardew, Cornelius. Concert guide : a handbook for music-lovers. (Westerman, Gerhart von). *Sphere. £0.90* A (B78-09117) ISBN 0-7221-9003-4
Care and nurture of your pianist partner or lesser spotted accompanist. (Duckenfield, Bridget). *P.O. Box 4, Ross-on-Wye, Herefordshire HR9 6EB : Hydatum. £1.25* AQ/ED (B78-33940) ISBN 0-905682-10-6
Carley, Lionel. Delius : a life in pictures. *Oxford University Press. £6.95* BDL(N/EM) (B78-05402) ISBN 0-19-315437-4
Carmina Burana. Selections. Songs from 'Carmina Burana'. *Edgefield Rd, Loanhead, Midlothian : Macdonald Publishers. Unpriced* ADW(XCH101) (B78-30833) ISBN 0-904265-20-x
Carnaval des animaux. Le cygne. *arr.* The swan ... : violoncello and piano. (Saint-Saëns, Camille). *Leonard, Gould and Bolttler. £0.50* SRPK (B78-50266)
Carnival de Venice. Op.14. Carnival of Venice : for flute and piano. (Genin, P A). *Chester Music. Unpriced* VRP/T (B78-51210)
Carnival of Venice : for flute and piano. (Genin, P A). *Chester Music. Unpriced* VRP/T (B78-51210)
Carol of the drum. *arr.* The little drummer boy. (Davis, Katherine Kennicott). *Chappell. Unpriced* NYDPK/DP/LF (B78-50951)
Carol y doethion = Carol of the kings a Cysgu yn y gwair = Lord Emmanuel. (Whelan, E L). *Hafod, St. Hilary, Cowbridge : E.L. Whelan. £0.25* FDP/LF (B78-50060)
Carol y doethion. Carol y doethion = Carol of the kings a Cysgu yn y gwair = Lord Emmanuel. (Whelan, E L). *Hafod, St. Hilary, Cowbridge : E.L. Whelan. £0.25* FDP/LF (B78-50060)
Carole King : her greatest hits, songs of long ago. (King, Carole). *Screen gems-EMI Music : Colgems-EMI Music : EMI. Unpriced* KDW/GB (B78-50864)
Caroline Pink and other nonsense rhymes. (Maw, Nicholas). *Boosey and Hawkes. £2.60* FDW (B78-50393)
Carré, Michel. Faust. Ah! je ris. *arr.* Jewel song ... (Gounod, Charles). *Leonard, Gould and Bolttler. Unpriced* KDW (B78-50115)
Carreras Arab lectures. Hage, Louis. Maronite music. *Longman for the University of Essex. £0.75* ADGTCX (B78-35472) ISBN 0-582-78085-3
Carroll, Lewis. Songs from Alice : Alice in Wonderland and Through the looking-glass. (Harper, Don). *Adam and Charles Black. Unpriced* JFDW (B78-50843) ISBN 0-7136-1879-5
Carry me Bach : themes and variations on original classical and jazz themes for guitar solo. (Puma, Joe). *Associated Music. £2.40* TSPM/T (B78-50611)
Carson, D. Regimental quick march of The Ulster Defence Regiment, 'The sprig of Shillelagh' 'Garry owen'. *Boosey and Hawkes. Unpriced* UMMGM/KH (B78-50280)
Carter, Andrew. A maiden most gentle : (a Christmas carol) ; S.A.T.B., French tune. *Oxford University Press. Unpriced* DP/LF (B78-50737) ISBN 0-19-343067-3
Carter, Anthony. Sigurd Jorsalfar. Op.56. Homage march. *arr.* Homage march. (Grieg, Edvard). *Oxford University Press. Unpriced* MK/AGM (B78-50485) ISBN 0-19-363848-7
Carter, Elliott.
A fantasy about Purcell's 'Fantasia upon one note' : for brass quintet. *Associated Music. £5.75* WNR (B78-50689)
The writings of Elliott Carter : an American composer looks at modern music. *Indiana University Press. £12.95* A(D/XNS40) (B78-33159) ISBN 0-253-36720-4
Carter, Roy E. Theory of harmony. (Schoenberg, Arnold). *Faber : Faber Music. £22.50 : CIP rev.* A/R (B78-12985) ISBN 0-571-10933-0
Carter, Sydney Horace. A catalogue of 'Clarion' & 'Ebonoid' records. *19 Glendale Rd, Bournemouth BH6 4JA : 'Talking machine review'. £2.00* A/FD(QB/WT) (B78-20766) ISBN 0-902338-29-3
Cartwright, Kenneth. Resurrection jazz : a cantata for schools. *Boosey and Hawkes. Unpriced* FDE/LL (B78-50388)
Carulli, Ferdinando. Fantasia, flute & guitar, op.337. Fantasie, op.337, für Flöte und Gitarre. *Heinrichshofen : Peters. Unpriced* VRPLTS (B78-50649)
Casals and the art of interpretation. (Blum, David). *Heinemann Educational. £8.50* ASR/E(P) (B78-06993) ISBN 0-435-81150-9
Case, Brian. The illustrated encyclopedia of jazz. *27 Old Gloucester St., WC1N 3AF : Salamander Books. £6.95* AMT(C) (B78-22169) ISBN 0-86101-013-2
Cash, Johnny. Man in black. *Hodder and Stoughton. £0.95* AKDW/GCW/E(P) (B78-02614) ISBN 0-340-22173-9
Casseus, Frantz. World's favorite selected masterpieces : for classic guitar
Vol.3 : compiled and edited by Frantz Cassens. *Ashley Phoenix. Unpriced* TSPMK/AAY (B78-50276)
Cassey, Chuck. The lemon drop kid. Silver bells. *arr.* Silver bells : SATB and piano. (Livingston, Jay). *Warner Blossom. Unpriced* DW (B78-50351)
Cassin-Scott, Jack. Military bands and their uniforms. *Blandford Press. £6.95* AUMM(X) (B78-26675) ISBN 0-7137-0895-6
Castellani, Marcello. Sonata, flute & continuo, op.3, no.6, D minor. Sonate, d-moll für Querflöte C (oder Violine) und Basso continuo = Sonata in D minor for transverse flute (or violin and basso continuo). (Cervetto, Giacobbe, *b.1682*). *Bärenreiter. £3.00* VRPE (B78-51212)
Castle of Arianrhod : for horn and piano. (McCabe, John). *Novello. £2.75* WTPJ (B78-51352)
Cat Stevens : hits. (Stevens, Cat). *Chappell. Unpriced* KDW/HKR (B78-50881)
Catalogue of 'Clarion' & 'Ebonoid' records. (Carter, Sydney Horace). *19 Glendale Rd, Bournemouth BH6 4JA : 'Talking machine review'. £2.00* A/FD(QB/WT) (B78-20766) ISBN 0-902338-29-3
Catalogue of music broadcast on Radio 3 and Radio 4
1974. (British Broadcasting Corporation). *B.B.C. £4.00* A/JT(WT) (B78-20763) ISBN 0-563-17369-6
Catalogue of musical instruments in the Victoria and Albert Museum
Vol.2: Non-keyboard instruments. (Victoria and Albert Museum). 2nd ed. *H.M.S.O. £8.75* AL/B(WJ) (B78-36278) ISBN 0-11-290263-4
Catalogue of the compositions of Frederick Delius : sources and references. (Threlfall, Robert). *Delius Trust : Distributed by Boosey and Hawkes. £10.00* BDL(TC) (B78-03908) ISBN 0-85162-028-0
Catalogue of the printed music published before 1850 in York Minster Library. (York Minster. *Library*). *Dean's Park, York YO1 2JD : The Library. £1.50* A(TC) (B78-20765)
Catelinet, Philip. The Isle of Avalon : suite for brass band. *R. Smith. Unpriced* WMG (B78-51303)
Causley, Charles. Saint Martha and the dragon. *Vocal score.* Saint Martha and the dragon : a dramatic legend set to music, for narrator, soprano and tenor soloists, chorus, children's chorus (with percussion) and chamber orchestra. (Tate, Phyllis). *Oxford University Press.*

Unpriced DE (B78-50718) ISBN 0-19-338397-7
Cavalli, Francesco. L'egisto. *Vocal score.* L'egisto : opera in three acts and a prologue. *Faber Music. Unpriced* CC (B78-50324)
Cavatina 'Avant de quitter ces lieux'. (Gounod, Charles). *Leonard, Gould & Bolttler. Unpriced* KDW (B78-50443)
Cavatine : for four double basses. (Lancen, Serge). *Yorke. Unpriced* SSNS (B78-51122)
Cearense, Catallo da Paixão. Luar do sertão. *arr.* Luar do sertão. *Arthur Napoleão : Essex Music. Unpriced* SPMK (B78-50594)
Celebraciones medievales : Spanish divertissements of the Middle Ages, for concert band with four-part chorus of mixed voices. (Surinach, Carlos). *Associated Music. £4.55* EUMMDW (B78-50359)
Celebration hymnal. Vocal/guitar ed. with supplement. *Mayhew-McCrimmon. Unpriced* JE/TSDM/LSB/AY (B78-50832) ISBN 0-85597-263-7
Celebration song. (Asprey, Jonathan). *57 Dorchester Rd, Lychett Minster, Poole : Celebration Services. Unpriced* FDM (B78-50059)
Cello sight-reading book : eighty studies
Part 1. (Smith, Doreen). *Oxford University Press. Unpriced* SR/EG (B78-51110) ISBN 0-19-358845-5
Part 2. (Smith, Doreen). *Oxford University Press. Unpriced* SR/EG (B78-51111) ISBN 0-19-358846-3
Centenãrio do choro : 20 choras para piano
Album no.2. *Fermata do Brasil : Essex Music. Unpriced* QPK/AAYUR (B78-50559)
Centenário do choro : 20 choros para piano
Album no.1. *Fermata do Brasil : Essex Music. Unpriced* QPK/AAYUR (B78-50558)
Centenario do choro : 20 choros para piano álbum No.3. *Fermata do Brasil : Essex Music. Unpriced* QPJ (B78-50528)
Cerney setting of Series 3 Holy Communion. (Fenton, Raymond). *All Hallows Church, South Cerney, Gloucestershire : Raymond Fenton. Unpriced* JDGS (B78-50078)
Cervetto, Giacobbe, *b.1682.* Sonata, flute & continuo, op.3, no.6, D minor. Sonate, d-moll für Querflöte C (oder Violine) und Basso continuo = Sonata in D minor for transverse flute (or violin and basso continuo). *Bärenreiter. £3.00* VRPE (B78-51212)
Chalumeau canons for clarinets. *Chappell. Unpriced* VVNK/X/AY (B78-50660)
Chancellor, John. Wagner. *Weidenfeld and Nicolson. £8.50* BWC(N) (B78-20436) ISBN 0-297-77429-8
Changing face of music. (Cole, Hugo). *Gollancz. £7.95* A(YC) (B78-35470) ISBN 0-575-02496-8
Chapman, Mike. Smokie's greatest hits. *Chappell. Unpriced* KDW/GB (B78-50127)
Chappell, Herbert. Teach me how to pray, Lord. *Chappell. Unpriced* KDM (B78-50440)
Chapple, Brian. Cantica. *Vocal score.* Cantica : for soprano and tenos soloists, chorus and orchestra. *Chester Music. Unpriced* DE (B78-50715)
Charles Ives Centennial Festival-Conference, *New York and New Haven, 1974.* An Ives celebration : papers and panels of the Charles Ives Centennial Festival-Conference. *University of Illinois Press. £8.40* BIV (B78-16383) ISBN 0-252-00619-4
Charpentier, Marc Antoine. Te Deum, D major. Prelude. *arr.* Trumpet tune. *J.B. Cramer. £0.45* RK (B78-51054)
Checkmate. *Selections : arr.* Four dances from the ballet ... (Bliss, *Sir* Arthur). *Novello. £4.85* WMK/HM (B78-51328)
Chester books of motets : sacred renaissance motets with Latin texts
4: The German school for 4 voices. *Chester. Unpriced* EZDJ/AY (B78-50780)
5: The Flemish school for 4 voices. *Chester. Unpriced* EZDJ/AY (B78-50781)
Chester recorder series.
Four Irish folksongs : for 2 descant, treble and tenor recorders. *Chester Music. Unpriced* VSNSK/DW/AYDM (B78-51245)
Greene, Maurice. Voluntary, organ, no.6, B flat major. *arr.* Voluntary in C major, for descant, treble and tenor recorders. *Chester Music. Unpriced* VSNTK (B78-51248)
Harvey, Raymond. Suite, recorder ensemble, no.1. Suite no.1 for recorder ensemble, for descant, treble, 2 tenor and bass recorders. *Chester Music. Unpriced* VSNG (B78-51240)
Scarlatti, Alessandro. Il tigrane. *Selections : arr.* Suite ... for 2 descant, treble (or tenor) recorders. *Chester Music. Unpriced* VSNTK (B78-51249)
Chester woodwind series.
Debussy, Claude. Syrinx : for solo flute. *Chester Music. Unpriced* VRPMJ (B78-51233)
Doppler, Franz. Fantaisie pastorale hongroise. Op.26. Hungarian pastoral fantasy : for flute and piano. *Chester Music. Unpriced* VRPJ (B78-51215)
Fauré, Gabriel. Fantasie, flute & piano, op.79. Fantasie for flute and piano, op.79. *Chester Music. Unpriced* VRPJ (B78-51216)
Fauré, Gabriel. Pelléas et Melisande. Op.80. Sicilienne. *arr.* Sicilienne from Pelléas et Melisande : for flute and piano. *Chester Music. Unpriced* VRPK/AHVQ/JM (B78-51221)
Flute duets
Vol.2. *Chester Music. Unpriced* VRNU/AY (B78-51204)
Flute duets
Vol.3: Six easy duos for two flutes. *Chester Music. Unpriced* VRNU (B78-51203)
Flute solos with piano accompaniment
Vol.3. *Chester Music. Unpriced* VRPK/AAY (B78-51220)
Genin, P A. Le carnival de Venice. Op.14. Carnival of Venice : for flute and piano. *Chester Music. Unpriced* VRP/T (B78-51210)
Godard, Benjamin. Suite de trois morçeaux : for flute and piano, op.116. *Chester Music. Unpriced* VRPJ (B78-51217)
Holst, Gustav. Terzetto (1925) : for flute, oboe and viola (or clarinet). 2nd revised ed. *Chester Music. Unpriced* VNT (B78-51198)
Oboe duets
Vol.1. *Chester Music. Unpriced* VTNUK/AAY (B78-51263)
Tessarini, Carlo. Sonata, oboe & continuo, op.2, no.1, F major. Sonata no.1 in F for oboe and piano. *Chester Music. Unpriced* VTPE (B78-51266)
Wye, Trevor. Flute duets
Vol.1: Thirty duets by Devienne, Berbiguier, Boismortier, Loeillet, Naudot, Tulou, Kohler and Mozart. *Chester Music. Unpriced* VRNU/AY (B78-51205)
Chester's concert pieces
From Bach to blues for the younger pianist. *Chester Music. Unpriced* QPK/AAY (B78-51023)
Chester's piano book : for two instruments. (Barratt, Carol). *London Pro Musica. Unpriced* LNU (B78-50908)
Chester's piano book
Number 1. (Barratt, Carol). *Chester Music. Unpriced* Q/AC (B78-50956)
Number 4. (Barratt, Carol). *Chester Music. Unpriced* Q/AC (B78-50957)
Chester's piano book written by Carol Barratt, illustrated by Wendy Hoile
Number 3. (Barratt, Carol). *Chester Music. Unpriced* Q/AC (B78-50958)
Chesterton, Gilbert Keith. Song under the silver umbrella : for children's voices and accompaniment
1: The Christ-Child : (S.A. and piano or harp). (Binkerd, Gordon). *Boosey and Hawkes. Unpriced* FDP/LF (B78-50809)
Chiffren : für Cembalo, (1976). (Zender, Hans). *Bote und Bock : Schirmer. £2.40* QRPJ (B78-51040)
Child, Harold. Hugh the drover. *Vocal score.* Hugh the drover or Love in the stocks : a romantic ballad opera in two acts. (Vaughan Williams, Ralph). New ed. based on the 1959 edition as revised in accordance with the composer's directions .. *Curwen : Faber Music. Unpriced* CC (B78-50010)
Children's dances series.
Higgins, Norman. Andantino. *Royal Academy of Dancing. Unpriced* QPH/H (B78-50218)
Higgins, Norman. Butterfly dance, and, Scherzo. *Royal Academy of Dancing. Unpriced* QPH/H (B78-50219)
Higgins, Norman. Two folk melodies. *Royal Academy of Dancing. Unpriced* QPH/H (B78-50220)
Higgins, Norman. Waltz in E. *Royal Academy of Dancing. Unpriced* QPHW/H (B78-50221)
Children's film favourites. *Chappell. Unpriced* QPK/DW/JR/AY (B78-51031)
Children's overture : an introduction to music listening and creative musical activities for young children. (Jenkins, David, *b.1944*). *Oxford University Press. £2.75* AJFDW(VC) (B78-33673) ISBN 0-19-321388-5
Children's songs and carols, including hymns and games : for easy guitar or recorder. *EMI. Unpriced* TSPMK/DW/GJ/AY (B78-51169)
Children's songs and carols, including hymns and games : for easy piano or organ. *EMI. Unpriced* QPK/DW/GJ/AY (B78-51030)
Childs, Lisa. Childs play for all. *Novello. £2.00* Q/AC (B78-50959)
Childs play for all. (Childs, Lisa). *Novello. £2.00* Q/AC (B78-50959)
Chinn, Nicky. Smokie's greatest hits. (Chapman, Mike). *Chappell. Unpriced* KDW/GB (B78-50127)
Chor-Archiv.
Briegel, Wolfgang Carl. Evangelischer Blumengarten. Machet die Töre weit. Machet die Töre weit : Du König der Ehren, wir danken Dir : für vierstimmigen gemischten Chor. *Bärenreiter. £0.84* EZDH (B78-50370)
Praetorius, Michael. Musae Sioniae. Tl.2. *Selections.* Weihnachtskonzerte : für zwei vierstimmige Chöre. *Bärenreiter. £1.96* EZDH/LF (B78-50374)
Choral fantasia, Op.51. (Holst, Gustav). *Eulenburg. £1.00* EZDE (B78-50042)
Choral music : a symposium. *Penguin. £1.25* AD(X) (B78-35474) ISBN 0-14-020533-0
Chorbajian, John.
A cradle song : for four-part chorus of women's voices with piano accompaniment. *Schirmer. Unpriced* FDW (B78-50062)
Vital spark of heavenly flame. (The dying Christian to his soul) : for full chorus of mixed voices a cappella. *Schirmer. Unpriced* EZDH (B78-50043)
Chormusik für Kinder
1: Advent, Weihnachten, Epiphanias. *Bärenreiter. Unpriced* FE/LDM/AYE (B78-50397)
2: Lob und Dank. *Bärenreiter. £3.36* FE/LDM/AYE (B78-50398)
Chorochronos 2 : für Bariton-Sprecher und Kammerochester = for baritone-narrator and chamber orchestra ; 1973. (Antoniou, Theodore). *Bärenreiter. £6.00* MRJ (B78-50939)
Chorus of the frogs : for four-part chorus of mixed voices with piano accompaniment. (Turok, Paul). *Schirmer. £0.45* DW (B78-50353)
Chorus : the Puffin Colony Song book. *Puffin Books. £0.70* JFE/TSDW (B78-50436) ISBN 0-14-030941-1
Christian, Frederick H . *For works of this author published under other names see* Nolan, Frederick.
Christian hymns. *Evangelical Movements of Wales : Henry E. Walter. Unpriced* DM/AY (B78-50024)
Christian songwriters' handbook. (Acott, Dennis). *65 Grace Ave., Maidstone, Kent : Third Day Enterprises. £0.40* ADW/GB/L(S) (B78-10624) ISBN 0-9505912-0-3
Christmas carols for guitar. *Charnwood Music. Unpriced* TSPMK/DP/LF/AY (B78-51168)
Christmas collection : for the junior school orchestra. *16 Anchor Way, Danes Green : Viking. Unpriced* MK/DP/LF/AY (B78-50915)
Christmas time. *Chappell. Unpriced* VRPK/DP/LF/AY (B78-51223)
Christopher, Mabel Linwood-. *See* Linwood-Christopher, Mabel.
Chronicles. (Brunelli, Louis Jean). *Boosey and Hawkes. Unpriced* UMMJ (B78-50629)
Chuck Berry : easy guitar. (Berry, Chuck). *Jewel Music : Chappell. Unpriced* KE/TSDW/GB (B78-50169)
Church and music. (Routley, Erik). Revised ed. *Duckworth. £12.50* AD/LD(X) (B78-30831) ISBN 0-7156-0062-1
Church choir library. In wonder, love and praise : a collection of fourteen anthems. *Novello. Unpriced* DH/AY (B78-50728)
Church sonatas. *Selections : arr.* Four church sonatas. (Mozart, Wolfgang Amadeus). *Boosey and Hawkes. £2.25* VVPK/AE (B78-50305)
Churchill downs : chamber concerto no.2. (Bazelon, Irwin). *Boosey and Hawkes. Unpriced* NYDF (B78-50207)
Cinq préludes : pour piano. (Staempfli, Edward). *Bote und Bock : Schirmer. £3.85* QPJ (B78-51020)
Clarinet. (Rutland, Jonathan Patrick). *F. Watts. £1.95* AVV/B (B78-50000) ISBN 0-85166-641-8
Clarinet scales and arpeggios. (Galper, Avrahm). *Boosey and Hawkes. Unpriced* VV/AF (B78-51274)
Clarinet technique. (Thurston, Frederick). 3rd ed. *Oxford University Press. £1.95* AVV/E (B78-05412) ISBN 0-19-318610-1
Clark, Keith. Three songs from 'A Shropshire lad' : for SATB choir unaccompanied with tenor solo. *Roberton. £0.24* EZDW (B78-50386)
Clarke, Garry E. Essays on American music. *Greenwood Press. £12.95* A(YT) (B78-09696) ISBN 0-8371-9484-9
Clarke, Jeremiah. Bishop Thorpe. *arr.* By cool Siloam's shady rill. *Galaxy : Stainer and Bell. Unpriced* EZDM (B78-50380)
Class in concert : graded music for classroom orchestra
Grade A. (Salaman, William). *7 Garrick St., W.C.2 : Middle Eight Music. Unpriced* MJ (B78-50180)
Grade B. (Salaman, William). *7 Garrick St., W.C.2 : Middle Eight Music. Unpriced* MJ (B78-50178)
Grade C. (Salaman, William). *7 Garrick St., W.C.2 : Middle Eight Music. Unpriced* MJ (B78-50914)
Classic Ash. (Wishbone Ash). *EMI. Unpriced* KE/TSDW/GB (B78-50170)
Classic guitar construction : diagrams, photographs and step-by-step instructions. (Sloane, Irving). *Omnibus Press. £2.95* ATS/BC (B78-01684) ISBN 0-86001-232-8
Classic melodies. *EMI. Unpriced* RPVCK (B78-51058)
Classical and romantic pieces
Book 1. *Oxford University Press. Unpriced* VRP/AY (B78-51208) ISBN 0-19-356538-2
Book 2. *Oxford University Press. Unpriced* VRP/AY (B78-51209) ISBN 0-19-356539-0
Classical Christmas music. *Columbia Pictures : EMI. Unpriced* R/LF/AY (B78-51046)
Classical music for clarinet, including music by Beethoven, Grétry, Haydn, Mozart, Stamitz. *Boosey and Hawkes. Unpriced* VVPK/AAY (B78-50303)
Clavierstücke für die Jugend. Op.68. *Selections : arr.* A Schumann suite : seven pieces from 'Album for the young'. opus 68. (Schumann, Robert). *Novello. Unpriced* VVNSK (B78-51276)
Cleare, Julia. Teach me how to pray, Lord. (Chappell, Herbert). *Chappell. Unpriced* KDM (B78-50440)
Clements, Patrick.
Slavonic dance, no.8, op.46, no.8, G minor. *arr.* Slavonic dance, no.8. (Dvořák, Antonín). *Boosey and Hawkes. Unpriced* UNNK/AH (B78-50642)
Slavonic dance, no.9, op.72, no.1. *arr.* Slavonic dance no.9. (Dvořák, Antonín). *Boosey and Hawkes. Unpriced* UNNK/AH (B78-50643)
Slavonic dance, no.15, op.72, no.7, C major. *arr.* Slavonic dance, no.15. (Dvořák, Antonín). *Boosey and Hawkes. Unpriced* UNNK/AH (B78-50644)
Clifford, Keith. Momentella : for clarinet in B flat. *Arts Lab Music. Unpriced* VVPMJ (B78-51287)
Clouds that veil the midnight moon. Clouds that veil the midnight moon and The straw hat : piano solo. (Dale, Mervyn). *Edwin Ashdown. £0.40* QPJ (B78-51009)
Clychau'r nadolig = Christmas bells a Bethlehem. (Whelan, E L). *Hafod, St. Hilary, Cowbridge : E.L. Whelan. £0.25* FDP/LF (B78-50061)
Clychau'r nadolig. Clychau'r nadolig = Christmas bells a Bethlehem. (Whelan, E L). *Hafod, St. Hilary, Cowbridge : E.L. Whelan. £0.25* FDP/LF (B78-50061)
Coates, John. Sing easy : twelve easy songs for mixed voices. *Oxford University Press. Unpriced* EZDW/AY (B78-50799) ISBN 0-19-330215-2
Cobbold, Sarah. Regina coeli. (White, Robert). *Oxenfor Imprint, dist. Blackwell's Music Shop. Unpriced* GEZDJ/LL (B78-50421)
Cockshott, Gerald. My boy Billy : folk song collected by R. Vaughan Williams. *Roberton. £0.18* FEZDW (B78-50066)
Coffin, Tristram Potter. The British traditional ballad in North America. Revised ed. reprinted. *University of Texas Press. £11.25* ADW/G(YT/TC) (B78-01317) ISBN 0-292-70719-3

Coker, Jerry. Listening to jazz. *Prentice-Hall. £6.55* AMT (B78-24453) ISBN 0-13-537217-8
Cole, Hugo. The changing face of music. *Gollancz. £7.95* A(YC) (B78-35470) ISBN 0-575-02496-8
Colin's fancy : for post horn solo and brass band. (Bryce, Frank). *Novello. Unpriced* WMPWTR (B78-51330)
Collage : for string quartet, wind quintet and percussion. (Lees, Benjamin). *Boosey and Hawkes. Unpriced* MRJ (B78-50942)
Collected lute music of John Dowland. (Dowland, John). 2nd ed. with 3 more pieces. *Faber Music. Unpriced* TW/AZ (B78-51171) ISBN 0-571-10024-4
Collection rock & folk Chappell. Lennon, John. Beatles album no.2. *Chappell. Unpriced* KDW/GB (B78-50451)

Collection rock et folk ballade. Ange. 'Par les fils de Mandrin'. *arr.* 'Par les fils de Mandrin'. *Chappell. Unpriced* KDW/GB (B78-50123)
Collection rock et folk Chappell.
Genesis. Genesis. *Chappell. Unpriced* KDW/HKR (B78-50459)
Malicorne. Recueil de vingt chansons et airs traditionnels. *Chappell. Unpriced* KE/LDW/GB (B78-50167)
Stevens, Cat. Cat Stevens : hits. *Chappell. Unpriced* KDW/HKR (B78-50881)
Yes. Yes. *Chappell. Unpriced* KDW/GB (B78-50141)
Collection rock et roll Chappell. Bijou. *Chappell. Unpriced* KDW/HKR (B78-50879)
Colles, Henry Cope. The growth of music : a study in musical history. 4th ed. *Oxford University Press. £4.50* A(XCH701) (B78-20435) ISBN 0-19-316116-8
Collier, James Lincoln. The making of jazz : a comprehensive history. *Hart-Davis MacGibbon. £10.00* AMT(X) (B78-33166) ISBN 0-246-11092-9
Collins, Ken. The fantasticks. *Vocal score.* The fantasticks : book and lyrics by Tom Jones. (Schmidt, Harvey). Revised ed. *Chappell. Unpriced* CM (B78-50327)
Collins, Mal. Big red songbook. *Unit 10, Specner Court, Chalcot Rd, N.W.1 : Plato Press. £1.00* JEZDW/AY (B78-50835) ISBN 0-904383-12-1
Comber, Chris. Jimmie the Kid : the life of Jimmie Rodgers. (Paris, Mike). *Eddison Press : 'Old time music' Magazine. £3.95* AKDW/GC/E(P) (B78-33931) ISBN 0-85649-019-9
Come all ye bold miners : ballads and songs of the coalfields. New, revised and enlarged ed. *Lawrence and Wishart. £10.00* AKDW/K/GNCC (B78-39786) ISBN 0-85315-412-0
Come, Christmas : an anthology of standard Christmas carols, new carols and favourite excerpts from major choral works. *Novello. £1.45* DH/LF/AY (B78-50730)
Come, my soul : SATB unacc. (Howells, Herbert). *Oxford University Press. Unpriced* EZDH (B78-50371)
Come sing and dance : S.A.T.B. (Lindley, Simon). *Banks Music. Unpriced* EZDP/LF (B78-50786)
Come thank now Jehovah = Kommt danket dem Helden : double chorus ; SATB with accompaniment. (Peter, Johann Friedrich). *Boosey and Hawkes. Unpriced* DH (B78-50341)
Comhar Cultúra Éireann. *See* Ireland *(Republic). Cultural Relations Committee of Ireland.*
Comic songs of Cork and Kerry. *25 Lower Abbey St., Dublin 1 : Mercier Press. £0.80* AKDW(YDQC) (B78-39235) ISBN 0-85342-498-5
Comic songs of Ireland. *25 Lower Abbey St., Dublin 1 : Mercier Press. £0.80* AKDW(YDM) (B78-39785) ISBN 0-85342-529-9
Committee of Enquiry into the Training of Musicians. Training musicians : a report to the Calouste Gulbenkian Foundation on the training of professional musicians. *98 Portland Place, W1N 4ET : The Foundation, UK and Commonwealth Branch. £1.50* A(VQ) (B78-18539) ISBN 0-903319-11-x
Communication and society. Frith, Simon. The sociology of rock. *Constable. £7.50* AKDW/HKR(Z) (B78-31211) ISBN 0-09-460220-4
Companion to the opera. (May, Robin). *Lutterworth Press. £5.95* AC (B78-01674) ISBN 0-7188-2123-8
Complete arias and sinfonias from cantatas, masses and oratorios : for solo voice, oboe, oboe d'amore, oboe de caccia, basso continuo/piano
Vol.8: Tenor, oboe, basso continuo/piano. (Bach, Johann Sebastian). *Musica rara. Unpriced* KE/VTNDH (B78-50888)
Vol.9: Tenor, bass, oboe, basso continuo/piano. (Bach, Johann Sebastian). *Musica rara. Unpriced* KE/VTNDH (B78-50889)
Vol.9: Tenor, bass, oboe, basso continuo/piano. (Bach, Johann Sebastian). *Musica rara. Unpriced* KE/VTNDH (B78-50890)
Vol.10: Bass, oboe, basso continuo/piano. (Bach, Johann Sebastian). *Musica rara. Unpriced* KE/VTNDH (B78-50891)
Complete Bottesini
Vol.1: For two double basses and piano. (Bottesini, Giovanni). *Yorke. Unpriced* SS/AZ (B78-51121)
Complete Crosby. (Thompson, Charles). Revised and augmented ed. *W.H. Allen. £5.95* AKDW/GB/E(P) (B78-20440) ISBN 0-491-02335-9
Complete operas of Mozart : a critical guide. (Osborne, Charles, *b.1927*). *Gollancz. £7.50* BMSAC (B78-33935) ISBN 0-575-02221-3
Complete string quartets with the horn and clarinet quintets ... (Mozart, Wolfgang Amadeus). *Dover Publications Constable. Unpriced* RXNR (B78-51076) ISBN 0-486-23603-x
Composers and their music. The dictionary of composers and their music : every listener's companion arranged chronologically and alphabetically. (Gilder, Eric). *Paddington Press. £6.95* A/D(M/C) (B78-26881) ISBN 0-448-22364-3
Composers and their world.
McLeish, Kenneth. Mozart. *Heinemann. £2.50* BMS (B78-29831) ISBN 0-434-95125-0
McLeish, Kenneth. Stravinsky. *Heinemann. £2.50* BSV(N) (B78-30825) ISBN 0-434-95126-9
Composers of Wales.
Boyd, Malcolm, *b.1932.* William Mathias. *University of Wales Press for the Welsh Arts Council. Unpriced* BMGH (B78-15753) ISBN 0-7083-0672-1
Deane, Basil. Alun Hoddinott. *University of Wales Pres for the Welsh Arts Council. £1.50* BHND (B78-39781) ISBN 0-7083-0695-0
Composicões de Ernesto NazarethAlbum 1: 25 tangos brasileiros (choras) para piano. (Nazareth, Ernesto). *Arthur Napoleāno : Essex Music. Unpriced* QPJ (B78-50545)
Album 2: 26 Obras para piano. (Nazareth, Ernesto). *Arthur Napoleão : Essex Music. Unpriced* QPJ (B78-50546)
Comus. Incidental music. Music for Comus : serenata a 9. (Handel, George Frideric). First modern ed. *23 Stanley Court, 1 Woodfield Rd, W.5 : Acca Music. Unpriced* JNDE/NXNQDW/JM (B78-50108)
Con brio
No.1- ; 1976-. *13 De Walden Court, 85 New Cavendish St., W.1 : New Philharmonia Club. Unpriced* AMM/E(QB/B) (B78-06990)
Concert de chambre, liv.1, no.1. Premier concert de chambre : for two descant recorders and keyboard. (Mouret, Jean Joseph). *Dolmetsch. Unpriced* VSRNTPWF (B78-51255)

Concert guide : a handbook for music-lovers. (Westerman, Gerhart von). *Sphere. £0.90* A (B78-09117) ISBN 0-7221-9003-4
Concertino.
Benker, Heinz. Mobile concertante : für Schlagwerk und Streicher. *Schott. £14.00* RXMPXF (B78-50252)
Henze, Hans Werner. Amicizia! : Quintett für Klarinette in A, Posaune, Violoncello, Schlagzeug und Klavier (1976). *Schott. £4.65* RXMK/AHW (B78-50247)
Lebrun, Ludwig August. Concerto, oboe, no.1, D minor. Konzert No.1, d-Moll für Oboe und Orchester. *Schott. £11.00* MPVTF (B78-50194)
Schubert, Franz. Valses nobles, D.969. *Selections: arr.* Valses nobles, opus 77. *Schott. £4.65* RXMK/AHW (B78-50248)
Sterkel, Franz Xaver. Concerto, piano, no.1, op.20, C major. *arr.* Erstes Konzert C-Dur, Ut majeur, für Klavier mit 2 Oboen, 2 Hörnern und Streichern, op.20. *Schott. £10.00* MPQF (B78-50192)
Torelli, Giuseppe. Sinfonia, trumpet & string orchestra, G.9, D major. Concerto D-Dur per tromba con archi e continuo. *Schott. £4.00* RXMPWSE (B78-50251)
Concise encyclopedia of music and musicians. 4th ed. (revised). *Hutchinson. £6.50* A(C) (B78-20430)
Concise history of modern music from Debussy to Boulez. (Griffiths, Paul). *Thames and Hudson. £5.50* A(XLK88) (B78-21398) ISBN 0-500-18167-5
Confidential matter : the letters of Richard Strauss and Stefan Zweig, 1931-1935. (Strauss, Richard). *University of California Press. £6.75* BSU(N/XNL5) (B78-04319) ISBN 0-520-03036-2
Congnetdale garland : a collection of tunes for fiddle and small-pipes. (Dagg, Archie). *Swinden, Sharperton, Morpeth : Archie Dagg. Unpriced* SPMJ (B78-51105)
Connor, Bill. A decade of The Who : an authorised history in music, paintings, words and photographs. (WHO). *Fabulous Music : Music Sales. Unpriced* KE/TSDW/HKR (B78-50172) ISBN 0-8256-2670-6
Conrad, Peter, *b.1948.* Romantic opera and literary form. *University of California Press. £5.50* AC(Z) (B78-12986) ISBN 0-520-03258-6
Consort and keyboard music of William Byrd. The music of William Byrd
Vol.3: The consort and keyboard music of William Byrd. (Kerman, Joseph). *Faber. £15.00 : CIP rev.* BBX (B78-19401) ISBN 0-571-10566-1
Consort-music, 1975. (Kelterborn, Rudolf). *Bote und Bock Associated Music. £5.75* KFLE/NYEP (B78-50472)
Consort music : for viols in four parts. (Jenkins, John). *Faber Music. Unpriced* STN (B78-51132)
'Constantine suite' : a Byzantine suite in seven movements for symphonic wind ensemble. (Newton, Rodney Stephen). *13 Chetwynd Ave., East Barnet, Herts. : Composer Edition. Unpriced* UMMG (B78-50278)
Contemporary choral series.
Berkeley, *Sir* Lennox. The hill of the graces : for unaccompanied chorus, SSAATTBB. *Chester Music. Unpriced* EZDW (B78-50794)
Brown, Christopher. Aubade, op.17 : for mixed chorus. *Chester Music. Unpriced* EZDW (B78-50795)
Contemporary church music series.
Berkeley, *Sir* Lennox. Judica me. Op.96 : for unaccompanied chorus, SSATBB. *Chester Music. Unpriced* EZDJ (B78-50776)
Payne, Anthony. A littel Ascensiontide cantata : for unaccompanied chorus SATB. *Chester Music. Unpriced* EZDE/LM (B78-50766)
Payne, Anthony. A little Whitsuntide cantata : for unaccompanied chorus SATB. *Chester Music. Unpriced* EZDE/LN (B78-50767)
Tavener, John. Canticle of the Mother of God. *Chester Music. Unpriced* EZDE (B78-50764)
Tavener, John. Little requiem for Father Malachy Lynch. *Vocal score.* Little requiem for Father Malachy Lynch. *Chester Music. Unpriced* DGKAV (B78-50722)
Tavener, John. Little requiem for Father Malachy Lynch. *Vocal score.* Little requiem for Father Malachy Lynch. *Chester Music. Unpriced* DGKAV (B78-50723)
Contemporary music for clarinet, including music by Copland, Goldman, Holloway, Reizenstein, Soproni. *Boosey and Hawkes. Unpriced* VVP/AY (B78-51282)
Conti, Annaberta. Sonata, flute & continuo, op.3, no.6, D minor. Sonate, d-moll für Querflöte C (oder Violine) und Basso continuo = Sonata in D minor for transverse flute (or violin and basso continuo). (Cervetto, Giacobbe, *b.1682*). *Bärenreiter. £3.00* VRPE (B78-51212)
Contributions in American history (ISSN 0084-9214).
Clarke, Garry E. Essays on American music. *Greenwood Press. £12.95* A(YT) (B78-09696) ISBN 0-8371-9484-9
Conyngham, Barry.
Ice carving. *Universal. Unpriced* RXMPS (B78-51071)
Three. *Universal. Unpriced* NYJNQ (B78-50955)
Water ... footsteps ... time. *Universal. Unpriced* MMJ (B78-50921)
Cook, Paul E G. Christian hymns. *Evangelical Movements of Wales : Henry E. Walter. Unpriced* DM/AY (B78-50024)
Cookie lady : a musical play for children. (Oliver, Donald). *Chappell. Unpriced* CN (B78-50706)
Coombes, Donald. Lindsay carol book. *Lindsay Music. Unpriced* FE/TSDP/LF/AY (B78-50822) ISBN 0-85957-007-x
Cooper, Martin. The concise encyclopedia of music and musicians. 4th ed. (revised). *Hutchinson. £6.50* A(C) (B78-20430)
Cope, Cecil. Sing for joy : ten Christmas carols. *Roberton. £0.28* FEZDP/LF (B78-50825)
Cope, David. New music composition. *Schirmer Books : Collier Macmillan. £6.75* A/D (B78-06259) ISBN 0-02-870630-7
Copland, Aaron. Midsummer nocturne : piano solo. *Boosey and Hawkes. Unpriced* QPJ (B78-50529)
Cops and robbers : for brass band. (Lear, W Hogarth). *Paxton. Unpriced* WMJ (B78-51312)
Corbetta, Francesco. La guitarre royalle. *Selections.* Suite in A minor ... : guitar solo. *Universal. Unpriced* TSPMJ (B78-51153)
Cornet cosmology : for brass band. (Woods, Stanley). *Chester Music. Unpriced* WMJ (B78-51314)
Cornets a-go-go. (Broadbent, Derek). *Polyphonic Reproductions : Studio Music. Unpriced* WMJ (B78-50677)
Cornish flower song : two-part song. (Graves, Richard). *Bosworth and Co. Unpriced* FDW (B78-50814)
Cotton : unison song with optional descant and piano music. (Fraser, Shena). *Roberton. £0.12* JFDW (B78-50091)
Country music. The illustrated encyclopedia of country music. (Dellar, Fred). *27 Old Gloucester St., WC1N 3AF : Salamander Books Ltd. £5.95* A/GC(C) (B78-05399) ISBN 0-86101-004-3
Country music round up
Vol.1, no.1- ; Dec. 1976-. *Country Music Round Up Publishing Co.; Roding Trading Estate, Barking, Essex : Distributed by A.M.D. Magazine Distributors Ltd. £0.20* A/GC(B) (B78-03571)
Courage, Alexander.
Star trek. *Selections : arr.* Theme from 'Star Trek'. (Roddenberry, Gene). *Warner : Blossom. Unpriced* UMMK/JS (B78-50640)
Star trek. Theme. *arr.* Theme from Star trek. (Roddenberry, Gene). *Warner : Blossom. Unpriced* UMMK/JS (B78-51189)
Cowan, Philip. Behind the Beatles songs. *159 Wardour St., W.1 : Polytantric Press. £2.50* AKDW/GB/E(P) (B78-28699) ISBN 0-905150-09-0
Coward, *Sir* Nöel. The Mermaid's 'Cowardy custard' : an entertainment. (Frow, Gerald). *French. £1.80* BCMWACM (B78-21400) ISBN 0-573-68079-5
Cowardy custard. The Mermaid's 'Cowardy custard' : an entertainment. (Frow, Gerald). *French. £1.80* BCMWACM (B78-21400) ISBN 0-573-68079-5
Cradle song : for four-part chorus of women's voices with piano accompaniment. (Chorbajian, John). *Schirmer. Unpriced* FDW (B78-50062)
Craft, Robert. Current convictions : views and reviews. *Secker and Warburg. £6.50* A (B78-11191) ISBN 0-436-11300-7
Cramer's library of church music. Hesford, Bryan. Holy communion series III. Missa in simplicitate. *Cramer. Unpriced* JDGS (B78-50831)
Crampton, Stephen. Music matters : a check-list for local music groups. *26 Bedford Sq., WC1B 3HU : Standing Conference for Amateur Music. Unpriced* A(WB/WT) (B78-20433)
Creation hymn. Songs for Sunday. Search me O God. Search me O God. (Parker, Alice). *Roberton. £0.18* FDH (B78-50389)
Creative piano : a modular approach for adult beginners. (Owyang, Lily Siao). *Houghton Mifflin. Unpriced* Q/AC (B78-50964) ISBN 0-395-25569-4
Credo. Crucifixus. *arr.* Crucifixus = (He was crucified) : for two-part chorus of women's voices with keyboard accompaniment. (Suidell, Padre). *Roberton. £0.15* FDJ (B78-50808)
Cremieux, Hector. Monsieur Choufleuri restera chez lui de. *Vocal score.* Salon Blumenkohl/Monsieur Choufleuri restera chez lui de ... : Buffo-Operette in einem Akt deutsch nach Karl Fr. Wiltmann von Heinz Balthes und Paul Vasil, opéra bouffe en un acte de St. Rémy, E. L'Epine, Hector Crémieux et Ludovic Halévy, musikalische Revision, neue Instrumentation und praktische Bearbeitung von Caspar Richter. (Offenbach, Jacques). *Bote und Bock : Associated music. £11.50* CF (B78-50703)
Cresswell, Lyell Richard. Drones 4 : for tuba, 1977. *Arts*

Lab Music. Unpriced WVPMJ (B78-51360)
Criancas. *arr.* As criancas. (Villa-Lobos, Heitor). *Arthur Napoleão : Essex Music. Unpriced* QPK (B78-50554)
Criswick, Mary. Italian intermezzo : six pieces. (Wolf-Ferrari, Ermanno). *Weinberger. Unpriced* VRPLTSK (B78-50650)
Crocker, John, *b.1925.* Potty pantomime. *Evans Bros. £0.40* BCQRACPP (B78-37098) ISBN 0-237-75031-7
Croft, William.
God is gone up with a merry noise : full anthem with verse for SSAATB. *Novello. £0.43* DK (B78-50343)
Musicus apparatus academicas. Laurus cruentas. *Overture.* Overture, Laurus cruentas. *Oxford University Press. Unpriced* MRJ (B78-50195) ISBN 0-19-362424-9
Croll, Gerhard. Vita di Giuseppe Afflisio = Lebensgeschichte des Giuseppe Afflisio. (Afflisio, Giuseppe). *17 Bucklersbury, Hitchin, Herts. : Bärenreiter. £4.48* AC(WB/P) (B78-19963)
Crookes, Brian. Way out west. *50 Ladbroke Grove, W.11 : Midland Music. Unpriced* WMJ (B78-50311)
Croquis : for double bass and piano. (Lancen, Serge). *Yorke. Unpriced* SSPJ (B78-51127)
Cross, Joan. The bartered bride. *Vocal score.* The bartered bride : a comic opera in three acts. (Smetana, Bedřich). Revised English libretto. *Boosey and Hawkes. Unpriced* CC (B78-50702)
Crosse, Gordon.
Concerto, violin, no.2, op.26. Violin concerto 2. *Oxford University Press. Unpriced* MPSF (B78-50193) ISBN 0-19-362479-6
Studies for string quartet. Op.34
Set 2: Fantasia, Aria (2) and Toccata. *Oxford University Press. Unpriced* RXNS (B78-51078) ISBN 0-19-355974-9
Crozier, Eric.
The bartered bride. *Vocal score.* The bartered bride : a comic opera in three acts. (Smetana, Bedřich). Revised English libretto. *Boosey and Hawkes. Unpriced* CC (B78-50702)
The little sweep ... *Boosey and Hawkes. Unpriced* BBUAC (B78-28697)
Crucifixus = (He was crucified) : for two-part chorus of women's voices with keyboard accompaniment. (Suidell, Padre). *Roberton. £0.15* FDJ (B78-50808)
Crumb, George. Four nocturnes. (Night Music II) : violin and piano. *Peters. Unpriced* SPJ (B78-51099)
Crumhorn consort anthology
Vol.2 ; edited by Pater Nothnagle and R.P. Block. *Musica rara. Unpriced* VTWN/AY (B78-51270)
Vol.3 ; edited by Peter Nothnagle and R.P. Block. *Musica rara. Unpriced* VTWN/AY (B78-51271)
Cryptic essay : for symphonic band. (Tull, Fisher). *Boosey and Hawkes. Unpriced* UMMJ (B78-50282)
Cultural Relations Committee of Ireland. *See* Ireland *(Republic). Cultural Relations Committee of Ireland.*
Cumming, Hildelith. Music for Evening Prayer from the Divine Office. *Collins. Unpriced* JEZDGKB (B78-50833) ISBN 0-00-599593-0
Cumming, Ray Fox. *See* Fox Cumming, Ray.
Current convictions : views and reviews. (Craft, Robert). *Secker and Warburg. £6.50* A (B78-11191) ISBN 0-436-11300-7
Cuthbert, Sheila Larchet. The Irish harp book : a tutor and companion. *Mercier Press. Unpriced* TQR/AC (B78-51139) ISBN 0-85342-279-6
Cyclorama 1 : flute ensemble. (Tull, Fisher). *Boosey and Hawkes. Unpriced* VRN (B78-51201)
Cyfarthfa High School. Dr Joseph Parry, 1841-1903. (Richards, W Mansel). *c/o Town Hall, Merthyr Tydfil, M. Glam. : W.M. Richards. Unpriced* BPEB(N) (B78-03577)
Cyngor Celfyddydau Cymru. *See* Welsh Arts Council.
Czerny, Carl. Das wohltemperirte Clavier. Well tempered clavier = Wohltemperiertes Clavier : forty-eight preludes and fugues, for the piano. (Bach, Johann Sebastian). *Ashley : Phoenix. Unpriced* QP/Y (B78-50989)
Da Gagliano, Marco. *See* Gagliano, Marco da.
Da Palestrina, Giovanni Pierluigi . *See* Palestrina, Giovanni Pierluigi da.
Da Palestrina, Giovanni Pierluigi. *See* Palestrina, Giovanni Pierluigi da.
Da Ponte, Lorenzo. Don Giovanni. The making of an opera : 'Don Giovanni' at Glyndebourne. (Higgins, John, *b.1934*). *Secker and Warburg. £7.95* BMSAC/E (B78-33162) ISBN 0-436-19595-x
Da Ponte, Lorenzo. Don Giovanni, KV527 : Dramma giocoso im zwei Akten
Textbuch italienisch-deutsch. *32 Gt Titchfield St., W1P 7AD : Bärenreiter. £2.24* BMSAC (B78-17615)
Dafne. (Gagliano, Marco da). *Cathedral Music. Unpriced* CC (B78-50325)
Dafne. *Vocal score.* La Dafne. (Gagliano, Marco da). *Cathedral Music. Unpriced* CC (B78-50325)
Dagg, Archie. The Congnetdale garland : a collection of tunes for fiddle and small-pipes. *Swinden, Sharperton, Morpeth : Archie Dagg. Unpriced* SPMJ (B78-51105)
Dalby, Stuart. Make your own musical instruments. *Batsford. £3.95* AL/BC (B78-26243) ISBN 0-7134-0545-7
Dale, Gordon. Twelve tunes for violin : for groups of mixed ability. *EMI Music. Unpriced* SPMJ (B78-51106)
Dale, Mervyn.
6 pieces for the piano. Polonaise napolitana. Polonaise napolitana : piano solo. *Edwin Ashdown. Unpriced* QPHVHM (B78-51001)
Clouds that veil the midnight moon. Clouds that veil the midnight moon and The straw hat : piano solo. *Edwin Ashdown. £0.40* QPJ (B78-51009)
Let the children sing
Book 1. *Edwin Ashdown. Unpriced* JFDW (B78-50430)
Dalmaine, Cyril. Ballet. *Warren and Phillips. Unpriced* QPK/HM/AY (B78-51032)
Dança campestre : piano a 4 mãos. (Mignone, Francisco). *Arthur Napoleão : Essex Music. Unpriced* QNVH (B78-50522)
Dance, Stanley. Duke Ellington in person : an intimate memoir. (Ellington, Mercer). *Hutchinson. £5.95* AMT(P) (B78-34740) ISBN 0-09-132750-4
Dances from 'Alcina'. (Handel, George Frideric). *Banks. Unpriced* QPK/AH (B78-51025)
Daniel quodlibet (based on three negro spirituals) : for two female, two male or one female and one male voices. (Hudson, Hazel). *Edwin Ashdown. Unpriced* FDW/LC (B78-50394)
Das stille Lied : für vier Männerstimmen = for four men's voices. (Schubert, Franz). Erstausgabe. *Bärenreiter. £0.90* GEZDW (B78-50830)
Davenant, William. Aubade, op.17 : for mixed chorus. (Brown, Christopher). *Chester Music. Unpriced* EZDW (B78-50795)
Davey, Brian. Recorder playing : for descant recorders
Junior book 2. *Chappell. Unpriced* VSRPMK/AAY (B78-51258)
Davies, Constance Bullock-. *See* Bullock-Davies, Constance.
Davies, Hunter. The Beatles : the authorized biography New ed.. *Mayflower. £1.25* AKDW/GB/E(P) (B78-26244) ISBN 0-583-11530-6
Davies, John Booth. The psychology of music. *Hutchinson. £8.95* A/CS (B78-11194) ISBN 0-09-129500-9
Davies, Peter Maxwell.
Five Klee pictures. *Boosey and Hawkes. Unpriced* MJ (B78-50179)
Le jongleur de Notre Dame : a masque, for mime, baritone, chamber ensemble and children's band. *Chester Music. Unpriced* CQPF (B78-50713)
The martyrdom of St Magnus : a chamber opera in nine scenes. *Boosey and Hawkes. £1.00* BDEAC (B78-06987)
A mirror of whitenbing light = Specolum luminis dealbensin : for chamber orchestra. *Boosey and Hawkes. Unpriced* MRJ (B78-50940)
Miss Donnithorne's maggot : for mezzo-soprano and chamber ensemble. *Boosey and Hawkes. £7.00* C/J (B78-50003)
Stedman doubles : for clarinet and percussion. *Boosey and Hawkes. Unpriced* VVPLX (B78-50664)
Stevie's ferry to Hoy : piano solo. *Boosey and Hawkes. Unpriced* QPJ (B78-50222)
Symphony. *Boosey and Hawkes. Unpriced* MME (B78-50185)
Taverner. Dances. Points and dances ... : for instrumental ensemble. *Boosey and Hawkes. Unpriced* LN (B78-50907)
Versalii icones : for dancer, solo cello and instrumental ensemble. *Boosey and Hawkes. Unpriced* NYDPNP (B78-50510)
Davis, Diane.
I am a rock. *Yeldall Manor, Hare Hatch, Reading : Celebration Services. Unpriced* KDH (B78-50110)
Yeldall carol, This is the day. *Yeldall Manor, Hare Hatch, Reading : Celebration Services. Unpriced* DP/LF (B78-50025)
Davis, John, *b.1946.* A decade of The Who : an authorised history in music, paintings, words and photographs. *Elm Tree Books for Fabulous Music Ltd. £4.50* AKDW/HKR/E(P) (B78-00388) ISBN 0-241-89809-9
Davis, Katherine Kennicott. Carol of the drum. *arr.* The little drummer boy. *Chappell. Unpriced* NYDPK/DP/LF (B78-50951)
Davisson, Walther. Études melodiques et progressives. Op.36. Études speciales. Opus 36 : neu herausgegeben und bezeichnet von Walther Davisson
Hft.1. (Mazas, Jacques Féréol). Neurevidierte Ausgabe. *Peters. Unpriced* S/AF (B78-51089)
Dawney, Michael. The ploughboy's glory : a selection of hitherto unpublished folk songs. *English Folk Dance and Song Society. Unpriced* KEZDW/G/AYD (B78-50467)
Day at the races. (Queen). *Beechwood Music : EMI. Unpriced* KDW/HKR (B78-50164)
Day at the races. *arr.* A day at the races. (Queen). *Beechwood Music : EMI. Unpriced* KDW/HKR (B78-50164)
Day of the donkey, and other songs of praise. *Vocal score.* The day of the donkey (and other songs of praise for juniors). (Race, Steve). *Weinberger. Unpriced* JFDM (B78-50839)
Day the world was born. (Walker, Sue). *Mayhew McCrimmon. £1.10* FDE (B78-50806) ISBN 0-85597-271-8
De Caix D'Herverlois, Louis. *See* Caix D'Hervelois, Louis de.
De Cormier, Robert. She'll be comin' round the mountain : American folk song, for full chorus of mixed voices unaccompanied. *Roberton. £0.32* EZDW (B78-50051)
De Haan, Stefan. *See* Haan, Stefan de.
De la Mare, Walter. *See* Mare, Walter de la.
De Lerma, Dominique-René. *See* Lerma, Dominique-René de.
De profundis : piano solo. (Griffes, Charles Tomlinson). *Peters. Unpriced* QPJ (B78-51010)
De tierra lejana venimos. (Weiss, Donn). *Roberton. £0.24* EZDP/LF (B78-50790)
De Victoria, Tomás Luis. *See* Victoria, Tomás Luis de.
De Victoria, Tomás Luis de. *See* Victoria, Tomás Luis de.
Deane, Basil. Alun Hoddinott. *University of Wales Press for the Welsh Arts Council. £1.50* BHND (B78-39781) ISBN 0-7083-0695-0
Dear anyone ... : a musical story of the agony behind the agony column ... from the concept album. (Stephens, Geoff). *Dick James : Music Sales (dist.). Unpriced* KDW/GB (B78-50870)
Dearnley, Christopher.
Evening service for men's voices. *36 Ranelagh Gdns., W.6 : Cathedral Music. Unpriced* GEZDGPP (B78-50416)
Hodie Christus natus est. (Palestrina, Giovanni Pierluigi da). *Cathedral Music. Unpriced* GEZDGKJ/LF (B78-50411)
Let thy hand be strengthened. *Cathedral Music. Unpriced* EZDK (B78-50379)
Paratum cor meum Deus. (Blow, John). *36 Ranelagh Gdns. W.6 : Cathedral Music. Unpriced* FLDJ (B78-50404)
Death on the Nile. Love theme. *arr.* Love theme from Death on the Nile : piano solo. (Rota, Nino). *EMI. Unpriced* QPK/JR (B78-51033)
Deathridge, John. Wagner's 'Rienzi' : a reappraisal based on a study of the sketches and drafts. *Clarendon Press. £12.00 : CIP rev.* BWCAC (B77-08491) ISBN 0-19-816131-x
Debrnov, Josef Srb-. *See* Srb-Debrnov, Josef.
Debussy, Claude.
En blanc et noir : three pieces for two pianos. *Peters. Unpriced* QNU (B78-50984)
Syrinx : for solo flute. *Chester Music. Unpriced* VRPMJ (B78-51233)
Decade of The Who : an authorised history in music, paintings, words and photographs. *Elm Tree Books for Fabulous Music Ltd. £4.50* AKDW/HKR/E(P) (B78-00388) ISBN 0-241-89809-9
Decade of The Who : an authorised history in music, paintings, words and photographs. (WHO). *Fabulous Music : Music Sales. Unpriced* KE/TSDW/HKR (B78-50172) ISBN 0-8256-2670-6
Deeper and deeper soul magazine
No.1- ; July 1977-. *18 Stretton Close, Holmlands Estate, Prenton, Birkenhead, Merseyside : K. Murray. £0.25* A/GBS(B) (B78-06258)
Del Mar, Norman.
Richard Strauss : a critical commentary on his life and works
Vol.1. *Barrie and Jenkins. £8.95* BSU(N) (B78-27521)
Vol.2. *Barrie and Jenkins. £8.95* BSU(N) (B78-27522)
Vol.3. *Barrie and Jenkins. £8.95* BSU(N) (B78-27523)
Deliège, Célestin. Pierre Boulez, conversations with Célestin Deliège. (Boulez, Pierre). *48 Great Marlborough St., W1V 2BN : Eulenburg Books. £3.00* BBRO (B78-11192) ISBN 0-903873-21-4
Delius, Frederick.
An arabesque = Eine Arabeske : for baritone solo, mixed chorus and orchestra = für Bariton-Solo, gemischter Chor und Orchester. *Boosey and Hawkes. Unpriced* EMDX (B78-50751)
Album of pianoforte solos. *Boosey and Hawkes. Unpriced* QPK (B78-51021)
Concerto, cello. Cello concerto. *Boosey and Hawkes. Unpriced* MPSRF (B78-50934)
Idyll 'Once I passed through a populous city'. *Vocal score.* Prelude and idyll : for soprano and baritone with orchestra. *Boosey and Hawkes. Unpriced* JNEDX (B78-50438)
Koanga. La calinda. *arr.* La calinda, and, Air and dance. *Boosey and Hawkes. Unpriced* VRPK (B78-50292)
Sea drift. *Boosey and Hawkes. Unpriced* EMDX (B78-50032)
Sleigh ride = Schlittenfahrt. 1st ed. *Boosey and Hawkes. Unpriced* MJ (B78-50911)
Sleigh ride = Schlittenfahrt. 1st ed. *Boosey and Hawkes. Unpriced* MJ (B78-50912)
Delius, Jelka. Idyll 'Once I passed through a populous city'. *Vocal score.* Prelude and idyll : for soprano and baritone with orchestra. (Delius, Frederick). *Boosey and Hawkes. Unpriced* JNEDX (B78-50438)
Delius : a life in pictures. *Oxford University Press. £6.95* BDL(N/EM) (B78-05402) ISBN 0-19-315437-4
Delius Trust. A catalogue of the compositions of Frederick Delius : sources and references. (Threlfall, Robert). *Delius Trust : Distributed by Boosey and Hawkes. £10.00* BDL(TC) (B78-03908) ISBN 0-85162-028-0
Dellar, Fred. The illustrated encyclopedia of country music. *27 Old Gloucester St., WC1N 3AF : Salamander Books Ltd. £5.95* A/GC(C) (B78-05399) ISBN 0-86101-004-3
Dellin, Martin Gregor-. *See* Gregor-Dellin, Martin.
Delrieu, Jean Philippe. À vous de jouer : cours d'initiation rapide et progressive à l'orgue electronique
Vol.1. *Chappell. Unpriced* RPV/AC (B78-50571)
Denkmann, Gertrud Meyer-. *See* Meyer-Denkmann, Gertrud.
Dennis, Peter, *b.1950.* Mozart : the young musician. (Kenyon, Nicholas). *Macdonald Educational. £1.95* BMS(N) (B78-30826) ISBN 0-356-05916-2
Dennison, Peter.
The tempest. Incidental music. Incidental music for The tempest : for strings and continuo. (Locke, Matthew). *Oxford University Press. Unpriced* RXM/JM (B78-50244) ISBN 0-19-365350-8
The works of Henry Purcell
Volume 8: Ode on St Cecilia's Day, 1692 ; edited under the supervision of the Purcell Society by Peter Dennison. (Purcell, Henry). *Novello. £10.00* C/AZ (B78-50002)
Derde musyck boexken. *Selections : arr.* Six Susato dances : for brass band ... (Susato, Thielman). *Chester Music. Unpriced* WMK/AH (B78-51321)
Derelinquat impius. (Tallis, Thomas). *Cathedral Music.*

Unpriced EZDJ (B78-50376)
Dering, Richard. Cantica sacra senis vocibus. Quem vidistis pastores? Quem vidistis pastores? : Motet for Christmas for six voices. *Chester Music. Unpriced* DJ/LF (B78-50731)
'Desert island discs'. (Plomley, Roy). *Fontana. £0.85* A/FD/JT(P/X) (B78-08479) ISBN 0-00-634227-2
Desnos, Robert. Les espaces du sommeil : for baritone and orchestra. (Lutoslawski, Witold). *Chester Music. Unpriced* KGNE/MDW (B78-50906)
Dessau, Paul. Sonatina, piano, no.2, (1975). Sonatine 2 für Klavier, 1975. *Bote und Bock : Yorke. £1.90* QPEM (B78-50997)
Detholiad y babanod. *Gwasg Gomer. Unpriced* JFEZDW/GJ/AY (B78-50855)
Devienne, François. Trio, flute, clarinet & bassoon, op.61, no.3, A minor. Trio für Flöte, Klarinette (Violine) und Fagott (Violoncello), Opus 61, Nr.3. *Litolff : Peters. Unpriced* VNT (B78-50646)
Dexter, Harry.
Mary and Martha : negro spiritual. *Edwin Ashdown. £0.20* FDW/LC (B78-50818)
Wake up, Jacob : negro spiritual. *Edwin Ashdown. £0.20* FDW/LC (B78-50819)
Di Lasso, Orlando. *See* Lasso, Orlando di.
Dialogue on a kiss : for two solo voices and continuo. (Lawes, Henry). *Oxford University Press. Unpriced* JNEDW (B78-50858) ISBN 0-19-345494-7
Diamond, Eileen. The little gingerbread man : a song/mime for children. *Chappell. Unpriced* JFDW/JN (B78-50435)

Dichter, Harry. Handbook of early American sheet music, 1768-1889. *Dover Publications etc. : Constable. £4.70* A(TC/YT/XFYH22) (B78-30339) ISBN 0-486-23364-2
Dick James Music presents 20 per volume greatest hits
Vol.1. *Dick James Music. £2.50* KDW/GB/AY (B78-50147)
Vol.2. *Dick James Music. Unpriced* KDW/GB/AY (B78-50148)
Vol.3. *Dick James Music. Unpriced* KDW/GB/AY (B78-50149)
Vol.4. *Dick James Music. Unpriced* KDW/GB/AY (B78-50150)
Dickinson, Peter, *b.1934*. Twenty British composers. *J. and W. Chester for the Feeney Trust. Unpriced* A(YC/XPQ17) (B78-33938) ISBN 0-9502767-3-1
Dicks, Ted.
Marc Bolan : a tribute. *19 Poland St., W1V 3DD : Essex House Publishing : Springwood Books. £5.95* AKDW/HKR/E(P) (B78-39783) ISBN 0-906445-00-0
Marc Bolan : a tribute. *19 Poland St., W1V 3DD : Essex House Publishing. £2.95* AKDW/HKR/E(P) (B78-39784) ISBN 0-906445-01-9
Dickson, Andrew Wilson-. *See* Wilson-Dickson, Andrew.
Dictionary of composers. *Bodley Head. £5.95* A/D(M/C) (B78-20434) ISBN 0-370-30016-5
Dictionary of composers and their music : every listener's companion arranged chronologically and alphabetically. (Gilder, Eric). *Paddington Press. £6.95* A/D(M/C) (B78-26881) ISBN 0-448-22364-3
Dieskau, Dietrich Fischer-. *See* Fischer-Dieskau, Dietrich.
Dietz, Howard. That's entertainment. That's entertainment. *arr.* That's entertainment : S.S.A. with piano. (Schwartz, Arthur). *Chappell. Unpriced* FDW/JR (B78-50817)
Dinerstein, Norman. Gather ye rosebuds : for four-part chorus of mixed voices a cappella. *Schirmer. Unpriced* EZDW (B78-50052)
Dingle, Patrick. An introduction to the clarinet
Book 1. *EMI. Unpriced* VV/AC (B78-50659)
Directory of British brass bands : associations, societies, contests
Vol.2 : 1978-79. *28 Marigold St., Rochdale OL11 1RJ British Federation of Brass Bands. £1.00* AWM(QB/YC/BC) (B78-27525)
Dismal land and the giant : a one act musical play for juniors. (Wade, Darrell). *(16 Anchor Way, Danes Green, Gnosall) : Viking. Unpriced* CN (B78-50011)
Divertimento for string orchestra, Op.32, no.4. (Baber, Joseph). *Oxford University Press. Unpriced* RXMJ (B78-50246)
Divertissement baroque en trois mouvements. (Baselli, Joss). *Chappell. Unpriced* QPG (B78-50998)
Django Reinhardt. (Reinhardt, Django). *EMI. Unpriced* TSPMHX (B78-51151)
D'Luhy, Gale R. Sir Arthur Sullivan : composer & personage. (Allen, Reginald). *Pierpont Morgan Library : Chappell. £12.95* BSW(N) (B78-05721) ISBN 0-87923-145-9
Dmitri Shostakovich, a complete catalogue. (MacDonald, Malcolm, *b.1948*). *Boosey and Hawkes. £1.50* BSGR(TC) (B78-02934)
Do-re-mi. (Rodgers, Richard). *Chappell. Unpriced* NYFPK/DW (B78-50516)
Dobree, Georgina. Sonata, clarinet & piano. Sonata for clarinet in B flat and piano. (Poulenc, Francis). 5th ed embodying corrections to the first ed., edited by Thea King and Georgina Dobree. *Chester Music. Unpriced* VVPE (B78-51283)
Dobrovolskis, Kunibertas. Nun jauchzt dem Herren, alle Welt : Chorsätze zu Gemeinsamen Kirchenliedern. *Bärenreiter. £3.20* EZDM/AYE (B78-50381)
Doce canciones = Twelve songs : with guitar accompaniment. (Moretti, Federico). Complete facsimile ed. *Tecla. Unpriced* KE/TSDW (B78-50885) ISBN 0-8494-0140-2
Doctor bonus. In festo sancti Andreae. (Victoria, Tomás Luis de). *Cathedral Music. Unpriced* EZDJ (B78-50378)

Dodgson, Stephen.
Duet, flute & harp. Duo for flute and harp in four movements. *Oxford University Press. Unpriced* VRPLTQ (B78-51230) ISBN 0-19-356269-3
Take two = A due = Für zwei : five guitar duets. *Ricordi. Unpriced* TSNU (B78-50609)
Doedd neb yn becso dam : hanes, lluniau a chaneuon Edward H. Dafis. (Wyn, Hefin). *Ffordd Llanllyfni, Penygroes, Gwynedd LL54 6DB : Sain (Recordiau) Cyf.. £1.50* AKDW/GB/E(P) (B78-09115)
Doflein, Erich. Sammlung kleiner Stücke für Violoncello = Collection of small pieces for violoncello : duets and solos from the 18th century
Vol.2: 1st to 4th position. *Schott. £4.00* SRNU/AY (B78-50264)
Doktor, Paul. Four epiphanies : for unaccompanied viola. (Schonthal, Ruth). *Oxford University Press. Unpriced* SQPMJ (B78-50262)
Dolly. Op.36 sic : suite pour piano à 4 mains. (Fauré, Gabriel). *Cramer. £2.75* QNVG (B78-50521)
Dolly. Op.56, no.1. Berceuse. *arr.* Berceuse. ('Listen with Mother' theme) ... (Fauré, Gabriel). *R. Smith. Unpriced* WMK (B78-51315)
Dolly suite, op.56. Dolly. Op.36 sic : suite pour piano à 4 mains. (Fauré, Gabriel). *Cramer. £2.75* QNVG (B78-50521)
Dolmetsch, Arnold.
Concert de chambre, liv.1, no.1. Premier concert de chambre : for two descant recorders and keyboard. (Mouret, Jean Joseph). *Dolmetsch. Unpriced* VSRNTPWF (B78-51255)
Fantasia a cinque : for recorder quintet. (Le Jeune, Henri). *Dolmetsch : Chappell. Unpriced* VSNR (B78-51243)
Dolmetsch, Jeanne.
Concert de chambre, liv.1, no.1. Premier concert de chambre : for two descant recorders and keyboard. (Mouret, Jean Joseph). *Dolmetsch. Unpriced* VSRNTPWF (B78-51255)
Suite, flute & continuo, op.6, no.4, C major. *arr.* Suite no.4, for descant recorder and keyboard. (Caix D'Hervelois, Louis de). *Dolmetsch : Chappell. Unpriced* VSRPK/AG (B78-51256)
Dolmetsch library.
Caix D'Hervelois, Louis de. Suite, flute & continuo, op.6, no.4, C major. *arr.* Suite no.4, for descant recorder and keyboard. *Dolmetsch : Chappell. Unpriced* VSRPK/AG (B78-51256)
Le Jeune, Henri. Fantasia a cinque : for recorder quintet. *Dolmetsch : Chappell. Unpriced* VSNR (B78-51243)
Mouret, Jean Joseph. Concert de chambre, liv.1, no.1. Premier concert de chambre : for two descant recorders and keyboard. *Dolmetsch. Unpriced* VSRNTPWF (B78-51255)
Neri, Massimiliano. Sonate e canzone a quatro. Canzone del terzo tuono : for recorder concert. *Dolmetsch : Chappell. Unpriced* VSN (B78-51239)
Dommett, Kenneth. Bartók. *Novello. £0.30* BBG(N)
Don Giovanni. *See* Mozart, Wolfgang Amadeus.
Don Giovanni. Deh vieni alla finestra. *arr.* Canzonetta. (Mozart, Wolfgang Amadeus). *Lengnick. £0.60* VRPK/DW (B78-51224)
Don Giovanni, KV527 : Dramma giocoso im zwei Akten Textbuch italienisch-deutsch. (Da Ponte, Lorenzo). *32 Gt Titchfield St., W1P 7AD : Bärenreiter. £2.24* BMSAC (B78-17615)
Donakowski, Conrad L. A muse for the masses : ritual and music in an age of democratic revolution, 1770-1870. *University of Chicago Press. £15.40* AD/L(XFYK101) (B78-11190) ISBN 0-226-15621-4
Donizetti, Gaetano. Favorita. La favorita : drama in four acts. (Royer, Alphonse). *140 Strand, WC2R 1HH : G. Schirmer. Unpriced* BDRAC (B78-26887)
Donne, John.
At the round earth's imagined corners : for unaccompanied voices S.M. S.A.T.B. (Routh, Francis). *Radcliffe. Unpriced* EZDH (B78-50774)
A hymne to God the Father. (Wyton, Alec). *Novello. £0.47* EXRPLRDH (B78-50363)
Doppler, Franz. Fantaisie pastorale hongroise. Op.26. Hungarian pastoral fantasy : for flute and piano. *Chester Music. Unpriced* VRPJ (B78-51215)
Double crossings : duo for trumpet and percussion. (Bazelon, Irwin). *Boosey and Hawkes. £4.50* WSPLX (B78-51347)
Douglas, Roy. Symphony no.3, 'Pastoral'. Pastoral symphony. (Vaughan Williams, Ralph). *Boosey and Hawkes. Unpriced* KFLE/MDX (B78-50175)
Doveton, Robin.
Magnificat and Nunc dimittis. *Cathedral Music. Unpriced* GEZDGPP (B78-50417)
Preces and responses. *arr.* Preces and responses. *36 Ranelagh Gdns W.6 : Cathedral Music. Unpriced* GEZDGMM (B78-50413)
Preces and responses (SATB). *36 Ranelagh Gdns., W.6 : Cathedral Music. Unpriced* EZDGMM (B78-50368)
A short Communion service : for ATB and organ. *Cathedral Music. Unpriced* GDGS (B78-50406)
Dower. Die Mitgift und Gebet : zwei Männerchöre a cappella nach Texten von Josef Srb-Debrnov. (Smetana, Bedřich). *Bärenreiter. £0.70* GEZDW (B78-50423)
Dowland, John.
Lute music. *Collections.* The collected lute music of John Dowland. 2nd ed. with 3 more pieces. *Faber Music. Unpriced* TW/AZ (B78-51171) ISBN 0-571-10024-4
Selected works for one and two lutes with original lute tablature and transcription for the guitar. *Ariel : Music Sales. £1.95* TSPMK (B78-51162) ISBN 0-86001-294-8
Downes, Edward. Everyman's guide to orchestral music. *Dent. £15.00 : CIP rev.* AMM (B78-03579) ISBN 0-460-03030-2
Downes, Edward. New York Philharmonic guide to the symphony. *For later reprint see* Downes, Edward. Everyman's guide to orchestral music.
Drake, Susan. Duet, flute & harp. Duo for flute and harp in four movements. (Dodgson, Stephen). *Oxford University Press. Unpriced* VRPLTQ (B78-51230) ISBN 0-19-356269-3
Dramatic genius of Verdi : studies of selected operas
Vol.2. (Godefroy, Vincent). *Gollancz. £7.50* BVEAC (B78-02610) ISBN 0-575-02166-7
Draths, W. Mein Heimatland : die schönsten Volks-, Wander-, Trink- und Scherzlieder. Neu- Ausgabe mit vollstandigem Text, Trompete oder Klarinette in B. *Schott. £7.20* WSPMK/DW/AYE (B78-50314)
Draths, Willi.
Das klingende Orgelbuch : Bekanntes und Beliebtes aus Klassik Volks- und Unterhaltungsmusik, für elektronische Orgel (alle Modelle)
Band 2. *Schott. £7.20* RK/AAY (B78-50233)
Orgelschule zum Selbstunterricht. *Schott. £4.00* RPV/AC (B78-50239)
Drei Lieder nach Texten von Friedrich Hölderlin : für höhe Stimme und Klavier, op.74. (Klebe, Giselher). *Bärenreiter. £3.90* KFTDW (B78-50900)
Drei Sonatinen für Viola solo, opus 70. Sonatinas, viola, op.70, nos 1-3. 3 Sonatinen für Viola solo, op.70. (Weiner, Stanley). *Bote und Bock : Associated Music. £4.80* SQPMEM (B78-50597)
Drei spanische Solostücke = Three Spanish solo pieces = Trois morceaux espagnoles : for guitar. *Schott. £2.40* TSPMK/AYK (B78-50277)
Dreissig kleine Choral-vorspiele zu den gebrauchlichsten Choralen, für Orgel, Opus 135A. (Reger, Max). *Peters. Unpriced* RJ (B78-51052)
Dresden trio sonatas. (Handel, George Frideric). *Eulenburg. Unpriced* NXNSE (B78-50204)
Drewar, Della. Mingled jingles : for recorders and piano. *16 Anchor Way, Danes Green : Viking. Unpriced* VSNTQ (B78-51250)
Dritte Streichquartett (1976). Quartet, strings, no.3. 3. Streichquartett (1976). (Henze, Hans Werner). *Schott. £12.80* RXNS (B78-50582)
Drone, Jeanette Marie. Index to opera, operetta and musical comedy synopses in collections and periodicals. *Scarecrow Press : Distributed by Bailey and Swinfen. £5.95* ACMBN(WT) (B78-19781) ISBN 0-8108-1100-6
Drones 4 : for tuba, 1977. (Cresswell, Lyell Richard). *Arts Lab Music. Unpriced* WVPMJ (B78-51360)
Dronke, Peter. The medieval lyric. 2nd ed. *Hutchinson. £5.95* AKDW(XCDXK451) (B78-09116) ISBN 0-09-132080-1
Drummer's delight : drum feature. (Siebert, Edrich). *Studio Music. Unpriced* WMJ (B78-51313)
Dtv-Atlas zur Musik : Tafeln und Texte
Bd 1. Systematischer Teil ; und, Historischer Teil: Von den Anfängen bis zur Renaissance. (Michels, Ulrich). 2.Aufl. *Bärenreiter etc.. £3.58* A(C) (B78-19397)
Duarte, John William.
Capirola lute book : seven pieces, guitar solo. (Capirola, Vincenzo). *Universal. Unpriced* TSPMK (B78-51161)
La guitarre royalle. *Selections.* Suite in A minor ... : guitar solo. (Corbetta, Francesco). *Universal. Unpriced* TSPMJ (B78-51153)
Neuen Lautenfrüchte. *Selections.* Two pieces ... : guitar solo. (Reusner, Esaias). *Universal. Unpriced* TSPMK (B78-51165)
Duckenfield, Bridget. The care and nurture of your pianist partner or lesser spotted accompanist. *P.O. Box 4, Ross-on-Wye, Herefordshire HR9 6EB : Hydatum. £1.25* AQ/ED (B78-33940) ISBN 0-905682-10-6
Duett in G nach dem Original für 2 Barytone, Hob XII, 4. (Haydn, Joseph). *Schott. £4.00* TSNUK (B78-50270)
Duetto concertante, flute & guitar, op.52. Gran duetto concertante, op.52 : für Flöte (Violine) und Gitarre. (Giuliani, Mauro). *Schott. £4.80* VRPLTSF (B78-50294)

Duke : a portrait of Duke Ellington. (Jewell, Derek). New ed.. *Sphere. £1.95* AMT(P) (B78-33939) ISBN 0-7221-5022-9
Duke Ellington in person : an intimate memoir. (Ellington, Mercer). *Hutchinson. £5.95* AMT(P) (B78-34740) ISBN 0-09-132750-4
Dunkley, Sally.
Magnificat. (White, Robert). *Oxenford Imprint : Blackwell's Music Shop. Unpriced* EZDGKK (B78-50772)
Mass, Puer natus est nobis. (Tallis, Thomas). *Oxenford Imprint : Dist. Blackwell's Music Shop. Unpriced* EZDG (B78-50365)
Dunn, Geoffrey.
L'egisto. *Vocal score.* L'egisto : opera in three acts and a prologue. (Cavalli, Francesco). *Faber Music. Unpriced* CC (B78-50324)
L'incoronazione di Poppea. *Choral score.* L'incoronazione di Poppea. (Monteverdi, Claudio). *Faber Music. Unpriced* DAC (B78-50331)
L'incoronazione di Poppea. Vocal score. L'incoronazione di Poppea = The coronation of Poppea : opera in two acts and prologue. (Monteverdi, Claudio). New ed. *Faber Music. Unpriced* CC (B78-50007)
Durante, Francesco. Sei sonate divise in studii e divertimenti. Sei sonate : (studii e divertimenti), per cembalo. *Bärenreiter. £4.80* QRPE (B78-51038)
Dürr, Walther.
Das stille Lied : für vier Männerstimmen = for four men's voices. (Schubert, Franz). Erstausgabe. *Bärenreiter. £0.90* GEZDW (B78-50830)
Don Giovanni, KV527 : Dramma giocoso im zwei Akten

Textbuch italienisch-deutsch. (Da Ponte, Lorenzo). *32 Gt Titchfield St., W1P 7AD : Bärenreiter. £2.24* BMSAC (B78-17615)
Franz Schubert Lieder
Heft 3: Lieder nach Texten von Goethe, für mittlere Stimme. (Schubert, Franz). *Bärenreiter. £4.80* KFVDW (B78-50903)
Dvořák, Antonín.
Romantic pieces. Op.75. Four romantic pieces : for violin and piano. *Schirmer. £2.10* SPJ (B78-50589)
Slavonic dance, no.8, op.46, no.8, G minor. *arr.* Slavonic dance, no.8. *Boosey and Hawkes. Unpriced* UNNK/AH (B78-50642)
Slavonic dance, no.9, op.72, no.1. *arr.* Slavonic dance no.9. *Boosey and Hawkes. Unpriced* UNNK/AH (B78-50643)

Slavonic dance, no.15, op.72, no.7, C major. *arr.* Slavonic dance, no.15. *Boosey and Hawkes. Unpriced* UNNK/AH (B78-50644)
Dvořák symphonies and concertos. (Layton, Robert). *British Broadcasting Corporation. £1.00* BDXAMME (B78-29839) ISBN 0-563-12676-0
'Earl of Salisbury' carol, adapted from 'The Earl of Salisbury's Pavane', two-part. (Byrd, William). *Banks. Unpriced* FDP/LF (B78-50810)
Earle of Oxford's march. (Byrd, William). *Chester Music. Unpriced* WMK/AGM (B78-51320)
Early American sheet music, its lure and its lore, 1768-1889. Handbook of early American sheet music, 1768-1889. (Dichter, Harry). *Dover Publications etc. : Constable. £4.70* A(TC/YT/XFYH22) (B78-30339) ISBN 0-486-23364-2
Early Beatles. *Chappell. Unpriced* KDW/GB/AY (B78-50151)
Early English church music.
Taverner, John. Six-part masses. *Stainer and Bell. Unpriced* EZDG (B78-50769) ISBN 0-85249-477-7
Tye, Christopher. English sacred music
Vol.1. *Stainer and Bell, for the British Academy. Unpriced* EZDK (B78-50046) ISBN 0-85249-449-1
Early Georgian songs
Book 1: Medium voice. *Stainer and Bell. £1.50* KDW/AYC (B78-50112) ISBN 0-85249-459-9
Book 2: Low voice. *Stainer and Bell. £1.50* KDW/AYC (B78-50113) ISBN 0-85249-460-2
Easter greeting : for unison voices with divisions and organ. (How, Martin). *Roberton. £0.15* JFDH (B78-50838)
Easton, Ken.
Pushover : a choral play in one act about Samson, Judge of Israel. *French. £1.20* BSGNHACM (B78-03576) ISBN 0-573-62425-9
Turnabout : a musical version of the Book of Esther French's acting ed.. *French. £1.65* BSGNHACM (B78-20438) ISBN 0-573-62527-1
Easy winners : nine piano rags. (Joplin, Scott). *Paxton. £1.25* QPHXJ (B78-50526)
Ebdon, Thomas. Preces and responses. *36 Ranelagh Gdns., W.6 : Cathedral Music. Unpriced* EZDGMM (B78-50369)
Eboracum choral series.
Byrd, William. Pavane, 'Earl of Salisbury', virginals. *arr.* The 'Earl of Salisbury' carol, adapted from 'The Earl of Salisbury's Pavane', two-part. *Banks. Unpriced* FDP/LF (B78-50810)
Jackson, Francis. Alleluia, laudate pueri dominum : S.S.A.A.T.T.B.B. *Banks. Unpriced* EZDJ (B78-50777)
Jackson, Francis. Praise God in his sanctuary : S.A.T.B. *Banks. Unpriced* DR (B78-50743)
Johnston, Peter Fyfe. When the kye comes home : T.T.B.B. unacc. *Banks Music. Unpriced* GEZDW (B78-50072)
Lindley, Simon. Come sing and dance : S.A.T.B. *Banks Music. Unpriced* EZDP/LF (B78-50786)
Ecce virgo concipiet. (Morales, Cristoval). *Cathedral Music. Unpriced* GEZDGKAH/LEZ (B78-50408)
Eccles, John. Eight songs. *Stainer and Bell. £1.50* KDW (B78-50114) ISBN 0-85249-463-7
Echo fantasia : for brass quartet. (Banchieri, Adriano). *Chester Music. Unpriced* WNSK (B78-51339)
Eddison blues books. Garon, Paul. Blues & the poetic spirit. *Eddison Press. £3.50* AKDW/HHW (B78-30829) ISBN 0-85649-018-0
Eddison musicbooks. Paris, Mike. Jimmie the Kid : the life of Jimmie Rodgers. *Eddison Press : 'Old time music' Magazine. £3.95* AKDW/GC/E(P) (B78-33931) ISBN 0-85649-019-9
Edgington, Harry. Abba. Revised ed. *Magnum Books. £0.95* AKDW/GB/E(P) (B78-28698) ISBN 0-417-03370-2
Edinburgh dances. (Kelly, Bryan). *Novello. £4.50* WMH (B78-51306)
Edinger, Christiane. Sonata, violin, op.47. Sonata für Solo-Violine, Opus 47. (Einem, Gottfried von). *Bote und Bock : Schirmer. £5.75* SPME (B78-51103)
Édith Piaf. *Wise. £3.95* KDW/GB/AY (B78-50152) ISBN 0-86001-112-7
Edition Eulenburg.
Arne, Thomas Augustine. Thomas and Sally : dramatic pastoral in two acts. *Eulenburg. Unpriced* CQC (B78-50329)
Fauré, Gabriel. Requiem, Op.48. *Eulenburg. Unpriced* EMDGKAV (B78-50031)
Handel, George Frideric. Concerto, organ, op.4, no.1, G minor. Organ concerto, G minor, Op.4, no.1. *Eulenburg. Unpriced* MPRF (B78-50926)
Handel, George Frideric. Concerto, organ, op.4, no.2, B flat major. Organ concerto, B flat major, Op.4, no.2. *Eulenburg. Unpriced* MPRF (B78-50927)
Handel, George Frideric. Concerto, organ, op.4, no.3, G minor. Organ concerto, G minor, Op.4, no.3. *Eulenburg. Unpriced* MPRF (B78-50928)
Handel, George Frideric. Concerto, organ, op.4, no.4, F major. Organ concerto, F major, Op.4, no.4. *Eulenburg. Unpriced* MPRF (B78-50929)
Handel, George Frideric. Concerto, organ, op.4, no.5, F major. Organ concerto, F major, Op.4, no.5. *Eulenburg. Unpriced* MPRF (B78-50930)
Handel, George Frideric. Concerto, organ, op.4, no.6, B flat major, 'Harp'. Organ concerto, (Harp concerto), B flat major, Op.4, no.6. *Eulenburg. Unpriced* MPRF (B78-50931)
Handel, George Frideric. Sonatas, violins (2) & continuo, Op.2, no.1-6. Trio sonatas
Op.2, nos.1-3. *Eulenburg. Unpriced* NXNSE (B78-50203)
Holst, Gustav. A choral fantasia, Op.51. *Eulenburg. £1.00* EZDE (B78-50042)
Mozart, Wolfgang Amadeus. Concerto, piano, no.17, K.453, G major. Piano concerto, G major, K.453. *Eulenburg. £1.60* MPQF (B78-50497)
Purcell, Henry. Sonatas in 4 parts, Z.802-811. Ten sonatas in four parts
Nos. 1-6. *Eulenburg. £2.00* NXNSE (B78-50506)
Purcell, Henry. Sonatas in 4 parts. Z.802-811. Ten sonatas in four parts
Nos.7-10. *Eulenburg. £2.00* NXNSE (B78-50507)
Weber, Carl Maria von, *Freiherr.* Trio, flute, cello & piano, J. 259, G minor. Trio for flute, cello and piano in G minor, J.259. *Eulenburg. Unpriced* NURNT (B78-50198)
Edition Eulenburg, no.1365. Handel, George Frideric. Sonatas, violins (2) & continuo, op.2, nos.1-6. Trio sonatas
Op.2, no.4-6. *Eulenburg. Unpriced* NXNSE (B78-50205)
Edmund Rubbra : composer-essays. *22 Pheasant Way, Rickmansworth, Herts. : Triad Press. £9.95 : CIP rev.* BRU (B77-18309) ISBN 0-902070-21-5
Edwards, Aneurin J. Y ffidil = The violin : y camau cyntaf = the first steps. *4-5, Thomas Row, Swansea : Christopher Davies. £1.25* S/AC (B78-51088) ISBN 0-7154-0299-4
Edwards, Gunvor. Musical merry-go-round : musical activities for the very young. (Willson, Robina Beckles). *Heinemann. £3.50* A/GR (B78-01459) ISBN 0-434-97257-6
Edwards, Warwick. Musica Britannica : a national collection of music
Vol.40: Music for mixed consort. *Stainer and Bell, for the Musica Britannica Trust. Unpriced* C/AYD (B78-50001) ISBN 0-85249-436-x
Egisto. *Vocal score.* L'egisto : opera in three acts and a prologue. (Cavalli, Francesco). *Faber Music. Unpriced* CC (B78-50324)
Egk, Werner.
Nachgefühl. *Vocal score.* Nachgefühl : Kantate für Sopran und Orchester nach Versen von Klabund. *Schott. £4.80* KFLDX (B78-50471)
Polonaise, Adagio und Finale : für vier Bläser (Oboe, Klarinette in B, Horn in F, Fagott) und Streichquintett (solistisch oder chorisch) = for four wind instruments (oboe, clarinet in B flat, horn in F, bassoon) and string quintet (solo or in chorus). Neufassung. *Schott. £12.00* NWNM (B78-50947)
Polonaise, Adagio und Finale : für vier Bläser und Streichquintett = for four wind instruments and string quintet. *Schott. Unpriced* NWNM (B78-50946)
Ehmann, Wilhelm.
Neue Musik für Bläser
Heft 4: Werke von Herbert Gadsch, Eberhard Wenzel, Theodor Hlouschek, Rolf Schweizer, Hans Friedrich Micheelsen. *Bärenreiter. £4.20* WN/AY (B78-51331)
Partita canonica. (Feld, Jindřich). *Bärenreiter. £3.60* WNQG (B78-51335)
Voce et tuba : gesammelte Reden und Aufsätze, 1934-1974. *32 Great Titchfield St., W.1 : Bärenreiter Kassel. Unpriced* A(D) (B78-03573)
Eibl, Joseph Heinz. Wolfgang Amadeus Mozart, Chronik eines Lebens. 2.Aufl. *Bärenreiter etc.. £1.90* BMS(N) (B78-21399)
Eight études : for piano. (Rorem, Ned). *Boosey and Hawkes. £3.25* QPG (B78-50217)
Eight lieder, 1570 : for four voices or instruments, ATTBB. (Vento, Ivo de). *London Pro Musica. Unpriced* EZDU (B78-50383)
Eight preludes, op.30 : for piano. (Kabeláč, Miloslav). *Supraphon : Schirmer. £3.65* QPJ (B78-50534)
Eight urban musical cultures : tradition and change. *University of Illinois Press. £10.50* BZ (B78-39229) ISBN 0-252-00208-3
Eight valses for four guitars. (Biberian, Gilbert). *Belwin Mills. Unpriced* TSNSHW (B78-50606)
Einem, Gottfried von.
Kabale und liebe. Op.44. *Vocal score.* Kabale und Liebe : Oper in 2 teilen (9 Bildern) nach Friedrich von Schiller. *Boosey and Hawkes. Unpriced* CC (B78-50006)
Kabale und Liebe : Oper in 2 Teilen (9 Bildern) nach Friedrich von Schiller. *Boosey and Hawkes. Unpriced* CQC (B78-50710)

Leibes- und Abendlieder : für höhe Stimme und Klavier, Opus 48 : von Gottfried von Einem. *Bote und Bock. £3.85* KFTDW (B78-50474)
Quartet, strings, no.1, op.45. Erstes Streichquartett, opus 45. *Boosey and Hawkes. Unpriced* RXNS (B78-51079)
Quartet, strings, no.1, op.45. Erstes Streichquartett, opus 45. *Boosey and Hawkes. Unpriced* RXNS (B78-51080)
Quintet, wind instruments, op.46. Bläserquintett. Op.46. *Boosey and Hawkes. Unpriced* UNR (B78-51195)
Quintet, wind instruments, op.46. Bläserquintett. Opus 46. *Boosey and Hawkes. Unpriced* UNR (B78-51196)
Sonata, violin, op.47. Sonata für Solo-Violine, Opus 47. *Bote und Bock : Schirmer. £5.75* SPME (B78-51103)
Wiener Symphonie, Opus 49. *Bote und Bock : Schirmer. £14.40* MME (B78-50918)
Electronic organ review
Nov.1976-. *Waldron, Heathfield, Sussex TN21 0QS Electronic Organ Review. £0.50(£5.00 yearly)* ARPV/B(B) (B78-11202)
Elegia. (Villa-Lobos, Heitor). *Arthur Napoleão : Essex Music. Unpriced* QPK (B78-50555)
Elegia. *arr.* Elegia. (Villa-Lobos, Heitor). *Arthur Napoleão Essex Music. Unpriced* QPK (B78-50555)
Elegy and dance : for small orchestra. (Jenni, Donald). *Associated Music. £13.60* MJ (B78-50484)
Elegy : for orchestra. (Washburn, Robert). *Boosey and Hawkes. Unpriced* MMJ (B78-50924)
Elegy for violin and piano. (Lombardi, Luca). *Schirmer. £2.40* SPJ (B78-51100)
Elektra : tragedy in one act. (Hofmannsthal, Hugo von). *Boosey and Hawkes. £9.00* BSUAC
Elgar, *Sir* Edward, *bart.*
Four unaccompanied part-songs. Opus.53 : for SATB with divisions. *Novello. £1.10* EZDW (B78-50796)
Selections. *arr.* Elgar organ album
Book 1. *Novello. £1.50* RK (B78-50232)
Seven anthems. *Novello. £1.30* DH (B78-50725)
Elgar Society. Elgar's interpreters on record : an Elgar discography. (Knowles, John, *b.1948*). *c/o F.B. Greatwich, 20 Geraldine Rd, Malvern, Worcs. WR14 3PA : The Elgar Society. £1.00* BEP/FD (B78-33481)
Elgar's interpreters on record : an Elgar discography. (Knowles, John, *b.1948*). *c/o F.B. Greatwich, 20 Geraldine Rd, Malvern, Worcs. WR14 3PA : The Elgar Society. £1.00* BEP/FD (B78-33481)
Elguera, Amalia. Primavera : for soprano and flute. (Musgrave, Thea). *Chester Music. Unpriced* KFLE/VRDW (B78-50896)
Elley, Derek. International music guide
1978. *Tantivy Press etc.. £3.25* A(BC) (B78-07707) ISBN 0-498-02107-6
Ellington, Mercer. Duke Ellington in person : an intimate memoir. *Hutchinson. £5.95* AMT(P) (B78-34740) ISBN 0-09-132750-4
Elliott Carter : a 70th birthday tribute. *Associated Music Publishers; 140 Strand, WC2 1HG : G. Schirmer Limited. Unpriced* BCBRS
Ellis, David. Sonata, double bass, op.42. Sonata for unaccompanied double bass. *Yorke. Unpriced* SSPME (B78-51128)
Ellis, Martin. In wonder, love and praise : a collection of fourteen anthems. *Novello. Unpriced* DH/AY (B78-50728)
Elsner, Constanze. Stevie Wonder. *Everest. £4.95* AKDW/GBS/E(P) (B78-15755) ISBN 0-905018-51-6
Elvis Presley - 1935-1977 : a tribute to the king
1. *2 Engine La., Wednesbury, W. Midlands : 'Bavie' Publications. £3.00* AKDW/HK/E(P) (B78-12098)
2. *2 Engine La., Wednesbury, W. Midlands : 'Bavie' Publications. £3.00* AKDW/HK/E(P) (B78-12099)
3. *2 Engine La., Wednesbury, W. Midlands : 'Bavie' Publications. £3.00* AKDW/HK/E(P) (B78-06988)
4. *2 Engine La., Wednesbury, W. Midlands : 'Bavie' Publications. £3.00* AKDW/HK/E(P) (B78-12100)
5. *2 Engine La., Wednesbury, W. Midlands : 'Bavie' Publications. £3.00* AKDW/HK/E(P) (B78-12101)
Elvis Presley quizbook. (Nash, Bruce M). *Warner Books : Distributed by New English Library. £0.90* AKDW/HK/E(P/DE) (B78-33163) ISBN 0-446-89823-6
Emblem XI. How shall my tongue express ...? : Motet. (Rubbra, Edmund). *Lengnick. £0.18* EZDH (B78-50372)

EMI music book of piano rags. *EMI. Unpriced* QPHXJ (B78-50525)
Emmerson, Simon. Variations, tuba. Variations for tuba. *Arts Lab Music. Unpriced* WVPM/T (B78-51359)
En blanc et noir : three pieces for two pianos. (Debussy, Claude). *Peters. Unpriced* QNU (B78-50984)
Encyclopaedia of the musical. (Green, Stanley, *b.1923*). *Cassell. £7.95* ACM(C) (B78-03575) ISBN 0-304-29930-8
Encyclopaedia of the musical theatre. Encyclopaedia of the musical. (Green, Stanley, *b.1923*). *Cassell. £7.95* ACM(C) (B78-03575) ISBN 0-304-29930-8
Encyclopedia of jazz. (Feather, Leonard). Completely revised, enlarged ed.. *Quartet Books. £9.95* AMT(C) (B78-25374) ISBN 0-7043-2173-4
Encyclopedia of jazz in the seventies. (Feather, Leonard). *Quartet Books. £9.95* AMT(XR9/C) (B78-26894) ISBN 0-7043-2175-0
Encyclopedia of jazz in the sixties. (Feather, Leonard). *Quartet Books. £9.95* AMT(XQ10/C) (B78-26893) ISBN 0-7043-2174-2
Encyclopedia of quotations about music. *David and Charles. £6.95 : CIP rev.* A(DD) (B78-19438) ISBN 0-7153-7611-x
Engel, Lehman. The making of a musical. *Macmillan : Collier Macmillan. £6.75* ACM/D (B78-32355) ISBN 0-02-536070-1
Engelbrecht, Christiane Bernsdorff-. *See* Bernsdorff-Engelbrecht, Christiane.
England expects : a musical entertainment for all those sick with sacrifice. (Richards, Gavin). *97 Ferme Park Rd, Crouch End, N8 9SA : Journeyman Press : Belt and Braces Roadshow Co. £1.20* BFKSACM (B78-01675) ISBN 0-904526-25-9
English church music : a collection of essays

1978. *Addington Palace, Croydon CR9 5AD : Royal School of Church Music. £1.70* AD/LD(YD/D) (B78-29836) ISBN 0-85402-075-6
English sacred music
Vol.1. (Tye, Christopher). *Stainer and Bell, for the British Academy. Unpriced* EZDK (B78-50046) ISBN 0-85249-449-1
English! Sing it! : a structured presentation of spoken English through the use of songs. *McGraw-Hill. Unpriced* KE/TSDW/AY (B78-50168) ISBN 0-07-024667-x
Enjoying music
Book 2. (Bennett, Roy). *Longman. £0.95* A/C(VF) (B78-37863) ISBN 0-582-22180-3
Enoch, Yvonne.
Group piano-teaching. *Oxford University Press. £2.95* AQ/E(VC) (B78-26247) ISBN 0-19-318423-0
Play the piano : a tutor for adults and late beginners. *Faber Music. Unpriced* Q/AC (B78-50960)
Enoch choral series. Pasfield, William Reginald. Jillian of Berry : four part song for male voices T.T.B.B. *Edwin Ashdown. £0.20* GEZDW (B78-50829)
Ensemble canzonas of Frescobaldi. Frescobaldi, Girolamo. Il primo libro delle canzoni a una, due, tre e quattro voci. *Selections.* Three canzonas for two treble, one bass instrument and continuo. *London Pro Musica Edition. Unpriced* LNSPW (B78-50483)
Ensembles with Orff instruments.
Odom, John. The last month of the year : eight carols for voices, Orff-instruments, recorders and guitars
1: Hodie, Vhristus natus est. *Schott. Unpriced* ENYESDP/LF (B78-50754)
Odom, John. The last month of the year : eight carols for voices, Orff-instruments, recorders and guitars
2: Children go where I send thee. *Schott. Unpriced* ENYESDP/LF (B78-50755)
Odom, John. The last month of the year : eight carols for voices, Orff-instruments, recorders and guitars
3: Virgin Mary, meek and mild. *Schott. Unpriced* ENYESDP/LF (B78-50756)
Odom, John. The last month of the year : eight carols for voices, Orff-instruments, recorders and guitars
4: O magnum mysterium. *Schott. Unpriced* ENYESDP/LF (B78-50757)
Odom, John. The last month of the year : eight carols for voices, Orff-instruments, recorders and guitars
5: Noël. *Schott. Unpriced* ENYESDP/LF (B78-50758)
Odom, John. The last month of the year : eight carols for voices, Orff-instruments, recorders and guitars
6: The last month of the year. *Schott. Unpriced* ENYESDP/LF (B78-50759)
Odom, John. The last month of the year : eight carols for voices, Orff-instruments, recorders and guitars
7: What you gonna call yo' pretty little baby? *Schott. Unpriced* ENYESDP/LF (B78-50760)
Odom, John. The last month of the year : eight carols for voices, Orff-instruments, recorders and guitars
8: A Christmas gloria. *Schott. Unpriced* ENYESDP/LF (B78-50761)
Entrerue : für Flöte und Orgel, 1976, 1977. (Wahren, Karl Heinz). *Bote und Bock : Schirmer. £4.30* VRPLR (B78-51228)
Enzensberger, Hans Magnus. 4 Songs nach Texten von Hans-Jurgen Heise, Heinz Piontek, Hans Magnus Enzensberger und Ror Wolf für Singstimme, Klavier, Kontrabass und Schlagzeug. (Wimberger, Gerhard). *Bärenreiter. £2.50* KE/NYGDW (B78-50883)
Epine, E L'. Monsieur Choufleuri restera chez lui de. *Vocal score.* Salon Blumenkohl/Monsieur Choufleuri restera chez lui de ... : Buffo-Operette in einem Akt deutsch nach Karl Fr. Wiltmann von Heinz Balthes und Paul Vasil, opéra bouffe en un acte de St. Rémy, E. L'Epine, Hector Crémieux et Ludovic Halévy, musikalische Revision, neue Instrumentation und praktische Bearbeitung von Caspar Richter. (Offenbach, Jacques). *Bote und Bock : Associated music. £11.50* CF (B78-50703)
Epstein, Dena J. Sinful tunes and spirituals : black folk music to the Civil War. *University of Illinois Press. £12.60* AKDW/G(YTLD/XA1867) (B78-15754) ISBN 0-252-00520-1
Equale 1 : Szene für drei Kontrabasse = Scene for three basses, 1974. (Acker, Dieter). *Bote und Bock : Yorke. Unpriced* SSNU (B78-51125)
Erber, James.
La Dafne. *Vocal score.* La Dafne. (Gagliano, Marco da). *Cathedral Music. Unpriced* CC (B78-50325)
Mass, no.2, E minor, (1896). *Vocal score.* Mass no.2, E minor, for eight part choir and wind instruments (1896 version). (Bruckner, Anton). Revised version of the edition of Kurt Soldan by James Erber. *Peters. Unpriced* DG (B78-50720)
Erbrecht, Lothar Hoffmann-. *See* Hoffman-Erbrecht, Lothar.
Erinnerung an Covent Garden. Op.329. *arr.* Memories of Covent Garden = Erinnerung an Covent Garden : waltz, op.329, based on English music hall songs. (Strauss, Johann, *b.1825*). *Bosworth & Co. Unpriced* MK/AHW (B78-50486)
Eröd, Iván.
Milchzahnlieder. *Choral score.* Milchzahnlieder = Milktooth songs. *Boosey and Hawkes. Unpriced* JFADW (B78-50836)
Milchzahnlieder. *Vocal score.* Milchzahnlieder = Milktooth songs : für Gesang oder Kinderchor, mit Klavier oder Kammerorchester = for solo voice, or children's chorus with piano or chamber orchestra. *Boosey and Hawkes. Unpriced* KDW (B78-50860)
Erste Streichquartett in vier Sätzen, 1976. Quartet, strings, no.1. 1. Streichquartett in vier Sätzen, 1976, von Ulrich Stranz. (Stranz, Ulrich). *Bärenreiter. £7.00* RXNS (B78-50583)
Erster Theil confortativae sacrae symphoniacae. Wenn der Herr die Gefangnen Zion erlösen wird. *arr.* Motet, Wenn der Herr die Gefangnen Zion erlösen wird. (Hartmann, Heinrich). *Tomus. Unpriced* VSNQK/DJ (B78-51242)
Espaces du sommeil : for baritone and orchestra. (Lutoslawski, Witold). *Chester Music. Unpriced* KGNE/MDW (B78-50906)
Essays on American music. (Clarke, Garry E). *Greenwood Press. £12.95* A(YT) (B78-09696) ISBN 0-8371-9484-9
Essence of Bruckner : an essay towards the understanding of his music. (Simpson, Robert). 2nd ed. *Gollancz. £4.95* BBUEAMME (B78-10360) ISBN 0-575-01189-0
Essential guitar skill = Tecnica essenziale per la chitarra = Grundlagen der Fertigkeit im Gittarenspiel
Book 1. *Ricordi. Unpriced* TS/AF (B78-50603)
Book 2. (Lester, Bryan). *Ricordi. Unpriced* TS/AF (B78-50602)
Essex University. *See* University of Essex.
Estro poetico-armonico. d Salmo 18. *arr.* 'The heavens devlare the glory of God'. (Marcello, Benedetto). *Cramer. Unpriced* RK/DR (B78-51056)
Ettlinger, Yona. Church sonatas. *Selections : arr.* Four church sonatas. (Mozart, Wolfgang Amadeus). *Boosey and Hawkes. £2.25* VVPK/AE (B78-50305)
Étude. (Walker, Timothy). *Belwin Mills. £0.50* TSPMJ (B78-50619)
Études melodiques et progressives. Op.36. Études speciales. Opus 36 : neu herausgegeben und bezeichnet von Walther Davisson
Hft.1. (Mazas, Jacques Féréol). Neurevidierte Ausgabe. *Peters. Unpriced* S/AF (B78-51089)
Études speciales. Opus 36 : neu herausgegeben und bezeichnet von Walther Davisson
Hft.1. (Mazas, Jacques Féréol). Neurevidierte Ausgabe. *Peters. Unpriced* S/AF (B78-51089)
Eustace and Hilda. *arr.* Eustace and Hilda : theme from the award-winning BBV tv trilogy, for piano solo. (Bennett, Richard Rodney). *Novello. Unpriced* QPK/JS (B78-51034)
Eustace and Hilda : theme from the award-winning BBV tv trilogy, for piano solo. (Bennett, Richard Rodney). *Novello. Unpriced* QPK/JS (B78-51034)
Evangelischer Blumengarten. Machet die Töre weit. Machet die Töre weit : Du König der Ehren, wir danken Dir : für vierstimmigen gemischten Chor. (Briegel, Wolfgang Carl). *Bärenreiter. £0.84* EZDH (B78-50370)
Evans, Colin. Sounds for swinging strings : four pieces in popular style for group music. *Paxton. £1.32* NX (B78-50505)
Evans, David, *b.1940 (May).* Sharing sounds : musical experiences with young children. *Longman. Unpriced* A/GJ (B78-31364) ISBN 0-582-25006-4
Evans, Mary, *b.1947.* Guitars : music, history, construction and players from the Renaissance to rock. (Evans, Tom, *b.1948*). *Paddington Press. £10.95* ATS/B (B78-25375) ISBN 0-448-22240-x
Evans, Mary Anne. *See* Evans, Mary, b.1947.
Evans, Ray.
The paleface. Buttons and bows. *arr.* Buttons and bows. (Livingston, Jay). *Warner : Blossom. Unpriced* UMMK/DW/JR (B78-51188)
The lemon drop kid. Silver bells. *arr.* Silver bells : SATB and piano. (Livingston, Jay). *Warner : Blossom. Unpriced* DW (B78-50351)
Evans, Tom, *b.1948.* Guitars : music, history, construction and players from the Renaissance to rock. *Paddington Press. £10.95* ATS/B (B78-25375) ISBN 0-448-22240-x
Evans one act plays. Crocker, John, *b.1925.* Potty pantomime. *Evans Bros. £0.40* BCQRACPP (B78-37098) ISBN 0-237-75031-7
Evening service for men's voices. (Dearnley, Christopher). *36 Ranelagh Gdns., W.6 : Cathedral Music. Unpriced* GEZDGPP (B78-50416)
Everett, Paul J.
L'alphabet de la musique, Op.30 : 24 sonatas in all the keys for treble recorder and basso continuo in 6 volumes
Vol.1: Nos 1-4. (Schickhard, Johann Christian). *Musica rara. Unpriced* VSSPE (B78-50655)
L'alphabet de la musique. Op.30 : 24 sonatas in all the keys for treble recorder and basso continuo in 6 volumes
Vol.2: Sonatas 5-8. (Schickhard, Johann Christian). *Musica rara. £6.50* VSSPE (B78-51259)
Sonatas, treble recorder & continuo, op.17, nos 5,9. Sonatas op.17, nos 5 and 9 for treble recorder and basso continuo. (Schickhard, Johann Christian). *Musica rara. Unpriced* VSSPE (B78-50656)
Sonatas, treble recorder & continuo, op.17, nos 10,11. Sonatas op.17, nos 10 and 11 for treble recorder and basso continuo. (Schickhard, Johann Christian). *Musica rara. Unpriced* VSSPE (B78-50657)
Sonatas, treble recorder & continuo, op.17, nos.1-2. Sonatas op.17, nos 1 and 2, for treble recorder and basso continuo. (Schickhard, Johann Christian). *Musica rara. Unpriced* VSSPE (B78-50658)
Everyman's guide to orchestral music. (Downes, Edward). *Dent. £15.00 : CIP rev.* AMM (B78-03579) ISBN 0-460-03030-2
Evita : the legend of Eva Peron, 1919-1952. (Webber, Andrew Lloyd). *Elm Tree Books. £3.95 : CIP rev.* BWKRACM (B78-12401) ISBN 0-241-89890-0
Ev'ry time I feel the spirit : spiritual for four-part chorus of mixed voices with accompaniment for organ and optional handbells. (Ferguson, Edwin Earle). *Roberton. £0.20* DW/LC (B78-50748)
Ewans, Michael. Janáček's tragic operas. *Faber. £7.95 : CIP rev.* BJFAC (B77-23620) ISBN 0-571-10959-4
Ewen, David. All the years of American popular music. *Prentice-Hall. Unpriced* A/GB(YT/X) (B78-20432) ISBN 0-13-022442-1
Exercitien 3 'Das Prinzip Hoffnung' (nach Ernst Bloch) : für sechs Ausführende (1974-1976). (Hufschmidt, Wolfgang). *Bärenreiter. £21.00* KFNE/NYDNQDX (B78-50898)
Experiments in sound : new directions in musical education for young children. (Meyer-Denkmann, Gertrud). *Universal Edition. £3.50* A/D(VC) (B78-10119) ISBN 0-900938-49-8
Exploring music series.
Baroque music for clarinet : including music by Couperin, Handel, Molter, Pokorny, Stamitz. *Boosey and Hawkes. Unpriced* VVPK/AAY (B78-51286)
Dvořák, Antonín. Slavonic dance, no.8, op.46, no.8, G minor. *arr.* Slavonic dance, no.8. *Boosey and Hawkes. Unpriced* UNNK/AH (B78-50642)
Dvořák, Antonín. Slavonic dance, no.9, op.72, no.1. *arr.* Slavonic dance no.9. *Boosey and Hawkes. Unpriced* UNNK/AH (B78-50643)
Dvořák, Antonín. Slavonic dance, no.15, op.72, no.7, C major. *arr.* Slavonic dance, no.15. *Boosey and Hawkes. Unpriced* UNNK/AH (B78-50644)
Exploring music series : Ensemble series.
Haydn, Joseph. Feld-Parthie in F, for wind ensemble. *Boosey and Hawkes. Unpriced* UNQ (B78-51193)
Mozart, Wolfgang Amadeus. Serenade, wind sextet, no.11, K.375, E flat major. Adagio. Adagio ... for wind ensemble. *Boosey and Hawkes. Unpriced* UNQ (B78-51194)
Exploring music series. Ensemble series. Haydn, Joseph. Divertimento, woodwind quartet, Hob.II, no.7, C major. Feld-Parthie in C for wind ensemble. *Boosey and Hawkes. Unpriced* UNN (B78-50284)
Eye level. *arr.* Eye level. (Trombey, Jack). *Chappell. Unpriced* NYFPK (B78-50514)
Fabb, John. Military bands and their uniforms. (Cassin-Scott, Jack). *Blandford Press. £6.95* AUMM(X) (B78-26675) ISBN 0-7137-0895-6
Fabulous phonograph, 1877-1977. (Gelatt, Roland). 2nd revised ed. *Cassell. £6.50* A/FD(XKS101) (B78-03423) ISBN 0-304-29904-9
Face out
No.1- ; Apr. 1978-. *c/o Chris Furse, 25 Lionel Ave., Wendover, Aylesbury, Bucks. : 'Face out'. Unpriced* AKDW/HKR(B) (B78-26879)
Fahnengruss. (Stephan, Wilhelm). *Bote und Bock Associated Music. £1.60* UMMGM (B78-50626)
Familiar music for 5 string banjo. *Lewis Music : Phoenix. Unpriced* TTPMJ (B78-50624)
Fanen, Pierre. Rock and roll-blues guitare. *Chappell. Unpriced* TS/AC (B78-50268)
Fanfare. Fanfare, Lullaby, Cherokee war dance. (Wade, Darrell). *16 Anchor Way, Danes Green, Gnosall : Viking. Unpriced* MJ (B78-50181)
Fanfare and processional : for concert band. (Schaefer, Will). *Schirmer. £18.20* UMMJ (B78-51182)
Fanfare, Lullaby, Cherokee war dance. (Wade, Darrell). *16 Anchor Way, Danes Green, Gnosall : Viking. Unpriced* MJ (B78-50181)
Fanshawe, David.
African Sanctus. Lord's Prayer. *arr.* The Lord's Prayer ... : S.A.B. and piano with optional guitar and drums. *Chappell. Unpriced* DTF (B78-50348)
African Sanctus. Lord's Prayer. *arr.* The Lord's Prayer ... : S.A.T.B. and piano with optional guitar and drums. *Chappell. Unpriced* DTF (B78-50347)
African Sanctus. Lord's Prayer. *arr.* The Lord's Prayer ... : unison chorus and piano. *Chappell. Unpriced* JDTF (B78-50425)
Fantaisie pastorale hongroise. Op.26. Hungarian pastoral fantasy : for flute and piano. (Doppler, Franz). *Chester Music. Unpriced* VRPJ (B78-51215)
Fantasia a cinque : for recorder quintet. (Le Jeune, Henri). *Dolmetsch : Chappell. Unpriced* VSNR (B78-51243)
Fantasia celestina. (Walker, Timothy). *Belwin Mills Music. £0.80* TSPMJ (B78-51159)
Fantasia concertante no.5 : for solo guitar. (Camilleri, Charles). *Basil Ramsey : Roberton. £2.00* TSPMF (B78-51149)
Fantasie, op.337, für Flöte und Gitarre. (Carulli, Ferdinando). *Heinrichshofen : Peters. Unpriced* VRPLTS (B78-50649)
Fantasie overo canzoni alla francese. Fantasie no.6. *arr.* Echo fantasia : for brass quartet. (Banchieri, Adriano). *Chester Music. Unpriced* WNSK (B78-51339)
Fantasticks : book and lyrics by Tom Jones. (Schmidt, Harvey). Revised ed. *Chappell. Unpriced* CM (B78-50327)
Fantasticks. *Vocal score.* The fantasticks : book and lyrics by Tom Jones. (Schmidt, Harvey). Revised ed. *Chappell. Unpriced* CM (B78-50327)
Fantasy about Purcell's 'Fantasia upon one note' : for brass quintet. (Carter, Elliott). *Associated Music. £5.75* WNR (B78-50689)
Fantasy for organ, Op.78. (Mathias, William). *Oxford University Press. Unpriced* RJ (B78-51051) ISBN 0-19-375552-1
Fantasy sonata for organ. (Jacob, Gordon). *Peters. Unpriced* RE (B78-50561)
Farewell recital : further memoirs. (Moore, Gerald, *b.1899*). *Hamilton. £4.95 : CIP rev.* AQ/ED(P/XQG11) (B77-33371) ISBN 0-241-89817-x
Farjeon, Eleanor.

Cotton : unison song with optional descant and piano music. (Fraser, Shena). *Roberton. £0.12* JFDW (B78-50091)
Songs of London town. *Selections.* Highgate and The tower. (Burtch, Mervyn). *Roberton. £0.18* JFDW (B78-50090)
Farmer, Paul. Pop workbook. (Attwood, Tony). *Edward Arnold. £1.75 : CIP rev.* A/GB (B77-28559) ISBN 0-7131-0155-5
Farnaby, Giles. Giles Farnaby suite. *Oxford University Press. Unpriced* UMMK (B78-50283)
Farra, Mimi. Hosanna Lord! *Celebration Services. Unpriced* JDH (B78-50079)
Farren, Mick. Rock 'n roll circus : the illustrated rock concert. *Pierrot Publishing Ltd; 219 Eversleigh Rd, SW11 5UY : Distributed by Big O Publishing Ltd. £3.95* AKDW/HKR/E(M) (B78-31595) ISBN 0-905310-10-1
Fasch, Johann Friedrich. Concerto, bassoon & string orchestra, C major. *arr.* Concerto C-dur für Fagott, Streicher und Basso continuo. Ausgabe für Fagott und Klavier. *Noetzel : Peters. Unpriced* VWPK/LF (B78-50666)
Fauré, Gabriel.
Dolly. Op.56, no.1. Berceuse. *arr.* Berceuse. ('Listen with Mother' theme) ... *R. Smith. Unpriced* WMK (B78-51315)
Dolly suite, op.56. Dolly. Op.36 sic : suite pour piano à 4 mains. *Cramer. £2.75* QNVG (B78-50521)
Fantasie, flute & piano, op.79. Fantasie for flute and piano, op.79. *Chester Music. Unpriced* VRPJ (B78-51216)
Messe basse and other sacred works : for female or boys voices and organ or piano. *Novello. Unpriced* DFF (B78-50016)
Pelléas et Melisande. Op.80. Sicilienne. *arr.* Sicilienne from Pelléas et Melisande : for flute and piano. *Chester Music. Unpriced* VRPK/AHVQ/JM (B78-51221)
Requiem, Op.48. *Eulenburg. Unpriced* EMDGKAV (B78-50031)
Faust. Ah! je ris. *arr.* Jewel song ... (Gounod, Charles). *Leonard, Gould and Bolttler. Unpriced* KDW (B78-50115)
Faust. Avant de quitter ces lieux. *arr.* Cavatina 'Avant de quitter ces lieux'. (Gounod, Charles). *Leonard, Gould & Bolttler. Unpriced* KDW (B78-50443)
Faustini, Giovanni. L'egisto. *Vocal score.* L'egisto : opera in three acts and a prologue. (Cavalli, Francesco). *Faber Music. Unpriced* CC (B78-50324)
Favorita : drama in four acts. (Royer, Alphonse). *140 Strand, WC2R 1HH : G. Schirmer. Unpriced* BDRAC (B78-26887)
Fear not, for I have redeemed you. (Page, Jodi). *Celebration Services. Unpriced* JDK (B78-50080)
Feather, Leonard.
The encyclopedia of jazz. Completely revised, enlarged ed.. *Quartet Books. £9.95* AMT(C) (B78-25374) ISBN 0-7043-2173-4
The encyclopedia of jazz in the seventies. *Quartet Books. £9.95* AMT(XR9/C) (B78-26894) ISBN 0-7043-2175-0
The encyclopedia of jazz in the sixties. *Quartet Books. £9.95* AMT(XQ10/C) (B78-26893) ISBN 0-7043-2174-2
Feed my sheep : a quodlibet based on negro spirituals. (Hudson, Hazel). *Ashdown. Unpriced* FDW/LC (B78-50065)
Feeney Trust. Twenty British composers. *J. and W. Chester for the Feeney Trust. Unpriced* A(YC/XPQ17) (B78-33938) ISBN 0-9502767-3-1
Feld, Jindřich.
Partita canonica. *Bärenreiter. £3.60* WNQG (B78-51335)
Three pieces : for oboe (or flute or clarinet) and piano. *Supraphon : Schirmer. Unpriced* VTPJ (B78-51267)
Feld-Parthie in C for wind ensemble. (Haydn, Joseph). *Boosey and Hawkes. Unpriced* UNN (B78-50284)
Feldman, Morton. Instruments 1. *Universal. Unpriced* NYH (B78-50954)
Fenby, Eric. Koanga. La calinda. *arr.* La calinda, and, Air and dance. (Delius, Frederick). *Boosey and Hawkes. Unpriced* VRPK (B78-50292)
Fenton, Ian. Looking at music. *Coventure. £2.93* A (B78-14493) ISBN 0-904576-42-6
Fenton, Raymond. The Cerney setting of Series 3 Holy Communion. *All Hallows Church, South Cerney, Gloucestershire : Raymond Fenton. Unpriced* JDGS (B78-50078)
Ferguson, Edwin Earle. Ev'ry time I feel the spirit : spiritual for four-part chorus of mixed voices with accompaniment for organ and optional handbells. *Roberton. £0.20* DW/LC (B78-50748)
Ferguson, Howard. Sonatas, piano. Complete pianoforte sonatas, including the unfinished works
Vol.1. (Schubert, Franz). *Associated Board of the Royal Schools of Music. Unpriced* QPE/AZ (B78-50996)
Ferneyhough, Brian.
Four miniatures : flute and piano. *Peters. Unpriced* VRPJ (B78-50291)
Sieben Sterne : for organ. *Peters. Unpriced* RJ (B78-50230)
Time and motion study 2 : for solo 'cello and electronics'. *Peters. Unpriced* SR (B78-51109)
Time and motion study I : solo bass clarinet. *Peters. Unpriced* VVUPMJ (B78-50306)
Transit : six solo voices and chamber orchestra. *Peters. Unpriced* JNAZE/MRDW (B78-50107)
Ferrari, Ermanno Wolf-. *See* Wolf-Ferrari, Ermanno.
Ffidil = The violin : y camau cyntaf = the first steps. (Edwards, Aneurin J). *4-5, Thomas Row, Swansea : Christopher Davies. £1.25* S/AC (B78-51088) ISBN 0-7154-0299-4
Fiala, Jaromir. The dower. Die Mitgift und Gebet : zwei Männerchöre a cappella nach Texten von Josef Srb-Debrnov. (Smetana, Bedřich). *Bärenreiter. £0.70* GEZDW (B78-50423)
Field, Eugene.
Jest 'fore Christmas. (Silverman, Jerry). *Schirmer. Unpriced* KDW (B78-50116)
Jest 'fore Christmas : for two-part chorus of young voices with piano and guitar accompaniment. (Silverman, Jerry). *Schirmer. Unpriced* FDW (B78-50063)
Fietta, Hector Lagna. Centenário do choro : 20 choros para piano
Album no.1. *Fermata do Brasil : Essex Music. Unpriced* QPK/AAYUR (B78-50558)
Fietta, Heitor Lagna. Centenário do choro : 20 choras para piano
Album no.2. *Fermata do Brasil : Essex Music. Unpriced* QPK/AAYUR (B78-50559)
Fifty first exercises for horn. (Tuckwell, Barry). *Oxford University Press. Unpriced* WT/AF (B78-51350) ISBN 0-19-359150-2
Figaro-Metamorphosen 'Voi che sapete' : für Horn (F) und Klavier, Opus 61. (Krol, Bernhard). *Bote und Bock Associated Music. £7.70* WTPJ (B78-50694)
Finger style folk : a guitar tutor for folk song accompaniment. (Green, E). *45 Riverside Drive, Hambleton, Blackpool FY6 9EH : Wyre Publications. Unpriced* ATS/ED (B78-06266)
Fink, Siegfried. Studien für Drum Set = Studies for drum set
Heft 2 = Vol.2: Mittelstufe = Intermediate. *Simrock. Unpriced* XQ/AF (B78-51363)
Finney, Ross Lee. Variations on a theme by Alban Berg : piano solo. *Henmar Press : Peters : Peters. Unpriced* QP/T (B78-50215)
First American Music Conference held at Keele University, England, Friday, April 18-21, 1975. (American Music Conference, *1st, University of Keele, 1975*). *Keele, Staffs. ST5 5BG : University of Keele, Department of Music. Unpriced* A(YT) (B78-30830)
First book of Irish ballads. Revised ed. *4 Bridge St., Cork : Mercier Press. £1.50* AKDW/K/G(YDM) (B78-37867) ISBN 0-85342-080-7
First book of treble recorder solos. *Faber Music. Unpriced* VSSPK/AAY (B78-51261)
First guitar pieces. (Garcia, Gerald). *Holley Music. Unpriced* TSPMJ (B78-51154)
First ideas. Ramsbottom, Edward. Sounds and music. *Macmillan. £0.48* A (B78-18538) ISBN 0-333-23169-4
Fischer-Dieskau, Dietrich. Wagner and Nietzsche. *Sidgwick and Jackson. £7.50* BWC(Z) (B78-39782) ISBN 0-283-98434-1
Fiske, Roger.
Requiem, Op.48. (Fauré, Gabriel). *Eulenburg. Unpriced* EMDGKAV (B78-50031)
Thomas and Sally : dramatic pastoral in two acts. (Arne, Thomas Augustine). *Eulenburg. Unpriced* CQC (B78-50329)
Thomas and Sally. *Vocal score.* Thomas and Sally : a dramatic pastoral in two acts. (Arne, Thomas Augustine). *Schott. Unpriced* CC (B78-50323)
Trio, flute, cello & piano, J. 259, G minor. Trio for flute, cello and piano in G minor, J.259. (Weber, Carl Maria von, *Freiherr*). *Eulenburg. Unpriced* NURNT (B78-50198)
Fitzenhagen, Wilhelm Carl Friedrich. Ave Maria. Op.42. *arr.* Ave Maria : for four double basses. *Yorke. Unpriced* SSNSK (B78-51124)
Fitzgerald, Edward. Symphony no.24, 'Majnun'. Letters in the sand. *arr.* Letters in the sand : SATB with trumpet solo and piano. (Hovhaness, Alan). *Associated Music. £0.35* EWSPDW (B78-50361)
Five canzonas for four instruments SATB. (Maschera, Florentio). *London Pro Musica. Unpriced* LNS (B78-50482)
Five Chinese songs, op.78 : for medium voice and piano. (Berkeley, *Sir* Lennox). *Chester Music. Unpriced* KFVDW (B78-50902)
Five greatest symphonies : for piano, two hands. *Ashley Phoenix. Unpriced* QPK/AE/AY (B78-51024)
Five Klee pictures. (Davies, Peter Maxwell). *Boosey and Hawkes. Unpriced* MJ (B78-50179)
Five sketches : for guitar and violin. (Brindle, Reginald Smith). *Schott. £0.70* SPLTS (B78-51102)
Five times of day : clarinet and piano. (Garland, Neil). *Emerson. £1.50* VVPJ (B78-50662)
Five traditional songs. *Oxford University Press. Unpriced* EZDW/AYC (B78-50800) ISBN 0-19-343717-1
Flanders, Michael. Ein Walzertraum. *Vocal score.* A waltz dream : operetta in three acts. (Straus, Oscar). *Weinberger. Unpriced* CF (B78-50326)
Flauto traverso. Giuliani, Mauro. Duetto concertante, flute & guitar, op.52. Gran duetto concertante, op.52 : für Flöte (Violine) und Gitarre. *Schott. £4.80* VRPLTSF (B78-50294)
Flecker and Delius : the making of 'Hassan'. (Redwood, Dawn). *14 Barlby Rd, W10 6AR : Thames Publishing. £5.50* BDL/JM (B78-29853) ISBN 0-905210-06-9
Fletcher, John.
Jillian of Berry : four part song for male voices T.T.B.B. (Pasfield, William Reginald). *Edwin Ashdown. £0.20* GEZDW (B78-50829)
Sleep = Cswg : for two-part choir and piano. (Hughes-Jones, Llifon). *Roberton. £0.20* FDW (B78-50815)
Flint, Berni. Berni Flint songbook. *Chappell. Unpriced* KDW/GB/AY (B78-50144)
Floraison : for horn and piano. (McCabe, John). *Novello. £1.65* WTPJ (B78-51353)
Flute duets
Vol.1: Thirty duets by Devienne, Berbiguier, Boismortier, Loeillet, Naudot, Tulou, Kohler and Mozart. (Wye, Trevor). *Chester Music. Unpriced* VRNU/AY (B78-51205)
Vol.2. *Chester Music. Unpriced* VRNU/AY (B78-51204)
Vol.3: Six easy duos for two flutes. *Chester Music. Unpriced* VRNU (B78-51203)
Flute solos with piano accompaniment
Vol.3. *Chester Music. Unpriced* VRPK/AAY (B78-51220)
Folk ballads of the English-speaking world. The Penguin book of folk ballads of the English-speaking world. *Penguin. £1.75* AKDW/K/G (B78-08525) ISBN 0-14-004241-5
Folk music and dances in Ireland. (Breathnach, Breandán). Revised ed. *25 Lower Abbey St., Dublin 1 : Mercier Press Ltd. £2.10* A/G(YDM) (B78-34736) ISBN 0-85342-509-4
Folk music in school. *Cambridge University Press. £4.95* A/G(VF) (B78-29835) ISBN 0-521-21595-1
Folk news
Vol.1, no.1- ; June 1977-. *28 Gordon Mansions, Torrington Place, WC1E 7HF : Folk News Publications. £0.20* A/G(B) (B78-00387)
Folkestone fiery serpent, and other Kentish poems : a selection. *Springfield, Maidstone, Kent : Kent County Library. £0.50* AKDW/G(YDCM) (B78-11199) ISBN 0-905155-13-0
Follow my leader : ten songs with percussion accompaniments for young singers and players. *Oxford University Press. Unpriced* JFE/XNDW (B78-50106) ISBN 0-19-330364-7
For joy that we are here : Rural Music Schools, 1929-1950. (Ibberson, Mary). *Bedford Square Press for the Rural Music Schools Association. £2.75* A(V/YD/XN31) (B78-03572) ISBN 0-7199-0930-9
Forbes, Watson.
Classical and romantic pieces
Book 1. *Oxford University Press. Unpriced* VRP/AY (B78-51208) ISBN 0-19-356538-2
Book 2. *Oxford University Press. Unpriced* VRP/AY (B78-51209) ISBN 0-19-356539-0
Foreman, Lewis. Edmund Rubbra : composer-essays. *22 Pheasant Way, Rickmansworth, Herts. : Triad Press. £9.95 : CIP rev.* BRU (B77-18309) ISBN 0-902070-21-5
Foreman, Ronald Lewis Edmund. *See* Foreman, Lewis.
Forte, Allen.
The harmonic organization of 'The rite of spring'. *Yale University Press. £10.80* BSVAMM/HM/R (B78-38605) ISBN 0-300-02201-8
The structure of atonal music. *Yale University Press. £4.50* A/PN (B78-24451) ISBN 0-300-02120-8
Fortner, Wolfgang.
Amicizia! : Quintett für Klarinette in A, Posaune, Violoncello, Schlagzeug und Klavier (1976). (Henze, Hans Werner). *Schott. £4.65* RXMK/AHW (B78-50247)
That time. *Schott. £12.00* JNDE/NXNT (B78-50109)
Valses nobles, D.969. *Selections: arr.* Valses nobles, opus 77. (Schubert, Franz). *Schott. £4.65* RXMK/AHW (B78-50248)
Forty songs for the class plus ten for the choir : a song book for primary children. *Schofield and Sims. Unpriced* JFE/TSDW/G/AY (B78-50853) ISBN 0-7217-2528-7
Forty songs for the class plus ten for the choir : a song book for primary children. *Schofield and Sims. Unpriced* JFDW/AY (B78-50844) ISBN 0-7217-2529-5
Foss, Peter. Édith Piaf. *Wise. £3.95* KDW/GB/AY (B78-50152) ISBN 0-86001-112-7
Four Australian songs. *Schott. Unpriced* VSNK/DW/AYX (B78-51241)
Four clock pieces. (Haydn, Joseph). *Novello. Unpriced* VVNTK/B/FJ (B78-51277)
Four dances (1611). (Peuerl, Paul). *Chester Music. Unpriced* WNSK/AH (B78-51340)
Four dances from the ballet ... (Bliss, *Sir* Arthur). *Novello. £4.85* WMK/HM (B78-51328)
Four epiphanies : for unaccompanied viola. (Schonthal, Ruth). *Oxford University Press. Unpriced* SQPMJ (B78-50262)
Four Irish folksongs : for 2 descant, treble and tenor recorders. *Chester Music. Unpriced* VSNSK/DW/AYDM (B78-51245)
Four miniatures : flute and piano. (Ferneyhough, Brian). *Peters. Unpriced* VRPJ (B78-50291)
Four nocturnes. (Night Music II) : violin and piano. (Crumb, George). *Peters. Unpriced* SPJ (B78-51099)
Four piano studies. (Berkeley, *Sir* Lennox). *Chester Music. Unpriced* QPJ (B78-51006)
Four pieces after the seasons : S.A.T.B. with instrumental accompaniment
1: Early May. (Nelson, Ron). *Boosey and Hawkes. £0.50* ENYLDW (B78-50035)
2: Wonder and wild honey. (Nelson, Ron). *Boosey and Hawkes. £0.40* ENYLDW (B78-50036)
3: Late September. (Nelson, Ron). *Boosey and Hawkes. £0.40* ENYLDW (B78-50037)
4: Winter journeyings. (Nelson, Ron). *Boosey and Hawkes. £0.40* ENYLDW (B78-50038)
Four pieces for flute and viola ... op.10. (Neubaur, Franz). *Schirmer. £2.50* VRPLSQ (B78-51229)
Four pieces for four cellos : Byrd, Tchaikovsky, Berlioz, Mozart. *Oxford University Press. Unpriced* SRNSK/AAY (B78-51112) ISBN 0-19-358850-1
Four poems of García Lorca : for solo guitar. (Brindle, Reginald Smith). *Schott. Unpriced* TSPMJ (B78-50615)
Four romantic pieces : for violin and piano. (Dvořák,

Antonín). *Schirmer. £2.10* SPJ (B78-50589)
Four shanties : for guitar. (Regan, Michael). *Schott. £0.70* TSPMJ (B78-51158)
Four songs from 'Rosina'. (Shield, William). *Boosey and Hawkes. Unpriced* KFTDW (B78-50901)
Four unaccompanied part-songs. Opus.53 : for SATB with divisions. (Elgar, *Sir* Edward, *bart*). *Novello. £1.10* EZDW (B78-50796)
Fowler, Frederick. The school recorder assembly book for pupils. *E.J. Arnold. Unpriced* VSRPMK/AAY (B78-51257) ISBN 0-560-00379-x
Fowler, G. Bell ringing, minimus : three and four bell methods. (Lewis, Harold). *36 Great Clarendon St., Oxford : J. Hannon and Co. £1.50* AXSR/E (B78-17617)
Fox, Charles.
Happy days. *arr.* Happy days : from the Paramount TV series 'Happy days'. *Warner : Blossom. Unpriced* UMMK/DW/JS (B78-50638)
One on one. *Selections: arr.* Songs from 'One on one' : a Warner Bros. film. *Warner : Blossom. Unpriced* KDW/JR (B78-50166)
Fox Cumming, Ray. Stevie Wonder. *44 Hill St., W1X 8LB : Mandabrook Books. £0.60* AKDW/HKR/E(P) (B78-50321) ISBN 0-427-00418-7
Fragment für Orgel, 1975. (Yun, Isang). *Bote und Bock Associated Music. £2.40* RJ (B78-50569)
Françaix, Jean. Quasi improvvisando : pour ensemble à vent = für Bläserenseble. *Schott. £6.00* UMJ (B78-51174)
Francis, John.
Don Giovanni. Deh vieni alla finestra. *arr.* Canzonetta. (Mozart, Wolfgang Amadeus). *Lengnick. £0.60* VRPK/DW (B78-51224)
Drei Albumblätter, no.1. Albumblatt. (Busoni, Ferruccio). *Lengnick. £0.60* VRPK (B78-51219)
Piramo e Tisbe. Tambourin. *arr.* Tambourin. (Hasse, Johann Adolf). *Lengnick. £0.60* VRPK/AHVQT (B78-51222)
Die Zauberflöte. Wie stark ist nicht dein Zauberton. *arr.* Andante. (Mozart, Wolfgang Amadeus). *Lengnick. Unpriced* VRPK/DW (B78-51225)
Francis and Day's community book of music hall songs
No.1. *EMI Music. Unpriced* JDW/JV/AY (B78-50083)
No.2. *EMI Music. Unpriced* JDW/JV/AY (B78-50084)
Frank, Alan. Sinatra. *Hamlyn. £4.50* AKDW/GB/E(P) (B78-37100) ISBN 0-600-38317-2
Franklin, Adele. We piano teachers. (Booth, Victor). Revised ed.. *Hutchinson. £2.95* AQ/E(VC) (B78-40354) ISBN 0-09-106191-1
Franz Schubert Lieder
Heft 3: Lieder nach Texten von Goethe, für mittlere Stimme. (Schubert, Franz). *Bärenreiter. £4.80* KFVDW (B78-50903)
Fraser, Shena. Cotton : unison song with optional descant and piano music. *Roberton. £0.12* JFDW (B78-50091)
Frazer, Alan.
3 Schubert dances. (Schubert, Franz). *7 Garrick St., W.C.2 : Middle Eight Music. Unpriced* VNSK/AH (B78-50287)
Theme from Z Cars ('Johnny Todd') : traditional. *7 Garrick St., W.C.2 : Middle Eight Music. Unpriced* MK/DW (B78-50916)
Theme from Z Cars ('Johnny Todd') : traditional. (Frazer, Alan). *7 Garrick St., W.C.2 : Middle Eight Music. Unpriced* MK/DW (B78-50916)
Freedland, Michael.
Jerome Kern. *Robson. £4.50 : CIP rev.* BKDN(N) (B78-20441) ISBN 0-86051-011-5
Sophie : the Sophie Tucker story. *Woburn Press. £6.50* AKDW/GB/E(P) (B78-05406) ISBN 0-7130-0153-4
French, Percy.
Percy French and his songs. (Healy, James N). *25 Lower Abbey St., Dublin 1 : Mercier Press. £1.70* BFUR(N) (B78-33936) ISBN 0-85342-394-6
Phil the fluter's ball. *arr.* Phil the fluter's ball. *Polyphonic Reproductions : Studio Music. Unpriced* WMK/DW (B78-50682)
French baroque music : from Beaujoyeulx to Rameau. (Anthony, James R). Revised ed. *Batsford. £12.50* A(YH/XDZA153) (B78-26886) ISBN 0-7134-1076-0
French horn : some notes on the evolution of the instrument and of its technique. (Morley-Pegge, Reginald). 2nd ed. *E. Benn etc.. £7.50* AWT/B
French's musical library.
Bimonte, Richard. Yankee ingenuity : a musical. French's acting ed. *French. £1.65* BWNTSACM (B78-12987) ISBN 0-573-68082-5
Frow, Gerald. The Mermaid's 'Cowardy custard' : an entertainment. *French. £1.80* BCMWACM (B78-21400) ISBN 0-573-68079-5
Patrick, John, *b.1907.* Noah's animals : a musical allegory in three acts. *French. £1.65* BPECACM (B78-02612) ISBN 0-573-68078-7
Frescobaldi, Girolamo.
Il primo libro delle canzoni a una, due, tre e quattro voci. *Selections.* Three canzonas for two treble, one bass instrument and continuo. *London Pro Musica Edition. Unpriced* LNSPW (B78-50483)
Recercari et canzoni francese. Libro primo. *Selections ; arr.* Ricercar et canzoni. *Novello. £1.30* MRK (B78-50196)
Frets and fingers : a guitar player's manual. (Pearse, John). *Paddington Press. £4.95* ATS/E (B78-34741) ISBN 0-7092-0625-9
Friedman, Albert Barron. The Penguin book of folk ballads of the English-speaking world. *Penguin. £1.75* AKDW/K/G (B78-08525) ISBN 0-14-004241-5
Frith, Simon. The sociology of rock. *Constable. £7.50* AKDW/HKR(Z) (B78-31211) ISBN 0-09-460220-4
Fröhliche Weihnachtszeit : eine Folge volkstümlicher Weihnachtslieder für Männerchor und Klavier oder a cappella. (Goedecke, Werner). *Schott. £4.40* GDP/LF (B78-50070)
Frow, Gerald. The Mermaid's 'Cowardy custard' : an entertainment. *French. £1.80* BCMWACM (B78-21400) ISBN 0-573-68079-5
Fry, Christopher. Sinfonia fidei. *Vocal score.* Sinfonia fidei : a cantata for soprano and tenor soloists, chorus and orchestra. (Hoddinott, Alan). *Oxford University Press. Unpriced* DE (B78-50716) ISBN 0-19-336842-0
Fucile ad ago. *arr.* Il fucile ad ago : revista de 1866. (Gomes, Antonio Carlos). *Arthur Napoleão : Essex Music. Unpriced* QPK (B78-50549)
Fucile ad ago : revista de 1866. (Gomes, Antonio Carlos). *Arthur Napoleão : Essex Music. Unpriced* QPK (B78-50549)
Fuenllana, Miguel de. Libro de musica para vihuela, intitulado Orphenica lyra. Orphenica lyra (Seville 1554). *Clarendon Press. £30.00* TVPMJ (B78-50625)
Fun music : for all organ
Vol.1. *Chappell. Unpriced* RK/DW/GB/AY (B78-50237)
Vol.2. *Chappell. Unpriced* RK/DW/GB/AY (B78-50238)
Fun music : for chord organ
Vol.1. *Chappell. Unpriced* RPVCK/DW/GB/AY (B78-50240)
Vol.2. *Chappell. Unpriced* RPVCK/DW/GB/AY (B78-50241)
Fun music : for piano
Vol.1. *Chappell. Unpriced* QPK/DW/GB/AY (B78-50226)
Vol.2. *Chappell. Unpriced* QPK/DW/GB/AY (B78-50227)
Fun on the piano : for very young music makers to start learning the happy way
Initial Book A. (Bailey, Freda O). *Regina Music. Unpriced* QPJ (B78-51004)
Fun organ : arrangements featuring automatic rhythm and accompaniment for all electronic and 'C' chord organs
Folio no.2 ; arranged by Jack Moore. *EMI. Unpriced* RPVK/AAY (B78-51060)
Fundação Calouste Gulbenkian. *See* Calouste Gulbenkian Foundation.
Fundação Gulbenkian. *See* Calouste Gulbenkian Foundation.
Fünf Details. 5 Details : für Klavier (1975). (Brandmüller, Theo). *Bote und Bock : Associated Music. Unpriced* QPJ (B78-50527)
Funniest man on earth : the story of Dan Leno. (Brandreth, Gyles). *Hamilton. £4.50* AKDW/JV/E(P) (B78-01692) ISBN 0-241-89810-2
Funny family : songs, rhymes and games for children. *Ward Lock. £3.95* JFDW/GJ/AY (B78-50847) ISBN 0-7062-3719-6
Fussell, Charles. Three processionals : for orchestra. *Schirmer. £5.45* MMJ (B78-50490)
G. Schirmer's collection of opera librettos. Royer, Alphonse. La favorita : drama in four acts. *140 Strand, WC2R 1HH : G. Schirmer. Unpriced* BDRAC (B78-26887)
Gabrieli, Giovanni. Sacrae symphoniae. Bk.1. Sonata pian'e forte. Sonata pian'e forte : for brass octet. *Chester Music. Unpriced* WNNE (B78-51333)
Gabrielli, Domenico.
Sonata, trumpet, string quartet & continuo, D major. Sonata, D.XI, 5 in D for trumpet, strings and basso continuo. *Musica rara. Unpriced* NUXSNQE (B78-50945)
Sonata, trumpet, string quartet & continuo, D major. *arr.* Sonata D. XI.5 in D for trumpet, strings and basso continuo. *Musica rara. Unpriced* WSPK/AE (B78-51345)
Sonata, trumpet, string quintet & continuo, D major. Sonata, D. XI, 4 in D for trumpet, strings and basso continuo. *Musica rara. Unpriced* NUXSNPE (B78-50944)
Sonata, trumpet, string quintet & continuo, D major. *arr.* Sonata D, XI, 4 in D for trumpet, strings and basso continuo. *Musica rara. Unpriced* WSPK/AE (B78-51346)
Gadsby, David.
Merrily to Bethlehem : a very unusual carol book. *A. and C. Black. Unpriced* JFE/LNDP/LF/AY (B78-50850) ISBN 0-7136-1887-6
Ta-ra-ra boom-de-ay : songs for everyone. *A. and C. Black. Unpriced* JFADW/AY (B78-50837) ISBN 0-7136-1790-x
Gagliano, Marco da. La Dafne. *Vocal score.* La Dafne. *Cathedral Music. Unpriced* CC (B78-50325)
Gál, Hans. The musician's world : letters of the great composers. *Thames and Hudson. £2.95* A/D(M) (B78-35467) ISBN 0-500-27130-5
Galician carol, Panxoliña sic de Nadal : for four-part chorus of mixed voices unaccompanied. (Wilkinson, Stephen). *Roberton. £0.18* EZDP/LF (B78-50048)
Gallagher, Benny.
Breakaway. *arr.* Breakaway. *Wise : Music Sales. Unpriced* KDW/GB (B78-50129) ISBN 0-86001-278-6
Showdown and other songs. *Rondor Music : Music Sales. Unpriced* KDW/GB (B78-50128)
Gallo, Armando. Genesis : the evolution of a rock band. *Sidgwick and Jackson. £7.50* AKDW/HKR/E(P) (B78-25373) ISBN 0-283-98439-2
Galloway, Malcolm. Recorder tutor : for descant recorders. *Regina Music. Unpriced* VSR/AC (B78-51254)
Galper, Avrahm. Clarinet scales and arpeggios. *Boosey and Hawkes. Unpriced* VV/AF (B78-51274)
Garcia, Gerald. First guitar pieces. *Holley Music. Unpriced* TSPMJ (B78-51154)
Gardner, John.
Bel and the dragon. Op.120. *Chorus score.* Bel and the dragon, opus 120. *Oxford University Press. Unpriced* FACN (B78-50804) ISBN 0-19-336205-8
Bel and the dragon. Op.120. *Vocal score.* Bel and the dragon : an opera for children. *Oxford University Press. Unpriced* CN (B78-50709) ISBN 0-19-336202-3
Sonata da chiesa sopra un tema di Claudio Monteverdi. *Oxford University Press. Unpriced* WSNTR (B78-51343) ISBN 0-19-356713-x
Sunny bank carol : S.A.T.B. (unacc.), opus 141. *Oxford University Press. Unpriced* EZDP/LF (B78-50785) ISBN 0-19-343063-0
Garland, Neil. Five times of day : clarinet and piano. *Emerson. £1.50* VVPJ (B78-50662)
Garland reference library of the humanities. Gooch, Bryan N S. Musical settings of late Victorian and modern British literature : a catalogue. *2 Holly Bush Hill, NW3 6SH : Garland Publishing, Inc. £55.35* AKDW(XKK101/T) (B78-14028) ISBN 0-8240-9981-8
Garon, Paul. Blues & the poetic spirit. *Eddison Press. £3.50* AKDW/HHW (B78-30829) ISBN 0-85649-018-0
Garoto. 15 choros. *Fermata do Brasil : Essex Music. Unpriced* QPJ (B78-50530)
Garten, Hugh Frederic. Wagner the dramatist. *J. Calder. £5.95* BWCAC (B78-09113) ISBN 0-7145-3620-2
Gartenberg, Egon. Mahler : the man and his music. *Cassell. £8.95* BME(N) (B78-25369) ISBN 0-304-30058-6
Gather ye rosebuds : for four-part chorus of mixed voices a cappella. (Dinerstein, Norman). *Schirmer. Unpriced* EZDW (B78-50052)
Gaudium : concert piece for wind symphony orchestra. (Sparke, Philip). *Boosey and Hawkes. Unpriced* UMMJ (B78-51183)
Gavotte for a Latin lady : for violin and piano. (Nieman, Alfred). *Roberton. £0.50* SPHM (B78-50259)
Gay, Bram. Edinburgh dances. (Kelly, Bryan). *Novello. £4.50* WMH (B78-51306)
Gegus, Erno. Spektralanalytische Untersuchung der Bestandteile der Orgel von Aquincum. Die römische Orgel von Aquincum (3. Jahrhundert). (Kaba, Melinda). *Bärenreiter. £11.20* AR/B(YGB/XBH) (B78-03580)
Geiger, George. I believe in God : a sacred song. *Lewis Music : Phoenix. Unpriced* KDH (B78-50111)
Geiringer, Karl. Instruments in the history of Western music. 3rd (revised and enlarged) ed. *Allen and Unwin. £10.50* AL/B(X) (B78-37097) ISBN 0-04-781005-x
Gelatt, Roland. The fabulous phonograph, 1877-1977. 2nd revised ed. *Cassell. £6.50* A/FD(XKS101) (B78-03423) ISBN 0-304-29904-9
Gellhorn, Peter. Mozart's 'Don Giovanni'. (Abert, Hermann). *48 Great Marlborough St., W1V 2BN : Eulenburg Books. £3.00* BMSAC (B78-11196) ISBN 0-903873-19-2
Gending. (Burgon, Geoffrey). *Chester Music. Unpriced* UMJ (B78-51173)
Genesis. Genesis. *Chappell. Unpriced* KDW/HKR (B78-50459)
Genesis. (Genesis). *Chappell. Unpriced* KDW/HKR (B78-50459)
Genesis : the evolution of a rock band. (Gallo, Armando). *Sidgwick and Jackson. £7.50* AKDW/HKR/E(P) (B78-25373) ISBN 0-283-98439-2
Genin, P A. Le carnival de Venice. Op.14. Carnival of Venice : for flute and piano. *Chester Music. Unpriced* VRP/T (B78-51210)
Gentle on my mind. (Hartford, John). *Warner : Blossom. Unpriced* UMMK/DW (B78-50634)
Gentle on my mind. *arr.* Gentle on my mind. (Hartford, John). *Warner : Blossom. Unpriced* UMMK/DW (B78-50634)
Gentle spirit : an opera in one act for soprano, tenor and chamber orchestra. (Tavener, John). *Chester Music. Unpriced* CQC (B78-50711)
Genzmer, Harald. Miniaturen : für Streicher. *Litolff : Peters. Unpriced* RXMJ (B78-50576)
George, Thom Ritter. Would I might go far over sea : for four-part chorus of mixed voices a cappella. *Chappell. Unpriced* EZDW (B78-50387)
Gershwin, George. Porgy and Bess. *Selections : arr.* Porgy and Bess. *Chappell. Unpriced* KDW (B78-50442)
Gershwin, Ira. Porgy and Bess. *Selections : arr.* Porgy and Bess. (Gershwin, George). *Chappell. Unpriced* KDW (B78-50442)
'Getting together' : a collection devised for the junior and middle school. (Wade, Darrell). *16 Anchor Way, Danes Green, Gnosall : Viking. Unpriced* NYDS (B78-50208)
Gibson, Gerald D. Bibliography of discographies
Vol.1: Classical music, 1925-1975. (Gray, Michael H). *Bowker. £15.00* A/FD(WT/T) (B78-09309) ISBN 0-8352-1023-5
Gibson guitar from 1950. (Bishop, Ian Courtney). *20 Denmark St., WC2H 8NE : Musical New Services Ltd. Unpriced* ATS/B
Giefer, Willy. Concerto, cello, op.3, E flat major. *arr.* Konzert für Violoncello und Orchester in Es-Dur, Opus 3 (1915). (Hindemith, Paul). *Schott. £20.00* SRPK/LF (B78-51118)
Giesen, Walter. Zur Geschichte des buddhistischen Ritualgesangs in Japan : Traktate des 9. bis 14. Jahrhunderts zum shomyo der Tendai-Sekte. *32 Gt Titchfield St., W1P 7AD : Bärenreiter. £12.60* BZHPADGVF (B78-35473)
Gift of December : for four-part chorus of men's voices and baritone solo with piano accompaniment. (Gump, Richard). *Schirmer. Unpriced* GDH/LF (B78-50068)
Gift of December : for four-part chorus of men's voices and baritone solo with piano accompaniment. (Gump, Richard). *Schirmer. Unpriced* GDH/LF (B78-50069)
Gilder, Eric.

The dictionary of composers and their music : every listener's companion arranged chronologically and alphabetically. *Paddington Press. £6.95* A/D(M/C) (B78-26881) ISBN 0-448-22364-3
Potty pantomime. (Crocker, John, *b.1925*). *Evans Bros. £0.40* BCQRACPP (B78-37098) ISBN 0-237-75031-7
Giles, Andrew.
Motecta. Ave Maria. Ave Maria. In Annuntiationis B. Maria Virginis,. (Victoria, Tomás Luis de). *36 Ranelagh Gdns. W.6 : Cathedral Music. Unpriced* EZDJ (B78-50377)
Motecta. Doctor bonus. Doctor bonus. In festo sancti Andreae. (Victoria, Tomás Luis de). *Cathedral Music. Unpriced* EZDJ (B78-50378)
Giles Farnaby suite. (Farnaby, Giles). *Oxford University Press. Unpriced* UMMK (B78-50283)
Gill, Donald. Gut-strung plucked instruments contemporary with the lute. *c/o The Administrator, 71 Priory Rd, Kew Gardens, Richmond, Surrey TW9 3DH : Lute Society. Unpriced* AT/B(XCSK301) (B78-01683)
Gillespie, John. Nineteenth-century American piano music. *Dover Publications : Constable. Unpriced* QP/AYT (B78-50988) ISBN 0-486-23602-1
Gillies, Douglas. Follow my leader : ten songs with percussion accompaniments for young singers and players. *Oxford University Press. Unpriced* JFE/XNDW (B78-50106) ISBN 0-19-330364-7
Gipsy wedding. (Siebert, Edrich). *Harmer Music : Studio Music. Unpriced* WMH (B78-50676)
Girdlestone, Cuthbert Morton. Mozart's piano concertos. 3rd ed. *Cassell. £6.50* BMSAMPQF (B78-22846) ISBN 0-304-30043-8
Gitarren-Archiv.
Drei spanische Solostücke = Three Spanish solo pieces = Trois morceaux espagnoles : for guitar. *Schott. £2.40* TSPMK/AYK (B78-50277)
Haydn, Joseph. Duet, barytones (2), Hob XII/4, G major. *arr.* Duett in G nach dem Original für 2 Barytone, Hob XII, 4. *Schott. £4.00* TSNUK (B78-50270)
Mendelssohn, Felix. Lieder ohne Worte. *Selections: arr.* 6 Lieder ohne Worte. *Schott. £4.80* TSPMK (B78-50275)
Sor, Fernando. Sonata, guitar, op.22, C major. *Selections.* Menuett und Rondo : für Gitarre. Revidierte Neuausgabe. *Schott. £3.20* TSPMJ (B78-50273)
Tarrega, Francisco. Zwei spanische Stücke = Two Spanish pieces = Deux pièces espagnoles : für Gitarre ... Revidierte Neuausgabe. *Schott. £3.20* TSPMH (B78-50271)
Weiss, Sylvias Leopold. Zwei Menuette = Two minuets. *Schott. £2.00* TSPMK/AHR (B78-51166)
Weiss, Sylvius Leopold. Duet, lute. *arr.* Duett für Gitarren = Duet for guitars. *Schott. £2.00* TSNU (B78-51146)
Zehm, Friedrich. Serenade für Flöte und Gitarre. *Schott. £6.00* VRPLTS (B78-50293)
Gitler, Ira. The encyclopedia of jazz in the seventies. (Feather, Leonard). *Quartet Books. £9.95* AMT(XR9/C) (B78-26894) ISBN 0-7043-2175-0
Giuliani, Mauro.
Duetto concertante, flute & guitar, op.52. Gran duetto concertante, op.52 : für Flöte (Violine) und Gitarre. *Schott. £4.80* VRPLTSF (B78-50294)
Overture, guitar, op.61. Grande ouverture for solo guitar, op.61. *Faber Music. £2.00* TSPMJ (B78-51155)
Six airs irlandois nationales variées, Op.125. *Belwin Mills Music. £1.50* TSPM/T (B78-51147)
Sonata, guitar, op.15, C major. Sonata in C major, opus 15. *Ariel : Music Sales. £1.95* TSPME (B78-51148) ISBN 0-86001-377-4
Twenty-five etudes. *Ariel : Music Sales. £1.95* TSPMJ (B78-51156) ISBN 0-86001-372-3
Gladiolus rag. (Joplin, Scott). *R. Smith. Unpriced* WMK/AHXJ (B78-51322)
Glass, Paul. Premieres leçons de piano. *Selections.* Six pieces in the early grades. (Lambert, Sydney). *Associated Music. £1.20* QPJ (B78-50536)
Globokar, Vinko.
Airs de voyages vers l'interieur : für acht Stimmen, Klarinette, Posaune und Elektronik. *Litolff : Peters. Unpriced* JNAYE/VVPLWTDX (B78-50857)
Vendre le vent : für einen Pianisten, einen Schlagzeuger und neun Bläser. *Litolff : Peters. Unpriced* UMPQ (B78-51190)
Glover, Jane. Cavalli. *Batsford. £8.50* BCBX(N) (B78-26885) ISBN 0-7134-1007-8
Glowatzki, Manfred.
Musae Sioniae. Tl.2. *Selections.* Weihnachtskonzerte : für zwei vierstimmige Chöre. (Praetorius, Michael). *Bärenreiter. £2.24* EWNDH/LF (B78-50360)
Musae Sioniae. Tl.2. *Selections.* Weihnachtskonzerte : für zwei vierstimmige Chöre. (Praetorius, Michael). *Bärenreiter. £1.96* EZDH/LF (B78-50374)
God is gone up with a merry noise : full anthem with verse for SSAATB. (Croft, William). *Novello. £0.43* DK (B78-50343)
Godard, Benjamin. Suite de trois morçeaux : for flute and piano, op.116. *Chester Music. Unpriced* VRPJ (B78-51217)
Goddard, Arthur. A selection of musical instruments to make for children. *Trident House, Brooks Mews, W1Y 2PN : Trident Television Ltd. £0.25* AX/BC (B78-05413)
Goddess trilogy. 3 : Shapeshifter. Shapeshifter : for horn and piano. (McCabe, John). *Novello. £1.80* WTPJ (B78-51351)
Goddess triology. 1 : The castle of Arianrhod. The castle of Arianrhod : for horn and piano. (McCabe, John). *Novello. £2.75* WTPJ (B78-51352)
Goddess triology. 2 : Floraison. Floraison : for horn and piano. (McCabe, John). *Novello. £1.65* WTPJ (B78-51353)
Godefroy, Vincent. The dramatic genius of Verdi : studies of selected operas
Vol.2. *Gollancz. £7.50* BVEAC (B78-02610) ISBN 0-575-02166-7
Godfather. *Selections : arr.* Themes from The godfather and The godfather, part II. (Rota, Nino). *Warner : Blossom. Unpriced* UMMK/JR (B78-50639)
Goedecke, Werner. Fröhliche Weihnachtszeit : eine Folge volkstümlicher Weihnachtslieder für Männerchor und Klavier oder a cappella. *Schott. £4.40* GDP/LF (B78-50070)
Goehr, Alexander. Musical ideas and ideas about music. *Birkbeck College. £0.25* A (B78-32354)
Goethe, Johann Wolfgang von. Franz Schubert Lieder
Heft 3: Lieder nach Texten von Goethe, für mittlere Stimme. (Schubert, Franz). *Bärenreiter. £4.80* KFVDW (B78-50903)
Going for the one. (Yes). *Warner : Blossom. Unpriced* KDW/HKR (B78-50165)
Going for the one. *arr.* Going for the one. (Yes). *Warner Blossom. Unpriced* KDW/HKR (B78-50165)
Golby, Ivor. Merrily to Bethlehem : a very unusual carol book. *A. and C. Black. Unpriced* JFE/LNDP/LF/AY (B78-50850) ISBN 0-7136-1887-6
Goldberg's dream. (Burgon, Geoffrey). *Chester Music. Unpriced* MM/HM (B78-50917)
Golden greats. *EMI Music. Unpriced* KDW/GB/AY (B78-50153)
Golden Latin : all organ. *Chappell. Unpriced* RPVK/DW/GB/AY (B78-51064)
Goldstein, Michael. Concerto, viola, op.2, no.1, E flat major. *arr.* Konzert Es-dur für Viola und Orchester = Concerto E-flat major for viola and orchestra. (Reicha, Joseph). *Simrock. £5.50* SQPK/LF (B78-50596)
Golland, John.
Bandkraft
1. *Forsyth. Unpriced* WM/AY (B78-51295)
2. *Forsyth. Unpriced* WM/AY (B78-51296)
3. *Forsyth. Unpriced* WM/AY (B78-51297)
Gomes, Antonio Carlos.
Il fucile ad ago. *arr.* Il fucile ad ago : revista de 1866. *Arthur Napoleão : Essex Music. Unpriced* QPK (B78-50549)
Variaç ões. *arr.* Variaç ês. *Arthur Napoleão : Essex Music. Unpriced* QPK (B78-50550)
Gooch, Bryan N S. Musical settings of late Victorian and modern British literature : a catalogue. *2 Holly Bush Hill, NW3 6SH : Garland Publishing, Inc. £55.35* AKDW(XKK101/T) (B78-14028) ISBN 0-8240-9981-8
Goodbye.
Elvis Presley - 1935-1977 : a tribute to the king
1. *2 Engine La., Wednesbury, W. Midlands : 'Bavie' Publications. £3.00* AKDW/HK/E(P) (B78-12098)
2. *2 Engine La., Wednesbury, W. Midlands : 'Bavie' Publications. £3.00* AKDW/HK/E(P) (B78-12099)
3. *2 Engine La., Wednesbury, W. Midlands : 'Bavie' Publications. £3.00* AKDW/HK/E(P) (B78-06988)
4. *2 Engine La., Wednesbury, W. Midlands : 'Bavie' Publications. £3.00* AKDW/HK/E(P) (B78-12100)
5. *2 Engine La., Wednesbury, W. Midlands : 'Bavie' Publications. £3.00* AKDW/HK/E(P) (B78-12101)
Goodyear, Stephen F. The recorder. *Teach Yourself Books. £1.25 : CIP rev.* AVS/E (B78-25376) ISBN 0-340-22247-6
Goran, Ulf. Accompniment guide for guitar. *Oxford University Press. Unpriced* TS/ED (B78-51144) ISBN 0-19-322213-2
Gordon, Christopher. A Mozart suite. (Mozart, Wolfgang Amadeus). *Janus Music. Unpriced* VSNS (B78-51244)
Gordon, Jennie. Detholiad y babanod. *Gwasg Gomer. Unpriced* JFEZDW/GJ/AY (B78-50855)
Gossec, François Joseph.
Le camp de Grand-Pré. Tambourin. *arr.* Tambourin. *Bosworth and Co. Unpriced* QPK/AHVQT (B78-51027)
Le camp de Grand-Pré. Tambourin. *arr.* Tambourin : solo for B flat cornet. *Studio Music. Unpriced* WMPWRK/AHVQT (B78-51329)
Gottlieb, Jack. Haiku souvenirs : for voice and piano. *Amberson : Boosey and Hawkes : Boosey and Hawkes. Unpriced* KDW (B78-50861)
Gottlieb, Jacob. Hakol kol Yaacov = The voice is the voice of Jacob : compositions for cantor and choir. Limited ed. *18 Station Tce, N.W.10 : Sinai Publishing House. Unpriced* DGU (B78-50724) ISBN 0-9506345-0-6
Gounod, Charles.
Faust. Ah! je ris. *arr.* Jewel song ... *Leonard, Gould and Bolttler. Unpriced* KDW (B78-50115)
Faust. Avant de quitter ces lieux. *arr.* Cavatina 'Avant de quitter ces lieux'. *Leonard, Gould & Bolttler. Unpriced* KDW (B78-50443)
Grabe. Parthia, viola d'amore, gamba & harpsichord, C minor. Parthia in C minor for viola d'amore, gamba & harpsichord. *Little Margaret, Penmans Green, Chipperfield : Ian White. Unpriced* NXNTG (B78-50508)
Graded wind music series.
Associated Board of the Royal Schools of Music. New pieces for clarinet : with piano accompaniment
Book 1: Grades 3 & 4. *Associated Board of the Royal Schools of Music. Unpriced* VVP/AY (B78-51279)
Associated Board of the Royal Schools of Music. New pieces for clarinet : with piano accompaniment
Book 1: Grades 3 & 4. *Associated Board of the Royal Schools of Music. Unpriced* VVP/AY (B78-51280)
Associated Board of the Royal Schools of Music. New pieces for clarinet : with piano accompaniment
Book 1: Grades 5 & 6. *Associated Board of the Royal Schools of Music. Unpriced* VVP/AY (B78-51281)
Associated Board of the Royal Schools of Music. New pieces for flute : with piano accompaniment
Book 1: Grades 3 & 4. *Associated Board of the Royal Schools of Music. Unpriced* VRP/AY (B78-51206)
Associated Board of the Royal Schools of Music. New pieces for oboe : with piano accompaniment
Book 1: Grades 3 & 4. *Associated Board of the Royal Schools of Music. Unpriced* VTP/AY (B78-51264)
Gradualia, lib.1. Ave verum corpus. *arr.* Ave verum corpus : for male voice choir unaccompanied. (Byrd, William). *Roberton. £0.20* GEZDJ (B78-50826)
Grainger (Percy) Society. *See* Percy Grainger Society.
Grainger journal
No.1- ; Spring 1978-. *c/o D. Tall, 21 Laburnum Ave., Kenilworth, Warks CV8 2DR : Percy Grainger Society. Unpriced* BGRT(B) (B78-37094)
Gran duetto 2 : for double basses. (Bottesini, Giovanni). *Yorke. Unpriced* SSNU (B78-51126)
Grant, Lawrence.
World's favorite popular classics for organ and other favorites
Vol.1. *Ashley : Phoenix. Unpriced* RK/AAY (B78-50234)
Vol.2 ; arranged by Lawrence Grant. *Ashley : Phoenix. Unpriced* RK/AAY (B78-50235)
Graves, Richard.
Cornish flower song : two-part song. *Bosworth and Co. Unpriced* FDW (B78-50814)
Pavane, 'Earl of Salisbury', virginals. *arr.* The 'Earl of Salisbury' carol, adapted from 'The Earl of Salisbury's Pavane', two-part. (Byrd, William). *Banks. Unpriced* FDP/LF (B78-50810)
Gray, Michael H. Bibliography of discographies
Vol.1: Classical music, 1925-1975. *Bowker. £15.00* A/FD(WT/T) (B78-09309) ISBN 0-8352-1023-5
Grayson, Martin. Purcell for the guitar : five pieces ... (Purcell, Henry). *Oxford University Press. Unpriced* TSPMK (B78-51164) ISBN 0-19-358356-9
Great all-time country hits : melody, lyrics and guitar chords, 60 of the greatest country songs ever written. *Southern Music : Music Sales (dist.). £1.95* KE/TSDW/GC/AY (B78-50886)
Great Britain. *Department of the Environment. Working Group on Pop Festivals. See* Great Britain. *Working Group on Pop Festivals.*
Great Britain. *Prime Minister, 1970-74 (Heath). See also* Heath, Edward.
Great Britain. *Public Record Office. See* Public Record Office.
Great Britain. *Working Group on Pop Festivals.* Pop festivals and their problems : second report of the Working Group on Pop Festivals. *H.M.S.O. £0.85* A/GB(WE) (B78-16620) ISBN 0-11-751254-0
Great composers.
Piggott, Patrick. Rachmaninov. *Faber. £3.95 : CIP rev.* BRC(N) (B77-12592) ISBN 0-571-10265-4
Reed, John, *b.1909.* Schubert. *Faber. £3.95 : CIP rev.* BSF(N) (B77-22755) ISBN 0-571-10327-8
Great days and jolly days : the story of girls' school songs. (Haddon, Celia). *Hodder and Stoughton. £3.50* AJFDW/GJS (B78-01679) ISBN 0-340-22230-1
Great opera stars in historic photographs : 343 portraits from the 1850s to the 1940s. *Dover Publications etc. : Constable. £4.35* AC/E(M/XJK100/EM) (B78-31599) ISBN 0-486-23575-0
Great song book. *Benn. Unpriced* DW/AY (B78-50747) ISBN 0-510-00037-1
Greaves, Terence. Beethoven's fifth bossa nova : wind quintet. *Emerson. Unpriced* UNRHJKS (B78-50286)
Green, Barbara. Rounds about rounds. *Franklin Watts. Unpriced* FDW/XC/AY (B78-50396) ISBN 0-531-00125-3
Green, David. Chorus : the Puffin Colony Song book. *Puffin Books. £0.70* JFE/TSDW (B78-50436) ISBN 0-14-030941-1
Green, Douglas B. The illustrated encyclopedia of country music. (Dellar, Fred). *27 Old Gloucester St., WC1N 3AF : Salamander Books Ltd. £5.95* A/GC(C) (B78-05399) ISBN 0-86101-004-3
Green, E. Finger style folk : a guitar tutor for folk song accompaniment. *45 Riverside Drive, Hambleton, Blackpool FY6 9EH : Wyre Publications. Unpriced* ATS/ED (B78-06266)
Green, Roy. Rock of the westies. *arr.* Rock of the westies : songs from the album. (John, Elton). *Big Pig Music : Music Sales. £1.95* KDW/HKR (B78-50162)
Green, Stanley, *b.1923.* Encyclopaedia of the musical. *Cassell. £7.95* ACM(C) (B78-03575) ISBN 0-304-29930-8
Greene, Maurice. Voluntary, organ, no.6, B flat major. *arr.* Voluntary in C major, for descant, treble and tenor recorders. *Chester Music. Unpriced* VSNTK (B78-51248)
Greenfield, Edward. The Penguin stereo record guide. 2nd ed. *Penguin. £4.50* A/FF(WT) (B78-23118)
Greening, Anthony. Six easy three-part anthems. *Royal School of Church Music. Unpriced* EZDH/AY (B78-50373)
Greenough, Millie. English! Sing it! : a structured presentation of spoken English through the use of songs. *McGraw-Hill. Unpriced* KE/TSDW/AY (B78-50168) ISBN 0-07-024667-x
Greensleeves. (Howarth, Elgar). *Chester Music. Unpriced* WMK/DW (B78-51326)
Greensleeves : for brass band. (Howarth, Elgar). *Chester Music. Unpriced* WMK/DW (B78-51327)
Gregor-Dellin, Martin. Cosima Wagner's diaries
Vol.1: 1869-1877. (Wagner, Cosima). *Collins. £15.00*

BWC(N) (B78-34737) ISBN 0-00-216130-3
Gregson, Edward. Concerto, tuba. *arr.* Tuba concerto. *Novello. £2.85* WVPK/LF (B78-50695)
Gresh, Margaret.
Selected works : for piano solo. (Liszt, Franz). *Schirmer. £3.60* QPJ (B78-50541)
Selected works : for piano solo. (Mozart, Wolfgang Amadeus). *Schirmer. £3.60* QPJ (B78-50544)
Gridley, Mark C. Jazz styles. *Prentice-Hall. £9.45* AMT(X) (B78-31600) ISBN 0-13-509885-8
Grieg, Edvard.
Holberg suite, op.40. *Selections : arr.* Sarabande and gavotte ... *Banks Music. Unpriced* VSNSK/AH (B78-50296)
Sigurd Jorsalfar. Op.56. Homage march. *arr.* Homage march. *Oxford University Press. Unpriced* MK/AGM (B78-50485) ISBN 0-19-363848-7
Griffes, Charles Tomlinson. De profundis : piano solo. *Peters. Unpriced* QPJ (B78-51010)
Griffiths, David. A catalogue of the printed music published before 1850 in York Minster Library. (York Minster. Library). *Dean's Park, York YO1 2JD : The Library. £1.50* A(TC) (B78-20765)
Griffiths, Paul. A concise history of modern music from Debussy to Boulez. *Thames and Hudson. £5.50* A(XLK88) (B78-21398) ISBN 0-500-18167-5
Grimley, Myra. Catalogue of music broadcast on Radio 3 and Radio 4
1974. (British Broadcasting Corporation). *B.B.C. £4.00* A/JT(WT) (B78-20763) ISBN 0-563-17369-6
Grindea, Carola.
Music books for schools : an annotated list. *School Library Association. £1.30(£0.90 to members)* A(VC/T) (B78-18775) ISBN 0-900641-30-4
Tensions in the performance of music : a symposium. *Kahn and Averill. £3.00* AL/CY (B78-16900) ISBN 0-900707-44-5
Grosch, Mal. The Christian songwriters' handbook. (Acott, Dennis). *65 Grace Ave., Maidstone, Kent : Third Day Enterprises. £0.40* ADW/GB/L(S) (B78-10624) ISBN 0-9505912-0-3
Gross, Michael. Bob Dylan : an illustrated history. (Alexander, Robert). *Elm Tree Books. £3.95* AKDW/HKR/E(P) (B78-33164) ISBN 0-241-10038-0
Group piano-teaching. (Enoch, Yvonne). *Oxford University Press. £2.95* AQ/E(VC) (B78-26247) ISBN 0-19-318423-0
Growth of music : a study in musical history. (Colles, Henry Cope). 4th ed. *Oxford University Press. £4.50* A(XCH701) (B78-20435) ISBN 0-19-316116-8
Gruber, Franz. Stille Nacht, heilige Nacht. *arr.* Silent night : all organ. *Chappell. Unpriced* RK/DP/LF (B78-50236)
Gruber, Heinz Karl. 6 Episoden aus einer unterbrochenen Chronik = 6 episodes from a discontinued chronicle : Klavier = for piano : op.20. *Boosey and Hawkes. Unpriced* QPJ (B78-51011)
Grundman, Clare.
Nocturne for harp and wind ensemble. *Boosey and Hawkes. Unpriced* TQPMJ (B78-51136)
Overture on a short theme. *Boosey and Hawkes. Unpriced* UMMJ (B78-51178)
Slanal. *arr.* Slava! : a concert overture. (Bernstein, Leonard). *Amberson : Boosey and Hawkes : Boosey and Hawkes. Unpriced* UMMK (B78-51186)
Guess what time of year it is! : for SATB chorus with piano accompaniment. (Lombardo, Mario). *Chappell. Unpriced* DW/LF (B78-50749)
Guess what time of year it is! : for SATB chorus with piano accompaniment. (Lombardo, Mario). *Chappell. Unpriced* FDW/LF (B78-50820)
Guest, George. Miserere. Miserere mei, Deus : for nine voices. (Allegri, Gregorio). *Chester Music. Unpriced* EZDGKHM/LH (B78-50771)
Guinness book of British hit singles : (the Guinness book of records records). (Rice, Jo). *Guinness Superlatives. £4.95* AKDW/GB/FD(XPM16) (B78-02936) ISBN 0-900424-77-x
Guitar ensemble series. Biberian, Gilbert. Eight valses for four guitars. *Belwin Mills. Unpriced* TSNSHW (B78-50606)
Guitar heroes. (Tobler, John). *Marshall Cavendish. £2.95* ATS/E(M) (B78-39236) ISBN 0-85685-438-7
Guitar masters of the 19th century : Italian masters, 19 original easy pieces, collected, edited and arranged in progressive order by June Yakeley. *Ricordi. Unpriced* TSPMJ (B78-50616)
Guitar repair : a manual of repair for guitars and fretted instruments. (Sloane, Irving). *Omnibus Press. £2.95* ATS/BT (B78-19402) ISBN 0-86001-157-7
Guitar scales and arpeggios
Grade 3-8. (Associated Board of the Royal Schools of Music). *Associated Board of the Royal Schools of Music. Unpriced* TS/AF (B78-51142)
Guitarre royalle. *Selections.* Suite in A minor ... : guitar solo. (Corbetta, Francesco). *Universal. Unpriced* TSPMJ (B78-51153)
Guitars : music, history, construction and players from the Renaissance to rock. (Evans, Tom, *b.1948*). *Paddington Press. £10.95* ATS/B (B78-25375) ISBN 0-448-22240-x
Gulbenkian (Calouste) Foundation. *See* Calouste Gulbenkian Foundation.
Gump, Richard.
The gift of December : for four-part chorus of men's voices and baritone solo with piano accompaniment. *Schirmer. Unpriced* GDH/LF (B78-50068)
The gift of December : for four-part chorus of men's voices and baritone solo with piano accompaniment. *Schirmer. Unpriced* GDH/LF (B78-50069)
Gunn, Douglas. Four Irish folksongs : for 2 descant, treble and tenor recorders. *Chester Music. Unpriced* VSNSK/DW/AYDM (B78-51245)
Gut-strung plucked instruments contemporary with the lute. (Gill, Donald). *c/o The Administrator, 71 Priory Rd, Kew Gardens, Richmond, Surrey TW9 3DH : Lute Society. Unpriced* AT/B(XCSK301) (B78-01683)
Gwyneth, John. That virgin's child : for S.A.T.B. unacc. (Ridout, Alan). *Williams School of Church Music. Unpriced* EZDP/LF (B78-50047)
Haan, Stefan de. Suite, brass sextet. Suite for brass sextet. *Chester Music. Unpriced* WNQ (B78-51334)
Haddon, Celia. Great days and jolly days : the story of girls' school songs. *Hodder and Stoughton. £3.50* AJFDW/GJS (B78-01679) ISBN 0-340-22230-1
Haec dies. (Shepherd, John, *b.1520*). *Oxenford Imprint : Blackwell's Music Shop. Unpriced* EZDJ/LL (B78-50784)
Hage, Louis. Maronite music. *Longman for the University of Essex. £0.75* ADGTCX (B78-35472) ISBN 0-582-78085-3
Haiku souvenirs : for voice and piano. (Gottlieb, Jack). *Amberson : Boosey and Hawkes : Boosey and Hawkes. Unpriced* KDW (B78-50861)
Hail to the Lord's anointed. (Pulkingham, Betty). *57 Dorchester Rd. Lytchett Minister, Poole : Celebration Services. Unpriced* JDM (B78-50082)
Hair today : for mixed chorus (SAATBB) a cappella. (Bach, Jan). *New Galaxy Music : Stainer and Bell. Unpriced* EZDW (B78-50049)
Hairston, Jester. Mary's boy child. *arr.* Mary's boy child. *Chappell. Unpriced* NYFPK/DW/LF (B78-50953)
Hakol kol Yaacov = The voice is the voice of Jacob : compositions for cantor and choir. (Gottlieb, Jacob). Limited ed. *18 Station Tce, N.W.10 : Sinai Publishing House. Unpriced* DGU (B78-50724) ISBN 0-9506345-0-6
Halévy, Ludovic. Monsieur Choufleuri restera chez lui de. *Vocal score.* Salon Blumenkohl/Monsieur Choufleuri restera chez lui de ... : Buffo-Operette in einem Akt deutsch nach Karl Fr. Wiltmann von Heinz Balthes und Paul Vasil, opéra bouffe en un acte de St. Rémy, E. L'Epine, Hector Crémieux et Ludovic Halévy, musikalische Revision, neue Instrumentation und praktische Bearbeitung von Caspar Richter. (Offenbach, Jacques). *Bote und Bock : Associated music. £11.50* CF (B78-50703)
Hall, Daryl.
Beauty on a back street. *arr.* Beauty on a back street. *Chappell. Unpriced* KDW/GB (B78-50131)
Best of Daryl Hall and John Oates. *Chappell. Unpriced* KDW/GB (B78-50130)
Hallé, 1858-1976 : a brief survey of the orchestra's history, travels and achievements. (Kennedy, Michael, *b.1926*) Revised ed.. *30 Cross St., Manchester M2 7BA : Hallé Concerts Society. £0.75* AMM/E(QB/X) (B78-06265)
Hallé Concerts Society. Hallé, 1858-1976 : a brief survey of the orchestra's history, travels and achievements. (Kennedy, Michael, *b.1926*). Revised ed.. *30 Cross St., Manchester M2 7BA : Hallé Concerts Society. £0.75* AMM/E(QB/X) (B78-06265)
Handbook for ex-trebles and young choirmen. RSCM chorister training scheme
Part 2. Handbook for ex-trebles and young choirmen. (Royal School of Church Music). *Addington Palace, Croydon, Surrey CR9 5AD : R.S.C.M.. £0.55* AD/LD/E (B78-22164) ISBN 0-85402-073-x
Handbook of early American sheet music, 1768-1889. (Dichter, Harry). *Dover Publications etc. : Constable. £4.70* A(TC/YT/XFYH22) (B78-30339) ISBN 0-486-23364-2
Handel, George Frideric.
Alcina. *Selections : arr.* Dances from 'Alcina'. *Banks. Unpriced* QPK/AH (B78-51025)
Comus. Incidental music. Music for Comus : serenata a 9. First modern ed. *23 Stanley Court, 1 Woodfield Rd, W.5 : Acca Music. Unpriced* JNDE/NXNQDW/JM (B78-50108)
Concerto, organ, op.4, no.1, G minor. Organ concerto, G minor, Op.4, no.1. *Eulenburg. Unpriced* MPRF (B78-50926)
Concerto, organ, op.4, no.2, B flat major. Organ concerto, B flat major, Op.4, no.2. *Eulenburg. Unpriced* MPRF (B78-50927)
Concerto, organ, op.4, no.3, G minor. Organ concerto, G minor, Op.4, no.3. *Eulenburg. Unpriced* MPRF (B78-50928)
Concerto, organ, op.4, no.4, F major. Organ concerto, F major, Op.4, no.4. *Eulenburg. Unpriced* MPRF (B78-50929)
Concerto, organ, op.4, no.5, F major. Organ concerto, F major, Op.4, no.5. *Eulenburg. Unpriced* MPRF (B78-50930)
Concerto, organ, op.4, no.6, B flat major, 'Harp'. Organ concerto, (Harp concerto), B flat major, Op.4, no.6. *Eulenburg. Unpriced* MPRF (B78-50931)
Selected solos and duets. *Ariel : Music Sales. £1.50* TSPMK (B78-51163) ISBN 0-86001-378-2
Sonatas, violins (2) & continuo, Op.2, no.1-6. Trio sonatas Op.2, nos.1-3. *Eulenburg. Unpriced* NXNSE (B78-50203)
Sonatas, violins (2) & continuo, op.2, nos. 3, 8, 9. Dresden trio sonatas. *Eulenburg. Unpriced* NXNSE (B78-50204)
Sonatas, violins (2) & continuo, op.2, nos.1-6. Trio sonatas Op.2, no.4-6. *Eulenburg. Unpriced* NXNSE (B78-50205)
Suite de pièces, 1st collection. Passacaille. *arr.* Passacaglia in G minor. *Oxford University Press. Unpriced* UMMK/AHT (B78-50632)
Suite, harpsichord, Craig Bell no.170, A major. Sarabande. Sarabande and air : for keyboard. *Banks Music. Unpriced* QPJ (B78-51012)
Utrecht Te Deum. *Vocal score.* The Utrecht Te Deum (1713) : for chorus of mixed voices and soloists with organ or piano accompaniment. *Schirmer. £2.40* DGNQ (B78-50336)
Handl, Jacob. Secundus tomus musici operis. Ascendo ad Patrem meum. *arr.* Ascendo ad Patrem meum. *Cathedral Music. Unpriced* GEZDJ/LM (B78-50422)
Hankey, Peter. The great song book. *Benn. Unpriced* DW/AY (B78-50747) ISBN 0-510-00037-1
Hanmer, Ronald. Ein Walzertraum. *Vocal score.* A waltz dream : operetta in three acts. (Straus, Oscar). *Weinberger. Unpriced* CF (B78-50326)
Hansen, Chadwick. Selections from the gutter : jazz portraits from the 'Jazz record'. *University of California Press. £8.75* AMT/FD(M) (B78-05409) ISBN 0-520-02999-2
Happy birthday, Jesus. *arr.* Happy birthday, Jesus. (Pockriss, Lee). *Chappell. Unpriced* DP/LF (B78-50742)
Happy birthday, Jesus. *arr.* Happy birthday, Jesus. (Pockriss, Lee). *Chappell. Unpriced* FDP/LF (B78-50811)
Happy days. *arr.* Happy days : from the Paramount TV series 'Happy days'. (Fox, Charles). *Warner : Blossom. Unpriced* UMMK/DW/JS (B78-50638)
Happy days : from the Paramount TV series 'Happy days'. (Fox, Charles). *Warner : Blossom. Unpriced* UMMK/DW/JS (B78-50638)
Haratyanyan, Narineh The Russian school of piano playing Vol.2. (Nikolaev, Aleksandr Aleksandrovich). English ed. *Boosey and Hawkes. Unpriced* Q/AC (B78-50963)
harbison, John. Incidental music for Shakespeare's 'The merchant of Venice' : for string orchestra (or string quintet). *Associated Music. Unpriced* RXMJ (B78-51066)
Harding, James, *b.1929.* My friends and myself : conversations with Francis Poulenc. (Audel, Stéphane). *Dobson. £4.95* BPO(N) (B78-39780) ISBN 0-234-77251-4
Hardy, Thomas. The oxen : S.A.T.B. (Rorem, Ned). *Boosey Hawkes. Unpriced* EZDW/LF (B78-50803)
Harker, Dave. Big red songbook. *Unit 10, Specner Court, Chalcot Rd, N.W.1 : Plato Press. £1.00* JEZDW/AY (B78-50835) ISBN 0-904383-12-1
Harkonen, Jorma. Ave Maria. Op.42. *arr.* Ave Maria : for four double basses. (Fitzenhagen, Wilhelm Carl Friedrich). *Yorke. Unpriced* SSNSK (B78-51124)
Harland, John. Ballads and songs of Lancashire
Part 2: Modern. 3rd ed. *EP Publishing. £5.25* AKDW/K/G(YDJD) (B78-02615) ISBN 0-7158-1182-7
Harlow, Frank. Rock of the westies. *arr.* Rock of the westies : songs from the album. (John, Elton). *Big Pig Music : Music Sales. £1.95* KDW/HKR (B78-50162)
Harmonic organization of 'The rite of spring'. (Forte, Allen). *Yale University Press. £10.80* BSVAMM/HM/R (B78-38605) ISBN 0-300-02201-8
Harper, Annette.
Almost caught red-pawed (or The cat who cried over spilt milk) : a musical play for children. (Oliver, Donald). *Chappell. Unpriced* CN (B78-50705)
The cookie lady : a musical play for children. (Oliver, Donald). *Chappell. Unpriced* CN (B78-50706)
The runaways : a musical play for children. (Oliver, Donald). *Chappell. Unpriced* CN (B78-50707)
Harper, Don. Songs from Alice : Alice in Wonderland and Through the looking-glass. *Adam and Charles Black. Unpriced* JFDW (B78-50843) ISBN 0-7136-1879-5
Harper, Edward. Ricercari, 'In memoriam Luigi Dallapiccola' : for 11 players. *Oxford University Press. Unpriced* MRJ (B78-50941) ISBN 0-19-356888-8
Harrison, Graham. Christian hymns. *Evangelical Movements of Wales : Henry E. Walter. Unpriced* DM/AY (B78-50024)
Harrison, Louis H. Hollywood on record : the film stars' discography. (Pitts, Michael R). *Scarecrow Press Distributed by Bailey and Swinfen. £13.60* AKDW/JR/FD(YT/WT) (B78-27785) ISBN 0-8108-1093-x
Harrison, Sidney. The Sidney Harrison adult piano tutor. *Chappell. Unpriced* Q/AC (B78-50961)
Harrop, Beatrice. Ta-ra-ra boom-de-ay : songs for everyone. *A. and C. Black. Unpriced* JFADW/AY (B78-50837) ISBN 0-7136-1790-x
Harry Mortimer souvenir album : a unique collection of famous cornet solos. *Boosey and Hawkes. Unpriced* WRPK/AAY (B78-51341)
Hart, Lorenz. Love me tonight. Mimi. *arr.* Mimi : SATB chorus and piano. (Rodgers, Richard). *Warner : Blossom. Unpriced* DW (B78-50746)
Hartford, John. Gentle on my mind. *arr.* Gentle on my mind. *Warner : Blossom. Unpriced* UMMK/DW (B78-50634)
Hartmann, Heinrich. Erster Theil confortativae sacrae symphoniaciae. Wenn der Herr die Gefangnen Zion erlösen wird. *arr.* Motet, Wenn der Herr die Gefangnen Zion erlösen wird. *Tomus. Unpriced* VSNQK/DJ (B78-51242)
Hartmann, Karl Amadeus.
Miserae : symphonische Dichtung für Orchester, (1933-34). *Schott. £10.00* MMJ (B78-50189)
Symphonische Ouverture für grosses Orchester (1942). *Schott. £14.00* MMJ (B78-50190)
Harutyanyan, Narineh. The Russian school of piano playing Vol.1. (Nikolaev, Aleksandr Aleksandrovich). English ed. *Boosey and Hawkes. Unpriced* Q/AC (B78-50962)
Harvey, Jonathan. Magnificat and Nunc dimittis : for choir and organ (1978). *Faber Music. £1.50* DGPP (B78-50337)

Harvey, Pamela. Paul McCartney & Wings. (Pascall, Jeremy). *Chartwell Books : Phoebus. £2.95* AKDW/GB/E(P) (B78-01677) ISBN 0-89009-125-0
Harvey, Paul. Saxophone quartets
Vol.1. *Chester Music. Unpriced* VUNSK/AAY (B78-51272)
Harvey, Raymond. Suite, recorder ensemble, no.1. Suite no.1 for recorder ensemble, for descant, treble, 2 tenor and bass recorders. *Chester Music. Unpriced* VSNG (B78-51240)
Haskins, James. The story of Stevie Wonder. *Panther. £0.65* AKDW/HKR/E(P) (B78-06263) ISBN 0-586-04541-4
Hasse, Johann Adolf. Piramo e Tisbe. Tambourin. *arr.* Tambourin. *Lengnick. £0.60* VRPK/AHVQT (B78-51222)
Hat trick. (Newsome, Roy). *Midland Music. Unpriced* WMJ (B78-50312)
Haul away! : 3 movements based on a sea shanties. *7 Garrick St., W.C.2 : Middle Eight Music. Unpriced* VNSK/DW/GMC/AY (B78-50288)
Haus, Karl. Schönster Schatz leb wohl eine Reise durch Deutschland mit Volksliedern und Tänzen : für Männerchor, zwei Klarinetten oder andere Holzbläser, Streicher oder Tasteninstrumente und Schlagzeug, Gitarre ad lib. *Schott. £5.20* GE/NYDPDW/G/AYE (B78-50071)
Havlice, Patricia Pate. Popular song index
1st supplement. *Scarecrow Press : Distributed by Bailey and Swinfen. £12.75* AKDW/GB(WT) (B78-27098) ISBN 0-8108-1099-9
Hawes, Stephen. A pair of wings. (Sackman, Nicholas). *Schott. £5.00* JNFLDE/NYEXPNQDW (B78-50439)
Hawkes pocket score. Davies, Peter Maxwell. A mirror of whitenbing light = Specolum luminis dealbensin : for chamber orchestra. *Boosey and Hawkes. Unpriced* MRJ (B78-50940)
Hawkes pocket scores.
Davies, Peter Maxwell. Symphony. *Boosey and Hawkes. Unpriced* MME (B78-50185)
Delius, Frederick. An arabesque = Eine Arabeske : for baritone solo, mixed chorus and orchestra = für Bariton-Solo, gemischter Chor und Orchester. *Boosey and Hawkes. Unpriced* EMDX (B78-50751)
Delius, Frederick. Concerto, cello. Cello concerto. *Boosey and Hawkes. Unpriced* MPSRF (B78-50934)
Delius, Frederick. Sea drift. *Boosey and Hawkes. Unpriced* EMDX (B78-50032)
Einem, Gottfried von. Kabale und Liebe : Oper in 2 Teilen (9 Bildern) nach Friedrich von Schiller. *Boosey and Hawkes. Unpriced* CQC (B78-50710)
Einem, Gottfried von. Quartet, strings, no.1, op.45. Erstes Streichquartett, opus 45. *Boosey and Hawkes. Unpriced* RXNS (B78-51080)
Einem, Gottfried von. Quintet, wind instruments, op.46. Bläserquintett. Opus 46. *Boosey and Hawkes. Unpriced* UNR (B78-51196)
Lees, Benjamin. Collage : for string quartet, wind quintet and percussion. *Boosey and Hawkes. Unpriced* MRJ (B78-50942)
Lees, Benjamin. Spectrum : for orchestra. *Boosey and Hawkes. Unpriced* MMJ (B78-50923)
Vaughan Williams, Ralph. Symphony no.3, 'Pastoral'. Pastoral symphony. *Boosey and Hawkes. Unpriced* KFLE/MDX (B78-50175)
Weinzweig, John. Divertimento 1 for flute and string orchestra. *Boosey and Hawkes. Unpriced* RXMPVR (B78-51073)
Weinzweig, John. Divertimento, oboe & string orchestra, no.2. Divertimento 2 for oboe and string orchestra. *Boosey and Hawkes. Unpriced* RXMPVT (B78-51074)
Hawkes pocket series. Davies, Peter Maxwell. Taverner. Dances. Points and dances ... : for instrumental ensemble. *Boosey and Hawkes. Unpriced* LN (B78-50907)
Hawkes school series.
Bach, Johann Sebastian. Three chorales. *Boosey and Hawkes. Unpriced* MK/DM (B78-50184)
Davies, Peter Maxwell. Five Klee pictures. *Boosey and Hawkes. Unpriced* MJ (B78-50179)
Delius, Frederick. Sleigh ride = Schlittenfahrt. 1st ed. *Boosey and Hawkes. Unpriced* MJ (B78-50911)
Delius, Frederick. Sleigh ride = Schlittenfahrt. 1st ed. *Boosey and Hawkes. Unpriced* MJ (B78-50912)
Haydn, Joseph.
Divertimento, woodwind quartet, Hob.II, no.7, C major. Feld-Parthie in C for wind ensemble. *Boosey and Hawkes. Unpriced* UNN (B78-50284)
Duet, barytones (2), Hob XII/4, G major. *arr.* Duett in G nach dem Original für 2 Barytone, Hob XII, 4. *Schott. £4.00* TSNUK (B78-50270)
Feld-Parthie in F, for wind ensemble. *Boosey and Hawkes. Unpriced* UNQ (B78-51193)
Quartet, strings, no.3. Klassische Tanze von Joseph Haydn und Wolfgang Amadeus Mozart : für Blockflöten - Ensemble ... Sopran, Alt, Tenor, Bass ... *Schott. £3.20* VSNSK/AH (B78-50298)
Werke für das Laufwerk. *Selections : arr.* Four clock pieces. *Novello. Unpriced* VVNTK/B/FJ (B78-51277)
Haydn at Eszterháza, 1766-1790. Haydn : chronicle and works
Haydn at Eszterháza, 1766-1790. (Landon, Howard Chandler Robbins). *Thames and Hudson. £30.00* BHE(N) (B78-40350) ISBN 0-500-01168-0
Head, Michael.
Trio, oboe, bassoon and piano. *Emerson. Unpriced* NWPNT (B78-50201)
The world is mad : song, for voice, clarinet and piano. *Emerson. Unpriced* KE/VVPDW (B78-50466)
Healy, James N.
Ballads from the pubs of Ireland. 3rd ed. *25 Lower Abbey St., Dublin 1 : Mercier Press. £1.50* AKDW/K/G(YDM) (B78-37866)
Comic songs of Cork and Kerry. *25 Lower Abbey St., Dublin 1 : Mercier Press. £0.80* AKDW(YDQC) (B78-39235) ISBN 0-85342-498-5
Comic songs of Ireland. *25 Lower Abbey St., Dublin 1 : Mercier Press. £0.80* AKDW(YDM) (B78-39785) ISBN 0-85342-529-9
The first book of Irish ballads. Revised ed. *4 Bridge St., Cork : Mercier Press. £1.50* AKDW/K/G(YDM) (B78-37867) ISBN 0-85342-080-7
Love songs of the Irish. *25 Lower Abbey St., Dublin 1 : Mercier Press. £1.10* AKDW(YDM) (B78-39234) ISBN 0-85342-497-7
Percy French and his songs. *25 Lower Abbey St., Dublin 1 : Mercier Press. £1.70* BFUR(N) (B78-33936) ISBN 0-85342-394-6
The second book of Irish ballads. 3rd ed. *4 Bridge St., Cork : Mercier Press. £1.50* AKDW/K/G(YDM) (B78-37868) ISBN 0-85342-081-5
Healy, James Nagle-. Irish ballads and songs of the sea. *4 Bridge St., Cork : Mercier Press. £1.50* AKDW/KC(YDM) (B78-34739) ISBN 0-85342-074-2
Heaney, E L. Alphabetical index of the Scottish metrical psalms : first line of every 4-line verse of the Psalms in metre. *23 Nairn St., Glasgow G3 8SE : The compiler. £0.50* ADR(YDL/WT) (B78-15373)
Heath, Edward. Music : a joy for life. *Sidgwick and Jackson. £5.95* A (B78-33160)
'Heavens devlare the glory of God'. (Marcello, Benedetto). *Cramer. Unpriced* RK/DR (B78-51056)
Heavy reductions : for tuba and tape, 1977. (Soaster, Timothy). *Arts Lab Music. Unpriced* WV (B78-51358)
Heber, Reginald. Bishop Thorpe. *arr.* By cool Siloam's shady rill. (Clarke, Jeremiah). *Galaxy : Stainer and Bell. Unpriced* EZDM (B78-50380)
Heiden, Bernhard.
Siena : for cello and piano. *Associated Music. £3.05* SRPJ (B78-50601)
Variations, tuba & horns (9). Variations for solo tuba and nine horns. *Associated Music. £9.05* WN/T (B78-50687)
Heilbut, Peter. Spass am Klavierspielen : Schule für Kinder aus Grund- un Früherziehungskursen. *Bärenreiter. £4.20* Q/AC (B78-50518)
Heise, Hans Jürgen. 4 Songs nach Texten von Hans-Jurgen Heise, Heinz Piontek, Hans Magnus Enzensberger und Ror Wolf für Singstimme, Klavier, Kontrabass und Schlagzeug. (Wimberger, Gerhard). *Bärenreiter. £2.50* KE/NYGDW (B78-50883)
Heloïse and Abelard. *Vocal score.* Heloïsw and Abelard : a dramatic cantata for soprano, tenor and baritone soloists, chorus and orchestra. (Maconchy, Elizabeth). *Chester Music. Unpriced* DE (B78-50717)
Help your patrol to make music. *Girl Guides Association. Unpriced* FEZDW/AY (B78-50403)
Helyer, Marjorie. Plum stones : for piano. *Novello. Unpriced* QPJ (B78-50531)
Hemingway, Roger. The sea of faith, Dover Beach. *Novello. £0.45* DH (B78-50726)
Hennessy, Val. In the gutter. *Quartet Books. £1.95* AKDW/HKQ (B78-24013) ISBN 0-7043-3230-2
Hentoff, Nat. Jazz is. *W.H. Allen. £5.95* AMT(M) (B78-08478) ISBN 0-491-02312-x
Henze, Hans Werner.
4. Streichquartett = 4th string quartet (1976). *Schott. £12.00* RXNS (B78-51081)
4. Streichquartett = 4th string quartet : (1976). *Schott. £26.00* TXNS (B78-51172)
Amicizia! : Quintett für Klarinette in A, Posaune, Violoncello, Schlagzeug und Klavier (1976). *Schott. £4.65* RXMK/AHW (B78-50247)
Amicizia! : Quintett für Klarinette in A, Posaune, Violoncello, Schlagzeug und Klavier (1976). *Schott. £8.00* NYDPNR (B78-50512)
Quartet, strings, no.3. 3. Streichquartett = 3rd string quartet. *Schott. £10.00* RXNS (B78-50581)
Quartet, strings, no.3. 3. Streichquartett (1976). *Schott. £12.80* RXNS (B78-50582)
Quartet, strings, no.5. 5. Streichquartett (1976-77). *Schott. £12.00* RXNS (B78-50254)
Herbert, George.
Antiphon : S.A.T.B. (Walton, *Sir* William). *Oxford University Press. Unpriced* DH (B78-50021) ISBN 0-19-350366-2
Antiphon : S.A.T.B. (unacc.). (Howells, Herbert). *Oxford University Press. Unpriced* EZDH (B78-50044) ISBN 0-19-350365-4
Herbst, Johannes. Three sacred songs of Johannes Herbert. *Boosey and Hawkes. Unpriced* KFTDH (B78-50899)
Herder, Johann von. Intermezzo, piano, op.117, no.1, E flat major. *arr.* Wiegenlied : for mixed chorus and piano four hands. (Brahms, Johannes). *Boosey and Hawkes. Unpriced* DW (B78-50349)
Heritage of 20th century British song
Vol.1. (Association of English Singers and Speakers). *Boosey and Hawkes. Unpriced* KDW/AYD (B78-50119)
Vol.2. (Association of English Singers and Speakers). *Boosey and Hawkes. Unpriced* KDW/AYC (B78-50118)
Herr, wie sind deine Werke so gross. *arr.* Lord, thy creations, how great they are = Herr, wie sind deine Werke so gross : S.A.T.B. with accompaniment. (Peter, Johann Friedrich). *Boosey and Hawkes. Unpriced* DH (B78-50339)
Herrick, Robert.
Aubade, op.17 : for mixed chorus. (Brown, Christopher). *Chester Music. Unpriced* EZDW (B78-50795)
Gather ye rosebuds : for four-part chorus of mixed voices a cappella. (Dinerstein, Norman). *Schirmer. Unpriced* EZDW (B78-50052)
Herrmann, William. Utrecht Te Deum. *Vocal score.* The Utrecht Te Deum (1713) : for chorus of mixed voices and soloists with organ or piano accompaniment. (Handel, George Frideric). *Schirmer. £2.40* DGNQ (B78-50336)
Herrnschmidt, Johann Daniel. Kommt danket dem Helden. *arr.* Come thank now Jehovah = Kommt danket dem Helden : double chorus ; SATB with accompaniment. (Peter, Johann Friedrich). *Boosey and Hawkes. Unpriced* DH (B78-50341)
Hersom, Herbert. Holberg suite, op.40. *Selections : arr.* Sarabande and gavotte ... (Grieg, Edvard). *Banks Music. Unpriced* VSNSK/AH (B78-50296)
Hertel, Johann Wilhelm. Concerto, bassoon & string orchestra, B flat major. *arr.* Concerto in B flat for bassoon, strings and basso continuo. *Musica rara. Unpriced* VWPK/LF (B78-51291)
Heseltine, Philip. An arabesque = Eine Arabeske : for baritone solo, mixed chorus and orchestra = für Bariton-Solo, gemischter Chor und Orchester. (Delius, Frederick). *Boosey and Hawkes. Unpriced* EMDX (B78-50751)
Hesford, Bryan.
Estro poetico-armonico. d Salmo 18. *arr.* 'The heavens devlare the glory of God'. (Marcello, Benedetto). *Cramer. Unpriced* RK/DR (B78-51056)
Holy communion series III. Missa in simplicitate. *Cramer. Unpriced* JDGS (B78-50831)
Te Deum, D major. Prelude. *arr.* Trumpet tune. (Charpentier, Marc Antoine). *J.B. Cramer. £0.45* RK (B78-51054)
Transcriptions for organ. (Bach, Johann Sebastian). *Cramer. Unpriced* RK/AAY (B78-50570)
Hewitt, Graham. How to sing. *Elm Tree Books : E.M.I. Music Publishing. £3.95 : CIP rev.* AB/E (B78-04325) ISBN 0-241-89897-8
Heyward, Du Bose. Porgy and Bess. *Selections : arr.* Porgy and Bess. (Gershwin, George). *Chappell. Unpriced* KDW (B78-50442)
Hicks, Anthony. Comus. Incidental music. Music for Comus : serenata a 9. (Handel, George Frideric). First modern ed. *23 Stanley Court, 1 Woodfield Rd, W.5 : Acca Music. Unpriced* JNDE/NXNQDW/JM (B78-50108)
Higgins, John, *b.1934.* The making of an opera : 'Don Giovanni' at Glyndebourne. *Secker and Warburg. £7.95* BMSAC/E (B78-33162) ISBN 0-436-19595-x
Higgins, Norman.
Andantino. *Royal Academy of Dancing. Unpriced* QPH/H (B78-50218)
Butterfly dance, and, Scherzo. *Royal Academy of Dancing. Unpriced* QPH/H (B78-50219)
Two folk melodies. *Royal Academy of Dancing. Unpriced* QPH/H (B78-50220)
Waltz in E. *Royal Academy of Dancing. Unpriced* QPHW/H (B78-50221)
Highgate and The tower. (Burtch, Mervyn). *Roberton. £0.18* JFDW (B78-50090)
Higson, G. Finger style folk : a guitar tutor for folk song accompaniment. (Green, E). *45 Riverside Drive, Hambleton, Blackpool FY6 9EH : Wyre Publications. Unpriced* ATS/ED (B78-06266)
Hill of the graces : for unaccompanied chorus, SSAATTBB. (Berkeley, *Sir* Lennox). *Chester Music. Unpriced* EZDW (B78-50794)
Hilton, John Anthony. Joseph Hatch : the Ulcombe bellfounder. *36 Great Clarendon St., Oxford : J. Hannon and Co. £2.50* AXSR/BC(P) (B78-18095)
Himmelstrand, Peter. Abba. (Edgington, Harry). Revised ed. *Magnum Books. £0.95* AKDW/GB/E(P) (B78-28698) ISBN 0-417-03370-2
Hindemith, Paul. Concerto, cello, op.3, E flat major. *arr.* Konzert für Violoncello und Orchester in Es-Dur, Opus 3 (1915). *Schott. £20.00* SRPK/LF (B78-51118)
Hinrichsen second band book : four original compositions and four arrangements of classical works. *Peters in conjunction with the National School Brass Band Association. Unpriced* WMK/AAY (B78-51316)
Hinrichsen second band book : four original compositions and four arrangements of classical works. *Peters in conjunction with the National School Brass Band Association. Unpriced* WMK/AAY (B78-51317)
Hinrichsen third band book : a miscellany of 6 popular pieces. *Peters in conjunction with the National School Brass Band Association. Unpriced* WMK/AAY (B78-51318)
Hinrichsen third band book : a miscellany of 6 popular pieces. *Peters in conjunction with the National School Brass Band Association. Unpriced* WMK/AAY (B78-51319)
Hiplips . (Philip's) : for brass quintet. (Pearson, Leslie). *Chester Music. Unpriced* WNR (B78-51337)
Hip'nes 1 (1973 I) : versions a and b, for one or more

instrument. (Lanza, Alcides). *Boosey and Hawkes. £2.50* LN (B78-50481)
Hitchcock, Hugh Wiley. An Ives celebration : papers and panels of the Charles Ives Centennial Festival-Conference. (Charles Ives Centennial Festival-Conference, *New York and New Haven, 1974*). *University of Illinois Press. £8.40* BIV (B78-16383) ISBN 0-252-00619-4
Hlaváč, Miroslav. Musica carnevalesca : rondo for piano. *Schirmer. £2.10* QP/Y (B78-50990)
Hoddinott, Alan.
Sinfonia fidei. *Vocal score.* Sinfonia fidei : a cantata for soprano and tenor soloists, chorus and orchestra. *Oxford University Press. Unpriced* DE (B78-50716) ISBN 0-19-336842-0
Sonata, violin & piano, no.4. Sonata no.4 for violin and piano. *Oxford University Press. Unpriced* SPE (B78-51098) ISBN 0-19-357166-8
Hodes, Art. Selections from the gutter : jazz portraits from the 'Jazz record'. *University of California Press. £8.75* AMT/FD(M) (B78-05409) ISBN 0-520-02999-2
Hodie Christus natus est. (Palestrina, Giovanni Pierluigi da). *Cathedral Music. Unpriced* GEZDGKJ/LF (B78-50411)

Hodie salvator apparuit : a sequence for Christmas, op.28. (Brown, Christopher). *Chester Music. Unpriced* EZDE/LF (B78-50765)
Hoffmann-Erbrecht, Lothar. Sonaten für Klavier zu zwei Händen
Band 2: Nr.16-32. (Beethoven, Ludwig van). *Litolff : Peters. Unpriced* QPE (B78-50991)
Hoffmeister, Franz Anton. Quartet, recorder, viola d'amore, violin & cello, D major. Quartetto in D for viola d'amore, recorder, violino con sordino and basso. *Little Margaret, Penmans Green, Chipperfield, Kings Langley : E.L. White. Unpriced* NVSNS (B78-50200)
Hofmannsthal, Hugo von.
Ariadne auf Naxos : Oper in einem Akt nebst einem Vorspiel. *Boosey and Hawkes. £0.85* BSUAC
Elektra : tragedy in one act. *Boosey and Hawkes. £9.00* BSUAC
Hogg, James. When the kye comes home : T.T.B.B. unacc. (Johnston, Peter Fyfe). *Banks Music. Unpriced* GEZDW (B78-50072)
Hoggard, Stuart. Bob Dylan : an illustrated discography. *113 Thame Rd, Oxford : Transmedia Express. £1.90* AKDW/HKR/FD(P/WT) (B78-17915) ISBN 0-906344-00-x
Hogwood, Christopher.
Music at court. *Folio Society. £4.95* A(KKR) (B78-08477)

Sonatas in 4 parts, Z.802-811. Ten sonatas in four parts Nos. 1-6. (Purcell, Henry). *Eulenburg. £2.00* NXNSE (B78-50506)
Sonatas in 4 parts. Z.802-811. Ten sonatas in four parts Nos.7-10. (Purcell, Henry). *Eulenburg. £2.00* NXNSE (B78-50507)
Holberg suite, op.40. *Selections : arr.* Sarabande and gavotte ... (Grieg, Edvard). *Banks Music. Unpriced* VSNSK/AH (B78-50296)
Hölderlin, Friedrich. Drei Lieder nach Texten von Friedrich Hölderlin : für höhe Stimme und Klavier, op.74. (Klebe, Giselher). *Bärenreiter. £3.90* KFTDW (B78-50900)
Holdsworth, Frank. An introduction to the clarinet
Book 1. (Dingle, Patrick). *EMI. Unpriced* VV/AC (B78-50659)
Holiday inn. White Christmas. *arr.* White Christmas. (Berlin, Irving). *Chappell. Unpriced* NYFPK/DW/JR/LF (B78-50952)
Holland, B J C. Suite, guitars (2). Suite for two guitars. *Schott. £0.50* TSNUG (B78-50269)
Holland, James. Percussion. *Macdonald and Jane's. £6.95* AX/B (B78-39787) ISBN 0-354-04173-8
Hollman, Peter. Parthia, viola d'amore, gamba & harpsichord, C minor. Parthia in C minor for viola d'amore, gamba & harpsichord. (Grabe). *Little Margaret, Penmans Green, Chipperfield : Ian White. Unpriced* NXNTG (B78-50508)
Holloway, Robin. This is just to say : for tenor and piano. *Boosey and Hawkes. Unpriced* KGHDW (B78-50904)
Hollywood on record : the film stars' discography. (Pitts, Michael R). *Scarecrow Press : Distributed by Bailey and Swinfen. £13.60* AKDW/JR/FD(YT/WT) (B78-27785) ISBN 0-8108-1093-x
Holst, Gustav.
A choral fantasia, Op.51. *Eulenburg. £1.00* EZDE (B78-50042)
Seven part-songs for female voices and strings. Revised ed. 1973. *Novello. Unpriced* FE/RXNRDW (B78-50821)
Terzetto (1925) : for flute, oboe and viola (or clarinet). 2nd revised ed. *Chester Music. Unpriced* VNT (B78-51198)
Holst, Imogen. Terzetto (1925) : for flute, oboe and viola (or clarinet). (Holst, Gustav). 2nd revised ed. *Chester Music. Unpriced* VNT (B78-51198)
Holy Bible. *See* Bible.
Holy communion series III. Missa in simplicitate. (Hesford, Bryan). *Cramer. Unpriced* JDGS (B78-50831)
Holy, holy, holy. Holy, Lord God almighty : verse anthem for Trinity Sunday. (Batten, Adrian). *36 Ranelagh Gdns., W.6 : Cathedral Music. Unpriced* DK/LNB (B78-50344)

Holy, Lord God almighty : verse anthem for Trinity Sunday. (Batten, Adrian). *36 Ranelagh Gdns., W.6 : Cathedral Music. Unpriced* DK/LNB (B78-50344)
Homage march. (Grieg, Edvard). *Oxford University Press. Unpriced* MK/AGM (B78-50485) ISBN 0-19-363848-7
Home organist and leisure music
Vol.1, no.1- ; Aug.-Sept. 1977-. *Cover Publications Ltd; 181 Queen Victoria St., EC4V 4DD : Distributed by Independent Magazines Ltd. £4.35 yearly* ARPV/E(B) (B78-06991)
Honky tonkin' : a guide to music USA. (Wootton, Richard). 2nd ed. *21 Melbourne Court, Anerley Rd, Penge, S.E.20 : The author. £2.50* A/GB(YT/BC) (B78-28695) ISBN 0-9506108-0-1
Honolka, Kurt. The dower. Die Mitgift und Gebet : zwei Männerchöre a cappella nach Texten von Josef Srb-Debrnov. (Smetana, Bedřich). *Bärenreiter. £0.70* GEZDW (B78-50423)
Horizon circled = Horizont umkreist : for orchestra = für Orchester, 1967 ; op.199 by Ernst Křenek. (Křenek, Ernst). *Bärenreiter. £10.50* MMJ (B78-50922)
Horizons circled : reflections on my music. (Krenek, Ernst). *University of California Press. £6.80* BKTM (B78-06254) ISBN 0-520-02338-2
Horn, the horn-. (Merewether, Richard). *116 Long Acre, WC2E 9PA : Paxman Musical Instruments Ltd. £1.50* AWT/B (B78-15125)
Hornplayer's companion series. Merewether, Richard. The horn, the horn-. *116 Long Acre, WC2E 9PA : Paxman Musical Instruments Ltd. £1.50* AWT/B (B78-15125)
Horovitz, Joseph.
Jubilee toy symphony. *Novello. £3.45* MVE (B78-50197)
String music of the second Elizabeth : twelve original pieces for string orchestra. *Belwin-Mills. Unpriced* RXM/AY (B78-50243)
Hortus musicus. Cervetto, Giacobbe, *b.1682.* Sonata, flute & continuo, op.3, no.6, D minor. Sonate, d-moll für Querflöte C (oder Violine) und Basso continuo = Sonata in D minor for transverse flute (or violin and basso continuo). *Bärenreiter. £3.00* VRPE (B78-51212)
Hosanna in the highest : a collection of descants for traditional hymns. *Dorchester Rd : Celebration Services. £1.50* FADM/AY (B78-50805) ISBN 0-906309-07-7
Hosanna Lord! (Farra, Mimi). *Celebration Services. Unpriced* JDH (B78-50079)
Hospodine. Höre mich, Herr : suli, coro, organo, arpa, trombe, 4 tromboni e tuba. (Janáček, Leoš). *Editio Dupraphone : Bärenreiter. £3.00* ENUXPNNDE (B78-50753)
Houseman, Alfred Edward. Three songs from 'A Shropshire lad' : for SATB choir unaccompanied with tenor solo. (Clark, Keith). *Roberton. £0.24* EZDW (B78-50386)
Hovhaness, Alan.
Simple mass. Op.282. *Vocal score.* Simple mass. Op.282 : for four-part unison chorus and soprano, alto, tenor and bass solos with organ accompaniment. *Associated Music. £1.80* DG (B78-50333)
Symphony no.24, 'Majnun'. Letters in the sand. *arr.* Letters in the sand : SATB with trumpet solo and piano. *Associated Music. £0.35* EWSPDW (B78-50361)
Symphony no.24, 'Majnun'. Majnun answered. *arr.* Majnun answered ... : SATB with trumpet solo and piano. *Associated Music. £0.30* EWSPDW (B78-50362)
How, Martin.
Advent message. *Weinberger. Unpriced* DK/LEZ (B78-50733)
An Easter greeting : for unison voices with divisions and organ. *Roberton. £0.15* JFDH (B78-50838)
How brightly beams the morning star = Wie schön leuchtet der Morgenstern : for four-part chorus of mixed voices, five solo voices and optional keyboard accompaniment. (Praetorius, Michael). *Schirmer. £0.35* EZDH/LF (B78-50375)
How brightly shine = Perite autem : for four part chorus of men's voices a cappella. (Mendelssohn, Felix). *Schirmer. £0.35* GEZDH/LF (B78-50420)
How t'make it as a rockstar. *IPC Magazines. £0.40* AKDW/HKR/E(MN)
How to dance : waltz, fox-trot, quick-step, tango, mambo, samba, cha-cha-cha, rumba, bossa-nova, jive ; plus! the music to 20 great dance numbers, plus! a detailed discography of dance records. *Omnibus Press : Books Sales. £3.50* KDW/GB/AY (B78-50873) ISBN 0-86001-380-4

How to sing. (Hewitt, Graham). *Elm Tree Books : E.M.I. Music Publishing. £3.95 : CIP rev.* AB/E (B78-04325) ISBN 0-241-89897-8
Howard, Brian. If I were a butterfly. *Celebration Services. Unpriced* JFDM (B78-50088)
Howarth, Elgar.
The battell. The marche before the battell. *arr.* The Earle of Oxford's march. (Byrd, William). *Chester Music. Unpriced* WMK/AGM (B78-51320)
Berne patrol : for brass band. *Chester Music. Unpriced* WMGM (B78-51304)
Greensleeves. *Chester Music. Unpriced* WMK/DW (B78-51326)
Greensleeves. (Howarth, Elgar). *Chester Music. Unpriced* WMK/DW (B78-51326)
Greensleeves : for brass band. *Chester Music. Unpriced* WMK/DW (B78-51327)
Two processional fanfares. *Chester Music. Unpriced* WMGN (B78-51305)
Howe, Lyn. Singalive! : twelve songs and a cakewalk. (Swann, Donald). *Collins. Unpriced* KDW (B78-50862) ISBN 0-00-599605-8

Howells, Herbert.
Antiphon : S.A.T.B. (unacc.). *Oxford University Press. Unpriced* EZDH (B78-50044) ISBN 0-19-350365-4
Come, my soul : SATB unacc. *Oxford University Press. Unpriced* EZDH (B78-50371)
Howell's clavichord : twenty pieces for clavichord or piano. *Novello. £3.80* PWPJ (B78-50517)
Howell's clavichord : twenty pieces for clavichord or piano. (Howells, Herbert). *Novello. £3.80* PWPJ (B78-50517)
Huber, Paul. Caprice. *R. Smith. Unpriced* WMJ (B78-51310)
Hudson, Hazel.
The Daniel quodlibet (based on three negro spirituals) : for two female, two male or one female and one male voices. *Edwin Ashdown. Unpriced* FDW/LC (B78-50394)
Feed my sheep : a quodlibet based on negro spirituals. *Ashdown. Unpriced* FDW/LC (B78-50065)
Hudson, Herman C. The black composer speaks. *Scarecrow Press : Distributed by Bailey and Swinfen. £17.00* A/D(YTLD/M) (B78-22844) ISBN 0-8108-1045-X
Hufschmidt, Wolfgang.
Exercitien 3 'Das Prinzip Hoffnung' (nach Ernst Bloch) : für sechs Ausführende (1974-1976). *Bärenreiter. £21.00* KFNE/NYDNQDX (B78-50898)
Trio 3. Partitur-Fassung 1975-1977 mit Versionen für eine oder drei Sprecherinnen und oder 1-9 Oboeinstrumente und oder 1-9 Gitarren oder andere zupfinstrumente. *Bärenreiter. £22.40* HYE/VTPLTN (B78-50424)
Hugh the drover or Love in the stocks : a romantic ballad opera in two acts. (Vaughan Williams, Ralph). New ed. based on the 1959 edition as revised in accordance with the composer's directions .. *Curwen : Faber Music. Unpriced* CC (B78-50010)
Hugh the drover. *Vocal score.* Hugh the drover or Love in the stocks : a romantic ballad opera in two acts. (Vaughan Williams, Ralph). New ed. based on the 1959 edition as revised in accordance with the composer's directions .. *Curwen : Faber Music. Unpriced* CC (B78-50010)
Hughes, Brian.
Jonah : spiritual for unaccompanied male choir or quartet. *Roberton. £0.12* GEZDW/LC (B78-50074)
Two Old Testament spirituals. *Roberton. £0.18* EZDW/LC (B78-50057)
Hughes, David E. Ring bells ring. *2 Highfield Close : David E. Hughes. Unpriced* DP/LF (B78-50738)
Hughes, Eric. Overture to youth. *Studio Music. Unpriced* WMJ (B78-51311)
Hughes, Martin.
The Russian school of piano playing
Vol.1. (Nikolaev, Aleksandr Aleksandrovich). English ed. *Boosey and Hawkes. Unpriced* Q/AC (B78-50962)
Vol.2. (Nikolaev, Aleksandr Aleksandrovich). English ed. *Boosey and Hawkes. Unpriced* Q/AC (B78-50963)
Hughes-Jones, Llifon. Sleep = Cswg : for two-part choir and piano. *Roberton. £0.20* FDW (B78-50815)
Hugill, Stan. Sea shanties. *Barrie and Jenkins. £2.95* ADW/GMC (B78-01680) ISBN 0-214-20329-8
Hume, Paul. Verdi : the man and his music. *Hutchinson. £5.50* BVE(N) (B78-08475) ISBN 0-09-132390-8
Humphries, John.
Concerto, string orchestra, op.3, no.10, D minor. Concerto in D minor, opus 3, no.10, for strings and continuo. *Oxford University Press. Unpriced* RXMF (B78-50245) ISBN 0-19-364804-0
Concerto, trumpet & string orchestra, op.2, no.12, D major. Concerto in D major, for trumpet (or horn), strings and continuo. *Oxford University Press. Unpriced* RXMPWSF (B78-51075) ISBN 0-19-364797-4
Hungarian pastoral fantasy : for flute and piano. (Doppler, Franz). *Chester Music. Unpriced* VRPJ (B78-51215)
Hurd, Michael.
Invitation to the partsong
3: Shakespeare settings by Bishop, Cooke, Hatton, MacFarren, Stevens, Webbe ; a selection of four- and five-part works newly transcribed and edited by Geoffrey Bush and Michael Hurd. *Stainer and Bell. £1.25* EZDW/AY (B78-50056) ISBN 0-85249-491-2
The ordeal of Ivor Gurney. *Oxford University Press. £5.95 : CIP rev.* BGYU(N) (B78-29833) ISBN 0-19-211752-1
The phoenix and the turtle. *Vocal score.* The phoenix and the turtle : for mezzo-soprano solo, SATB timpani (2) and string orchestra. *Novello. £0.78* DX (B78-50029)
Pilgrim. *Vocal score.* Pilgrim : a musical morality in popular style for unison voices (with divisions) and piano with guitar chord symbols. *Novello. £0.86* DE (B78-50332)
Shepherd's calendar. *Vocal score.* Shepherd's calendar : choral symphony for baritone solo, SATB and orchestra. *Novello. £1.45* DX (B78-50354)
Hurford, Peter.
Bristol suite. *Novello. £1.20* RG (B78-50562)
Sonata, organ, C minor. Sonata in C minor for organ. (Pescetti, Giovanni Battista). *Oxford University Press. Unpriced* RE (B78-50229) ISBN 0-19-375634-x
Husa, Karel. Twelve Moravian songs : for voice and piano. *Associated Music. £3.05* KDW (B78-50444)
Hutchings, Arthur. The baroque concerto. 3rd revised ed. *Faber. £3.95 : CIP rev.* ALF(XFQ31) (B78-30835) ISBN 0-571-10865-2
Hyman, Alan. Sullivan and his satellites : a survey of English operettas, 1860-1914. *Chappell : Elm Tree Books. £7.50* ACF(YD/XK55) (B78-26888) ISBN 0-903443-24-4
Hymne to God the Father. (Wyton, Alec). *Novello. £0.47* EXRPLRDH (B78-50363)
I am a rock. (Davis, Diane). *Yeldall Manor, Hare Hatch, Reading : Celebration Services. Unpriced* KDH (B78-50110)
I believe in God : a sacred song. (Geiger, George). *Lewis Music : Phoenix. Unpriced* KDH (B78-50111)
I speak in wisdom's voice (Ego sapienta) : for full chorus of men's voices a cappella. (Loudová, Ivana). *Schirmer. Unpriced* GEZDH (B78-50419)

I will clothe thy priests with salvation = Ihre Priester will ich mit Heil kleiden : S.A.T.B. with accompaniment. (Peter, Johann Friedrich). *Boosey and Hawkes. Unpriced* DH (B78-50340)

Ibberson, Mary. For joy that we are here : Rural Music Schools, 1929-1950. *Bedford Square Press for the Rural Music Schools Association. £2.75* A(V/YD/XN31) (B78-03572) ISBN 0-7199-0930-9

Ice break : an opera in three acts. (Tippett, *Sir* Michael). *Schott. £13.00* CC (B78-50009)

Ice break. *Vocal score.* The ice break : an opera in three acts. (Tippett, *Sir* Michael). *Schott. £13.00* CC (B78-50009)

Ice carving. (Conyngham, Barry). *Universal. Unpriced* RXMPS (B78-51071)

Idyll 'Once I passed through a populous city'. *Vocal score.* Prelude and idyll : for soprano and baritone with orchestra. (Delius, Frederick). *Boosey and Hawkes. Unpriced* JNEDX (B78-50438)

If I were a butterfly. (Howard, Brian). *Celebration Services. Unpriced* JFDM (B78-50088)

Ihre Priester will ich mit Heil kleiden. *arr.* I will clothe thy priests with salvation = Ihre Priester will ich mit Heil kleiden : S.A.T.B. with accompaniment. (Peter, Johann Friedrich). *Boosey and Hawkes. Unpriced* DH (B78-50340)

Illustrated encyclopedia of country music. (Dellar, Fred). *27 Old Gloucester St., WC1N 3AF : Salamander Books Ltd. £5.95* A/GC(C) (B78-05399) ISBN 0-86101-004-3

Illustrated encyclopedia of jazz. (Case, Brian). *27 Old Gloucester St., WC1N 3AF : Salamander Books. £6.95* AMT(C) (B78-22169) ISBN 0-86101-013-2

Illustrated history of rock music. (Pascall, Jeremy). *Hamlyn. £5.95* AKDW/HKR(X) (B78-39779) ISBN 0-600-37605-2

Illustrated 'New musical express' encyclopedia of rock. (Logan, Nick). 1978 ed.. *27 Old Gloucester St., WC1N 3AF : Salamander Books Limited. £3.95* A/HKR(C) (B78-12095) ISBN 0-86101-009-4

Illustrated 'New musical express' encyclopedia of rock. (Logan, Nick). Revised ed. *Hamlyn. £5.95* AKDW/HKR(C) (B78-15752) ISBN 0-600-33171-7

I'm Popeye the sailor man. (Lerner, Sammy). *Warner Blossom. Unpriced* UMMK/DW/JR (B78-50636)

I'm Popeye the sailor man. *arr.* I'm Popeye the sailor man. (Lerner, Sammy). *Warner : Blossom. Unpriced* EWMDW/JR (B78-50762)

In changing mood : nine short easy piano pieces. (Last, Joan). *Oxford University Press. Unpriced* QPJ (B78-50223) ISBN 0-19-373122-3

In defence of opera. (Swanston, Hamish). *Penguin. £1.25* AC (B78-05403) ISBN 0-14-022005-4

In defence of opera. (Swanston, Hamish). *Allen Lane. £6.50* AC (B78-09697) ISBN 0-7139-1063-1

In excelsis gloria : two carols for three-part female voice choir and piano with optional recorders. (Smith, Robert F). *Roberton. £0.28* FDP/LF (B78-50390)

In search of Buddy Bolden, first man of jazz. (Marquis, Donald M). *Louisiana State University Press. £7.00* AMT(P) (B78-33167) ISBN 0-8071-0356-x

In the gutter. (Hennessy, Val). *Quartet Books. £1.95* AKDW/HKQ (B78-24013) ISBN 0-7043-3230-2

In wonder, love and praise : a collection of fourteen anthems. *Novello. Unpriced* DH/AY (B78-50728)

In words and music. Andy Williams. *Wise : Music Sales. £1.95* KDW/GB/AY (B78-50143) ISBN 0-86001-115-1

Incidental music for Shakespeare's 'The merchant of Venice' : for string orchestra (or string quintet). (harbison, John). *Associated Music. Unpriced* RXMJ (B78-51066)

Incoronazione di Poppea. (Monteverdi, Claudio). *Faber Music. Unpriced* DAC (B78-50331)

Incoronazione di Poppea. *Choral score.* L'incoronazione di Poppea. (Monteverdi, Claudio). *Faber Music. Unpriced* DAC (B78-50331)

Incoronazione di Poppea. Vocal score. L'incoronazione di Poppea = The coronation of Poppea : opera in two acts and prologue. (Monteverdi, Claudio). New ed. *Faber Music. Unpriced* CC (B78-50007)

Index of musical wind-instrument makers. (Langwill, Lyndesay Graham). 5th ed. *7 Dick Place, Edinburgh EH9 2JS : The author. £10.00* AV/BC(M/WT) (B78-14459)

Index to opera, operetta and musical comedy synopses in collections and periodicals. (Drone, Jeanette Marie). *Scarecrow Press : Distributed by Bailey and Swinfen. £5.95* ACMBN(WT) (B78-19781) ISBN 0-8108-1100-6

Indiana University. *Afro-American Arts Institute.* The black composer speaks. *Scarecrow Press : Distributed by Bailey and Swinfen. £17.00* A/D(YTLD/M) (B78-22844) ISBN 0-8108-1045-X

Ingrisch, Lotte.
- Kabale und liebe. Op.44. *Vocal score.* Kabale und Liebe : Oper in 2 teilen (9 Bildern) nach Friedrich von Schiller. (Einem, Gottfried von). *Boosey and Hawkes. Unpriced* CC (B78-50006)
- Kabale und Liebe : Oper in 2 Teilen (9 Bildern) nach Friedrich von Schiller. (Einem, Gottfried von). *Boosey and Hawkes. Unpriced* CQC (B78-50710)
- Kabale und Liebe : Opera in 2 Teilen (9 Bildern) nach Friedrich von Schiller. (Einem, Gottfried von). *Boosey and Hawkes. Unpriced* CC (B78-50005)

Initiation a l'accordeon de concert = Initiation to the concert accordion = Einführung zum Konzertakkordeon. (Abbott, Alain). *Chappell. Unpriced* RS/AC (B78-50574)

Inness, Peter. Six pieces : for organ. *Novello. £2.40* RJ (B78-51048)

Inside the pop scene. (Watson, Pat). *Thornhill Press. £1.50* AKDW/GB/E(M) (B78-14832) ISBN 0-904110-57-5

Instruments 1. (Feldman, Morton). *Universal. Unpriced* NYH (B78-50954)

Instruments in the history of Western music. (Geiringer, Karl). 3rd (revised and enlarged) ed. *Allen and Unwin. £10.50* AL/B(X) (B78-37097) ISBN 0-04-781005-x

Instruments of the orchestra.
- Bate, Philip. The trumpet and trombone : an outline of their history, development and construction. 2nd ed. *E. Benn etc.. £8.50* AWS/B (B78-09121) ISBN 0-510-36412-8
- Morley-Pegge, Reginald. The French horn : some notes on the evolution of the instrument and of its technique. 2nd ed. *E. Benn etc.. £7.50* AWT/B

Intavolatura di liutto, lib.2. Canzona a 8. *arr.* Canzona in 8 parts. (Terzi, Giovanni Antonio). *Schott. £0.70* TSNSK (B78-50608)

Intermediate band book
- Book 1: Sandwell festival march, by Stuart Johnson and arrangements of songs, hymns, and carols. *R. Smith. Unpriced* WM/AY (B78-50669)

International music guide
- 1978. *Tantivy Press etc.. £3.25* A(BC) (B78-07707) ISBN 0-498-02107-6

International piper
- Vol.1, no.1- ; May 1978-. *Seton Works, Edinburgh Rd, Cockenzie, East Lothian EH32 0HQ : International Piper Ltd. £0.35* AVY/E(B) (B78-26248)

Internationale Stiftung Mozarteum Salzburg. Mozarts italienische Texte mit deutscher Ubersetzung. Arien, Szenen, Ensembles
- Textbuch italienisch-deutsch. *32 Gt Titchfield St., W1P 7AD : Bärenreiter. £1.68* BMSADW (B78-26890)

Internationale Stiftung Mozarteum Salzburg. Mozarts italienische Texte mit deutscher Übersetzung. Da Ponte, Lorenzo. Don Giovanni, KV527 : Dramma giocoso im zwei Akten
- Textbuch italienisch-deutsch. *32 Gt Titchfield St., W1P 7AD : Bärenreiter. £2.24* BMSAC (B78-17615)

Internationale Stiftung Mozarteum Salzburg. Schriftenreiche. Afflisio, Giuseppe. Vita di Giuseppe Afflisio = Lebensgeschichte des Giuseppe Afflisio. *17 Bucklersbury, Hitchin, Herts. : Bärenreiter. £4.48* AC(WB/P) (B78-19963)

Interplay : für sieben Spieler, 1975. (Redel, Martin Christoph). *Bote und Bock : Associated Music. £7.70* NYDPNP (B78-50511)

Interpretation for the piano student. Interpretation in piano study. (Last, Joan). *Oxford University Press. £2.50* AQ/E (B78-26895) ISBN 0-19-318424-9

Interpretation in piano study. (Last, Joan). *Oxford University Press. £2.50* AQ/E (B78-26895) ISBN 0-19-318424-9

Introduction and allegro. (Wood, Gareth). *R. Smith. Unpriced* WMJ (B78-50680)

Introduction, elegy and caprice. (Calvert, Morley). *R. Smith. Unpriced* WMJ (B78-51309)

Introduction to the clarinet
- Book 1. (Dingle, Patrick). *EMI. Unpriced* VV/AC (B78-50659)

'Introduction to the guitar. (Bolton, Cecil). *EMI Music. Unpriced* TS/AC (B78-51140)

Introduction to the melodica : a beginner's guide to the melodica with well known tunes to play and sing. (Slack, Roy). *EMI. Unpriced* VXR/AC (B78-51294)

Introduction to the recorder : a tutor for adults. (Rowland-Jones, A). *Oxford University Press. £1.95* AVS/E (B78-23598) ISBN 0-19-322341-4

Invitation to medieval music
- 4: Music of the mid-fifteenth century (ii) : an advanced selection of 11 compositions for 1-3 voices and/or instruments newly transcribed and edited by Brian Trowell. *Stainer and Bell. £1.25* CB/AY(XCH 301) (B78-50004) ISBN 0-85249-317-7

Invitation to the partsong
- 3: Shakespeare settings by Bishop, Cooke, Hatton, MacFarren, Stevens, Webbe ; a selection of four- and five-part works newly transcribed and edited by Geoffrey Bush and Michael Hurd. *Stainer and Bell. £1.25* EZDW/AY (B78-50056) ISBN 0-85249-491-2

Invocation and toccata : guitar. (Walters, Gareth). *Oxford University Press. Unpriced* TSPMJ (B78-50274) ISBN 0-19-359380-7

Inwood, Paul. Requiem, Op.48. (Fauré, Gabriel). *Eulenburg. Unpriced* EMDGKAV (B78-50031)

Iona boat song. For a dead king : traditional Scottish air for 4-part male chorus unaccompanied. (Lees, Heath). *Roberton. £0.15* GEZDW (B78-50828)

Ireland *(Republic). Cultural Relations Committee of Ireland.* Irish life and culture. *See* Irish life and culture.

Irish ballads and songs of the sea. *4 Bridge St., Cork : Mercier Press. £1.50* AKDW/KC(YDM) (B78-34739) ISBN 0-85342-074-2

Irish environmental library series. McMahon, Tony. Irish traditional music. *Folens. Unpriced* A/G(YDM) (B78-15122)

Irish harp. (Rimmer, Joan). 2nd ed. *4 Bridge St., Cork : Mercier Press for the Cultural Relations Committee. £1.50* ATQS/B (B78-35478) ISBN 0-85342-151-x

Irish harp book : a tutor and companion. (Cuthbert, Sheila Larchet). *Mercier Press. Unpriced* TQR/AC (B78-51139) ISBN 0-85342-279-6

Irish heritage series. Acton, Charles. Irish music & musicians. *65 Middle Abbey St., Dublin 1 : Eason and Son Ltd. £0.90* A(YDM/X) (B78-33934) ISBN 0-900346-22-1

Irish life and culture. Rimmer, Joan. The Irish harp. 2nd ed. *4 Bridge St., Cork : Mercier Press for the Cultural Relations Committee. £1.50* ATQS/B (B78-35478) ISBN 0-85342-151-x

Irish music & musicians. (Acton, Charles). *65 Middle Abbey St., Dublin 1 : Eason and Son Ltd. £0.90* A(YDM/X) (B78-33934) ISBN 0-900346-22-1

Irish street ballads. *Pan Books. £0.90* KEZDW/K/G/AYDM (B78-50468) ISBN 0-330-25316-6

Irish traditional music. (McMahon, Tony). *Folens. Unpriced* A/G(YDM) (B78-15122)

Isle of Avalon : suite for brass band. (Catelinet, Philip). *R. Smith. Unpriced* WMG (B78-51303)

Italian 17th & 18th century sinfonias and sonatas for trumpets and strings. Gabrielli, Domenico. Sonata, trumpet, string quartet & continuo, D major. Sonata, D.XI, 5 in D for trumpet, strings and basso continuo. *Musica rara. Unpriced* NUXSNQE (B78-50945)

Italian 17th & 18th century sinfonias and sonatas for trumpets & strings.
- Gabrielli, Domenico. Sonata, trumpet, string quintet & continuo, D major. Sonata, D. XI, 4 in D for trumpet, strings and basso continuo. *Musica rara. Unpriced* NUXSNPE (B78-50944)
- Gabrielli, Domenico. Sonata, trumpet, string quintet & continuo, D major. *arr.* Sonata D, XI, 4 in D for trumpet, strings and basso continuo. *Musica rara. Unpriced* WSPK/AE (B78-51346)

Italian 17th and 18th century sinfonias and sonatas for trumpets and strings.
- Lazari, Ferdinando Antonio. Sonata, trumpets (2) & string orchestra, D major. Sonata à 6 for trumpets, strings and continuo. *Musica rara. Unpriced* RXMPWSNUE (B78-50579)
- Lazari, Ferdinando Antonio. Sonata, trumpets (2) & string orchestra, D major. *arr.* Sonata à 6, for 2 trumpets, strings and continuo. *Musica rara. Unpriced* WSNTQK/AE (B78-50693)

Italian 17th & 18th century sinofonias and sonatas for trumpets and strings. Gabrielli, Domenico. Sonata, trumpet, string quartet & continuo, D major. *arr.* Sonata D. XI.5 in D for trumpet, strings and basso continuo. *Musica rara. Unpriced* WSPK/AE (B78-51345)

Italian instrumental music of the renaissance.
- Barratt, Carol. Chester's piano book : for two instruments. *London Pro Musica. Unpriced* LNU (B78-50908)
- Lupacchino, Bernadino. Primo libro a due voci. *Selections.* Nine fantasies : for two instruments. *London Pro Musica. Unpriced* LNU (B78-50909)

Italian intermezzo : six pieces. (Wolf-Ferrari, Ermanno). *Weinberger. Unpriced* VRPLTSK (B78-50650)

Ives, Charles.
- 3 quarter-tone pieces. Quarter-tone chorale. *arr.* Quarter-tone chorale. *Peters. Unpriced* RXMJ (B78-51067)
- Sunrise : voice, violin and piano. *Peters. Unpriced* KE/SPDW (B78-50462)

Ives celebration : papers and panels of the Charles Ives Centennial Festival-Conference. (Charles Ives Centennial Festival-Conference, *New York and New Haven, 1974*). *University of Illinois Press. £8.40* BIV (B78-16383) ISBN 0-252-00619-4

Iveson, John.
- Het derde musyck boexken. *Selections : arr.* Six Susato dances : for brass band ... (Susato, Thielman). *Chester Music. Unpriced* WMK/AH (B78-51321)
- A suite of dances. (Susato, Thielman). *Chester Music. Unpriced* WNK/AH (B78-51332)
- Three rags for five. (Joplin, Scott). *Chester Music. Unpriced* WNRK/AHXJ (B78-51338)

Izitso. *arr.* Izitso. (Stevens, Cat). *Columbia Pictures Publications : EMI. Unpriced* KDW/GB (B78-50139)

Jackson, Arthur. The book of musicals : from 'Show Boat' to 'A Chorus Line'. *Mitchell Beazley. £7.95* ACM(XKF112) (B78-16385) ISBN 0-85533-116-x

Jackson, Chuck. Our love : a Marvin Yancy, Chuck Jackson songbook. (Yancy, Marvin). *Chappell. Unpriced* KDW/GB (B78-50871)

Jackson, Francis.
- Alleluia, laudate pueri dominum : S.S.A.A.T.T.B.B. *Banks. Unpriced* EZDJ (B78-50777)
- Praise God in his sanctuary : S.A.T.B. *Banks. Unpriced* DR (B78-50743)

Jacob, Gordon.
- Concerto, viola, new version. *arr.* Concerto for viola and orchestra : für viola und Orchester. *Simrock. Unpriced* SQPK/LF (B78-50595)
- Fantasy sonata for organ. *Peters. Unpriced* RE (B78-50561)
- Tribute to Canterbury. *Boosey and Hawkes. Unpriced* UMMJ (B78-50281)

Jacobs, Arthur.
- Choral music : a symposium. *Penguin. £1.25* AD(X) (B78-35474) ISBN 0-14-020533-0
- The new Penguin dictionary of music. 4th ed. *Allen Lane. £5.50* A(C) (B78-27519) ISBN 0-7139-1121-2

Jacobs, Charles. Libro de musica para vihuela, intitulado Orphenica lyra. Orphenica lyra (Seville 1554). (Fuenllana, Miguel de). *Clarendon Press. £30.00* TVPMJ (B78-50625)

Jacobsen, Jens Peter. An arabesque = Eine Arabeske : for baritone solo, mixed chorus and orchestra = für Bariton-Solo, gemischter Chor und Orchester. (Delius, Frederick). *Boosey and Hawkes. Unpriced* EMDX (B78-50751)

Jami. Symphony no.24, 'Majnun'. Letters in the sand. *arr.* Letters in the sand : SATB with trumpet solo and piano. (Hovhaness, Alan). *Associated Music. £0.35* EWSPDW (B78-50361)

Janáček, Leoš. Lord, have mercy upon us. Hospodine. Höre mich, Herr : suli, coro, organo, arpa, trombe, 4 tromboni

e tuba. *Editio Dupraphone : Bärenreiter. £3.00* ENUXPNNDE (B78-50753)
Janáček's tragic operas. (Ewans, Michael). *Faber. £7.95 : CIP rev.* BJFAC (B77-23620) ISBN 0-571-10959-4
Jannetti, Francesco. La favorita : drama in four acts. (Royer, Alphonse). *140 Strand, WC2R 1HH : G. Schirmer. Unpriced* BDRAC (B78-26887)
Janz, Curt Paul.
Works. Der musikalische Nachlass. (Nietzsche, Friedrich). *Bärenreiter. Unpriced* C/AZ (B78-50699)

Japanese fragments : for soprano, viola and guitar. (Williams, Graham). *Chester Music. Unpriced* KFLE/SQPLTSDW (B78-50895)
Jarvis, Roger S. Voluntary, organ, no.6, B flat major. *arr.* Voluntary in C major, for descant, treble and tenor recorders. (Greene, Maurice). *Chester Music. Unpriced* VSNTK (B78-51248)
Jasper, Tony. British records charts, 1955-1978. Revised and updated ed.. *Macdonald and Jane's. £4.95* AKDW/GB/FD(XPQ24) (B78-37424) ISBN 0-354-08523-9
Jazz is. (Hentoff, Nat). *W.H. Allen. £5.95* AMT(M) (B78-08478) ISBN 0-491-02312-x
'Jazz record'. Selections from the gutter : jazz portraits from the 'Jazz record'. *University of California Press. £8.75* AMT/FD(M) (B78-05409) ISBN 0-520-02999-2
Jazz styles. (Gridley, Mark C). *Prentice-Hall. £9.45* AMT(X) (B78-31600) ISBN 0-13-509885-8
Jefferson, Alan. Richard Strauss. *Novello. £0.30* BSU(N) (B78-31596)
Jeffery, Brian. Doce canciones = Twelve songs : with guitar accompaniment. (Moretti, Federico). Complete facsimile ed. *Tecla. Unpriced* KE/TSDW (B78-50885) ISBN 0-8494-0140-2
Jenkins, Colin J. Four Australian songs. *Schott. Unpriced* VSNK/DW/AYX (B78-51241)
Jenkins, David, *b.1944.*
Children's overture : an introduction to music listening and creative musical activities for young children. *Oxford University Press. £2.75* AJFDW(VC) (B78-33673) ISBN 0-19-321388-5
Mendelssohn in Scotland. *Chappell : Elm Tree Books. £5.95* BMJ(N/YDL/XHJ) (B78-19674) ISBN 0-903443-18-x
Jenkins, John. Consort music : for viols in four parts. *Faber Music. Unpriced* STN (B78-51132)
Jenner, Gustav. Serenade für Orchester. *Bärenreiter. £22.40* MMJ (B78-50491)
Jenni, Donald.
Elegy and dance : for small orchestra. *Associated Music. £13.60* MJ (B78-50484)
Gloria for four-part chorus of mixed voices a cappella. *Associated Music. £0.30* EZDGC (B78-50366)
Musica dell'autumno : for organ. *Associated Music. £3.05* RJ (B78-50563)
Jest 'fore Christmas. (Silverman, Jerry). *Schirmer. Unpriced* KDW (B78-50116)
Jest 'fore Christmas : for two-part chorus of young voices with piano and guitar accompaniment. (Silverman, Jerry). *Schirmer. Unpriced* FDW (B78-50063)
Jesu dulcis memoria. Jusu! the very thought is sweet : for 4-part female choir unaccompanied. (Victoria, Tomás Luis de). *Roberton. £0.15* FEZDJ (B78-50824)
Jesus nimmt die Sunder an : aria from cantata 113 for tenor, flute and continuo. (Bach, Johann Sebastian). *Oxford University Press. Unpriced* KGHE/VRPDH (B78-50177)
Jeune, Henri le. *See* Le Jeune, Henri.
Jewel song ... (Gounod, Charles). *Leonard, Gould and Bolttler. Unpriced* KDW (B78-50115)
Jewell, Derek. Duke : a portrait of Duke Ellington. New ed.. *Sphere. £1.95* AMT(P) (B78-33939) ISBN 0-7221-5022-9
Jillian of Berry : four part song for male voices T.T.B.B. (Pasfield, William Reginald). *Edwin Ashdown. £0.20* GEZDW (B78-50829)
Jimmie the Kid : the life of Jimmie Rodgers. (Paris, Mike). *Eddison Press : 'Old time music' Magazine. £3.95* AKDW/GC/E(P) (B78-33931) ISBN 0-85649-019-9
Jingle bells. (Pierpont, James S). *EMI. Unpriced* KDW/LF (B78-50882)
Jobim, Antonio Carlos.
Álbum para piano. *Editôra Musical Arapuã : Essex Music. Unpriced* QPJ (B78-50532)
Sinfonia do Rio de Janeiro : piano. *Arapua : Essex Music. Unpriced* QPE (B78-50995)
John, Elton.
Blue moves. *arr.* Blue moves. *Big Pig Music : Music Sales. £4.95* KDW/HKR (B78-50161)
Rock of the westies. *arr.* Rock of the westies : songs from the album. *Big Pig Music : Music Sales. £1.95* KDW/HKR (B78-50162)
John, Timothy. The great song book. *Benn. Unpriced* DW/AY (B78-50747) ISBN 0-510-00037-1
John of the Cross, *Saint.* Ultimos ritos. En honor de San Juan de la Cruz. (Tavener, John). *Chester Music. Unpriced* EMDH (B78-50750)
John Roberts, telynor Cymru. (Roberts, E Ernest). *Gwasg Gee. £1.50* ATQ/E(P) (B78-33170)
Johnson, J Rosamond. The books of American negro spirituals, including The book of American negro spirituals and The second book of negro spirituals. *Da Capo Press : Robert Hale. £6.50* KDW/LC/AY (B78-50461)
Johnson, James Weldon. The books of American negro spirituals, including The book of American negro spirituals and The second book of negro spirituals. *Da Capo Press : Robert Hale. £6.50* KDW/LC/AY (B78-50461)
Johnson, Lucile. Sonata, harp. Sonata, für Harfe, for harp. (Rossini, Gioacchino Antonio). *Schott. £2.40* TQPME (B78-51133)
Johnson, Michael. Tune and repair your own piano : a practical and theoretical guide to the tuning of all keyboard stringed instruments, and to the running repair of the piano. *Harcourt Brace Jovanovich. Unpriced* AQ/BT (B78-24454) ISBN 0-15-191383-8
Johnson, Robert Sherlaw. Sonata, flute (alto) & cello. Sonata for alto flute and cello. *Oxford University Press. Unpriced* VRSPLSRE (B78-51236) ISBN 0-19-357337-7
Johnson, Stuart.
Hinrichsen second band book : four original compositions and four arrangements of classical works. *Peters in conjunction with the National School Brass Band Association. Unpriced* WMK/AAY (B78-51316)
Hinrichsen second band book : four original compositions and four arrangements of classical works. *Peters in conjunction with the National School Brass Band Association. Unpriced* WMK/AAY (B78-51317)
Hinrichsen third band book : a miscellany of 6 popular pieces. *Peters in conjunction with the National School Brass Band Association. Unpriced* WMK/AAY (B78-51318)
Hinrichsen third band book : a miscellany of 6 popular pieces. *Peters in conjunction with the National School Brass Band Association. Unpriced* WMK/AAY (B78-51319)
Intermediate band book
Book 1: Sandwell festival march, by Stuart Johnson and arrangements of songs, hymns, and carols. *R. Smith. Unpriced* WM/AY (B78-50669)
A march overture. *R. Smith. Unpriced* WMGM (B78-50674)
Johnson, Thomas Arnold. Le camp de Grand-Pré. Tambourin. *arr.* Tambourin. (Gossec, François Joseph). *Bosworth and Co. Unpriced* QPK/AHVQT (B78-51027)

Johnston, Peter Fyfe. When the kye comes home : T.T.B.B. unacc. *Banks Music. Unpriced* GEZDW (B78-50072)
Jolivet, André. Alla rustica. *arr.* Alla rustica : divertissement pour flûte et harpe ou deux flûtes et harpe. *Boosey and Hawkes. Unpriced* VRPLTQ (B78-50648)
Jonah : spiritual for unaccompanied male choir or quartet. (Hughes, Brian). *Roberton. £0.12* GEZDW/LC (B78-50074)
Jones, A Rowland-. *See* Rowland-Jones, A.
Jones, Eirlys.
Carol y doethion. Carol y doethion = Carol of the kings a Cysgu yn y gwair = Lord Emmanuel. (Whelan, E L). *Hafod, St. Hilary, Cowbridge : E.L. Whelan. £0.25* FDP/LF (B78-50060)
Clychau'r nadolig. Clychau'r nadolig = Christmas bells a Bethlehem. (Whelan, E L). *Hafod, St. Hilary, Cowbridge : E.L. Whelan. £0.25* FDP/LF (B78-50061)
Jones, Ivor Wynne. Opera at Llandudno. *c/o I.W. Jones, 'Pegasus', 71 Llandudno Rd, Penrhyn Bay, Llandudno, Gwynedd LL30 3HN : Welsh National Opera Company. Unpriced* AC/E(YDKPL) (B78-28696)
Jones, Kenneth. Sonata for solo violin. *Chester Music. Unpriced* SPME (B78-51104)
Jones, Llifon Hughes-. *See* Hughes-Jones, Llifon.
Jones, Michael Leighton. Preces and responses for men's voices. Revised ed. *36 Ranelagh Gdns., W.6 : Cathedral Music. Unpriced* GEZDGMM (B78-50414)
Jones, Philip.
Equali, trombones(4), nos.1-3. Three equali for four trombones. (Beethoven, Ludwig van). *Chester Music. Unpriced* WUNS (B78-51354)
Fantasie overo canzoni alla francese. Fantasie no.6. *arr.* Echo fantasia : for brass quartet. (Banchieri, Adriano). *Chester Music. Unpriced* WNSK (B78-51339)
Paduana, galliarda .... Cantus 18. Canzon cornetto : for four trumpets. (Scheidt, Samuel). *Chester Music. Unpriced* WSNS (B78-51342)
Sacrae symphoniae. Bk.1. Sonata pian'e forte. Sonata pian'e forte : for brass octet. (Gabrieli, Giovanni). *Chester Music. Unpriced* WNNE (B78-51333)
Jones, Stanley. Ein musikalischen Spass. K.522. Presto. *arr.* A musical joke : theme from 'The horse of the year show' and other equestrian events. (Mozart, Wolfgang Amadeus). *Fentone Music. Unpriced* QPK (B78-51022)
Jones, Stephen. The lantern song : ten Chinese songs arranged for voices, recorders and percussion by Kenneth Pont. (Pont, Kenneth). *Oxford University Press. Unpriced* JFE/NYHSDW (B78-50851) ISBN 0-19-330613-1
Jongleur de Notre Dame : a masque, for mime, baritone, chamber ensemble and children's band. (Davies, Peter Maxwell). *Chester Music. Unpriced* CQPF (B78-50713)
Joplin, Scott.
Easy winners : nine piano rags. *Paxton. £1.25* QPHXJ (B78-50526)
Gladiolus rag. *R. Smith. Unpriced* WMK/AHXJ (B78-51322)
Maple leaf rag. *arr.* Maple leaf rag. *Bosworth and Co. Unpriced* QPK/AHXJ (B78-51028)
Piano music. *Selections : arr.* Rags for guitar. *Schirmer. £1.50* TSPMK/AHXJ (B78-51167)
Three rags for five. *Chester Music. Unpriced* WNRK/AHXJ (B78-51338)
Jordan, Ruth. Nocturne : a life of Chopin. *Constable. £6.95* BCE(N) (B78-26246) ISBN 0-09-462330-9
Josephs, Wilfred.
Rail. Op.57. *arr.* Rail. *Galaxy : Stainer and Bell. Unpriced* UMMK (B78-50630)
Symphony no.3, op.59, 'Philadelphia'. Symphony no.3 (Philadelphia), op.59. *Novello. £3.45* MME (B78-50488)

Josquin des Prés. Seven secular pieces : for four voices or instruments, ATTB. *London Pro Musica. Unpriced* EZDU (B78-50382)
Joubert, John.
Concerto, bassoon & chamber orchestra, Op.77. *arr.* Concerto for bassoon and chamber orchestra, Opus 77. *Novello. £3.15* VWPK/LF (B78-50667)
Sonata, piano, no.2, op.71. Sonata no.2 for piano, op.71. *Novello. £2.50* QPE (B78-50216)
Joyce, James. The mime of Mick, Nick and the Maggies : on part 2 of 'Finnegans Wake'. (Buller, John). *Schirmer. £17.50* EMDX (B78-50355)
Juba-mirum-Fantasia nach W.A. Mozart, K.V.626 : für Orgel, op.65. (Krol, Bernhard). *Bote und Bock Schirmer. £7.70* RJ (B78-51049)
Jubilee toy symphony. (Horovitz, Joseph). *Novello. £3.45* MVE (B78-50197)
Jubilen da quarânia, 1927-1977 : 20 melhores quarânias de todus os tempos. *Fermata da Brasil : Essex Music. Unpriced* KDW/AYUR (B78-50121)
Jubileu de guarânia, 1927-1977 : melhores guarânias de todos os tempos. *Fermata do Brasil : Essex Music. Unpriced* QPJ (B78-50533)
Judica me. Op.96 : for unaccompanied chorus, SSATBB. (Berkeley, *Sir* Lennox). *Chester Music. Unpriced* EZDJ (B78-50776)
Junior orchestra, series 1. Wade, Darrell. Fanfare. Fanfare, Lullaby, Cherokee war dance. *16 Anchor Way, Danes Green, Gnosall : Viking. Unpriced* MJ (B78-50181)
Just brass.
Banchieri, Adriano. Fantasie overo canzoni alla francese. Fantasie no.6. *arr.* Echo fantasia : for brass quartet. *Chester Music. Unpriced* WNSK (B78-51339)
Beethoven, Ludwig van. Equali, trombones(4), nos.1-3. Three equali for four trombones. *Chester Music. Unpriced* WUNS (B78-51354)
Butterworth, Arthur. Nightflight : symphonic study for brass band. *Chester Music. Unpriced* WMJ (B78-51307)
Butterworth, Arthur. Nightflight : symphonic study for brass band. *Chester Music. Unpriced* WMJ (B78-51308)
Byrd, William. The battell. The marche before the battell. *arr.* The Earle of Oxford's march. *Chester Music. Unpriced* WMK/AGM (B78-51320)
Gabrieli, Giovanni. Sacrae symphoniae. Bk.1. Sonata pian'e forte. Sonata pian'e forte : for brass octet. *Chester Music. Unpriced* WNNE (B78-51333)
Howarth, Elgar. Berne patrol : for brass band. *Chester Music. Unpriced* WMGM (B78-51304)
Howarth, Elgar. Greensleeves. *Chester Music. Unpriced* WMK/DW (B78-51326)
Howarth, Elgar. Greensleeves : for brass band. *Chester Music. Unpriced* WMK/DW (B78-51327)
Howarth, Elgar. Two processional fanfares. *Chester Music. Unpriced* WMGN (B78-51305)
Joplin, Scott. Three rags for five. *Chester Music. Unpriced* WNRK/AHXJ (B78-51338)
Pearson, Leslie. Hiplips . (Philip's) : for brass quintet. *Chester Music. Unpriced* WNR (B78-51337)
Peuerl, Paul. Newe Padouan, Intrada, Täntz unnd Galliarda. *Selections.* Four dances (1611). *Chester Music. Unpriced* WNSK/AH (B78-51340)
Scheidt, Samuel. Paduana, galliarda .... Cantus 18. Canzon cornetto : for four trumpets. *Chester Music. Unpriced* WSNS (B78-51342)
Susato, Thielman. Het derde musyck boexken. *Selections : arr.* Six Susato dances : for brass band ... *Chester Music. Unpriced* WMK/AH (B78-51321)
Susato, Thielman. A suite of dances. *Chester Music. Unpriced* WNK/AH (B78-51332)
Woods, Stanley. Cornet cosmology : for brass band. *Chester Music. Unpriced* WMJ (B78-51314)
Jusu! the very thought is sweet : for 4-part female choir unaccompanied. (Victoria, Tomás Luis de). *Roberton. £0.15* FEZDJ (B78-50824)
Kaba, Melinda. Die römische Orgel von Aquincum (3. Jahrhundert). *Bärenreiter. £11.20* AR/B(YGB/XBH) (B78-03580)
Kabale und liebe. Op.44. *Vocal score.* Kabale und Liebe : Oper in 2 teilen (9 Bildern) nach Friedrich von Schiller. (Einem, Gottfried von). *Boosey and Hawkes. Unpriced* CC (B78-50006)
Kabale und Liebe : Oper in 2 Teilen (9 Bildern) nach Friedrich von Schiller. (Einem, Gottfried von). *Boosey and Hawkes. Unpriced* CQC (B78-50710)

Kabeláč, Miloslav.
Eight preludes, op.30 : for piano. *Supraphon : Schirmer. £3.65* QPJ (B78-50534)
Fantasia, organ, op.32, no.1. Fantasia, op.32, no.1, for organ. *Supraphon : Schirmer. £2.10* RJ (B78-50564)
Kail, Robert.
Beloved Scotch & Irish songs & ballads. *Ashley : Phoenix. Unpriced* KDW/AYDM (B78-50120)
Five greatest symphonies : for piano, two hands. *Ashley Phoenix. Unpriced* QPK/AE/AY (B78-51024)
Kalisch, Alfred. Elektra : tragedy in one act. (Hofmannsthal, Hugo von). *Boosey and Hawkes. £9.00* BSUAC
Kalliwoda, Jan Vaclav. Concertino, flute & oboe, F major. *arr.* Concertino for flute, oboe and orchestra. *Musica rara. Unpriced* NWPNTK/LF (B78-50202)
Kalliwoda, Jan Václav. Introduction & rondo, orchestra, op.51. *arr.* Introduction and rondo, op.51, for horn and orchestra. *Musica rara. Unpriced* VWPK/W (B78-51293)

Karp, Michael. Piano music. *Selections : arr.* Rags for guitar. (Joplin, Scott). *Schirmer. £1.50* TSPMK/AHXJ (B78-51167)
Kaul, Alexander. Concerto, piano, no.1, op.20, C major. *arr.* Erstes Konzert C-Dur, Ut majeur, C major, für Klavier mit 2 Oboen, 2 Hörnern und Streichern, Opus 20. (Sterkel, Johann Franz Xaver). *Schott. £10.00* QNUK/LF (B78-50211)
Keele University. *See* University of Keele.
Keetman, Gunild.
Musik für Kinder
7: Rhythmische Übung. *Schott. Unpriced* X/AF (B78-50318)
8: Paralipomena. (Orff, Carl). *Schott. Unpriced* JFE/NYEPDW (B78-50105)
Kelkel, Manfred. Melancolia und Mirabilis : zwei Stücke für Harfe solo = deux morçeaux pour pour harpe seule = two pieces for solo harp : opus 23. *Bote und Bock Schirmer. £2.90* TQPMJ (B78-51137)
Kelly, Bryan.
At the round earth's imagined corners. *Vocal score.* At the round earth's imagined corners : cantata for tenor solo, SATB and string orchestra. *Novello. Unpriced* DE (B78-50015)
Basque suite : for guitar and harpsichord (or piano). *Oxford University Press. Unpriced* TSPJ (B78-50610) ISBN 0-19-357423-3
Edinburgh dances. *Novello. £4.50* WMH (B78-51306)
Pastorale and paean. *Novello. £1.45* RJ (B78-50565)
Watt's cradle song : S.A.T.B. *Oxford University Press. Unpriced* DP/LF (B78-50739) ISBN 0-19-343065-7
Zodiac : twelve pieces for clarinet in B flat and piano, in two sets
Set 1. *Oxford University Press. Unpriced* VVPJ (B78-51284) ISBN 0-19-357442-x
Set 2. *Oxford University Press. Unpriced* VVPJ (B78-51285) ISBN 0-19-357443-8
Kelterborn, Rudolf. Consort-music, 1975. *Bote und Bock Associated Music. £5.75* KFLE/NYEP (B78-50472)
Kemp's music & recording industry year book (international)
1978. *Kemps. £5.50* A/GB(YC/BC) (B78-09409) ISBN 0-905255-30-5
Kendall, Alan, *b.1939.*
The life of Beethoven. *Hamlyn. £4.50* BBJ(N) (B78-26882) ISBN 0-600-31431-6
Vivaldi. *Chappell : Elm Tree Books. £8.95* BVJ(N) (B78-18541) ISBN 0-903443-26-0
Kennedy, Jimmy. The works of Jimmy Kennedy. *EMI. Unpriced* KDW/GB (B78-50872)
Kennedy, Michael, *b.1926.* Hallé, 1858-1976 : a brief survey of the orchestra's history, travels and achievements Revised ed.. *30 Cross St., Manchester M2 7BA : Hallé Concerts Society. £0.75* AMM/E(QB/X) (B78-06265)
Kennedy, Mikel. Never in my life. *57 Dorchester Rd. Lytchett Minister, Poole : Celebration Services. Unpriced* JDM (B78-50081)
Kenney, A R. Sounds of music. *Nelson. £0.45* A/B (B78-29834) ISBN 0-17-438332-0
Kenny, Courtney. L'incoronazione di Poppea. Vocal score. L'incoronazione di Poppea = The coronation of Poppea : opera in two acts and prologue. (Monteverdi, Claudio). New ed. *Faber Music. Unpriced* CC (B78-50007)
Kent County Library. The Folkestone fiery serpent, and other Kentish poems : a selection. *Springfield, Maidstone, Kent : Kent County Library. £0.50* AKDW/G(YDCM) (B78-11199) ISBN 0-905155-13-0
Kenyon, Nicholas. Mozart : the young musician. *Macdonald Educational. £1.95* BMS(N) (B78-30826) ISBN 0-356-05916-2
Kerman, Joseph.
The Beethoven quartets. *Oxford University Press. £3.95* BBJARXNS (B78-37869) ISBN 0-19-315145-6
The music of William Byrd
Vol.3: The consort and keyboard music of William Byrd. *Faber. £15.00 : CIP rev.* BBX (B78-19401) ISBN 0-571-10566-1
Keune, Eckehardt. Schlaginstrumente = Percussion instruments : a method of instruction
Teil 2: Pauken = Timpani. *Bärenreiter. £7.00* X/AC (B78-50696)
Killmayer, Wilhelm.
Brahms-Bildnis : für Violine, Violoncello und Klavier. *Schott. £12.00* NXNT (B78-50948)
Quartet, strings. Quartett für Violinen, Viola abd Violoncello. *Schott. £4.00* RXNS (B78-51082)
Speranza : für fünfstimmigen gemischten Chor a cappella. *Schott. £0.72* EZDW (B78-50797)
Kind ist uns geboren : das Ottowinder Christspiel, für Sprecher, Soli ad lib. (Sopran, Tenor, Bariton) - Kinderstimmen, Frauen - , gemischten Chor und Gemeindegesang - Instrumentalkreis (Stabspiele, Schlagzeng) - Orgel (wahlweise oder zusätzlich auch Streicher, Holz und Blechbläser). (Möckl, Franz). *Schott. £8.00* CQM/LF (B78-50014)
Kinderlieder in leichten Sätzen : elektronische Orgel (1 Manual). *Nagel : Bärenreiter. £3.36* RPVK/DW/GJ/AYE (B78-50573)
Kindermann, Jürgen. New edition of the complete works
Vol.9: Grande messe des morts ; edited by Jürgen Kindermann. (Berlioz, Hector). *Bärenreiter. Unpriced* C/AZ (B78-50698)
King, Alexander Hyatt. Mozart wind and string concertos. *British Broadcasting Corporation. £1.00* BMSAMPSF (B78-28702) ISBN 0-563-12770-8
King, Carole.
Carole King : her greatest hits, songs of long ago. *Screen gems-EMI Music : Colgems-EMI Music : EMI. Unpriced* KDW/GB (B78-50864)
Simple things : piano, vocal, chords. *Colgems-EMI : EMI. Unpriced* KDW/GB (B78-50132)
Welcome home : piano, vocal, chords. *Colgems-EMI Music : EMI. Unpriced* KDW/GB (B78-50865)
King, Thea. Sonata, clarinet & piano. Sonata for clarinet in B flat and piano. (Poulenc, Francis). 5th ed. embodying corrections to the first ed., edited by Thea King and Georgina Dobree. *Chester Music. Unpriced* VVPE (B78-51283)
King of glory : series 3 (mixolydian). (Pulkingham, Betty). *57 Dorchester Rd, Lytchett Minster, Poole : Celebration Services. Unpriced* ETSPLRDGS (B78-50040)
Kipnis, Igor. Overture, orchestra, E flat major. *arr.* Overture in E flat. (Telemann, Georg Phillip). *Oxford University Press. Unpriced* QRPK/AG (B78-51041) ISBN 0-19-385586-0
Kirk, Theron. Now's the time to sing : for three-part chorus of treble voices with descant solo, piano four-hands accompaniment and percussion. *Schirmer. Unpriced* FLE/NYLDW (B78-50067)
Kirkpatrick, John. Sunrise : voice, violin and piano. (Ives, Charles). *Peters. Unpriced* KE/SPDW (B78-50462)
Kisell, E.
The Russian school of piano playing
Vol.1. (Nikolaev, Aleksandr Aleksandrovich). English ed. *Boosey and Hawkes. Unpriced* Q/AC (B78-50962)
Vol.2. (Nikolaev, Aleksandr Aleksandrovich). English ed. *Boosey and Hawkes. Unpriced* Q/AC (B78-50963)
Klabund. Nachgefühl. *Vocal score.* Nachgefühl : Kantate für Sopran und Orchester nach Versen von Klabund. (Egk, Werner). *Schott. £4.80* KFLDX (B78-50471)
Klapil, Pavel. Aus dem alten tschechischen Sammlungen : zweistimmige Sätze, für Sopran-und Altblockflöte. *Bärenreiter. £1.40* VSNUK/AYF (B78-50653)
Klappentexte : für Flöte oder Piccolo und Oboe oder English Horn, 1976. (Schweizer, Klaus). *Bärenreiter. £8.96* VNU (B78-50647)

Klassische Tanze von Joseph Haydn und Wolfgang Amadeus Mozart : für Blockflöten - Ensemble ... Sopran, Alt, Tenor, Bass ... (Haydn, Joseph). *Schott. £3.20* VSNSK/AH (B78-50298)
Klebe, Giselher.
Alborada : per arpa sola, op.77 : *Bärenreiter. £4.50* TQPMJ (B78-51138)
'Beuge dich, du Menschenseele' : geistliche Szene für mittlere Stimme und Orgel. *Bärenreiter. £5.60* KFVDE (B78-50476)
Drei Lieder nach Texten von Friedrich Hölderlin : für höhe Stimme und Klavier, op.74. *Bärenreiter. £3.90* KFTDW (B78-50900)
Neun Klavierstücke für Sonja. Op.76. *Bärenreiter. £5.04* QPJ (B78-50535)
Sechs Stücke : für Kontrabass solo, Op.68. *Bärenreiter. £2.70* SSPMJ (B78-51130)
Klingemann, Karl. Mendelssohn in Scotland. (Jenkins, David, *b.1944*). *Chappell : Elm Tree Books. £5.95* BMJ(N/YDL/XHJ) (B78-19674) ISBN 0-903443-18-x
Klingende Orgelbuch : Bekanntes und Beliebtes aus Klassik Volks- und Unterhaltungsmusik, für elektronische Orgel (alle Modelle)
Band 2. *Schott. £7.20* RK/AAY (B78-50233)
Klopčič, Rok. Romantic pieces. Op.75. Four romantic pieces : for violin and piano. (Dvořák, Antonín). *Schirmer. £2.10* SPJ (B78-50589)
Knight, Max. A confidential matter : the letters of Richard Strauss and Stefan Zweig, 1931-1935. (Strauss, Richard). *University of California Press. £6.75* BSU(N/XNL5) (B78-04319) ISBN 0-520-03036-2
Knowles, John, *b.1948.* Elgar's interpreters on record : an Elgar discography. *c/o F.B. Greatwich, 20 Geraldine Rd, Malvern, Worcs. WR14 3PA : The Elgar Society. £1.00* BEP/FD (B78-33481)
Knussen, Oliver.
Rosary songs = Rosenkranzlieder : three poems of Georg Trakl, for soprano, clarinet, viola and piano, Op.9. *Faber Music. Unpriced* KFLE/NUVNTDW (B78-50893)
Trumpets : for soprano and three clarinets, op.12. *Faber Music. Unpriced* KFLE/VVNTDW (B78-50897)
Koanga. La calinda. *arr.* La calinda, and, Air and dance. (Delius, Frederick). *Boosey and Hawkes. Unpriced* VRPK (B78-50292)
Koch, Johannes H E. Symphony, wind instruments, no.6, B flat major. *arr.* Bläser-Sinfonie für Blechbläser. (Bach, Johann Christian). *Bärenreiter. Unpriced* WMK/AE (B78-50681)
Koch, Lothar. Concerto, oboe, no.1, D minor. *arr.* Konzert No.1, d-moll, für Oboe und Orchester. (Lebrun, Ludwig August). *Schott. £9.60* VTPK/LF (B78-50302)
Kodály, Zoltán.
Intermezzo, string trio. Intermezzo per trio d'archi. *Editio musica : Boosey and Hawkes. Unpriced* RXNT (B78-51086)

Old Hungarian soldier songs. Magyar rondo = Hungarian rondo : vonószenekarra, két klarinéta és két fagottra = for string orchestra, two clarinets and two bassoons. *Editio musica : Boosey and Hawkes. Unpriced* RXMPVNS/W (B78-51072)
Kohs, Ellis B. Musical form : studies in analysis and synthesis. *Houghton Mifflin. £10.95* A/S (B78-25371) ISBN 0-395-18613-7
Kolb, Barbara.
Looking for Claudio : solo and tape. *Boosey and Hawkes. Unpriced* TSPMJ (B78-51157)
Rebuttal : two clarinets. *Henmar Press : Peters : Peters. Unpriced* VVNU (B78-51278)
Kölbel, Herbert. Sonata, flute, violin & continuo, G major. Triosonate, G-dur, G major, für Querflöte (Violine), Violine (Oboe) und B.C., for German flute (violin), violin (oboe) and b.c. (Platti, Giovanni Benedetto). Erstausgabe. *Heinrichshofen : Peters. Unpriced* NURNTE (B78-50501)
Kommt danket dem Helden. *arr.* Come thank now Jehovah = Kommt danket dem Helden : double chorus ; SATB with accompaniment. (Peter, Johann Friedrich). *Boosey and Hawkes. Unpriced* DH (B78-50341)
Köneke, Hans Wilhelm. Musikalische Grundausbildung in der Musikschule
Lehrerhandbuch. Teil 1 : Didaktik und Methodik. *Schott. £9.50* A(VF) (B78-33930)
Konfrontationen : für grosses Orchester, 1974. (Redel, Martin Christoph). *Bote und Bock : Associated Music. £5.75* MMJ (B78-50494)
Königliches Thema : für Violine solo, 1976. (Yun, Isang). *Bote und Bock : Associated Music. £2.40* SPM/T (B78-50592)
Kornemann, Helmut. Voce et tuba : gesammelte Reden und Aufsätze, 1934-1974. (Ehmann, Wilhelm). *32 Great Titchfield St., W.1 : Bärenreiter Kassel. Unpriced* A(D) (B78-03573)
Kozeluch, Johann Anton. Concerto, bassoon, C major. *arr.* Concerto in C for bassoon and orchestra. *Musica rara. Unpriced* VWPK/LF (B78-51292)
Kozikova, Marcelo. Sonata, harp. Sonata, für Harfe, for harp. (Rossini, Gioacchino Antonio). *Schott. £2.40* TQPME (B78-51133)
Kraemer, Timothy.
Bel and the dragon. Op.120. *Chorus score.* Bel and the dragon, opus 120. (Gardner, John). *Oxford University Press. Unpriced* FACN (B78-50804) ISBN 0-19-336205-8
Bel and the dragon. Op.120. *Vocal score.* Bel and the dragon : an opera for children. (Gardner, John). *Oxford University Press. Unpriced* CN (B78-50709) ISBN 0-19-336202-3
Kreidler, Dieter.
Duet, lute. *arr.* Duett für Gitarren = Duet for guitars. (Weiss, Sylvius Leopold). *Schott. £2.00* TSNU (B78-51146)
Zwei Menuette = Two minuets. (Weiss, Sylvias Leopold). *Schott. £2.00* TSPMK/AHR (B78-51166)
Křenek, Ernst. Horizon circled = Horizont umkreist : for orchestra = für Orchester, 1967 ; op.199 by Ernst Křenek. *Bärenreiter. £10.50* MMJ (B78-50922)
Krenek, Ernst. Horizons circled : reflections on my music. *University of California Press. £6.80* BKTM (B78-06254) ISBN 0-520-02338-2
Kriedler, Dieter.
Drei spanische Solostücke = Three Spanish solo pieces = Trois morceaux espagnoles : for guitar. *Schott. £2.40* TSPMK/AYK (B78-50277)
Duet, barytones (2), Hob XII/4, G major. *arr.* Duett in G nach dem Original für 2 Barytone, Hob XII, 4. (Haydn, Joseph). *Schott. £4.00* TSNUK (B78-50270)
Kroeger, Karl.
Herr, wie sind deine Werke so gross. *arr.* Lord, thy creations, how great they are = Herr, wie sind deine Werke so gross : S.A.T.B. with accompaniment. (Peter, Johann Friedrich). *Boosey and Hawkes. Unpriced* DH (B78-50339)
Ihre Priester will ich mit Heil kleiden. *arr.* I will clothe thy priests with salvation = Ihre Priester will ich mit Heil kleiden : S.A.T.B. with accompaniment. (Peter, Johann Friedrich). *Boosey and Hawkes. Unpriced* DH (B78-50340)
Kommt danket dem Helden. *arr.* Come thank now Jehovah = Kommt danket dem Helden : double chorus ; SATB with accompaniment. (Peter, Johann Friedrich). *Boosey and Hawkes. Unpriced* DH (B78-50341)
Original anthems. Make a joyful noise unto the Lord. *Vocal score.* Psalm 100, Make a joyful noise unto the Lord. (Latrobe, Christian Ignatius). *Boosey and Hawkes. Unpriced* DR (B78-50346)
Three sacred songs of Johannes Herbert. (Herbst, Johannes). *Boosey and Hawkes. Unpriced* KFTDH (B78-50899)
Unser Herr Jesus Christus. *arr.* Our dear Lord Jesus Christ = Unser Herr Jesus Christus : SATB with accompaniment. (Peter, Johann Friedrich). *Boosey and Hawkes. Unpriced* DH (B78-50342)
Krol, Bernhard.
Capricetten : für Oboe und Streichorchester, op.49. *Bote und Bock : Schirmer. £7.70* VTPK (B78-51268)
Figaro-Metamorphosen 'Voi che sapete' : für Horn (F) und Klavier, Opus 61. *Bote und Bock : Associated Music. £7.70* WTPJ (B78-50694)
Juba-mirum-Fantasia nach W.A. Mozart, K.V.626 : für Orgel, op.65. *Bote und Bock : Schirmer. £7.70* RJ (B78-51049)
Orgelbüchlein für Vincenz : 10 festliche kleine Präliudien, op.66. *Bote und Bock : Schirmer. £3.85* RJ (B78-51050)
Krzemioniecka, L. Three children's songs for three equal voices (SSA). (Lutoslawski, Witold). *Chester Music. Unpriced* FDW/GJ (B78-50816)
Kümmerling, Harold. Evangelischer Blumengarten. Machet die Töre weit. Machet die Töre weit : Du König der Ehren, wir danken Dir : für vierstimmigen gemischten Chor. (Briegel, Wolfgang Carl). *Bärenreiter. £0.84* EZDH (B78-50370)
La musique que j'aime : chansons. *Tanday Music : Chappell : Chappell. Unpriced* KDW/GB/AY (B78-50452)
La Roche, Renée. *See* Roche, Renée la.

Lagerlöf, Selma. 'Beuge dich, du Menschenseele' : geistliche Szene für mittlere Stimme und Orgel. (Klebe, Giselher). *Bärenreiter. £5.60* KFVDE (B78-50476)
Laine, Denny.
The best of McCartney : for easy piano. (McCartney, Paul). *MPL Communications : Music Sales (Dist.). Unpriced* QPK/DW/GB (B78-51029)
London town. *arr.* London town. (McCartney, Paul). *Music Sales. Unpriced* KDW/GB (B78-50868)
Laken, Alan. Christmas time. *Chappell. Unpriced* VRPK/DP/LF/AY (B78-51223)
Lally, Maureen.
Listen, sing and play
2 : First class, lessons 11-20, second class, lessons 21-30. Workbook. *Educational Company of Ireland. £0.48* A/M (B78-24450)
3 : classes 3 and 4, lessons 31-45. Workbook. *Educational Company of Ireland. £0.48* A/M (B78-21396)
Lam, Basil.
Lute music. *Collections.* The collected lute music of John Dowland. (Dowland, John). 2nd ed. with 3 more pieces. *Faber Music. Unpriced* TW/AZ (B78-51171) ISBN 0-571-10024-4
Sonatas, violins (2) & continuo, Op.2, no.1-6. Trio sonatas Op.2, nos.1-3. (Handel, George Frideric). *Eulenburg. Unpriced* NXNSE (B78-50203)
Sonatas, violins (2) & continuo, op.2, nos. 3, 8, 9. Dresden trio sonatas. (Handel, George Frideric). *Eulenburg. Unpriced* NXNSE (B78-50204)
Sonatas, violins (2) & continuo, op.2, nos.1-6. Trio sonatas Op.2, no.4-6. (Handel, George Frideric). *Eulenburg. Unpriced* NXNSE (B78-50205)
Lambert, Sydney. Premieres leçons de piano. *Selections.* Six pieces in the early grades. *Associated Music. £1.20* QPJ (B78-50536)
Lambeth *(London Borough). Directorate of Amenity Services.* Lambeth and Music Hall : a treasury of Music Hall memorabilia : including articles, biographies, photographs, engravings and reproductions of original material. *Leisure Centre, Loughborough Park, S.W.9 : London Borough of Lambeth Directorate of Amenity Services. £1.00* AKDW/JV(YDBL) (B78-20450) ISBN 0-905208-02-1
Lambeth and Music Hall : a treasury of Music Hall memorabilia : including articles, biographies, photographs, engravings and reproductions of original material. *Leisure Centre, Loughborough Park, S.W.9 : London Borough of Lambeth Directorate of Amenity Services. £1.00* AKDW/JV(YDBL) (B78-20450) ISBN 0-905208-02-1
Lament : for strings. (Sculthorpe, Peter). *Faber Music. Unpriced* RXMJ (B78-51068)
Lancen, Serge.
Cavatine : for four double basses. *Yorke. Unpriced* SSNS (B78-51122)
Croquis : for double bass and piano. *Yorke. Unpriced* SSPJ (B78-51127)
Landon, Howard Chandler Robbins.
Haydn : chronicle and works
Haydn at Eszterháza, 1766-1790. *Thames and Hudson. £30.00* BHE(N) (B78-40350) ISBN 0-500-01168-0
Kyrie, K.322, E flat major. *Vocal score.* Kyrie, (K.322), for four-part chorus of mixed voices with piano accompaniment. (Mozart, Wolfgang Amadeus). *Schirmer. Unpriced* DGB (B78-50017)
Kyrie, K.323, C major. *Vocal score.* Kyrie, (K.323), for four-part chorus of mixed voices with piano accompaniment. (Mozart, Wolfgang Amadeus). *Schirmer. Unpriced* DGB (B78-50018)
Kyrie, K.341, D minor. *Vocal score.* Kyrie, K.341, for four-part chorus of mixed voices with piano accompaniment. (Mozart, Wolfgang Amadeus). *Schirmer. Unpriced* DGB (B78-50019)
Lands : two settings for unaccompanied mixed voice choir of poems by W.H. Auden, music by Antonin Tučapský. (Tučapský, Antonin). *Roberton. £0.32* EZDW (B78-50055)
Lane, John. The best of McCartney : for easy piano. (McCartney, Paul). *MPL Communications : Music Sales (Dist.). Unpriced* QPK/DW/GB (B78-51029)
Lane, Margaret, *b.1899.* Edgar A. Lane : musician, 1865-1938 : memories of Edgar Alfred Lane. *'Purbeck mail'. Unpriced* AD/E(P) (B78-09112)
Langwill, Lyndesay Graham. An index of musical wind-instrument makers. 5th ed. *7 Dick Place, Edinburgh EH9 2JS : The author. £10.00* AV/BC(M/WT) (B78-14459)
Lantern song : ten Chinese songs arranged for voices, recorders and percussion by Kenneth Pont. (Pont, Kenneth). *Oxford University Press. Unpriced* JFE/NYHSDW (B78-50851) ISBN 0-19-330613-1
Lanza, Alcides. Hip'nes 1 (1973 I) : versions a and b, for one or more instrument. *Boosey and Hawkes. £2.50* LN (B78-50481)
Larkin, Rochelle. The Beatles, yesterday, today, tomorrow. *161 Fulham Rd, S.W.3 : Scholastic Book Services. Unpriced* AKDW/GB/E(P) (B78-06261)
Lasso, Orlando di. Magnificat septimi toni for mixed voices and instruments. *Oxford University Press. Unpriced* EZDGKK (B78-50773) ISBN 0-19-337335-1
Last, Joan.
Alphabetically yours : 26 short fragments for piano. *Oxford University Press. Unpriced* QPJ (B78-51013) ISBN 0-19-373099-5
In changing mood : nine short easy piano pieces. *Oxford University Press. Unpriced* QPJ (B78-50223) ISBN 0-19-373122-3
Last, Joan. Interpretation for the piano student. *For later reprint see* Last, Joan. Interpretation in piano study.
Last, Joan.
Interpretation in piano study. *Oxford University Press. £2.50* AQ/E (B78-26895) ISBN 0-19-318424-9
Lyric pieces : for piano
Set 1. *Chappell. Unpriced* QPJ (B78-50537)
Set 2. *Chappell. Unpriced* QPJ (B78-50538)
Two hand duos : nine pieces having equal interest for both hands. *Leonard, Gould and Bolttler. Unpriced* QPJ (B78-50539)
Last month of the year : eight carols for voices, Orff-instruments, recorders and guitars
1: Hodie, Vhristus natus est. (Odom, John). *Schott. Unpriced* ENYESDP/LF (B78-50754)
2: Children go where I send thee. (Odom, John). *Schott. Unpriced* ENYESDP/LF (B78-50755)
3: Virgin Mary, meek and mild. (Odom, John). *Schott. Unpriced* ENYESDP/LF (B78-50756)
4: O magnum mysterium. (Odom, John). *Schott. Unpriced* ENYESDP/LF (B78-50757)
5: Noël. (Odom, John). *Schott. Unpriced* ENYESDP/LF (B78-50758)
6: The last month of the year. (Odom, John). *Schott. Unpriced* ENYESDP/LF (B78-50759)
7: What you gonna call yo' pretty little baby? (Odom, John). *Schott. Unpriced* ENYESDP/LF (B78-50760)
8: A Christmas gloria. (Odom, John). *Schott. Unpriced* ENYESDP/LF (B78-50761)
Latin-Americana : a selection of famous melodies and rhythms. *Bosworth and Co. £3.50* MK/AH/AYU (B78-50182)
Latin-Americana : a selection of famous melodies and rhythms for piano. *Bosworth & Co. Unpriced* QPK/AH/AYU (B78-51026)
Latin church music in England, c.1460-1575. (Benham, Hugh). *Barrie and Jenkins. £10.00* ADFF(YD/XCT116) (B78-26889) ISBN 0-~14-20059-0
Latrobe, Christian Ignatius.
Credo. Crucifixus. *arr.* Crucifixus = (He was crucified) : for two-part chorus of women's voices with keyboard accompaniment. (Suidell, Padre). *Roberton. £0.15* FDJ (B78-50808)
Original anthems. Make a joyful noise unto the Lord. *Vocal score.* Psalm 100, Make a joyful noise unto the Lord. *Boosey and Hawkes. Unpriced* DR (B78-50346)
Lauder, *Sir* Harry. The best of Sir Harry Lauder. *EMI. Unpriced* KDW/JV (B78-50460)
Laudi : for orchestra. (Mathias, William). *Oxford University Press. Unpriced* MMJ (B78-50191) ISBN 0-19-365661-2
Laufe, Abe. Broadway's greatest musicals. *David and Charles. £9.50* ACM/E(YT/X) (B78-37865) ISBN 0-7153-7712-4
Lavender, Peter. The authentic Gilbert & Sullivan songbook : 92 unabridged selections from all 14 operas reproduced from early vocal scores. (Sullivan, *Sir* Arthur Seymour). *Dover : Constable. £5.35* DW (B78-50028) ISBN 0-486-23482-7
Law, Leslie. A space age suite : six easy guitar pieces for the young beginner. *Charnwood Music. Unpriced* TSPMG (B78-50612)
Lawes, Henry. Ayres and dialogues. Dialogue on a kiss. A dialogue on a kiss : for two solo voices and continuo. *Oxford University Press. Unpriced* JNEDW (B78-50858) ISBN 0-19-345494-7
Lawson-Gould sacred choral series.
Victoria, Tomás Luis de. Liber primus qui missas ... aliaque cumplectitut, 1576. Nigra sum. Nigra sum de beata virgine : for six-part chorus of mixed voices unaccompanied. *Roberton. £0.20* EZDJ (B78-50779)
West, John A. Shepherd, shepherd : spiritual for full chorus of mixed voices unaccompanied. *Roberton. £0.20* EZDW/LC (B78-50801)
Lawton, Sidney. Cantata no.208 : Was mir behagt. Schafe können sicher weiden. *arr.* Sheep may safely graze. (Bach, Johann Sebastian). *Oxford University Press. Unpriced* VRNTQK/DW (B78-50289) ISBN 0-19-355280-9
Layton, Robert.
Dvořák symphonies and concertos. *British Broadcasting Corporation. £1.00* BDXAMME (B78-29839) ISBN 0-563-12676-0
The Penguin stereo record guide. (Greenfield, Edward). 2nd ed. *Penguin. £4.50* A/FF(WT) (B78-23118)
Lazari, Ferdinando Antonio.
Sonata, trumpets (2) & string orchestra, D major. Sonata à 6 for trumpets, strings and continuo. *Musica rara. Unpriced* RXMPWSNUE (B78-50579)
Sonata, trumpets (2) & string orchestra, D major. *arr.* Sonata à 6, for 2 trumpets, strings and continuo. *Musica rara. Unpriced* WSNTQK/AE (B78-50693)
Lazarof, Henri. Textures. Cadence IV. Cadence IV : for piano. *Associated Music. £1.50* QPJ (B78-50540)
Le Jeune, Henri. Fantasia a cinque : for recorder quintet. *Dolmetsch : Chappell. Unpriced* VSNR (B78-51243)
Leach, Joel. Love me tonight, Mimi. *arr.* Mimi. (Rogers, Richard). *Warner : Blossom. Unpriced* UMMK/DW (B78-50635)
Leach, Robert, *b.1942.* Folk music in school. *Cambridge University Press. £4.95* A/G(VF) (B78-29835) ISBN 0-521-21595-1
Leaper, Kenneth. Three Victorian scenes. *Chappell. Unpriced* JFE/NYHSDX (B78-50852)
Lear, Edward. The courtship of the Yongli Bongli Bo sic : for voice and piano. (Thomson, Virgil). *Schirmer. £1.50* KDW (B78-50448)
Lear, W Hogarth. Cops and robbers : for brass band. *Paxton. Unpriced* WMJ (B78-51312)
Lebrun, Ludwig August.
Concerto, oboe, no.1, D minor. Konzert No.1, d-Moll für Oboe und Orchester. *Schott. £11.00* MPVTF (B78-50194)
Concerto, oboe, no.1, D minor. *arr.* Konzert No.1, d-moll, für Oboe und Orchester. *Schott. £9.60* VTPK/LF (B78-50302)
Lecky, Zip. How t'make it as a rockstar. *IPC Magazines. £0.40* AKDW/HKR/E(MN)
Leclair, Jean Marie. Sonata, violins (2) & continuo, A major. Sonata Opus 4 Nr.6 A-Dur für zwei Violinen und Basso continuo, A major for two violins and basso continuo, La majeur pour deux Violons et basse continue. *Edizioni Pegasus : Peters. Unpriced* SNTPWE (B78-50586)
Ledger, Philip.
The Oxford book of English madrigals. *Oxford University Press. Unpriced* EZDU/AYD (B78-50792) ISBN 0-19-343664-7
Two carols. *Oxford University Press. Unpriced* DP/LF (B78-50740) ISBN 0-19-343066-5
Lees, Benjamin.
Collage : for string quartet, wind quintet and percussion. *Boosey and Hawkes. Unpriced* MRJ (B78-50942)
Spectrum : for orchestra. *Boosey and Hawkes. Unpriced* MMJ (B78-50923)
Lees, Heath. Iona boat song. For a dead king : traditional Scottish air for 4-part male chorus unaccompanied. *Roberton. £0.15* GEZDW (B78-50828)
Léhar, Franz. Concertino, violin, B minor. *arr.* Concertino for violin and orchestra, für Violine und Orchester. *Glocken Verlag. Unpriced* SPK/LFL (B78-50590)
Lehár, Franz.
Six rhymes from Mother Goose : for four-part chorus of mixed voices and piano accompaniment. *Schirmer. £1.60* DW (B78-50350)
Twelve melodies for organ : twelve favourite Lehár melodies. *Glocken Verlag. Unpriced* RPVK/DW (B78-51061)
Leibes- und Abendlieder : für höhe Stimme und Klavier, Opus 48 : von Gottfried von Einem. (Einem, Gottfried von). *Bote und Bock. £3.85* KFTDW (B78-50474)
Leighton, Kenneth. Sequence for All Saints : for SATB choir, baritone solo and organ, words from English Hymnal 731. *Roberton. £1.20* DE/LQ (B78-50719)
Lennon, John.
Beatles album no.2. *Chappell. Unpriced* KDW/GB (B78-50451)
The Beatles : the singles collections, 1962-1970. *Wise : Music Sales. Unpriced* KDW/GB (B78-50133) ISBN 0-86001-274-3
Yellow submarine. *arr.* Yellow submarine. *Chappell. Unpriced* NYFPK/DW (B78-50515)
Leppard, Raymond.
L'egisto. *Vocal score.* L'egisto : opera in three acts and a prologue. (Cavalli, Francesco). *Faber Music. Unpriced* CC (B78-50324)
L'incoronazione di Poppea. *Choral score.* L'incoronazione di Poppea. (Monteverdi, Claudio). *Faber Music. Unpriced* DAC (B78-50331)
L'incoronazione di Poppea. Vocal score. L'incoronazione di Poppea = The coronation of Poppea : opera in two acts and prologue. (Monteverdi, Claudio). New ed. *Faber Music. Unpriced* CC (B78-50007)
Lerma, Dominique-René de. Requiem mass. *Vocal score.* Requiem mass for four-part chorus of mixed voices and alto, tenor and bass solos with piano accompaniment. (Nunes Garcia, Jose Mauricio). *Associated Music. £2.40* DGKAV (B78-50334)
Lerner, Sammy.
I'm Popeye the sailor man. *arr.* I'm Popeye the sailor man. *Warner : Blossom. Unpriced* EWMDW/JR (B78-50762)
Popeye the sailor. I'm Popeye the sailor man. *arr.* I'm Popeye the sailor man. *Warner : Blossom. Unpriced* UMMK/DW/JR (B78-50636)
Leslie Bricusse and Anthony Newley's The travelling music show. (Bricusse, Leslie). *Tro-Essex. Unpriced* KDW (B78-50441)
Lester, Bryan. Essential guitar skill = Tecnica essenziale per la chitarra = Grundlagen der Fertigkeit im Gittarenspiel
Book 2. *Ricordi. Unpriced* TS/AF (B78-50602)
Essential guitar skill = Tecnica essenziale per la chitarra = Grundlagen der Fertigkeit im Gittarenspiel
Book 1. *Ricordi. Unpriced* TS/AF (B78-50603)
Let it shine : spiritual for 3-part chorus of female voices with piano and optional percussion. (Stockton, Robert). *Roberton. £0.18* FDW/LC (B78-50395)
Let the children sing
Book 1. (Dale, Mervyn). *Edwin Ashdown. Unpriced* JFDW (B78-50430)
Let thy hand be strengthened. (Dearnley, Christopher). *Cathedral Music. Unpriced* EZDK (B78-50379)
Let's build a city : for two-part chorus of young voices with piano accompaniment. (Winfrey, Robert). *Schirmer. Unpriced* FDW (B78-50064)
Letters in the sand : SATB with trumpet solo and piano. (Hovhaness, Alan). *Associated Music. £0.35* EWSPDW (B78-50361)
Levitt, Estelle.
Happy birthday, Jesus. *arr.* Happy birthday, Jesus. (Pockriss, Lee). *Chappell. Unpriced* DP/LF (B78-50742)
Happy birthday, Jesus. *arr.* Happy birthday, Jesus. (Pockriss, Lee). *Chappell. Unpriced* FDP/LF (B78-50811)
Lewis, Harold. Bell ringing, minimus : three and four bell methods. *36 Great Clarendon St., Oxford : J. Hannon and Co. £1.50* AXSR/E (B78-17617)
Liber primus qui missas ... aliaque cumplectitut, 1576. Nigra sum. Nigra sum de beata virgine : for six-part chorus of

mixed voices unaccompanied. (Victoria, Tomás Luis de). *Roberton. £0.20* EZDJ (B78-50779)
Libera nos, salva nos : two settings. (Shepherd, John, *b.1520*). *Oxenford : Blackwell's Music Shop (dist.). Unpriced* EZDJ (B78-50778)
Libro de musica para vihuela, intitulado Orphenica lyra. Orphenica lyra (Seville 1554). (Fuenllana, Miguel de). *Clarendon Press. £30.00* TVPMJ (B78-50625)
Libro primo de canzoni da sonare. *Selections.* Five canzonas for four instruments SATB. (Maschera, Florentio). *London Pro Musica. Unpriced* LNS (B78-50482)
Lieder ohne Worte. *Selections: arr.* 6 Lieder ohne Worte. (Mendelssohn, Felix). *Schott. £4.80* TSPMK (B78-50275)
Lieder und Volksmusik aus der Tschechoslowakei : Materialien für den Musikunterricht in den Sekundarstufen. (Tschache, Helmut). *Schott. £4.80* AKDW/G(YF) (B78-33161)
Life and work of Sir Arthur Sullivan. Sir Arthur Sullivan : composer & personage. (Allen, Reginald). *Pierpont Morgan Library : Chappell. £12.95* BSW(N) (B78-05721) ISBN 0-87923-145-9
Life of Beethoven. (Kendall, Alan, *b.1939*). *Hamlyn. £4.50* BBJ(N) (B78-26882) ISBN 0-600-31431-6
Ligeti, Gyorgy. Monument, Selbstportrait, Bewegung : drei Stücke für zwei Klaviere ... (1976). *Schott. £10.00* QNU (B78-50210)
Lincolnshire poacher. (Broadbent, Derek). *Logo Music : Studio Music (dist.). Unpriced* WMK/DW (B78-51324)
Lindley, Simon. Come sing and dance : S.A.T.B. *Banks Music. Unpriced* EZDP/LF (B78-50786)
Lindsay carol book. *Lindsay Music. Unpriced* FE/TSDP/LF/AY (B78-50822) ISBN 0-85957-007-x
Lindvall, Marianne. Abba : the ultimate pop group. *Pop Universal Ltd : Souvenir Press. £2.95* AKDW/GB/E(P) (B78-17616) ISBN 0-285-62312-5
Linedecker, Cliff. My life with Elvis. (Yancey, Becky). *W.H. Allen. £5.95* AKDW/HK/E(P) (B78-01678) ISBN 0-491-02084-8
Linwood-Christopher, Mabel. The amateur singer : a series of practical hints on the use of the voice for conductors, soloists and choristers. *9 Museum Place, Cardiff : Welsh Amateur Music Federation. Unpriced* AB/E (B78-06264)
Listen! music and civilization. (Brace, Geoffrey). *Cambridge University Press. £2.25* A/KD(X) (B78-22160) ISBN 0-521-21153-0
Listen, sing and play
2 : First class, lessons 11-20, second class, lessons 21-30. Workbook. (Lally, Maureen). *Educational Company of Ireland. £0.48* A/M (B78-24450)
3 : classes 3 and 4, lessons 31-45. Workbook. (Lally, Maureen). *Educational Company of Ireland. £0.48* A/M (B78-21396)
Listening to jazz. (Coker, Jerry). *Prentice-Hall. £6.55* AMT (B78-24453) ISBN 0-13-537217-8
Liszt, Cosima. *See* Wagner, Cosima.
Liszt, Franz.
Liszt Society publications
Vol.7: Unfamiliar piano pieces. *Schott. £3.00* C/AZ (B78-50322)
Selected works : for piano solo. *Schirmer. £3.60* QPJ (B78-50541)
Liszt Society. The Liszt Society journal
Vol.1- ; 1975-. *78 Wimbledon Park Side, SW19 5LH : The Society. £3.50(for members)* BLJ(B) (B78-11193)
Liszt Society. Newsletter. *For later issues of this periodical see* Liszt Society. The Liszt Society journal.
Liszt Society publications
Vol.7: Unfamiliar piano pieces. (Liszt, Franz). *Schott. £3.00* C/AZ (B78-50322)
Litanei : für 3 Violoncello (1976). (Zender, Hans). *Bote und Bock : Schirmer. £5.75* SRNT (B78-51113)
Littel Ascensiontide cantata : for unaccompanied chorus SATB. (Payne, Anthony). *Chester Music. Unpriced* EZDE/LM (B78-50766)
Littell, Barbara.
March for a free spirit. *Warner : Blossom. Unpriced* UMMJ (B78-51180)
Slightly lightly Latin. *Warner : Blossom. Unpriced* UMMJ (B78-51181)
Little donkey. (Boswell, Eric). *Chappell. Unpriced* NYDPK/DP/LF (B78-50950)
Little donkey. *arr.* Little donkey. (Boswell, Eric). *Chappell. Unpriced* NYDPK/DP/LF (B78-50950)
Little drummer boy. (Davis, Katherine Kennicott). *Chappell. Unpriced* NYDPK/DP/LF (B78-50951)
Little gingerbread man : a song/mime for children. (Diamond, Eileen). *Chappell. Unpriced* JFDW/JN (B78-50435)
Little requiem for Father Malachy Lynch. *Vocal score.* Little requiem for Father Malachy Lynch. (Tavener, John). *Chester Music. Unpriced* DGKAV (B78-50722)
Little sad sound : a melodrama for double bass and narrator. (Ridout, Alan). *Yorke. Unpriced* SSPMJ (B78-51131)
Little sweep ... (Crozier, Eric). *Boosey and Hawkes. Unpriced* BBUAC (B78-28697)
Little Whitsuntide cantata : for unaccompanied chorus SATB. (Payne, Anthony). *Chester Music. Unpriced* EZDE/LN (B78-50767)
Livingston, Jay.
The paleface. Buttons and bows. *arr.* Buttons and bows. *Warner : Blossom. Unpriced* UMMK/DW/JR (B78-51188)
The lemon drop kid. Silver bells. *arr.* Silver bells : SATB and piano. *Warner : Blossom. Unpriced* DW (B78-50351)
The paleface. Buttons and bows. *arr.* Buttons and bows. *Warner : Blossom. Unpriced* UMMK/DW/JR (B78-50637)
Lloyd, Albert Lancaster. Come all ye bold miners : ballads and songs of the coalfields. New, revised and enlarged ed. *Lawrence and Wishart. £10.00* AKDW/K/GNCC (B78-39786) ISBN 0-85315-412-0
Lobos, Heiter Villa-. *See* Villa-Lobos, Heitor.
Lobos, Heitor Villa-. *See* Villa-Lobos, Heitor.
Lochlainn, Colm O. *See* O Lochlainn, Colm.
Locke, Matthew. The tempest. Incidental music. Incidental music for The tempest : for strings and continuo. *Oxford University Press. Unpriced* RXM/JM (B78-50244) ISBN 0-19-365350-8
Logan, Nick.
The illustrated 'New musical express' encyclopedia of rock. 1978 ed.. *27 Old Gloucester St., WC1N 3AF : Salamander Books Limited. £3.95* A/HKR(C) (B78-12095) ISBN 0-86101-009-4
The illustrated 'New musical express' encyclopedia of rock. Revised ed. *Hamlyn. £5.95* AKDW/HKR(C) (B78-15752) ISBN 0-600-33171-7
Lombardi, Luca. Elegy for violin and piano. *Schirmer. £2.40* SPJ (B78-51100)
Lombardo, Mario.
Guess what time of year it is! : for SATB chorus with piano accompaniment. *Chappell. Unpriced* DW/LF (B78-50749)
Guess what time of year it is! : for SATB chorus with piano accompaniment. *Chappell. Unpriced* FDW/LF (B78-50820)
London Association of Organists. Newsletter
Issue no.1- ; 1976-. *c/o P. Lea-Cox, St Jude-on-the-Hill, Central Sq., N.W.11 : The Association. Unpriced* AR(YDB/B) (B78-09120)
London musical shows on record, 1897-1976. (Rust, Brian Arthur Lovell). *177 Kenton Rd, Harrow, Middx HA3 0HA : General Gramophone Publications Ltd. £11.00* ACM/FD(XL596) (B78-02935) ISBN 0-902470-07-8
London Oriental series. Wright, O. The modal system of Arab and Persian music, AD 1250-1300. *Oxford University Press. £32.00 : CIP rev.* BZCW/PR (B77-07528) ISBN 0-19-713575-7
London town. (McCartney, Paul). *Music Sales. Unpriced* KDW/GB (B78-50868)
London town. *arr.* London town. (McCartney, Paul). *Music Sales. Unpriced* KDW/GB (B78-50868)
London University. *See* University of London.
Long, M. Singing together
Window cleaning man ; words by M. Long. (Wade, Darrell). *16 Anchor Way, Danes Green, Gnosall : Viking. Unpriced* JFDW (B78-50104)
Long, Odean. Musical settings of late Victorian and modern British literature : a catalogue. (Gooch, Bryan N S). *2 Holly Bush Hill, NW3 6SH : Garland Publishing, Inc. £55.35* AKDW(XKK101/T) (B78-14028) ISBN 0-8240-9981-8
Longman early childhood education. Evans, David, *b.1940 (May).* Sharing sounds : musical experiences with young children. *Longman. Unpriced* A/GJ (B78-31364) ISBN 0-582-25006-4
Longyear, Rey Morgan. Nineteenth-century Romanticism in music. 2nd ed. *Prentice-Hall. £5.05* A(YB/XG101) (B78-22843) ISBN 0-13-622647-7
Look-in books. Tobler, John. Pop quest : so you think you know all about rock 'n' pop. *Independent Television Books : Arrow Books. £0.65* A/GB (B78-20431) ISBN 0-09-917570-3
Looking at music. (Fenton, Ian). *Coventure. £2.93* A (B78-14493) ISBN 0-904576-42-6
Looking for Claudio : solo and tape. (Kolb, Barbara). *Boosey and Hawkes. Unpriced* TSPMJ (B78-51157)
Lopez-Calo, Jose. Missa scala aretina : para 11 voces in 3 cores, instrumentos y continuo = for 11 voices in 3 choirs, instruments and continuo. (Valls, Francisco). *Novello. £3.15* ENUDG (B78-50752)
Lord, have mercy upon us. Hospodine. Höre mich, Herr : suli, coro, organo, arpa, trombe, 4 tromboni e tuba. (Janáček, Leoš). *Editio Dupraphone : Bärenreiter. £3.00* ENUXPNNDE (B78-50753)
Lord's Prayer ... : S.A.B. and piano with optional guitar and drums. (Fanshawe, David). *Chappell. Unpriced* DTF (B78-50348)
Lord's Prayer ... : S.A.T.B. and piano with optional guitar and drums. (Fanshawe, David). *Chappell. Unpriced* DTF (B78-50347)
Lord's Prayer ... : unison chorus and piano. (Fanshawe, David). *Chappell. Unpriced* JDTF (B78-50425)
Lorenzo-Fernandez, Oscar. Noturno das folhas soltas. *arr.* Noturno das folhas soltas. *Arthur Napoleão : Essex Music. Unpriced* QPK (B78-50551)
Loudová, Ivana. I speak in wisdom's voice (Ego sapienta) : for full chorus of men's voices a cappella. *Schirmer. Unpriced* GEZDH (B78-50419)
Louis Moyse flute collection.
Moyse, Louis. Sonata, flute & piano, no.1 (1975). First sonata (1975) for flute and piano. *Schirmer. £3.95* VRPE (B78-51213)
Mozart, Wolfgang Amadeus. Concerto, flute & harp, K.299, C major. *arr.* Concerto in C major (K.299) for flute, harp and orchestra. *Schirmer. £2.75* VRPK/LF (B78-51227)
Neubaur, Franz. Four pieces for flute and viola ... op.10. *Schirmer. £2.50* VRPLSQ (B78-51229)
Telemann, Georg Philipp. Concerto, flutes (2), E minor. *arr.* Concerto in E minor for two flutes and piano. *Schirmer. £2.75* VRNTQK/LF (B78-51202)
Love, Kelly.
Happy days. *arr.* Happy days : from the Paramount TV series 'Happy days'. (Fox, Charles). *Warner : Blossom. Unpriced* UMMK/DW/JS (B78-50638)
Popeye the sailor. I'm Popeye the sailor man. *arr.* I'm Popeye the sailor man. (Lerner, Sammy). *Warner Blossom. Unpriced* UMMK/DW/JR (B78-50636)
The paleface. Buttons and bows. *arr.* Buttons and bows. (Livingston, Jay). *Warner : Blossom. Unpriced* UMMK/DW/JR (B78-50637)
Love me tonight, Mimi. *arr.* Mimi. (Rogers, Richard). *Warner : Blossom. Unpriced* UMMK/DW (B78-50635)
Love me tonight. Mimi. *arr.* Mimi : SATB chorus and piano. (Rodgers, Richard). *Warner : Blossom. Unpriced* DW (B78-50746)
Love songs of the Irish. *25 Lower Abbey St., Dublin 1 : Mercier Press. £1.10* AKDW(YDM) (B78-39234) ISBN 0-85342-497-7
Love theme from Death on the Nile : piano solo. (Rota, Nino). *EMI. Unpriced* QPK/JR (B78-51033)
Lovelie Jemmie. (Potter, Archibald James). *Ashdown. Unpriced* JFDW (B78-50092)
Lowe, Thomas. Suite of dances : wind ensemble. *Emerson. £3.50* UNNHG (B78-50285)
Lowman, Roger.
Ecce virgo concipiet. (Morales, Cristoval). *Cathedral Music. Unpriced* GEZDGKAH/LEZ (B78-50408)
O magnum mysterium. (Morales, Cristoval). *36 Ranelagh Gdns., W.6 : Cathedral Music. Unpriced* GEZDGKH/LF (B78-50410)
Luar do sertão. (Cearense, Catallo da Paixão). *Arthur Napoleão : Essex Music. Unpriced* SPMK (B78-50594)
Luar do sertão. *arr.* Luar do sertão. (Cearense, Catallo da Paixão). *Arthur Napoleão : Essex Music. Unpriced* SPMK (B78-50594)
Lucy Van-Jung Page, 1892-1972 : recollections of pupils and friends. *26 Chalfont Rd, Oxford : Miss C.J. Gibson. Unpriced* AQ/E(VC/P) (B78-09119)
Ludewig, Wolfgang. Reflexionen : fünf Psychogramme für Flöte (Alt-Flöte), Violoncello und Klavier, 1975. *Bote und Bock : Associated Music. £3.85* NURNT (B78-50500)
Luhy, Gale R D'. *See* D'Luhy, Gale R.
Lupacchino, Bernadino. Primo libro a due voci. *Selections.* Nine fantasies : for two instruments. *London Pro Musica. Unpriced* LNU (B78-50909)
Lute music. *Collections.* The collected lute music of John Dowland. (Dowland, John). 2nd ed. with 3 more pieces. *Faber Music. Unpriced* TW/AZ (B78-51171) ISBN 0-571-10024-4
Lute Society. Booklets (ISSN 0140-6353). Gill, Donald. Gut-strung plucked instruments contemporary with the lute. *c/o The Administrator, 71 Priory Rd, Kew Gardens, Richmond, Surrey TW9 3DH : Lute Society. Unpriced* AT/B(XCSK301) (B78-01683)
Luther, Martin. Apokalyptische Vision : für Basstimme und Orgel. (Brandmüller, Theo). *Bote und Bock : Associated Music. £4.80* KGXDE (B78-50479)
Lutoslawski, Witold.
Les espaces du sommeil : for baritone and orchestra. *Chester Music. Unpriced* KGNE/MDW (B78-50906)
Three children's songs for three equal voices (SSA). *Chester Music. Unpriced* FDW/GJ (B78-50816)
Lyle, Graham. Showdown and other songs. (Gallagher, Benny). *Rondor Music : Music Sales. Unpriced* KDW/GB (B78-50128)
Lynn, *Dame* Vera. Vocal refrain : an autobiography. Large print ed. *Magna Print Books. £4.25* AKDW/GB/E(P) (B78-05405) ISBN 0-86009-046-9
Lyric pieces : for piano
Set 1. (Last, Joan). *Chappell. Unpriced* QPJ (B78-50537)
Set 2. (Last, Joan). *Chappell. Unpriced* QPJ (B78-50538)
Lyttleton, Humphrey. Basin Street to Harlem : jazz masters and masterpieces, 1917-1930. *Robson. £5.25 : CIP rev.* AMT(M/XMS14) (B78-27526) ISBN 0-903895-91-9
Macaulay, Tony. The Tony Macaulay songbook. *Macaulay Music : Noel Gay Music. Unpriced* KDW/GB (B78-50866)
McBeth, Francis. Songs of heritage : symphonic band. (Williams, Clifton). *Rubank : Novello. Unpriced* UMMJ (B78-51185)
McCabe, John.
Concerto, piano & wind quintet. Concerto for piano and wind quintet. *Novello. £6.25* NWNQF (B78-50504)
The goddess trilogy. 3 : Shapeshifter. Shapeshifter : for horn and piano. *Novello. £1.80* WTPJ (B78-51351)
The goddess triology. 1 : The castle of Arianrhod. The castle of Arianrhod : for horn and piano. *Novello. £2.75* WTPJ (B78-51352)
The goddess triology. 2 : Floraison. Floraison : for horn and piano. *Novello. £1.65* WTPJ (B78-51353)
Sonata on a motet. *Novello. £2.10* RXME (B78-50575)
McCarthy, John. Oh, father : an English music hall medley, for four-part chorus of mixed voices with piano accompniment. *Roberton. £0.32* DW (B78-50745)
McCartney, Paul.
Band on the run. *arr.* Band on the run. *MPL : Music Sales. Unpriced* KDW/GB (B78-50134) ISBN 0-86001-479-7
Beatles album no.2. (Lennon, John). *Chappell. Unpriced* KDW/GB (B78-50451)
The Beatles : the singles collections, 1962-1970. (Lennon, John). *Wise : Music Sales. Unpriced* KDW/GB (B78-50133) ISBN 0-86001-274-3
The best of McCartney. *MPL Communications : Music Sales. Unpriced* KDW/GB (B78-50867)
The best of McCartney : for easy piano. *MPL Communications : Music Sales (Dist.). Unpriced* QPK/DW/GB (B78-51029)
London town. *arr.* London town. *Music Sales. Unpriced*

KDW/GB (B78-50868)
Red rose speedway. *arr.* Red rose speedway. *MPL : Music Sales. Unpriced* KDW/GB (B78-50135) ISBN 0-86001-478-9
Yellow submarine. *arr.* Yellow submarine. (Lennon, John). *Chappell. Unpriced* NYFPK/DW (B78-50515)
Macdonald, Hugh, *b.1940.* Skryabin. *Oxford University Press. £2.95* BSGNC (B78-35469) ISBN 0-19-315438-2
MacDonald, Malcolm, *b.1948.*
Dmitri Shostakovich, a complete catalogue. *Boosey and Hawkes. £1.50* BSGR(TC) (B78-02934)
The symphonies of Havergal Brian
Vol.2: Symphonies 13-29. *Kahn and Averill. £6.25* BBTNAMME (B78-23596) ISBN 0-900707-43-7
MacDonald, Peter. Two plainsong preludes = Deux preludes de plain-chant = Zwei Choralmusik Vorspiele : for organ. *64 Pineheath Rd., High Kelling, Holt, Nflk. : St Gregory. £1.25* RJ (B78-50566)
Macdonald famous people. Kenyon, Nicholas. Mozart : the young musician. *Macdonald Educational. £1.95* BMS(N) (B78-30826) ISBN 0-356-05916-2
McGrady, Richard. Ayres and dialogues. Dialogue on a kiss. A dialogue on a kiss : for two solo voices and continuo. (Lawes, Henry). *Oxford University Press. Unpriced* JNEDW (B78-50858) ISBN 0-19-345494-7
Machet die Töre weit : Du König der Ehren, wir danken Dir : für vierstimmigen gemischten Chor. (Briegel, Wolfgang Carl). *Bärenreiter. £0.84* EZDH (B78-50370)
Machlis, Joseph. Celebraciones medievales : Spanish divertissements of the Middle Ages, for concert band with four-part chorus of mixed voices. (Surinach, Carlos). *Associated Music. £4.55* EUMMDW (B78-50359)
Mack, Dietrich. Cosima Wagner's diaries
Vol.1: 1869-1877. (Wagner, Cosima). *Collins. £15.00* BWC(N) (B78-34737) ISBN 0-00-216130-3
McKnight, Cathy. Pop quest : so you think you know all about rock 'n' pop. (Tobler, John). *Independent Television Books : Arrow Books. £0.65* A/GB (B78-20431) ISBN 0-09-917570-3
Mackworth-Young, *Sir* Robin. Tune and repair your own piano : a practical and theoretical guide to the tuning of all keyboard stringed instruments, and to the running repair of the piano. (Johnson, Michael). *Harcourt Brace Jovanovich. Unpriced* AQ/BT (B78-24454) ISBN 0-15-191383-8
McLarnon, Gerard. A gentle spirit : an opera in one act for soprano, tenor and chamber orchestra. (Tavener, John). *Chester Music. Unpriced* CQC (B78-50711)
McLean, Mervyn. Traditional songs of the Maori. *A.H. and A.W. Reed. Unpriced* KDW/AYXR (B78-50449) ISBN 0-589-00748-3
MacLeish, Archibald. What any lover learns : for four-part chorus of mixed voices a cappella. (Trubitt, Allen). *Chappell. Unpriced* EZDW (B78-50054)
McLeish, Craig. Preces and responses for trebles. *36 Ranelagh Gdns., W.6 : Cathedral Music. Unpriced* FLEZDGMM (B78-50405)
McLeish, Kenneth.
Mozart. *Heinemann. £2.50* BMS (B78-29831) ISBN 0-434-95125-0
Stravinsky. *Heinemann. £2.50* BSV(N) (B78-30825) ISBN 0-434-95126-9
McLeish, Valerie.
Mozart. (McLeish, Kenneth). *Heinemann. £2.50* BMS (B78-29831) ISBN 0-434-95125-0
Stravinsky. (McLeish, Kenneth). *Heinemann. £2.50* BSV(N) (B78-30825) ISBN 0-434-95126-9
McMahon, Tony. Irish traditional music. *Folens. Unpriced* A/G(YDM) (B78-15122)
McMorland, Alison. The funny family : songs, rhymes and games for children. *Ward Lock. £3.95* JFDW/GJ/AY (B78-50847) ISBN 0-7062-3719-6
McNeice, Louis. The world is mad : song, for voice, clarinet and piano. (Head, Michael). *Emerson. Unpriced* KE/VVPDW (B78-50466)
Maconchy, Elizabeth.
Heloïse and Abelard. *Vocal score.* Heloïsw and Abelard : a dramatic cantata for soprano, tenor and baritone soloists, chorus and orchestra. *Chester Music. Unpriced* DE (B78-50717)
Notebook for harpsichord. *Chester Music. Unpriced* QRPJ (B78-51039)
Madden, John.
Complete arias and sinfonias from cantatas, masses and oratorios : for solo voice, oboe, oboe d'amore, oboe de caccia, basso continuo/piano
Vol.8: Tenor, oboe, basso continuo/piano. (Bach, Johann Sebastian). *Musica rara. Unpriced* KE/VTNDH (B78-50888)
Vol.9: Tenor, bass, oboe, basso continuo/piano. (Bach, Johann Sebastian). *Musica rara. Unpriced* KE/VTNDH (B78-50889)
Vol.10: Bass, oboe, basso continuo/piano. (Bach, Johann Sebastian). *Musica rara. Unpriced* KE/VTNDH (B78-50891)
Complete arias and sinfonias from the cantatas, masses and oratorios, for solo voice, oboe, oboe d'amore, oboe da caccia, basso continuo/piano in 31 volumes
Vol.5. (Bach, Johann Sebastian). *Musica rara. Unpriced* KE/VTPDH (B78-50463)
Complete arias and sinfonias from the cantatas, masses and oratorios, for solo voice, oboe, oboe d'amore, oboe da caccia, basso continuo/piano in 31 volumes
Vol.6. (Bach, Johann Sebastian). *Musica rara. Unpriced* KE/VTPDH (B78-50465)
Vol.7. (Bach, Johann Sebastian). *Musica rara. Unpriced* KE/VTPDH (B78-50464)
Concerto, clarinet, op.1, B flat major. *arr.* Concerto no.1 for clarinet and orchestra, op.1. (Beer, Joseph). *Musica rara. Unpriced* VVPK/LF (B78-50663)
Introduction & rondo, orchestra, op.51. *arr.* Introduction and rondo, op.51, for horn and orchestra. (Kalliwoda, Jan Václav). *Musica rara. Unpriced* VWPK/W (B78-51293)
Magic of music. (Baker, Richard, *b.1925*). *Sphere. £1.25* A(X) (B78-33932) ISBN 0-7221-1422-2
Magic show. *Selections : arr.* The magic show : vocal selection ... (Schwartz, Stephen). *Belwin Mills. Unpriced* KDW (B78-50446)
Magic show : vocal selection ... (Schwartz, Stephen). *Belwin Mills. Unpriced* KDW (B78-50446)
Magnificat and Nunc dimittis. (Mendelssohn, Felix). *36 Ralelagh Gdns., W.6 : Cathedral Music. Unpriced* DGPP (B78-50338)
Magnificat and Nunc dimittis : for choir and organ (1978). (Harvey, Jonathan). *Faber Music. £1.50* DGPP (B78-50337)
Magnificat septimi toni for mixed voices and instruments. (Lasso, Orlando di). *Oxford University Press. Unpriced* EZDGKK (B78-50773) ISBN 0-19-337335-1
Magyar rondo = Hungarian rondo : vonószenekarra, két klarinéta és két fagottra = for string orchestra, two clarinets and two bassoons. (Kodály, Zoltán). *Editio musica : Boosey and Hawkes. Unpriced* RXMPVNS/W (B78-51072)
Maiden most gentle : (a Christmas carol) ; S.A.T.B., French tune. (Carter, Andrew). *Oxford University Press. Unpriced* DP/LF (B78-50737) ISBN 0-19-343067-3
Mailman, Martin. A simple ceremony, 'In memorian John Barnes Chance', Op.53 : for symphonic band and unison voices. *Boosey and Hawkes. Unpriced* JFE/UMMDGF (B78-50854)
Main course. *arr.* Main course : songs. (Bee Gees). *Wise : Music Sales. Unpriced* KDW/GB (B78-50124) ISBN 0-86001-254-9
Main course : songs. (Bee Gees). *Wise : Music Sales. Unpriced* KDW/GB (B78-50124) ISBN 0-86001-254-9
Majewski, Anne. Sonata, violins (2) & continuo, A major. Sonata Opus 4 Nr.6 A-Dur für zwei Violinen und Basso continuo, A major for two violins and basso continuo, La majeur pour deux Violons et basse continue. (Leclair, Jean Marie). *Edizioni Pegasus : Peters. Unpriced* SNTPWE (B78-50586)
Majnun answered ... : SATB with trumpet solo and piano. (Hovhaness, Alan). *Associated Music. £0.30* EWSPDW (B78-50362)
Make your own musical instruments. (Dalby, Stuart). *Batsford. £3.95* AL/BC (B78-26243) ISBN 0-7134-0545-7
Make your own musical instruments : a bibliography. (Woodrow, Martin). *14 Wisden Rd, Stevenage, Herts. : Clover Publications. £2.40* AL/BC(T)
Making music. The tin whistle. (Vallely, Eithne). 2nd ed. *6 Dublin Rd, Belfast : Appletree Press. Unpriced* VSQW (B78-50301) ISBN 0-904651-19-3
Making musical instruments. Musical instruments. (Tolley, Bryan). *Wayland. £1.75* AL/BC (B78-31598) ISBN 0-85340-529-8
Making of a musical. (Engel, Lehman). *Macmillan : Collier Macmillan. £6.75* ACM/D (B78-32355) ISBN 0-02-536070-1
Making of an opera : 'Don Giovanni' at Glyndebourne. (Higgins, John, *b.1934*). *Secker and Warburg. £7.95* BMSAC/E (B78-33162) ISBN 0-436-19595-x
Making of jazz : a comprehensive history. (Collier, James Lincoln). *Hart-Davis MacGibbon. £10.00* AMT(X) (B78-33166) ISBN 0-246-11092-9
Malicorne. Recueil de vingt chansons et airs traditionnels. *Chappell. Unpriced* KE/LDW/GB (B78-50167)
Malm, William Paul. Music cultures of the Pacific, the Near East, and Asia. 2nd ed. *Prentice-Hall. £7.95* BZB (B78-04322) ISBN 0-13-608000-6
Man in black. (Cash, Johnny). *Hodder and Stoughton. £0.95* AKDW/GCW/E(P) (B78-02614) ISBN 0-340-22173-9
Mancini, Henry.
Baby elephant walk. *arr.* Baby elephant walk. *Warner Blossom. Unpriced* UMMK (B78-50631)
Baby elephant walk. *arr.* Baby elephant walk. *Warner Blossom. Unpriced* UMMK (B78-51187)
Henry Mancini. *EMI. Unpriced* KDW/GB (B78-50136)
Manifold, John Streeter. The Penguin Australian song book. *Penguin Books. £1.25* JEZDW/AYX (B78-50085) ISBN 0-14-070004-8
Mann, Robert. The second Vienna school : expressionism and dodecaphony. (Rognoni, Luigi). *J. Calder Distributed by Calder and Boyars. £12.50* A/D(M/YEM/XLQ51) (B78-06256) ISBN 0-7145-3528-1
Maple leaf rag. (Joplin, Scott). *Bosworth and Co. Unpriced* QPK/AHXJ (B78-51028)
Maple leaf rag. *arr.* Maple leaf rag. (Joplin, Scott). *Bosworth and Co. Unpriced* QPK/AHXJ (B78-51028)
Mar, Norman Del. *See* Del Mar, Norman.
Marais, Marin. Pièces de violes, liv 4. Le Basque. *arr.* Le Basque : old French dance. *116 Long Acre, W.C.2 : Paxman. Unpriced* WTPK/AH (B78-50316)
Marc Bolan : a tribute. *19 Poland St., W1V 3DD : Essex House Publishing : Springwood Books. £5.95* AKDW/HKR/E(P) (B78-39783) ISBN 0-906445-00-0
Marc Bolan : a tribute. *19 Poland St., W1V 3DD : Essex House Publishing. £2.95* AKDW/HKR/E(P) (B78-39784) ISBN 0-906445-01-9
Marcello, Benedetto. Estro poetico-armonico. d Salmo 18. *arr.* 'The heavens devlare the glory of God'. *Cramer. Unpriced* RK/DR (B78-51056)
March, Ivan. The Penguin stereo record guide. (Greenfield, Edward). 2nd ed. *Penguin. £4.50* A/FF(WT) (B78-23118)
March for a free spirit. (Littell, Barbara). *Warner : Blossom. Unpriced* UMMJ (B78-51180)
March overture. (Johnson, Stuart). *R. Smith. Unpriced* WMGM (B78-50674)
Marching band news
No.1- ; Apr. 1978-. *64 London End, Beaconsfield, Bucks. : 'Marching band news'. £2.50 yearly* AUMM/E(B) (B78-26891)
Marciniak, Thad. The building of the house. *arr.* The building of the house : for concert band. (Britten, Benjamin, *Baron Britten*). *Faber Music. Unpriced* UMMK (B78-50628)
Marcus, Greil. Mystery train : images of America in rock 'n' roll music. *Omnibus Press. Unpriced* A/HK(X) (B78-06253) ISBN 0-86001-311-1
Mare, Walter de la. Another spring. Op.93 : three songs to poems by Walter de la Mare. (Berkeley, *Sir* Lennox). *Chester Music. Unpriced* KDW (B78-50859)
Margaretten, Bill.
Guess what time of year it is! : for SATB chorus with piano accompaniment. (Lombardo, Mario). *Chappell. Unpriced* DW/LF (B78-50749)
Guess what time of year it is! : for SATB chorus with piano accompaniment. (Lombardo, Mario). *Chappell. Unpriced* FDW/LF (B78-50820)
Margittag, Sándor.
Anthologia organi : Orgelmusik aus acht Jahrhunderten
Band 1: Die Anfänge der Orgelmusik. *Edito Musica : Schott. £8.00* R/AY (B78-51042)
Band 2: Die Niederlander und die Venezianische Schule. *Edito Musica : Schott. £8.00* R/AY (B78-51043)
Band 3: Die Römische Schule und ihre Nachfolger. *Edito Musica : Schott. £8.00* R/AY (B78-51044)
Band 4: Englische Orgelmusik bis Purcell. *Edito Musica : Schott. £8.00* R/AY (B78-51045)
Maronite music. (Hage, Louis). *Longman for the University of Essex. £0.75* ADGTCX (B78-35472) ISBN 0-582-78085-3
Marquis, Donald M. In search of Buddy Bolden, first man of jazz. *Louisiana State University Press. £7.00* AMT(P) (B78-33167) ISBN 0-8071-0356-x
Marsh, John. Musica britannica : a national collection of music
Vol.41: Confitebor tibi, Domine by Samuel Wesley ; transcribed and edited by John Marsh. *Stainer and Bell, for the Musica Britannica Trust. Unpriced* C/AYD (B78-50697)
Marshall, Michael, *b.1930.* Top hat & tails : the story of Jack Buchanan. *Elm Tree Books. £6.95 : CIP rev.* AKDW/GB/E(P) (B78-06268) ISBN 0-241-89602-9
Marshall, Nicholas. Nine recorder quartets. *Oxford University Press. Unpriced* VSNSK/AAY (B78-50295) ISBN 0-19-357749-6
Martin, Frank. Two pieces, overture and foxtrot : for two pianos, four hands. *Schirmer. £3.65* QNUHKEF (B78-50986)
Martin, Morris.
Workers' carol. *arr.* The workers' carol. (Petrokino, Paul). *Roberton. Unpriced* DP/LF (B78-50026)
Workers' carol. *arr.* The workers' carol. (Petrokino, Paul). *Roberton. £0.12* JE/VSPDP/LF (B78-50426)
Martin, Ruth. Twelve Moravian songs : for voice and piano. (Husa, Karel). *Associated Music. £3.05* KDW (B78-50444)
Martyrdom of St Magnus : a chamber opera in nine scenes. (Davies, Peter Maxwell). *Boosey and Hawkes. £1.00* BDEAC (B78-06987)
Mary and Martha : negro spiritual. (Dexter, Harry). *Edwin Ashdown. £0.20* FDW/LC (B78-50818)
Mary, Queen of Scots : opera in three acts. (Musgrave, Thea). *Novello. £15.00* CC (B78-50008)
Mary, Queen of Scots. *Vocal score.* Mary, Queen of Scots : opera in three acts. (Musgrave, Thea). *Novello. £15.00* CC (B78-50008)
Mary's boy child. (Hairston, Jester). *Chappell. Unpriced* NYFPK/DW/LF (B78-50953)
Mary's boy child. *arr.* Mary's boy child. (Hairston, Jester). *Chappell. Unpriced* NYFPK/DW/LF (B78-50953)
Marz, Karl Robert.
L'egisto. *Vocal score.* L'egisto : opera in three acts and a prologue. (Cavalli, Francesco). *Faber Music. Unpriced* CC (B78-50324)
L'incoronazione di Poppea. *Choral score.* L'incoronazione di Poppea. (Monteverdi, Claudio). *Faber Music. Unpriced* DAC (B78-50331)
L'incoronazione di Poppea. Vocal score. L'incoronazione di Poppea = The coronation of Poppea : opera in two acts and prologue. (Monteverdi, Claudio). New ed. *Faber Music. Unpriced* CC (B78-50007)
Maschera, Florentio. Libro primo de canzoni da sonare. *Selections.* Five canzonas for four instruments SATB. *London Pro Musica. Unpriced* LNS (B78-50482)
Mason, Tony.
Haul away! : 3 movements based on a sea shanties. *7 Garrick St., W.C.2 : Middle Eight Music. Unpriced* VNSK/DW/GMC/AY (B78-50288)
Masque of angels. Sanctus. *arr.* Sanctus : double chorus and piano or organ from the opera 'The masque of angels'. (Argento, Dominick). *Boosey and Hawkes. Unpriced* DGE (B78-50721)

Mass, Puer natus est nobis. (Tallis, Thomas). *Oxenford Imprint : Dist. Blackwell's Music Shop. Unpriced* EZDG (B78-50365)
Master of the Rolls. *See also* Public Record Office.
Mathews, Emrys G. Titta Ruffo : a centenary discography. *'Neuadd Deg', Penybanc, Llandeilo, Dyfed SA19 7TA : The author. £0.60* AKGN/FD(P/WT) (B78-27784)
Mathews, Eve.
Sound tracks
1: Pattern music. (Paynter, John). *Cambridge University Press. £1.95* A/D(VF) (B78-23589) ISBN 0-521-20581-6
2: Rites and ceremonies. (Paynter, John). *Cambridge University Press. £1.95* A/D(VF) (B78-23590) ISBN 0-521-20579-4
4: Magic songs. (Paynter, John). *Cambridge University Press. £1.95* A/D(VF) (B78-23592) ISBN 0-521-20578-6
Mathias, William.
Arise, shine, for your light has come : S.A.T.B. *Oxford University Press. Unpriced* DK (B78-50732) ISBN 0-19-350367-0
Fantasy for organ, Op.78. *Oxford University Press. Unpriced* RJ (B78-51051) ISBN 0-19-375552-1
Laudi : for orchestra. *Oxford University Press. Unpriced* MMJ (B78-50191) ISBN 0-19-365661-2
Nativity carol : S.A.T.B. : by William Mathias. *Oxford University Press. Unpriced* DP/LF (B78-50741) ISBN 0-19-343064-9
A royal garland : for unaccompanied mixed voices, op.77. *Oxford University Press. Unpriced* EZDW (B78-50798) ISBN 0-19-337440-4
Sonatina, clarinet & piano, op.3. Sonatina for clarinet in B flat and piano, Op.3. *Oxford University Press. Unpriced* VUPEM (B78-51273) ISBN 0-19-357777-1
Vivat regina : suite for brass band. *Oxford University Press. Unpriced* WMG (B78-50672)
Vivat regina : suite for brass band, op.75. *Oxford University Press. Unpriced* WMG (B78-50673) ISBN 0-19-365694-9
Zodiac trio, op.70 : for flute, viola, and harp. *Oxford University Press. Unpriced* NVRNT (B78-50199) ISBN 0-19-335774-7
Mathis collection : 27 of my favorite songs. *Chappell. Unpriced* KDW/GB/AY (B78-50154)
Matthews, Colin.
Night music : for orchestra. *Faber Music. Unpriced* MMJ (B78-50492)
Toccata, nocturne and scherzo (1977) : for piano. *Faber Music. Unpriced* QPJ (B78-51014)
Matthews, Denis.
Brahms piano music. *British Broadcasting Corporation. £1.00* BBTAQ (B78-28703) ISBN 0-563-12981-6
Fantasia and sonata, piano, K.475, K.457, C minor. Fantasia and sonata in C minor, K.475 and 457. (Mozart, Wolfgang Amadeus). *Associated Board of the Royal Schools of Music. Unpriced* QPE (B78-50993)
Sonata, piano, no.2, K.280, F major. Sonata in F. K.280. (Mozart, Wolfgang Amadeus). *Associated Board of the Royal Schools of Music. Unpriced* QPE (B78-50994)
Maw, Nicholas.
Calico pie and other nonsense rhymes : songs and rounds for children. *Boosey and Hawkes. £2.60* FDW (B78-50392)
Caroline Pink and other nonsense rhymes. *Boosey and Hawkes. £2.60* FDW (B78-50393)
Max Boyce songbook
Vol.1. (Boyce, Max). *EMI. Unpriced* KDW/GB (B78-50125)
Vol.2. (Boyce, Max). *EMI. Unpriced* KDW/GB (B78-50126)
Maxwell, Peter J. Le carnaval des animaux. Le cygne. *arr.* The swan ... : violoncello and piano. (Saint-Saëns, Camille). *Leonard, Gould and Bolttler. £0.50* SRPK (B78-50266)
Maxwell-Timmins, Donald. Forty songs for the class plus ten for the choir : a song book for primary children. *Schofield and Sims. Unpriced* JFE/TSDW/G/AY (B78-50853) ISBN 0-7217-2528-7
May, Helmut. Concerto, oboe, no.1, D minor. *arr.* Konzert No.1, d-moll, für Oboe und Orchester. (Lebrun, Ludwig August). *Schott. £9.60* VTPK/LF (B78-50302)
May, Jane. I speak in wisdom's voice (Ego sapienta) : for full chorus of men's voices a cappella. (Loudová, Ivana). *Schirmer. Unpriced* GEZDH (B78-50419)
May, Kenneth. Music matters : a check-list for local music groups. (Crampton, Stephen). *26 Bedford Sq., WC1B 3HU : Standing Conference for Amateur Music. Unpriced* A(WB/WT) (B78-20433)
May, Robin. A companion to the opera. *Lutterworth Press. £5.95* AC (B78-01674) ISBN 0-7188-2123-8
Mayes, Jerry. Christmas carols for guitar. *Charnwood Music. Unpriced* TSPMK/DP/LF/AY (B78-51168)
Mayhew, Kevin.
20th century folk hymnal
Vol.1. *55 Leigh Rd, Leigh-on-Sea : Kevin Mayhew. Unpriced* JEZDM/AY (B78-50427) ISBN 0-905725-27-1
Vol.3. *55 Leigh Rd, Leigh-on-Sea : Kevin Mayhew. Unpriced* JEZDM/AY (B78-50428) ISBN 0-905725-00-x
Maynfrank, Claus E. Neue Sonatinen, nos.2,5. Two new sonatinas, for treble recorder and basso continuo. (Telemann, Georg Philipp). 1st ed. *Musica rara. Unpriced* VSSPE (B78-51260)
Mazas, Jacques Féréol. Études melodiques et progressives. Op.36. Études speciales. Opus 36 : neu herausgegeben und bezeichnet von Walther Davisson
Hft.1. Neurevidierte Ausgabe. *Peters. Unpriced* S/AF (B78-51089)
Mead, Stella. Song under the silver umbrella : for children's voices and accompaniment
4: The merry man of Paris : (unison children's voices and piano). (Binkerd, Gordon). *Boosey and Hawkes. Unpriced* JFDW (B78-50842)
Mears, Caroline. Music for today. *Oxford University Press. £9.50* A/R (B78-12984) ISBN 0-19-570082-1
Medieval lyric. (Dronke, Peter). 2nd ed. *Hutchinson. £5.95* AKDW(XCDXK451) (B78-09116) ISBN 0-09-132080-1
Medieval music. (Caldwell, John, *b.1938*). *Hutchinson. £12.50* A(XCE601) (B78-17613) ISBN 0-09-120900-5
Meditations on a Byzantine hymn 'O quando in croce', op.117a. (Rubbra, Edmund). *Lengnick. Unpriced* SQNUK (B78-51108)
Meditations on a Byzantine hymn. Op.117a. *arr.* Meditations on a Byzantine hymn 'O quando in croce', op.117a. (Rubbra, Edmund). *Lengnick. Unpriced* SQNUK (B78-51108)
Meerwein, Georg. Trio, flute, clarinet & bassoon, op.61, no.3, A minor. Trio für Flöte, Klarinette (Violine) und Fagott (Violoncello), Opus 61, Nr.3. (Devienne, François). *Litolff : Peters. Unpriced* VNT (B78-50646)
Meggett, Joan M. Music periodical literature : an annotated bibliography of indexes and bibliographies. *Scarecrow Press : Distributed by Bailey and Swinfen. Unpriced* A(B/T/WT) (B78-23111) ISBN 0-8108-1109-X
Meiklem, Colin L. Starter's whistle, or, How to play the penny whistle. *Feldman. Unpriced* VSX/AC (B78-51262)
Meilensteine eines Komponistenlebens : kleine Festschrift zum 70. Geburtstag von Günter Bialas. *32 Gt Titchfield St., W1P 7AD : Bärenreiter. £10.08* BBNO(D) (B78-19399)
Mein Heimatland : die schönsten Volks-, Wander-, Trink- und Scherzlieder. Neu- Ausgabe mit vollstandigem Text, Trompete oder Klarinette in B. *Schott. £7.20* WSPMK/DW/AYE (B78-50314)
Melancolia und Mirabilis : zwei Stücke für Harfe solo = deux morçeaux pour pour harpe seule = two pieces for solo harp : opus 23. (Kelkel, Manfred). *Bote und Bock Schirmer. £2.90* TQPMJ (B78-51137)
Membership list
Jan. 1977. (Player Piano Group). *358 High St., Brentford, Middx : The Group. Unpriced* AQ/FH(Q/BC) (B78-01685)
Memento vivere : für Mezzosopran, Bariton, 3 Sprechstimmen, gemischten Chor und Orchester. (Wimberger, Gerhard). *Bärenreiter. £12.60* EMDX (B78-50356)
Memories of Covent Garden = Erinnerung an Covent Garden : waltz, op.329, based on English music hall songs. (Strauss, Johann, *b.1825*). *Bosworth & Co. Unpriced* MK/AHW (B78-50486)
Mendelssohn, Felix.
Lieder ohne Worte. *Selections: arr.* 6 Lieder ohne Worte. *Schott. £4.80* TSPMK (B78-50275)
Magnificat & Nunc dimittis, op.69, nos.3, 1. Magnificat and Nunc dimittis. *36 Ralelagh Gdns., W.6 : Cathedral Music. Unpriced* DGPP (B78-50338)
Mendelssohn in Scotland. (Jenkins, David, *b.1944*). *Chappell : Elm Tree Books. £5.95* BMJ(N/YDL/XHJ) (B78-19674) ISBN 0-903443-18-x
Perite autem. Op.115, no.2. How brightly shine = Perite autem : for four part chorus of men's voices a cappella. *Schirmer. £0.35* GEZDH/LF (B78-50420)
Mendelssohn in Scotland. (Jenkins, David, *b.1944*). *Chappell : Elm Tree Books. £5.95* BMJ(N/YDL/XHJ) (B78-19674) ISBN 0-903443-18-x
Menestrellorum multitudo : minstrels at a royal feast. (Bullock-Davies, Constance). *University of Wales Press. £7.50* AL/E(YD/XCKF) (B78-12983) ISBN 0-7083-0656-x
Menuhin, Yehudi. My favourite music stories. *Lutterworth Press. £2.95* A (B78-18540) ISBN 0-7188-2308-7
Menuhin (Yehudi) music guides. *See* Yehudi Menuhin music guides.
Merewether, Richard. The horn, the horn-. *116 Long Acre, WC2E 9PA : Paxman Musical Instruments Ltd. £1.50* AWT/B (B78-15125)
Mermaid's 'Cowardy custard' : an entertainment. (Frow, Gerald). *French. £1.80* BCMWACM (B78-21400) ISBN 0-573-68079-5
Merrily to Bethlehem : a very unusual carol book. *A. and C. Black. Unpriced* JFE/LNDP/LF/AY (B78-50850) ISBN 0-7136-1887-6
Merulo, Claudio. Canzona in 4 parts. *Schott. Unpriced* TSNSK (B78-50607)
Messe basse and other sacred works : for female or boys voices and organ or piano. (Fauré, Gabriel). *Novello. Unpriced* DFF (B78-50016)
Metis, Frank.
bat out of hell. (Steinman, Jim). *Dick James. Unpriced* KDW/HKR (B78-50880)
Originals. (Brubeck, Dave). *EMI. Unpriced* QPHX (B78-51002)
Metropolitan Opera Guild. Composer series.
Hume, Paul. Verdi : the man and his music. *Hutchinson. £5.50* BVE(N) (B78-08475) ISBN 0-09-132390-8
Weaver, William, *b.1923*. Puccini : the man and his music. *Hutchinson. £5.50* BPU(N) (B78-20437) ISBN 0-09-132380-0
Meyer, Lucy Rider-. *See* Rider-Meyer, Lucy.
Meyer-Denkmann, Gertrud. Experiments in sound : new directions in musical education for young children. *Universal Edition. £3.50* A/D(VC) (B78-10119) ISBN 0-900938-49-8
Meyerolbersleben, Ernst. Sonata, flute, violin & continuo, G major. Triosonate, G-dur, G major, für Querflöte (Violine), Violine (Oboe) und B.C., for German flute (violin), violin (oboe) and b.c. (Platti, Giovanni Benedetto). Erstausgabe. *Heinrichshofen : Peters. Unpriced* NURNTE (B78-50501)
Michael, Frank. Yantra : für Klavier, Violine und Violoncello, Opus 41 (1974). *Bote und Bock : Schirmer. £15.35* NXNT (B78-50949)
Michaelides, Solon. The music of ancient Greece : an encyclopaedia. *Faber. £15.00* A(C/YBD) (B78-04320) ISBN 0-571-10021-x
Michels, Ulrich. dtv-Atlas zur Musik : Tafeln und Texte
Bd 1. Systematischer Teil ; und, Historischer Teil: Von den Anfängen bis zur Renaissance. 2.Aufl. *Bärenreiter etc.. £3.58* A(C) (B78-19397)
Midnight baby : an autobiography. (Previn, Dory). *Corgi. £0.75* AKDW/GB/E(P/B) (B78-18542) ISBN 0-552-10643-7
Midsummer nocturne : piano solo. (Copland, Aaron). *Boosey and Hawkes. Unpriced* QPJ (B78-50529)
Mignone, Francisco.
4 choros : piano. *Arthur Napoleão : Essex Music. Unpriced* QPJ (B78-50542)
Caixinha de bringnedos. Dança compestre. Dança campestre : piano a 4 mãos. *Arthur Napoleão : Essex Music. Unpriced* QNVH (B78-50522)
Cantiga de roda. *arr.* Cantiga de roda. (Villa-Lobos, Heitor). *Arthur Napoleão : Essex Music. Unpriced* QPK (B78-50552)
Capricho, op.49. *arr.* Capricho, Op.49. (Villa-Lobos, Heitor). *Arthur Napoleão : Essex Music. Unpriced* QPK (B78-50553)
As criancas. *arr.* As criancas. (Villa-Lobos, Heitor). *Arthur Napoleão : Essex Music. Unpriced* QPK (B78-50554)
Elegia. *arr.* Elegia. (Villa-Lobos, Heitor). *Arthur Napoleão : Essex Music. Unpriced* QPK (B78-50555)
Il fucile ad ago. *arr.* Il fucile ad ago : revista de 1866. (Gomes, Antonio Carlos). *Arthur Napoleão : Essex Music. Unpriced* QPK (B78-50549)
Nazarethiana : 5 pegas para piano. *Arthur Napoleão Essex Music. Unpriced* QPJ (B78-50543)
Noturno das folhas soltas. *arr.* Noturno das folhas soltas. (Lorenzo-Fernandez, Oscar). *Arthur Napoleão : Essex Music. Unpriced* QPK (B78-50551)
Prelude, cello & piano, op.20, no.2, F minor. *arr.* Prelúdio op.20, no.2 em lá bemol. (Villa-Lobos, Heitor). *Arthur Napoleão : Essex Music. Unpriced* QPK (B78-50556)
Sonhar. Op.14. *arr.* Sonhar, Op.14. (Villa-Lobos, Heitor). *Arthur Napoleão : Essex Music. Unpriced* QPK (B78-50557)
Valsa de esquina : para violão. *Arthur Napoleão : Essex Music. Unpriced* SPMHW (B78-50593)
Variaç ões. *arr.* Variaç ěs. (Gomes, Antonio Carlos). *Arthur Napoleão : Essex Music. Unpriced* QPK (B78-50550)
Variaç ões para violão sobro o tema 'Luar do sertão' de Catullo da Paixão Cearense. *Arthur Napoleão : Essex Music. Unpriced* SPM/T (B78-50591)
Milchzahnlieder = Milktooth songs. (Eröd, Iván). *Boosey and Hawkes. Unpriced* JFADW (B78-50836)
Milchzahnlieder = Milktooth songs : für Gesang oder Kinderchor, mit Klavier oder Kammerorchester = for solo voice, or children's chorus with piano or chamber orchestra. (Eröd, Iván). *Boosey and Hawkes. Unpriced* KDW (B78-50860)
Milchzahnlieder. *Choral score.* Milchzahnlieder = Milktooth songs. (Eröd, Iván). *Boosey and Hawkes. Unpriced* JFADW (B78-50836)
Milchzahnlieder. *Vocal score.* Milchzahnlieder = Milktooth songs : für Gesang oder Kinderchor, mit Klavier oder Kammerorchester = for solo voice, or children's chorus with piano or chamber orchestra. (Eröd, Iván). *Boosey and Hawkes. Unpriced* KDW (B78-50860)
Military bands and their uniforms. (Cassin-Scott, Jack). *Blandford Press. £6.95* AUMM(X) (B78-26675) ISBN 0-7137-0895-6
Miller, Thomas E. Sing we now Christmas : traditional French carol for 4-part chorus of female voices unaccompanied. *Roberton. £0.20* FEZDP/LF (B78-50399)
Milligan, Spike. Let the children sing
Book 1. (Dale, Mervyn). *Edwin Ashdown. Unpriced* JFDW (B78-50430)
Mime of Mick, Nick and the Maggies : on part 2 of 'Finnegans Wake'. (Buller, John). *Schirmer. £17.50* EMDX (B78-50355)
Mimi. (Rogers, Richard). *Warner : Blossom. Unpriced* UMMK/DW (B78-50635)
Mimi : SATB chorus and piano. (Rodgers, Richard). *Warner : Blossom. Unpriced* DW (B78-50746)
Mingled jingles : for recorders and piano. (Drewar, Della). *16 Anchor Way, Danes Green : Viking. Unpriced* VSNTQ (B78-51250)
Miniature scores:.
Arne, Thomas Augustine. Thomas and Sally : dramatic pastoral in two acts. *Eulenburg. Unpriced* CQC (B78-50329)
Berkeley, *Sir* Lennox. Voices of the night : for orchestra. *Chester Music. Unpriced* MMJ (B78-50920)
Davies, Peter Maxwell. Symphony. *Boosey and Hawkes. Unpriced* MME (B78-50185)
Davies, Peter Maxwell. Taverner. Dances. Points and dances ... : for instrumental ensemble. *Boosey and Hawkes. Unpriced* LN (B78-50907)
Delius, Frederick. An arabesque = Eine Arabeske : for baritone solo, mixed chorus and orchestra = für Bariton-Solo, gemischter Chor und Orchester. *Boosey and Hawkes. Unpriced* EMDX (B78-50751)
Delius, Frederick. Concerto, cello. Cello concerto. *Boosey*

and Hawkes. *Unpriced* MPSRF (B78-50934)
Einem, Gottfried von. Kabale und Liebe : Opera in 2 Teilen (9 Bildern) nach Friedrich von Schiller. *Boosey and Hawkes. Unpriced* CC (B78-50005)
Einem, Gottfried von. Quartet, strings, no.1, op.45. Erstes Streichquartett, opus 45. *Boosey and Hawkes. Unpriced* RXNS (B78-51080)
Einem, Gottfried von. Quintet, wind instruments, op.46. Bläserquintett. Opus 46. *Boosey and Hawkes. Unpriced* UNR (B78-51196)
Fauré, Gabriel. Requiem, Op.48. *Eulenburg. Unpriced* EMDGKAV (B78-50031)
Handel, George Frideric. Concerto, organ, op.4, no.1, G minor. Organ concerto, G minor, Op.4, no.1. *Eulenburg. Unpriced* MPRF (B78-50926)
Handel, George Frideric. Concerto, organ, op.4, no.2, B flat major. Organ concerto, B flat major, Op.4, no.2. *Eulenburg. Unpriced* MPRF (B78-50927)
Handel, George Frideric. Concerto, organ, op.4, no.3, G minor. Organ concerto, G minor, Op.4, no.3. *Eulenburg. Unpriced* MPRF (B78-50928)
Handel, George Frideric. Concerto, organ, op.4, no.4, F major. Organ concerto, F major, Op.4, no.4. *Eulenburg. Unpriced* MPRF (B78-50929)
Handel, George Frideric. Concerto, organ, op.4, no.5, F major. Organ concerto, F major, Op.4, no.5. *Eulenburg. Unpriced* MPRF (B78-50930)
Handel, George Frideric. Concerto, organ, op.4, no.6, B flat major, 'Harp'. Organ concerto, (Harp concerto), B flat major, Op.4, no.6. *Eulenburg. Unpriced* MPRF (B78-50931)
Handel, George Frideric. Sonatas, violins (2) & continuo, Op.2, no.1-6. Trio sonatas
Op.2, nos.1-3. *Eulenburg. Unpriced* NXNSE (B78-50203)
Handel, George Frideric. Sonatas, violins (2) & continuo, op.2, nos. 3, 8, 9. Dresden trio sonatas. *Eulenburg. Unpriced* NXNSE (B78-50204)
Handel, George Frideric. Sonatas, violins (2) & continuo, op.2, nos.1-6. Trio sonatas
Op.2, no.4-6. *Eulenburg. Unpriced* NXNSE (B78-50205)
Holst, Gustav. A choral fantasia, Op.51. *Eulenburg. £1.00* EZDE (B78-50042)
Lees, Benjamin. Collage : for string quartet, wind quintet and percussion. *Boosey and Hawkes. Unpriced* MRJ (B78-50942)
Lees, Benjamin. Spectrum : for orchestra. *Boosey and Hawkes. Unpriced* MMJ (B78-50923)
Mozart, Wolfgang Amadeus. Concerto, piano, no.17, K.453, G major. Piano concerto, G major, K.453. *Eulenburg. £1.60* MPQF (B78-50497)
Purcell, Henry. Sonatas in 4 parts, Z.802-811. Ten sonatas in four parts
Nos. 1-6. *Eulenburg. £2.00* NXNSE (B78-50506)
Purcell, Henry. Sonatas in 4 parts. Z.802-811. Ten sonatas in four parts
Nos.7-10. *Eulenburg. £2.00* NXNSE (B78-50507)
Vaughan Williams, Ralph. Symphony no.3, 'Pastoral'. Pastoral symphony. *Boosey and Hawkes. Unpriced* KFLE/MDX (B78-50175)
Weber, Carl Maria von, *Freiherr.* Trio, flute, cello & piano, J. 259, G minor. Trio for flute, cello and piano in G minor, J.259. *Eulenburg. Unpriced* NURNT (B78-50198)
Weinzweig, John. Divertimento 1 for flute and string orchestra. *Boosey and Hawkes. Unpriced* RXMPVR (B78-51073)
Weinzweig, John. Divertimento, oboe & string orchestra, no.2. Divertimento 2 for oboe and string orchestra. *Boosey and Hawkes. Unpriced* RXMPVT (B78-51074)
Miniaturen : für Streicher. (Genzmer, Harald). *Litolff : Peters. Unpriced* RXMJ (B78-50576)
Minstrel man : for bass trombone, bass drum and hi-hat cymbals (1977). (Anderson, Thomas Jefferson). *Bote und Bock : Schirmer. £2.40* WUUPLX (B78-51357)
Mirror of love : lute songs of love and lust. *Chester Music. Unpriced* KE/TWDW/AY (B78-50887)
Mirror of whitenbing light = Specolum luminis dealbensin : for chamber orchestra. (Davies, Peter Maxwell). *Boosey and Hawkes. Unpriced* MRJ (B78-50940)
Miserae : symphonische Dichtung für Orchester, (1933-34). (Hartmann, Karl Amadeus). *Schott. £10.00* MMJ (B78-50189)
Miserere. Miserere mei, Deus : for nine voices. (Allegri, Gregorio). *Chester Music. Unpriced* EZDGKHM/LH (B78-50771)
Miserere mei, Deus : for nine voices. (Allegri, Gregorio). *Chester Music. Unpriced* EZDGKHM/LH (B78-50771)
Mish, Violet. 'Stringing along' : a tutor for the first year schools' cello class. *(16 Anchor Way, Danes Green, Gnosall) : Viking. Unpriced* SRN/AC (B78-50263)
Misletoe bough, p.61 : traditional carol for SSATBB and piano woodwork or string orchestra and percussion. (Blyton, Carey). *Roberton. £0.20* EZDW (B78-50050)
Miss Donnithorne's maggot : for mezzo-soprano and chamber ensemble. (Davies, Peter Maxwell). *Boosey and Hawkes. £7.00* C/J (B78-50003)
Missa scala aretina : para 11 voces in 3 cores, instrumentos y continuo = for 11 voices in 3 choirs, instruments and continuo. (Valls, Francisco). *Novello. £3.15* ENUDG (B78-50752)
Mitgift und Gebet : zwei Männerchöre a cappella nach Texten von Josef Srb-Debrnov. (Smetana, Bedřich). *Bärenreiter. £0.70* GEZDW (B78-50423)
Mobile concertante : für Schlagwerk und Streicher. (Benker, Heinz). *Schott. £14.00* RXMPXF (B78-50252)
Mobile : für Oboe (Oboe d'amore ad lib.), Klarinette und Fagott, 1976. (Redel, Martin Christoph). *Bote und Bock : Schirmer. £4.80* VNT (B78-51199)
Möckl, Franz. Ein Kind ist uns geboren : das Ottowinder Christspiel, für Sprecher, Soli ad lib. (Sopran, Tenor, Bariton) - Kinderstimmen, Frauen - , gemischten Chor und Gemeindegesang - Instrumentalkreis (Stabspiele, Schlagzeng) - Orgel (wahlweise oder zusätzlich auch Streicher, Holz und Blechbläser). *Schott. £8.00* CQM/LF (B78-50014)
Modal system of Arab and Persian music, AD 1250-1300. (Wright, O). *Oxford University Press. £32.00 : CIP rev.* BZCW/PR (B77-07528) ISBN 0-19-713575-7
Moelwyn, Lewys. Sleep = Cswg : for two-part choir and piano. (Hughes-Jones, Llifon). *Roberton. £0.20* FDW (B78-50815)
Momentella : for clarinet in B flat. (Clifford, Keith). *Arts Lab Music. Unpriced* VVPMJ (B78-51287)
Monolog 1 : für Violoncello solo (1976). (Schlumpf, Martin). *Bote und Bock : Schirmer. £5.75* SRPMJ (B78-51120)
Monsieur Choufleuri restera chez lui de. *Vocal score.* Salon Blumenkohl/Monsieur Choufleuri restera chez lui de ... : Buffo-Operette in einem Akt deutsch nach Karl Fr. Wiltmann von Heinz Balthes und Paul Vasil, opéra bouffe en un acte de St. Rémy, E. L'Epine, Hector Crémieux et Ludovic Halévy, musikalische Revision, neue Instrumentation und praktische Bearbeitung von Caspar Richter. (Offenbach, Jacques). *Bote und Bock Associated music. £11.50* CF (B78-50703)
Monteverdi, Claudio.
L'incoronazione di Poppea. *Choral score.* L'incoronazione di Poppea. *Faber Music. Unpriced* DAC (B78-50331)
L'incoronazione di Poppea. Vocal score. L'incoronazione di Poppea = The coronation of Poppea : opera in two acts and prologue. New ed. *Faber Music. Unpriced* CC (B78-50007)
Tenmadrigals : for mixed voices. *Oxford University Press. Unpriced* EZDU (B78-50791) ISBN 0-19-343676-0
Montgomery, James. Hail to the Lord's anointed. (Pulkingham, Betty). *57 Dorchester Rd. Lytchett Minister, Poole : Celebration Services. Unpriced* JDM (B78-50082)
Monument, Selbstportrait, Bewegung : drei Stücke für zwei Klaviere ... (1976). (Ligeti, Gyorgy). *Schott. £10.00* QNU (B78-50210)
Moody Blues. The Moody Blues caught live + 5. *TRO : Essex Music International : Essex Music. Unpriced* KDW/HKR (B78-50163)
Moody Blues caught live + 5. (Moody Blues). *TRO : Essex Music International : Essex Music. Unpriced* KDW/HKR (B78-50163)
Moore, Clement Clark. A visit from St Nicholas. (The night before Christmas). (Silverman, Jerry). *Schirmer. Unpriced* KDW (B78-50117)
Moore, Gerald, *b.1899.* Farewell recital : further memoirs. *Hamilton. £4.95 : CIP rev.* AQ/ED(P/XQG11) (B77-33371) ISBN 0-241-89817-x
Moore, Jack.
An introduction to the guitar. (Bolton, Cecil). *EMI Music. Unpriced* TS/AC (B78-51140)
The best of Christmas songs : chord organ. *EMI. Unpriced* RPVCK/DW/LF/AY (B78-51059)
The best of Christmas songs : clarinet. *EMI. Unpriced* VVPMK/DW/LF/AY (B78-51288)
The best of Christmas songs : guitar or recorder. *EMI. Unpriced* TSPMK/DW/LF/AY (B78-51170)
The best of Christmas songs : piano or organ. *EMI. Unpriced* RK/DW/LF/AY (B78-51057)
The best of Christmas songs : trumpet. *EMI. Unpriced* WSPMK/DW/LF/AY (B78-51348)
Children's songs and carols, including hymns and games : for easy guitar or recorder. *EMI. Unpriced* TSPMK/DW/GJ/AY (B78-51169)
Children's songs and carols, including hymns and games : for easy piano or organ. *EMI. Unpriced* QPK/DW/GJ/AY (B78-51030)
Classic melodies. *EMI. Unpriced* RPVCK (B78-51058)
Moore, Thomas.
Song under the silver umbrella : for children's voices and accompaniment
5: Child's song : (three-part children's chorus and piano). (Binkerd, Gordon). *Boosey and Hawkes. Unpriced* FDW (B78-50812)
Two Thomas Moore songs : for solo voice and piano. (Raphael, Mark). *Roberton. £0.50* KDW (B78-50445)
Morales, Cristoval.
Ecce virgo concipiet. *Cathedral Music. Unpriced* GEZDGKAH/LEZ (B78-50408)
O magnum mysterium. *36 Ranelagh Gdns., W.6 : Cathedral Music. Unpriced* GEZDGKH/LF (B78-50410)
Moramus edition.
Herbst, Johannes. Three sacred songs of Johannes Herbert. *Boosey and Hawkes. Unpriced* KFTDH (B78-50899)
Peter, Johann Friedrich. Ihre Priester will ich mit Heil kleiden. *arr.* I will clothe thy priests with salvation = Ihre Priester will ich mit Heil kleiden : S.A.T.B. with accompaniment. *Boosey and Hawkes. Unpriced* DH (B78-50340)
Peter, Johann Friedrich. Kommt danket dem Helden. *arr.* Come thank now Jehovah = Kommt danket dem Helden : double chorus ; SATB with accompaniment. *Boosey and Hawkes. Unpriced* DH (B78-50341)
Peter, Johann Friedrich. Unser Herr Jesus Christus. *arr.* Our dear Lord Jesus Christ = Unser Herr Jesus Christus : SATB with accompaniment. *Boosey and Hawkes. Unpriced* DH (B78-50342)
Moramus editions. Peter, Johann Friedrich. Herr, wie sind deine Werke so gross. *arr.* Lord, thy creations, how great they are = Herr, wie sind deine Werke so gross : S.A.T.B. with accompaniment. *Boosey and Hawkes. Unpriced* DH (B78-50339)
More clarinet virtuosi of the past. (Weston, Pamela). *1 Rockland Rd, SW15 2LN : The author. £5.40* AVV/E(M) (B78-00390)
More Irish street ballads. *Pan Books. £0.90* KEZDW/K/G/AYDM (B78-50469) ISBN 0-330-25317-4
More songs for chord organ. *EMI Music. Unpriced* RPVK/DW (B78-50242)
Morehen, John. English sacred music
Vol.1. (Tye, Christopher). *Stainer and Bell, for the British Academy. Unpriced* EZDK (B78-50046) ISBN 0-85249-449-1
Moretti, Federico. Doce canciones = Twelve songs : with guitar accompaniment. Complete facsimile ed. *Tecla. Unpriced* KE/TSDW (B78-50885) ISBN 0-8494-0140-2
Morgan, Hilda.
Gradualia, lib.1. Ave verum corpus. *arr.* Ave verum corpus : for male voice choir unaccompanied. (Byrd, William). *Roberton. £0.20* GEZDJ (B78-50826)
Jesu dulcis memoria. Jusu! the very thought is sweet : for 4-part female choir unaccompanied. (Victoria, Tomás Luis de). *Roberton. £0.15* FEZDJ (B78-50824)
Morgan (Pierpont) Library. *See* Pierpont Morgan Library.
Morley, Thomas. A plaine and easy introduction to practicall musicke. O amica mea. *arr.* O amica mea. *Edizioni Pegasus : Peters. Unpriced* VSNRK/DJ (B78-50652)
Morley-Pegge, Reginald. The French horn : some notes on the evolution of the instrument and of its technique. 2nd ed. *E. Benn etc.. £7.50* AWT/B
Moroder, Giorgio. Zodiacs. *Hansa Productions : ATV Music : Music Sales. Unpriced* KFDW (B78-50174)
Morowitz, Gary. Simple things : piano, vocal, chords. (King, Carole). *Colgems-EMI : EMI. Unpriced* KDW/GB (B78-50132)
Mortimer, Harry.
Bandkraft
1. *Forsyth. Unpriced* WM/AY (B78-51295)
2. *Forsyth. Unpriced* WM/AY (B78-51296)
3. *Forsyth. Unpriced* WM/AY (B78-51297)
Harry Mortimer souvenir album : a unique collection of famous cornet solos. *Boosey and Hawkes. Unpriced* WRPK/AAY (B78-51341)
Moshe Timloch : fantasy for brass quintet. (Bishop, Jeffrey). *Novello. £1.30* WNR (B78-51336)
Motecta. Ave Maria. Ave Maria. In Annuntiationis B. Maria Virginis,. (Victoria, Tomás Luis de). *36 Ranelagh Gdns. W.6 : Cathedral Music. Unpriced* EZDJ (B78-50377)
Motecta. Doctor bonus. Doctor bonus. In festo sancti Andreae. (Victoria, Tomás Luis de). *Cathedral Music. Unpriced* EZDJ (B78-50378)
Motet, Wenn der Herr die Gefangnen Zion erlösen wird. (Hartmann, Heinrich). *Tomus. Unpriced* VSNQK/DJ (B78-51242)
Motettorum ... portim quinis ... vocibus ... liber primus. O magnum mysterium. O magnum mysterium. (Palestrina, Giovanni Pierluigi da). *36 Ranelagh Gdns., W.6 : Cathedral Music. Unpriced* EZDGKH/LF (B78-50367)
Mountain dance : for violin and piano. (Nieman, Alfred). *Roberton. £0.60* SPH (B78-50258)
'Mountains in cloud' : 8 minatures sic after Chinese scrolls and album leaves for chamber ensemble. (Newton, Rodney Stephen). *13 Chetwynd Ave., East Barnet, Herts. : Composer Edition. Unpriced* NYEPNQ (B78-50209)
Mouret, Jean Joseph. Concert de chambre, liv.1, no.1. Premier concert de chambre : for two descant recorders and keyboard. *Dolmetsch. Unpriced* VSRNTPWF (B78-51255)
Moyse, Louis.
Concerto, flute & harp, K.299, C major. *arr.* Concerto in C major (K.299) for flute, harp and orchestra. (Mozart, Wolfgang Amadeus). *Schirmer. £2.75* VRPK/LF (B78-51227)
Concerto, flutes (2), E minor. *arr.* Concerto in E minor for two flutes and piano. (Telemann, Georg Philipp). *Schirmer. £2.75* VRNTQK/LF (B78-51202)
Four pieces for flute and viola ... op.10. (Neubaur, Franz). *Schirmer. £2.50* VRPLSQ (B78-51229)
Sonata, flute & piano, no.1 (1975). First sonata (1975) for flute and piano. *Schirmer. £3.95* VRPE (B78-51213)
Mozart, Wolfgang Amadeus.
Arien, Szenen, Ensembles
Textbuch italienisch-deutsch. *32 Gt Titchfield St., W1P 7AD : Bärenreiter. £1.68* BMSADW (B78-26890)
Church sonatas. *Collections.* Sämtliche Kirchensonaten = Complete church sonatas
III/IV: Zwei Sonaten in C für Orgel und Orchester, KV278 (271e), KV329 (317a) : Generalbassausetzung, Werner Bittinger. *Bärenreiter. £2.80* MPRE/AZ (B78-50498)
Church sonatas. *Selections : arr.* Four church sonatas. *Boosey and Hawkes. £2.25* VVPK/AE (B78-50305)
Complete string quartets with the horn and clarinet quintets ... *Dover Publications : Constable. Unpriced* RXNR (B78-51076) ISBN 0-486-23603-x
Concerto, flute & harp, K.299, C major. *arr.* Concerto in C major (K.299) for flute, harp and orchestra. *Schirmer. £2.75* VRPK/LF (B78-51227)
Concerto, horn, no.3, K.447, E flat major. Rondo. *arr.* Rondo from horn concerto no.3, K.447. *50 Ladbroke Grove, W.11 : Midland Music. Unpriced* WTPK/LW (B78-50317)
Mozart, Wolfgang Amadeus. Don Giovanni. The making of an opera : 'Don Giovanni' at Glyndebourne. (Higgins, John, *b.1934*). *Secker and Warburg. £7.95* BMSAC/E (B78-33162) ISBN 0-436-19595-x
Mozart, Wolfgang Amadeus.
Don Giovanni. Deh vieni alla finestra. *arr.* Canzonetta.

Lengnick. £0.60 VRPK/DW (B78-51224)
Don Giovanni, KV527 : Dramma giocoso im zwei Akten Textbuch italienisch-deutsch. (Da Ponte, Lorenzo). *32 Gt Titchfield St., W1P 7AD : Bärenreiter. £2.24* BMSAC (B78-17615)
Fantasia and sonata, piano, K.475, K.457, C minor. Fantasia and sonata in C minor, K.475 and 457. *Associated Board of the Royal Schools of Music. Unpriced* QPE (B78-50993)
Klassische Tänze von Joseph Haydn und Wolfgang Amadeus Mozart : für Blockflöten - Ensemble ... Sopran, Alt, Tenor, Bass ... (Haydn, Joseph). *Schott. £3.20* VSNSK/AH (B78-50297)
Kyrie, K.322, E flat major. *Vocal score.* Kyrie, (K.322), for four-part chorus of mixed voices with piano accompaniment. *Schirmer. Unpriced* DGB (B78-50017)
Kyrie, K.323, C major. *Vocal score.* Kyrie, (K.323), for four-part chorus of mixed voices with piano accompaniment. *Schirmer. Unpriced* DGB (B78-50018)
Kyrie, K.341, D minor. *Vocal score.* Kyrie, K.341, for four-part chorus of mixed voices with piano accompaniment. *Schirmer. Unpriced* DGB (B78-50019)
Mozart : morçeaux choisis a l'usage des mains petites de la 2e année de piano (assez facile) a la moyenne difficulté. *Chappell. Unpriced* QPJ (B78-51015)
A Mozart suite. *Janus Music. Unpriced* VSNS (B78-51244)
Ein musikalischen Spass. K.522. Presto. *arr.* A musical joke : theme from 'The horse of the year show' and other equestrian events. *Fentone Music. Unpriced* QPK (B78-51022)
Piano concertos nos 17-22 in full score. *Dover Publications : Constable. Unpriced* MPQF (B78-50925) ISBN 0-486-23599-8
Quartet, strings, no.3. Klassische Tanze von Joseph Haydn und Wolfgang Amadeus Mozart : für Blockflöten - Ensemble ... Sopran, Alt, Tenor, Bass ... (Haydn, Joseph). *Schott. £3.20* VSNSK/AH (B78-50298)
Concerto, piano, no.17, K.453, G major. Piano concerto, G major, K.453. *Eulenburg. £1.60* MPQF (B78-50497)
Selected works : for piano solo. *Schirmer. £3.60* QPJ (B78-50544)
Serenade, wind sextet, no.11, K.375, E flat major. Adagio. Adagio ... for wind ensemble. *Boosey and Hawkes. Unpriced* UNQ (B78-51194)
Sonata, piano, no.2, K.280, F major. Sonata in F. K.280. *Associated Board of the Royal Schools of Music. Unpriced* QPE (B78-50994)
Die Zauberflöte. Wie stark ist nicht dein Zauberton. *arr.* Andante. *Lengnick. Unpriced* VRPK/DW (B78-51225)
Mozart & Beethoven : the concept of love in their operas. (Singer, Irving). *Johns Hopkins University Press. £7.00* BMSAC(ZC) (B78-15123) ISBN 0-8018-1987-3
Mozart : morçeaux choisis a l'usage des mains petites de la 2e année de piano (assez facile) a la moyenne difficulté. (Mozart, Wolfgang Amadeus). *Chappell. Unpriced* QPJ (B78-51015)
Mozart piano concertos. (Radcliffe, Philip). *British Broadcasting Corporation. £1.00* BMSAMPQF (B78-33168) ISBN 0-563-12771-6
Mozart suite. (Mozart, Wolfgang Amadeus). *Janus Music. Unpriced* VSNS (B78-51244)
Mozart wind and string concertos. (King, Alexander Hyatt). *British Broadcasting Corporation. £1.00* BMSAMPSF (B78-28702) ISBN 0-563-12770-8
Mozart's 'Don Giovanni'. (Abert, Hermann). *48 Great Marlborough St., W1V 2BN : Eulenburg Books. £3.00* BMSAC (B78-11196) ISBN 0-903873-19-2
Mozarts italienische Texte mit deutscher Übersetzung. *See* Internationale Stiftung Mozarteum Salzburg. Mozarts italienische Texte mit deutscher Übersetzung.
Mozart's piano concertos. (Girdlestone, Cuthbert Morton). 3rd ed. *Cassell. £6.50* BMSAMPQF (B78-22846) ISBN 0-304-30043-8
Mr Mulberry's toyshop : a one act musical play for infants or lower juniors. (Wade, Darrell). *16 Anchor Way, Danes Green, Gnosall : Viking. Unpriced* CN (B78-50012)
Mrs Pennyweather's garden : a musical play for infants (with optional percussion). (Wade, Darrell). *16 Anchor Way, Danes Green, Gnosall : Viking. Unpriced* CN (B78-50328)
Mueller, Frank.
Perite autem. Op.115, no.2. How brightly shine = Perite autem : for four part chorus of men's voices a cappella. (Mendelssohn, Felix). *Schirmer. £0.35* GEZDH/LF (B78-50420)
Romanzen für Frauenstimmen, Op.69. Tamburin schlägerin. The tambourine player = Tamburin schlägerin : for four-part chorus of women's voices a cappella. (Schumann, Robert). *Schirmer. £0.30* FEZDW (B78-50401)
Mug grant. (Orton, Richard H). *Arts Lab Music. Unpriced* CB/J (B78-50701)
Muir, Donna M. How to dance : waltz, fox-trot, quick-step, tango, mambo, samba, cha-cha-cha, rumba, bossa-nova, jive ; plus! the music to 20 great dance numbers, plus! a detailed discography of dance records. *Omnibus Press : Books Sales. £3.50* KDW/GB/AY (B78-50873) ISBN 0-86001-380-4
Mundy, William. Evening service for men's voices 'in three parts'. *Cathedral Music. Unpriced* GEZDGPP (B78-50418)
Murray, Albert. Stomping the blues. *Quartet Books. £4.95* AKDW/HHW(X) (B78-22168) ISBN 0-7043-2172-6
Musae Sioniae. Tl.2. *Selections.* Weihnachtskonzerte : für zwei vierstimmige Chöre. (Praetorius, Michael). *Bärenreiter. £2.24* EWNDH/LF (B78-50360)
Musae Sioniae. Tl.2. *Selections.* Weihnachtskonzerte : für zwei vierstimmige Chöre. (Praetorius, Michael). *Bärenreiter. £1.96* EZDH/LF (B78-50374)
Muse for the masses : ritual and music in an age of democratic revolution, 1770-1870. (Donakowski, Conrad L). *University of Chicago Press. £15.40* AD/L(XFYK101) (B78-11190) ISBN 0-226-15621-4
Musgrave, Thea.
Mary, Queen of Scots : an opera in three acts. *Novello. £1.00* BMTPAC (B78-12097)
Mary, Queen of Scots. *Vocal score.* Mary, Queen of Scots : opera in three acts. *Novello. £15.00* CC (B78-50008)
Primavera : for soprano and flute. *Chester Music. Unpriced* KFLE/VRDW (B78-50896)
Sir Patrick Spens : a ballad for tenor and guitar. *Chester Music. Unpriced* KGHE/TSDW (B78-50905)
Music. (Palmer, King). 4th ed. *Teach Yourself Books. £1.50* A (B78-16899) ISBN 0-340-05666-5
Music 70 choral series.
Stockton, Robert. Let it shine : spiritual for 3-part chorus of female voices with piano and optional percussion. *Roberton. £0.18* FDW/LC (B78-50395)
Suidell, Padre. Credo. Crucifixus. *arr.* Crucifixus = (He was crucified) : for two-part chorus of women's voices with keyboard accompaniment. *Roberton. £0.15* FDJ (B78-50808)
Music : a joy for life. (Heath, Edward). *Sidgwick and Jackson. £3.95* A (B78-33160)
Music & recording industry year book (international). Kemp's music & recording industry year book (international)
1978. *Kemps. £5.50* A/GB(YC/BC) (B78-09409) ISBN 0-905255-30-5
Music at court. (Hogwood, Christopher). *Folio Society. £4.95* A(KKR) (B78-08477)
Music books for schools : an annotated list. (Grindea, Carola). *School Library Association. £1.30(£0.90 to members)* A(VC/T) (B78-18775) ISBN 0-900641-30-4
Music cultures of the Pacific, the Near East, and Asia. (Malm, William Paul). 2nd ed. *Prentice-Hall. £7.95* BZB (B78-04322) ISBN 0-13-608000-6
Music education review : a handbook for music teachers
Vol.1 : 1977. *Chappell. £5.95* A(VC)
Music : for 4-part choir of mixed voices unaccompanied. (Smith, Robert). *Roberton. £0.18* EZDW (B78-50053)
Music for Comus : serenata a 9. (Handel, George Frideric). First modern ed. *23 Stanley Court, 1 Woodfield Rd, W.5 : Acca Music. Unpriced* JNDE/NXNQDW/JM (B78-50108)
Music for Evening Prayer from the Divine Office. *Collins. Unpriced* JEZDGKB (B78-50833) ISBN 0-00-599593-0
Music for listeners. (Thomson, William). *Prentice-Hall. £8.70* A/C (B78-29828) ISBN 0-13-608026-x
Music for memorial and thanksgiving services for manuals. *Elkin. £1.30* RK/AAY (B78-51055)
Music for orchestras. (Wiltshire Library and Museum Service). *Bythesea Rd, Trowbridge, Wilts. : Wiltshire County Council Library and Museum Service. £0.20* A(TC) (B78-23116) ISBN 0-86080-010-5
Music for piano and seven players = Musik für einen Pianisten und sieben Spieler, Opus 44. (Steffen, Wolfgang). *Bote und Bock : Associated Music. £5.75* NYDPNN (B78-50509)
Music for today. (Mears, Caroline). *Oxford University Press. £9.50* A/R (B78-12984) ISBN 0-19-570082-1
Music in American life.
Charles Ives Centennial Festival-Conference, *New York and New Haven, 1974.* An Ives celebration : papers and panels of the Charles Ives Centennial Festival-Conference. *University of Illinois Press. £8.40* BIV (B78-16383) ISBN 0-252-00619-4
Epstein, Dena J. Sinful tunes and spirituals : black folk music to the Civil War. *University of Illinois Press. £12.60* AKDW/G(YTLD/XA1867) (B78-15754) ISBN 0-252-00520-1
Music in worship : a quarterly journal for Christians
No.1- ; Sept. 1977-. *c/o The editor, 78 Trevellance Way, Garston, Herts. WD2 6LZ : 'Music in worship'. £0.15* AD/LD(B) (B78-23593)
Music kit. Frazer, Alan. Theme from Z Cars ('Johnny Todd') : traditional. *7 Garrick St., W.C.2 : Middle Eight Music. Unpriced* MK/DW (B78-50916)
Music makers. Reinhardt, Django. Django Reinhardt. *EMI. Unpriced* TSPMHX (B78-51151)
Music master
1978. *1 De Cham Ave., Hastings, Sussex : John Humphries. £30.00* A/FD(WT) (B78-11519) ISBN 0-904520-06-4
Music matters : a check-list for local music groups. (Crampton, Stephen). *26 Bedford Sq., WC1B 3HU : Standing Conference for Amateur Music. Unpriced* A(WB/WT) (B78-20433)
Music notation : a manual of modern practice. (Read, Gardner). 2nd ed.. *Gollancz. £3.95* A(QU) (B78-30828) ISBN 0-575-02554-9
Music of ancient Greece : an encyclopaedia. (Michaelides, Solon). *Faber. £15.00* A(C/YBD) (B78-04320) ISBN 0-571-10021-x
Music of Rosemary Brown. (Parrott, Ian). *Regency Press. £2.40* A(Z) (B78-19809)
Music of William Byrd
Vol.3: The consort and keyboard music of William Byrd. (Kerman, Joseph). *Faber. £15.00 : CIP rev.* BBX (B78-19401) ISBN 0-571-10566-1
Music periodical literature : an annotated bibliography of indexes and bibliographies. (Meggett, Joan M). *Scarecrow Press : Distributed by Bailey and Swinfen. Unpriced* A(B/T/WT) (B78-23111) ISBN 0-8108-1109-X
Music quiz. Robin Ray's music quiz. (Ray, Robin). *Batsford. £3.50* A(DE) (B78-35466) ISBN 0-7134-1492-8
Music speaks louder than words. *arr.* Music speaks louder than words : SATB chorus and piano with optional guitar, bass and drums. (Payne, Harold). *Warner Blossom. Unpriced* DW (B78-50352)
Music speaks louder than words : SATB chorus and piano with optional guitar, bass and drums. (Payne, Harold). *Warner : Blossom. Unpriced* DW (B78-50352)
Music therapy in the community : papers read at the conference held in London on the 16th October 1976. *48 Lanchester Rd, N6 4TA : British Society for Music Therapy. Unpriced* A(ZD) (B78-12810)
Music trades directory. Music trades international directory 1978. *Wheatland Journals. £3.00* A(YC/BC) (B78-11702)
Music trades international directory
1978. *Wheatland Journals. £3.00* A(YC/BC) (B78-11702)
'Music week'. British records charts, 1955-1978. Revised and updated ed.. *Macdonald and Jane's. £4.95* AKDW/GB/FD(XPQ24) (B78-37424) ISBN 0-354-08523-9
Musica Britannica : a national collection of music
Vol.40: Music for mixed consort. *Stainer and Bell, for the Musica Britannica Trust. Unpriced* C/AYD (B78-50001) ISBN 0-85249-436-x
Vol.41: Confitebor tibi, Domine by Samuel Wesley ; transcribed and edited by John Marsh. *Stainer and Bell, for the Musica Britannica Trust. Unpriced* C/AYD (B78-50697)
Musica carnevalesca : rondo for piano. (Hlaváč, Miroslav). *Schirmer. £2.10* QP/Y (B78-50990)
Musica da camera.
Croft, William. Musicus apparatus academicas. Laurus cruentas. *Overture.* Overture, Laurus cruentas. *Oxford University Press. Unpriced* MRJ (B78-50195) ISBN 0-19-362424-9
Humphries, John. Concerto, string orchestra, op.3, no.10, D minor. Concerto in D minor, opus 3, no.10, for strings and continuo. *Oxford University Press. Unpriced* RXMF (B78-50245) ISBN 0-19-364804-0
Humphries, John. Concerto, trumpet & string orchestra, op.2, no.12, D major. Concerto in D major, for trumpet (or horn), strings and continuo. *Oxford University Press. Unpriced* RXMPWSF (B78-51075) ISBN 0-19-364797-4
Lawes, Henry. Ayres and dialogues. Dialogue on a kiss. A dialogue on a kiss : for two solo voices and continuo. *Oxford University Press. Unpriced* JNEDW (B78-50858) ISBN 0-19-345494-7
Locke, Matthew. The tempest. Incidental music. Incidental music for The tempest : for strings and continuo. *Oxford University Press. Unpriced* RXM/JM (B78-50244) ISBN 0-19-365350-8
Musica dell'autumno : for organ. (Jenni, Donald). *Associated Music. £3.05* RJ (B78-50563)
Musical form : studies in analysis and synthesis. (Kohs, Ellis B). *Houghton Mifflin. £10.95* A/S (B78-25371) ISBN 0-395-18613-7
Musical ideas and ideas about music. (Goehr, Alexander). *Birkbeck College. £0.25* A (B78-32354)
Musical instruments. (Tolley, Bryan). *Wayland. £1.75* AL/BC (B78-31598) ISBN 0-85340-529-8
Musical instruments at the Victoria & Albert Museum : an introduction. (Victoria and Albert Museum). *H.M.S.O. £0.95* AL/B(YDB) (B78-39230) ISBN 0-11-290274-x
Musical instruments of the West. (Remnant, Mary). *Batsford. £10.00* AL/B (B78-24452) ISBN 0-7134-0569-4
Musical joke : theme from 'The horse of the year show' and other equestrian events. (Mozart, Wolfgang Amadeus). *Fentone Music. Unpriced* QPK (B78-51022)
Musical merry-go-round : musical activities for the very young. (Willson, Robina Beckles). *Heinemann. £3.50* A/GR (B78-01459) ISBN 0-434-97257-6
Musical settings of late Victorian and modern British literature : a catalogue. (Gooch, Bryan N S). *2 Holly Bush Hill, NW3 6SH : Garland Publishing, Inc. £55.35* AKDW(XKK101/T) (B78-14028) ISBN 0-8240-9981-8
Musician's world : letters of the great composers. *Thames and Hudson. £2.95* A/D(M) (B78-35467) ISBN 0-500-27130-5
Musicologia Hungarica. Neue Folge. Kaba, Melinda. Die römische Orgel von Aquincum (3. Jahrhundert). *Bärenreiter. £11.20* AR/B(YGB/XBH) (B78-03580)
Musicus apparatus academicas. Laurus cruentas. *Overture.* Overture, Laurus cruentas. (Croft, William). *Oxford University Press. Unpriced* MRJ (B78-50195) ISBN 0-19-362424-9
Musik für Kinder
7: Rhythmische Übung. (Keetman, Gunild). *Schott. Unpriced* X/AF (B78-50318)
8: Paralipomena. (Orff, Carl). *Schott. Unpriced* JFE/NYEPDW (B78-50105)
Musikalische Grundausbildung in der Musikschule
Lehrerhandbuch. Teil 1 : Didaktik und Methodik. *Schott. £9.50* A(VF) (B78-33930)
Musikalische Nachlass. (Nietzsche, Friedrich). *Bärenreiter. Unpriced* C/AZ (B78-50699)
Musikalischen Spass. K.522. Presto. *arr.* A musical joke : theme from 'The horse of the year show' and other equestrian events. (Mozart, Wolfgang Amadeus). *Fentone Music. Unpriced* QPK (B78-51022)
Muston, Jeff. Rick Wakeman's criminal record. (Wakeman, Rick). *Rondor Music : Music Sales. Unpriced* QPJ (B78-50224)
My boy Billy : folk song collected by R. Vaughan Williams. (Cockshott, Gerald). *Roberton. £0.18* FEZDW

(B78-50066)
My favourite music stories. *Lutterworth Press. £2.95* A (B78-18540) ISBN 0-7188-2308-7
My friends and myself : conversations with Francis Poulenc. (Audel, Stéphane). *Dobson. £4.95* BPO(N) (B78-39780) ISBN 0-234-77251-4
My life with Elvis. (Yancey, Becky). *W.H. Allen. £5.95* AKDW/HK/E(P) (B78-01678) ISBN 0-491-02084-8
Myler, Terry. Irish traditional music. (McMahon, Tony). *Folens. Unpriced* A/G(YDM) (B78-15122)
Mystery train : images of America in rock 'n' roll music. (Marcus, Greil). *Omnibus Press. Unpriced* A/HK(X) (B78-06253) ISBN 0-86001-311-1
Nachgefühl. *Vocal score.* Nachgefühl : Kantate für Sopran und Orchester nach Versen von Klabund. (Egk, Werner). *Schott. £4.80* KFLDX (B78-50471)
Nagel, Frank. Duetto concertante, flute & guitar, op.52. Gran duetto concertante, op.52 : für Flöte (Violine) und Gitarre. (Giuliani, Mauro). *Schott. £4.80* VRPLTSF (B78-50294)
Nagels Musik-Archiv. Durante, Francesco. Sei sonate divise in studii e divertimenti. Sei sonate : (studii e divertimenti), per cembalo. *Bärenreiter. £4.80* QRPE (B78-51038)
Nagle-Healy, James. *See* Healy, James Nagle-.
Napoli. *arr.* Napoli : cornet solo. (Bellstedt, Herman). *R. Smith. Unpriced* WRPK (B78-50692)
Napoli : cornet solo. (Bellstedt, Herman). *R. Smith. Unpriced* WMPWR (B78-50683)
Narmour, Eugene. Beyond Schenkerism : the need for alternatives in music analysis. *University of Chicago Press. £14.00* A/AM(P) (B78-03570) ISBN 0-226-56847-4
Nash, Bruce M. The Elvis Presley quizbook. *Warner Books : Distributed by New English Library. £0.90* AKDW/HK/E(P/DE) (B78-33163) ISBN 0-446-89823-6
Nat King Cole golden greats. *EMI. Unpriced* KDW/GB/AY (B78-50453)
Natanson, V.
The Russian school of piano playing
Vol.1. (Nikolaev, Aleksandr Aleksandrovich). English ed. *Boosey and Hawkes. Unpriced* Q/AC (B78-50962)
Vol.2. (Nikolaev, Aleksandr Aleksandrovich). English ed. *Boosey and Hawkes. Unpriced* Q/AC (B78-50963)
National Association of Accordion and Fiddle Clubs. Box and fiddle
No.1- ; Oct. 1977-. *c/o The editor, 50 Mount Vernon Rd, Stranraer : National Association of Accordion and Fiddle Clubs. £0.10* ARS(B) (B78-03581)
Nativity carol : S.A.T.B. : by William Mathias. (Mathias, William). *Oxford University Press. Unpriced* DP/LF (B78-50741) ISBN 0-19-343064-9
Naylor, C B.
Complete arias and sinfonias from the cantatas, masses and oratorios, for solo voice, oboe d'amore, oboe da caccia, basso continuo/piano in 31 volumes
Vol.5. (Bach, Johann Sebastian). *Musica rara. Unpriced* KE/VTPDH (B78-50463)
Complete arias and sinfonias from the cantatas, masses and oratorios, for solo voice, oboe, oboe d'amore, oboe da caccia, basso continuo/piano in 31 volumes
Vol.6. (Bach, Johann Sebastian). *Musica rara. Unpriced* KE/VTPDH (B78-50465)
Vol.7. (Bach, Johann Sebastian). *Musica rara. Unpriced* KE/VTPDH (B78-50464)
Naylor, Frank.
Erinnerung an Covent Garden. Op.329. *arr.* Memories of Covent Garden = Erinnerung an Covent Garden : waltz, op.329, based on English music hall songs. (Strauss, Johann, *b.1825*). *Bosworth & Co. Unpriced* MK/AHW (B78-50486)
Latin-Americana : a selection of famous melodies and rhythms. *Bosworth and Co. £3.50* MK/AH/AYU (B78-50182)
Latin-Americana : a selection of famous melodies and rhythms for piano. *Bosworth & Co. Unpriced* QPK/AH/AYU (B78-51026)
Maple leaf rag. *arr.* Maple leaf rag. (Joplin, Scott). *Bosworth and Co. Unpriced* QPK/AHXJ (B78-51028)
Nazareth, Ernesto.
Composicôes de Ernesto NazarethAlbum 1: 25 tangos brasileiros (choras) para piano. *Arthur Napoleâno : Essex Music. Unpriced* QPJ (B78-50545)
Album 2: 26 Obras para piano. *Arthur Napoleão : Essex Music. Unpriced* QPJ (B78-50546)
Nazareth, Ernesto, *b.1863.* 20 obras para piano
Album no.3. *Arthur Napoleão : Essex Music. Unpriced* QPJ (B78-51016)
Nazareth family. 20 obras para piano
Album no.3. (Nazareth, Ernesto, *b.1863*). *Arthur Napoleão : Essex Music. Unpriced* QPJ (B78-51016)
Nazarethiana : 5 pegas para piano. (Mignone, Francisco). *Arthur Napoleão : Essex Music. Unpriced* QPJ (B78-50543)
Neander, Johann. All my hope on God is founded. (Watson, Ronald). *Deacon House, Brundall : Braydeston Press : William Elkin. Unpriced* DH (B78-50022)
Neighbour, Oliver Wray. The music of William Byrd
Vol.3: The consort and keyboard music of William Byrd. (Kerman, Joseph). *Faber. £15.00 : CIP rev.* BBX (B78-19401) ISBN 0-571-10566-1
Neil, John. Company section song book. (Boys' Brigade. *Glasgow Battalion*). *168 Bath St., G.2 : Boys' Brigade, Glasgow Battalion. Unpriced* JFVBDW/AY (B78-50856)
Nelson, Esther L. Singing and dancing games for the very young. *Sterling etc. : Distributed by Ward Lock. £3.50* JFDW/GS (B78-50434) ISBN 0-7061-2558-4
Nelson, Ron.
Four pieces after the seasons : S.A.T.B. with instrumental accompaniment
1: Early May. *Boosey and Hawkes. £0.50* ENYLDW (B78-50035)
2: Wonder and wild honey. *Boosey and Hawkes. £0.40* ENYLDW (B78-50036)
3: Late September. *Boosey and Hawkes. £0.40* ENYLDW (B78-50037)
4: Winter journeyings. *Boosey and Hawkes. £0.40* ENYLDW (B78-50038)
Processional and prayer of Emperor of China on the Altar of Heaven, December 21, 1539. *Oxford University Press. Unpriced* EUMDE (B78-50041)
Nemser, Lipton.
The best bluegrass songbook - yet! *Lewis : Phoenix. Unpriced* KDW/GCG/AY (B78-50157)
World's favorite folk explosion : for all fretted instruments, guitar, banjo, ukulele, mandolin, tenor banjo, tenor guitar, baritone uke. *Ashley : Phoenix. Unpriced* TPMK/DW/G/AYT (B78-50267)
Neri, Massimiliano. Sonate e canzone a quatro. Canzone del terzo tuono : for recorder concert. *Dolmetsch : Chappell. Unpriced* VSN (B78-51239)
Nessling, Pat. Sounds and music. (Ramsbottom, Edward). *Macmillan. £0.48* A (B78-18538) ISBN 0-333-23169-4
Nettl, Bruno. Eight urban musical cultures : tradition and change. *University of Illinois Press. £10.50* BZ (B78-39229) ISBN 0-252-00208-3
Neubaur, Franz. Four pieces for flute and viola ... op.10. *Schirmer. £2.50* VRPLSQ (B78-51229)
Neue Musik für Bläser. Feld, Jindřich. Partita canonica. *Bärenreiter. £3.60* WNQG (B78-51335)
Neue Musik für Bläser
Heft 4: Werke von Herbert Gadsch, Eberhard Wenzel, Theodor Hlouschek, Rolf Schweizer, Hans Friedrich Micheelsen. *Bärenreiter. £4.20* WN/AY (B78-51331)
Neue Sonatinen, nos.2,5. Two new sonatinas, for treble recorder and basso continuo. (Telemann, Georg Philipp). 1st ed. *Musica rara. Unpriced* VSSPE (B78-51260)
Neuen Lautenfrüchte. *Selections.* Two pieces ... : guitar solo. (Reusner, Esaias). *Universal. Unpriced* TSPMK (B78-51165)
Neugroschel, Joachim. Wagner and Nietzsche. (Fischer-Dieskau, Dietrich). *Sidgwick and Jackson. £7.50* BWC(Z) (B78-39782) ISBN 0-283-98434-1
Neun Klavierstücke für Sonja. Op.76. (Klebe, Giselher). *Bärenreiter. £5.04* QPJ (B78-50535)
Never in my life. (Kennedy, Mikel). *57 Dorchester Rd. Lytchett Minister, Poole : Celebration Services. Unpriced* JDM (B78-50081)
New directions for clarinet. (Rehfeldt, Phillip). *University of California Press. £10.50* AVV/E (B78-27527) ISBN 0-520-03379-5
New edition of the complete works
Vol.9: Grande messe des morts ; edited by Jürgen Kindermann. (Berlioz, Hector). *Bärenreiter. Unpriced* C/AZ (B78-50698)
New instrumentation. Rehfeldt, Phillip. New directions for clarinet. *University of California Press. £10.50* AVV/E (B78-27527) ISBN 0-520-03379-5
New Jubilate Deo : simple Gregorian chants for the faithful to learn. 2nd ed. *Catholic Truth Society. Unpriced* JEZDTD (B78-50834)
New music composition. (Cope, David). *Schirmer Books : Collier Macmillan. £6.75* A/D (B78-06259) ISBN 0-02-870630-7
'New musical express'.
The illustrated 'New musical express' encyclopedia of rock. (Logan, Nick). 1978 ed.. *27 Old Gloucester St., WC1N 3AF : Salamander Books Limited. £3.95* A/HKR(C) (B78-12095) ISBN 0-86101-009-4
The illustrated 'New musical express' encyclopedia of rock. (Logan, Nick). Revised ed. *Hamlyn. £5.95* AKDW/HKR(C) (B78-15752) ISBN 0-600-33171-7
New national song book. *Vocal score.* The new national song book. (Blake, Howard). *Lengnick. £1.95* CP (B78-50013)
New Orleans jazz : a family album. (Rose, Al). Revised ed.. *Louisiana State University Press. £17.50* AMT(YTRN/M) (B78-23597) ISBN 0-8071-0374-8
New Penguin dictionary of music. (Jacobs, Arthur). 4th ed. *Allen Lane. £5.50* A(C) (B78-27519) ISBN 0-7139-1121-2
New Philharmonia Club. Con brio
No.1- ; 1976-. *13 De Walden Court, 85 New Cavendish St., W.1 : New Philharmonia Club. Unpriced* AMM/E(QB/B) (B78-06990)
New pieces for bassoon : with piano accompaniment
Book 1: Grades 3 and 4. *Associated Board of the Royal Schools of Music. Unpriced* VWP/AY (B78-51289)
Book 2: Grades 5 and 6. *Associated Board of the Royal Schools of Music. Unpriced* VWP/AY (B78-51290)
New pieces for clarinet : with piano accompaniment
Book 1: Grades 3 & 4. (Associated Board of the Royal Schools of Music). *Associated Board of the Royal Schools of Music. Unpriced* VVP/AY (B78-51279)
Book 1: Grades 3 & 4. (Associated Board of the Royal Schools of Music). *Associated Board of the Royal Schools of Music. Unpriced* VVP/AY (B78-51280)
Book 1: Grades 5 & 6. (Associated Board of the Royal Schools of Music). *Associated Board of the Royal Schools of Music. Unpriced* VVP/AY (B78-51281)
New pieces for flute : with piano accompaniment
Book 1: Grades 3 & 4. (Associated Board of the Royal Schools of Music). *Associated Board of the Royal Schools of Music. Unpriced* VRP/AY (B78-51206)
Book 2: Grades 5 and 6. *Associated Board of the Royal Schools of Music. Unpriced* VRP/AY (B78-51207)
New pieces for oboe : with piano accompaniment
Book 1: Grades 3 & 4. (Associated Board of the Royal Schools of Music). *Associated Board of the Royal Schools of Music. Unpriced* VTP/AY (B78-51264)
Book 2: Grades 5 and 6. *Associated Board of the Royal Schools of Music. Unpriced* VTP/AY (B78-51265)
New York Philharmonic guide to the symphony. Everyman's guide to orchestral music. (Downes, Edward). *Dent. £15.00 : CIP rev.* AMM (B78-03579) ISBN 0-460-03030-2
Newe Padouan, Intrada, Täntz unnd Galliarda. *Selections.* Four dances (1611). (Peuerl, Paul). *Chester Music. Unpriced* WNSK/AH (B78-51340)
Newe teutsche Lieder, mit viern, fünff, und sechs Stimmen. *Selections.* Eight lieder, 1570 : for four voices or instruments, ATTBB. (Vento, Ivo de). *London Pro Musica. Unpriced* EZDU (B78-50383)
Newley, Anthony. The travelling music show. *Selections : arr.* Leslie Bricusse and Anthony Newley's The travelling music show. (Bricusse, Leslie). *Tro-Essex. Unpriced* KDW (B78-50441)
Newman, Archie. Beecham stories : anecdotes, sayings and impressions of Sir Thomas Beecham. *Robson. £3.50 : CIP rev.* A/EC(P/E) (B78-26892) ISBN 0-86051-044-1
News of the world. (Queen). *EMI. Unpriced* KE/TSDW/HKR (B78-50173)
Newsletter
Issue no.1- ; 1976-. (London Association of Organists). *c/o P. Lea-Cox, St Jude-on-the-Hill, Central Sq., N.W.11 The Association. Unpriced* AR(YDB/B) (B78-09120)
Newsome, Roy.
Concerto, horn, no.3, K.447, E flat major. Rondo. *arr.* Rondo from horn concerto no.3, K.447. (Mozart, Wolfgang Amadeus). *50 Ladbroke Grove, W.11 : Midland Music. Unpriced* WTPK/LW (B78-50317)
Hat trick. *Midland Music. Unpriced* WMJ (B78-50312)
Newton, J. Come, my soul : SATB unacc. (Howells, Herbert). *Oxford University Press. Unpriced* EZDH (B78-50371)
Newton, Rodney Stephen.
'The path of the just' : poem, for chamber orchestra. *Composer Edition. Unpriced* MRJ (B78-50499)
'The silmarillion' : a symphonic prelude after J.R.R. Tolkien ; for orchestra. *13 Chetwynd Ave., East Barnet, Herts. : Composer Edition. Unpriced* MMJ (B78-50493)
Byzantine sketches : for clarinet quartet. *Composer Edition. Unpriced* VVNS (B78-50661)
Canzonietta sic : for cello and piano. *Composer Edition. Unpriced* SRPJ (B78-50265)
Concerto da camera no.1 for guitar, mandolin and strings. *13 Chetwynd Ave., East Barnet, Herts. : Composer Edition. Unpriced* RXMPTSPLTXF (B78-50249)
Concerto da camera no.2 for flute and string orchestra. *Composer Edition. Unpriced* RXMPVRF (B78-50250)
'Constantine suite' : a Byzantine suite in seven movements for symphonic wind ensemble. *13 Chetwynd Ave., East Barnet, Herts. : Composer Edition. Unpriced* UMMG (B78-50278)
'Mountains in cloud' : 8 minatures sic after Chinese scrolls and album leaves for chamber ensemble. *13 Chetwynd Ave., East Barnet, Herts. : Composer Edition. Unpriced* NYEPNQ (B78-50209)
Sonata, violin & piano. Sonata for violin and piano. *13 Chetwynd Ave., East Barnet, Herts. : Composer Edition. Unpriced* SPE (B78-50257)
Nichols, Robert. Idyll 'Once I passed through a populous city'. *Vocal score.* Prelude and idyll : for soprano and baritone with orchestra. (Delius, Frederick). *Boosey and Hawkes. Unpriced* JNEDX (B78-50438)
Nicholson, Sydney H. Practical methods in choir training. *Addington Palace, Croydon CR9 5AD : Royal School of Church Music. £0.65* AD/E (B78-01055) ISBN 0-85402-069-1
Nicolai, Philipp. Polyhymnia caduceatrix et panegyrica. Wie schön leuchtet der Morgenstern. How brightly beams the morning star = Wie schön leuchtet der Morgenstern : for four-part chorus of mixed voices, five solo voices and optional keyboard accompaniment. (Praetorius, Michael). *Schirmer. £0.35* EZDH/LF (B78-50375)
Nieman, Alfred.
Arie fantasie : for organ. *Novello. £1.20* RJ (B78-50567)
Gavotte for a Latin lady : for violin and piano. *Roberton. £0.50* SPHM (B78-50259)
Mountain dance : for violin and piano. *Roberton. £0.60* SPH (B78-50258)
Nietsche, Friedrich. Tre notturni : drei Gedichte von Friedrich Nietzsche, für tiefe Männerstimme, Klavier und Bläser. (Reutter, Hermann). *Schott. £6.00* KFXE/NWPNQDW (B78-50176)

Works. Der musikalische Nachlass. *Bärenreiter. Unpriced* C/AZ (B78-50699)

Night music : for orchestra. (Matthews, Colin). *Faber Music. Unpriced* MMJ (B78-50492)
Nightflight : symphonic study for brass band. (Butterworth, Arthur). *Chester Music. Unpriced* WMJ (B78-51307)
Nightflight : symphonic study for brass band. (Butterworth, Arthur). *Chester Music. Unpriced* WMJ (B78-51308)
Nigra sum de beata virgine : for six-part chorus of mixed voices unaccompanied. (Victoria, Tomás Luis de). *Roberton. £0.20* EZDJ (B78-50779)
Nikolaev, A. The Russian school of piano playing
Vol.2. (Nikolaev, Aleksandr Aleksandrovich). English ed. *Boosey and Hawkes. Unpriced* Q/AC (B78-50963)
Nikolaev, A A. The Russian school of piano playing
Vol.1. (Nikolaev, Aleksandr Aleksandrovich). English ed.

Boosey and Hawkes. Unpriced Q/AC (B78-50962)
Nikolaev, Aleksandr Aleksandrovich.
The Russian school of piano playing
Vol.1. English ed. *Boosey and Hawkes. Unpriced* Q/AC (B78-50962)
Vol.2. English ed. *Boosey and Hawkes. Unpriced* Q/AC (B78-50963)
Nine fantasies : for two instruments. (Lupacchino, Bernadino). *London Pro Musica. Unpriced* LNU (B78-50909)
Nine recorder quartets. *Oxford University Press. Unpriced* VSNSK/AAY (B78-50295) ISBN 0-19-357749-6
Nineteenth century. Smetana, Bedřich. The dower. Die Mitgift und Gebet : zwei Männerchöre a cappella nach Texten von Josef Srb-Debrnov. *Bärenreiter. £0.70* GEZDW (B78-50423)
Nineteenth-century American piano music. *Dover Publications : Constable. Unpriced* QP/AYT (B78-50988) ISBN 0-486-23602-1
Nineteenth-century Romanticism in music. (Longyear, Rey Morgan). 2nd ed. *Prentice-Hall. £5.05* A(YB/XG101) (B78-22843) ISBN 0-13-622647-7
Ninety golden years of Irving Berlin. 90 golden years of Irving Berlin. (Berlin, Irving). *Chappell. Unpriced* RPVK/DW/GB (B78-51062)
Noad, Frederick. Popular Elizabethan tunes : for recorder and guitar. *Ariel : Music Sales. Unpriced* VSPLTSK (B78-51252) ISBN 0-86001-371-5
Noad, Frederick M.
Selected solos and duets. (Handel, George Frideric). *Ariel : Music Sales. £1.50* TSPMK (B78-51163) ISBN 0-86001-378-2
Selected works for one and two lutes with original lute tablature and transcription for the guitar. (Dowland, John). *Ariel : Music Sales. £1.95* TSPMK (B78-51162) ISBN 0-86001-294-8
Sonata, guitar, op.15, C major. Sonata in C major, opus 15. (Giuliani, Mauro). *Ariel : Music Sales. £1.95* TSPME (B78-51148) ISBN 0-86001-377-4
Twenty-five etudes. (Giuliani, Mauro). *Ariel : Music Sales. £1.95* TSPMJ (B78-51156) ISBN 0-86001-372-3
Noad guitar library : ensemble series. Popular Elizabethan tunes : for recorder and guitar. *Ariel : Music Sales. Unpriced* VSPLTSK (B78-51252) ISBN 0-86001-371-5
Noad guitar library : performance series.
Dowland, John. Selected works for one and two lutes with original lute tablature and transcription for the guitar. *Ariel : Music Sales. £1.95* TSPMK (B78-51162) ISBN 0-86001-294-8
Giuliani, Mauro. Sonata, guitar, op.15, C major. Sonata in C major, opus 15. *Ariel : Music Sales. £1.95* TSPME (B78-51148) ISBN 0-86001-377-4
Handel, George Frideric. Selected solos and duets. *Ariel Music Sales. £1.50* TSPMK (B78-51163) ISBN 0-86001-378-2
Noad guitar library : study series. Giuliani, Mauro. Twenty-five etudes. *Ariel : Music Sales. £1.95* TSPMJ (B78-51156) ISBN 0-86001-372-3
Noah's animals : a musical allegory in three acts. (Patrick, John, *b.1907*). *French. £1.65* BPECACM (B78-02612) ISBN 0-573-68078-7
Nocturne : a life of Chopin. (Jordan, Ruth). *Constable. £6.95* BCE(N) (B78-26246) ISBN 0-09-462330-9
Nocturne for harp and wind ensemble. (Grundman, Clare). *Boosey and Hawkes. Unpriced* TQPMJ (B78-51136)
Noeltner, Robert H. The fantasticks. *Vocal score.* The fantasticks : book and lyrics by Tom Jones. (Schmidt, Harvey). Revised ed. *Chappell. Unpriced* CM (B78-50327)
Nolan, Frederick. The sound of their music : the story of Rodgers & Hammerstein. *Dent. £6.50 : CIP rev.* BRK(N) (B78-09114) ISBN 0-460-04315-3
Noramus edition. Latrobe, Christian Ignatius. Original anthems. Make a joyful noise unto the Lord. *Vocal score.* Psalm 100, Make a joyful noise unto the Lord. *Boosey and Hawkes. Unpriced* DR (B78-50346)
Nordenstrom, Gladys. Quintet, wind instruments. Wind quintet = Bläser Quintett. *Bärenreiter. £13.50* UNR (B78-51197)
'Not the Count of Monte Cristo?!' : a musical comedy in three acts for 3 players and a piano. (Reiser, Dave). *French. £1.65* BSGNHACM (B78-12096) ISBN 0-573-68085-x
Notebook for harpsichord. (Maconchy, Elizabeth). *Chester Music. Unpriced* QRPJ (B78-51039)
Nothnagle, Peter.
Crumhorn consort anthology
Vol.2 ; edited by Pater Nothnagle and R.P. Block. *Musica rara. Unpriced* VTWN/AY (B78-51270)
Vol.3 ; edited by Peter Nothnagle and R.P. Block. *Musica rara. Unpriced* VTWN/AY (B78-51271)
Notturni : für sechs Singstimmen, Violine, Klarinette, Schlaginstramente. (Terzakis, Dimitri). *Bärenreiter. £16.80* JNAZE/NYEVDW (B78-50437)
Noturno das folhas soltas. *arr.* Noturno das folhas soltas. (Lorenzo-Fernandez, Oscar). *Arthur Napoleão : Essex Music. Unpriced* QPK (B78-50551)
Novello brass band series. Bliss, *Sir* Arthur. Checkmate. *Selections : arr.* Four dances from the ballet ... *Novello. £4.85* WMK/HM (B78-51328)
Novello Brass Band Series. Kelly, Bryan. Edinburgh dances. *Novello. £4.50* WMH (B78-51306)
Novello early church music. Croft, William. God is gone up with a merry noise : full anthem with verse for SSAATB. *Novello. £0.43* DK (B78-50343)
Novello modern organ repertory.
Hurford, Peter. Bristol suite. *Novello. £1.20* RG (B78-50562)
Kelly, Bryan. Pastorale and paean. *Novello. £1.45* RJ (B78-50565)
Novello short biographies.
Dommett, Kenneth. Bartók. *Novello. £0.30* BBG(N)
Jefferson, Alan. Richard Strauss. *Novello. £0.30* BSU(N) (B78-31596)
Small, Christopher, *b.1927.* Schoenberg. *Novello. £0.47* BSET(N) (B78-02607)
Now's the time to sing : for three-part chorus of treble voices with descant solo, piano four-hands accompaniment and percussion. (Kirk, Theron). *Schirmer. Unpriced* FLE/NYLDW (B78-50067)
Noyce, John Leonard. Rock music index. *Noyce. £1.20* A/HKR(T) (B78-02933)
Nun jauchzt dem Herren, alle Welt : Chorsätze zu Gemeinsamen Kirchenliedern. *Bärenreiter. £3.20* EZDM/AYE (B78-50381)
Nunes Garcia, Jose Mauricio. Requiem mass. *Vocal score.* Requiem mass for four-part chorus of mixed voices and alto, tenor and bass solos with piano accompaniment. *Associated Music. £2.40* DGKAV (B78-50334)
Nurmi, Ruth. A plain & easy introduction to the harpsichord. *University of New Mexico Press : Distributed by Heinemann. £9.50* AQR/E (B78-28705) ISBN 0-434-52470-0
O amica mea. (Morley, Thomas). *Edizioni Pegasus : Peters. Unpriced* VSNRK/DJ (B78-50652)
Ó Canainn, Tomás. Traditional music in Ireland. *Routledge and Kegan Paul. £3.60 : CIP rev.* A/G(YDM) (B78-31597) ISBN 0-7100-0021-9
O Lochlainn, Colm.
Irish street ballads. *Pan Books. £0.90* KEZDW/K/G/AYDM (B78-50468) ISBN 0-330-25316-6
More Irish street ballads. *Pan Books. £0.90* KEZDW/K/G/AYDM (B78-50469) ISBN 0-330-25317-4
O magnum mysterium. (Morales, Cristoval). *36 Ranelagh Gdns., W.6 : Cathedral Music. Unpriced* GEZDGKH/LF (B78-50410)
O magnum mysterium. (Palestrina, Giovanni Pierluigi da). *36 Ranelagh Gdns., W.6 : Cathedral Music. Unpriced* EZDGKH/LF (B78-50367)
O magnum mysterium : S.A.T.B. (Rorem, Ned). *Boosey and Hawkes. Unpriced* EZDJ/LF (B78-50782)
O waly waly : for SSA unaccompanied, Somerset folk song. (Phillips, John Charles). *Roberton. £0.12* FEZDW (B78-50400)
Oates, John.
Beauty on a back street. *arr.* Beauty on a back street. (Hall, Daryl). *Chappell. Unpriced* KDW/GB (B78-50131)
Best of Daryl Hall and John Oates. (Hall, Daryl). *Chappell. Unpriced* KDW/GB (B78-50130)
Breakaway. *arr.* Breakaway. (Gallagher, Benny). *Wise : Music Sales. Unpriced* KDW/GB (B78-50129) ISBN 0-86001-278-6
Oboe Bibliothek. Lebrun, Ludwig August. Concerto, oboe, no.1, D minor. *arr.* Konzert No.1, d-moll, für Oboe und Orchester. *Schott. £9.60* VTPK/LF (B78-50302)
Oboe duets
Vol.1. *Chester Music. Unpriced* VTNUK/AAY (B78-51263)
Observer's book of big bands. (White, Mark). *F. Warne. £1.25* AMT(M) (B78-37101) ISBN 0-7232-1589-8
Observer's book of jazz. (White, Mark). *F. Warne. £1.25* AMT(C) (B78-35477) ISBN 0-7232-1588-x
Observer's pocket series. White, Mark. The observer's book of jazz. *F. Warne. £1.25* AMT(C) (B78-35477) ISBN 0-7232-1588-x
Observer's pocket series (ISSN 0305-4837). White, Mark. The observer's book of big bands. *F. Warne. £1.25* AMT(M) (B78-37101) ISBN 0-7232-1589-8
Odom, John.
The last month of the year : eight carols for voices, Orff-instruments, recorders and guitars
1: Hodie, Vhristus natus est. *Schott. Unpriced* ENYESDP/LF (B78-50754)
2: Children go where I send thee. *Schott. Unpriced* ENYESDP/LF (B78-50755)
3: Virgin Mary, meek and mild. *Schott. Unpriced* ENYESDP/LF (B78-50756)
4: O magnum mysterium. *Schott. Unpriced* ENYESDP/LF (B78-50757)
5: Noël. *Schott. Unpriced* ENYESDP/LF (B78-50758)
6: The last month of the year. *Schott. Unpriced* ENYESDP/LF (B78-50759)
7: What you gonna call yo' pretty little baby? *Schott. Unpriced* ENYESDP/LF (B78-50760)
8: A Christmas gloria. *Schott. Unpriced* ENYESDP/LF (B78-50761)
Odom, Lawrence. Rail. Op.57. *arr.* Rail. (Josephs, Wilfred). *Galaxy : Stainer and Bell. Unpriced* UMMK (B78-50630)
O'Donovan, Con.
Comic songs of Cork and Kerry. *25 Lower Abbey St., Dublin 1 : Mercier Press. £0.80* AKDW(YDQC) (B78-39235) ISBN 0-85342-498-5
Comic songs of Ireland. *25 Lower Abbey St., Dublin 1 : Mercier Press. £0.80* AKDW(YDM) (B78-39785) ISBN 0-85342-529-9
Love songs of the Irish. *25 Lower Abbey St., Dublin 1 : Mercier Press. £1.10* AKDW(YDM) (B78-39234) ISBN 0-85342-497-7
Offenbach, Jacques. Monsieur Choufleuri restera chez lui de. *Vocal score.* Salon Blumenkohl/Monsieur Choufleuri restera chez lui de ... : Buffo-Operette in einem Akt deutsch nach Karl Fr. Wiltmann von Heinz Balthes und Paul Vasil, opéra bouffe en un acte de St. Rémy, E. L'Epine, Hector Crémieux et Ludovic Halévy, musikalische Revision, neue Instrumentation und praktische Bearbeitung von Caspar Richter. *Bote und Bock : Associated music. £11.50* CF (B78-50703)
Ogdon, Will. Horizons circled : reflections on my music. (Krenek, Ernst). *University of California Press. £6.80* BKTM (B78-06254) ISBN 0-520-02338-2
Oh, father : an English music hall medley, for four-part chorus of mixed voices with piano accompniment. (McCarthy, John). *Roberton. £0.32* DW (B78-50745)
Oh! it's a lovely war : songs, ballads and parodies of the Great War. *EMI. Unpriced* KDW/GB/AY (B78-50874)
O'Keeffe, Daniel. The first book of Irish ballads. Revised ed. *4 Bridge St., Cork : Mercier Press. £1.50* AKDW/K/G(YDM) (B78-37867) ISBN 0-85342-080-7
Old English carol. *arr.* An old English carol : old English ballad tune. (Sternfeld, Frederick William). *Oxford University Press. Unpriced* EZDP/LF (B78-50789) ISBN 0-19-343068-1
Old English carol : old English ballad tune. (Sternfeld, Frederick William). *Oxford University Press. Unpriced* EZDP/LF (B78-50789) ISBN 0-19-343068-1
Old Father Time : a family musical. (Wood, David, *b.1944*). *French. £1.20* BWPDACN (B78-39232) ISBN 0-573-05046-5
Old Hungarian soldier songs. Magyar rondo = Hungarian rondo : vonószenekarra, két klarinéta és két fagottra = for string orchestra, two clarinets and two bassoons. (Kodály, Zoltán). *Editio musica : Boosey and Hawkes. Unpriced* RXMPVNS/W (B78-51072)
Old songs of Skye : Frances Tolmie and her circle. (Bassin, Ethel). *Routledge and Kegan Paul. £5.95* ADW/G(YDLZS/P) (B78-03578) ISBN 0-7100-8546-x
'Old time music'. Jimmie the Kid : the life of Jimmie Rodgers. (Paris, Mike). *Eddison Press : 'Old time music' Magazine. £3.95* AKDW/GC/E(P) (B78-33931) ISBN 0-85649-019-9
Oliver, Donald.
Almost caught red-pawed (or The cat who cried over spilt milk) : a musical play for children. *Chappell. Unpriced* CN (B78-50705)
The cookie lady : a musical play for children. *Chappell. Unpriced* CN (B78-50706)
The runaways : a musical play for children. *Chappell. Unpriced* CN (B78-50707)
On tiptoe. (Page, Jodi). *Yeldall Manor, Hare Hatch, Reading : Celebration Services. Unpriced* JFDM (B78-50089)
One and only Bing. (Thomas, Bob). *Joseph. £5.50* AKDW/GB/E(P) (B78-09699) ISBN 0-7181-1698-4
One on one. *Selections: arr.* Songs from 'One on one' : a Warner Bros. film. (Fox, Charles). *Warner : Blossom. Unpriced* KDW/JR (B78-50166)
Only now, and again : winds, piano and percussion (3). (Reynolds, Roger). *Peters. Unpriced* UMPQ (B78-51191)
Onorati, Henry.
Carol of the drum. *arr.* The little drummer boy. (Davis, Katherine Kennicott). *Chappell. Unpriced* NYDPK/DP/LF (B78-50951)
Carol of the drum. *arr.* The little drummer boy. (Davis, Katherine Kennicott). *Chappell. Unpriced* NYDPK/DP/LF (B78-50951)
Opera at Llandudno. (Jones, Ivor Wynne). *c/o I.W. Jones, 'Pegasus', 71 Llandudno Rd, Penrhyn Bay, Llandudno, Gwynedd LL30 3HN : Welsh National Opera Company. Unpriced* AC/E(YDKPL) (B78-28696)
Opera before Mozart. (Robinson, Michael Finlay). 3rd ed. *Hutchinson. £3.25* AC(XE182) (B78-40352) ISBN 0-09-136221-0
Opera guide. (Westerman, Gerhart von). *Sphere. £0.90* AC (B78-05404) ISBN 0-7221-9004-2
Opera library. Garten, Hugh Frederic. Wagner the dramatist. *J. Calder. £5.95* BWCAC (B78-09113) ISBN 0-7145-3620-2
Opera, operetta and musical comedy synopses. Index to opera, operetta and musical comedy synopses in collections and periodicals. (Drone, Jeanette Marie). *Scarecrow Press : Distributed by Bailey and Swinfen. £5.95* ACMBN(WT) (B78-19781) ISBN 0-8108-1100-6
Operas of Verdi
2: From 'Il trovatore' to 'La forza del destina'. (Budden, Julian). *Cassell. £17.50* BVEAC (B78-39231) ISBN 0-304-30056-x
Opticus 4 woodwind. Schubert, Franz. 3 Schubert dances. *7 Garrick St., W.C.2 : Middle Eight Music. Unpriced* VNSK/AH (B78-50287)
Option 4 woodwind.
Haul away! : 3 movements based on a sea shanties. *7 Garrick St., W.C.2 : Middle Eight Music. Unpriced* VNSK/DW/GMC/AY (B78-50288)
Haul away! : 3 movements based on sea shanties. *7 Garrick St., W.C.2 : Middle Eight Music. Unpriced* VNSK/DW/GMC/AY (B78-50645)
Orakel : für Kontrabass solo, 1974. (Acker, Dieter). *Bote und Bock : Yorke. Unpriced* SSPMJ (B78-51129)
Orbell, Margaret. Traditional songs of the Maori. *A.H. and A.W. Reed. Unpriced* KDW/AYXR (B78-50449) ISBN 0-589-00748-3
Orchestra : a history. (Raynor, Henry). *Scribner's : Hale. £4.50* AMM (B78-12988) ISBN 0-7091-6333-9
Ordeal of Ivor Gurney. (Hurd, Michael). *Oxford University Press. £5.95 : CIP rev.* BGYU(N) (B78-29833) ISBN 0-19-211752-1
Orff, Carl.
Musik für Kinder
8: Paralipomena. *Schott. Unpriced* JFE/NYEPDW (B78-50105)
Sprechstücke : für Sprecher, Sprechchor und Schlagwerk.

Schott. £7.20 HY (B78-50076)
Orff-Schulwerk.
Keetman, Gunild. Musik für Kinder
7: Rhythmische Übung. *Schott. Unpriced* X/AF (B78-50318)
Orff, Carl. Musik für Kinder
8: Paralipomena. *Schott. Unpriced* JFE/NYEPDW (B78-50105)
Orga, Ateş. Beethoven : his life and times. *Midas Books etc.. £6.50* BBJ(N) (B78-26883) ISBN 0-85936-082-2
Organising music in libraries
Vol.1: Arrangement and classification. (Redfern, Brian). Revised and rewritten ed. *Bingley etc.. £3.25* A(U) (B78-50319) ISBN 0-85157-231-6
Orgelbüchlein für Vincenz : 10 festliche kleine Präliudien, op.66. (Krol, Bernhard). *Bote und Bock : Schirmer. £3.85* RJ (B78-51050)
Orgeldisposition : eine Heranführung. (Supper, Walter). Grossausgabe. *Bärenreiter. £13.44* AR/E (B78-01682)
Orgelschule zum Selbstunterricht. (Draths, Willi). *Schott. £4.00* RPV/AC (B78-50239)
Original anthems. Make a joyful noise unto the Lord. *Vocal score.* Psalm 100, Make a joyful noise unto the Lord. (Latrobe, Christian Ignatius). *Boosey and Hawkes. Unpriced* DR (B78-50346)
Originals. (Brubeck, Dave). *EMI. Unpriced* QPHX (B78-51002)
O'Rourke, Eva. Lambeth and Music Hall : a treasury of Music Hall memorabilia : including articles, biographies, photographs, engravings and reproductions of original material. *Leisure Centre, Loughborough Park, S.W.9 : London Borough of Lambeth Directorate of Amenity Services. £1.00* AKDW/JV(YDBL) (B78-20450) ISBN 0-905208-02-1
Orphenica lyra (Seville 1554). (Fuenllana, Miguel de). *Clarendon Press. £30.00* TVPMJ (B78-50625)
Orton, Richard. Pièce de resistance. *Arts Lab Music. Unpriced* QPJ (B78-51017)
Orton, Richard H.
Ambierce : for bass trombone and tape. *Arts Lab Music. Unpriced* WUU (B78-51356)
Mug grant. *Arts Lab Music. Unpriced* CB/J (B78-50701)
Osborne, Charles, *b.1927.*
The complete operas of Mozart : a critical guide. *Gollancz. £7.50* BMSAC (B78-33935) ISBN 0-575-02221-3
The dictionary of composers. *Bodley Head. £5.95* A/D(M/C) (B78-20434) ISBN 0-370-30016-5
Verdi. *Macmillan. £5.95 : CIP rev.* BVE(N) (B77-21346) ISBN 0-333-21483-8
O'Shaughnessy, Arthur. Would I might go far over sea : for four-part chorus of mixed voices a cappella. (George, Thom Ritter). *Chappell. Unpriced* EZDW (B78-50387)
Osthoft, Wolfgang. Concerto, cello, A minor, op. posth, (1888). Konzert für Violoncello und Orchester (1888), Op. posth. (Pfitzner, Hans). *Schott. £6.00* MPSRF (B78-50935)
Ostinati : for piano solo. (Parke, Dorothy). *Banks Music. Unpriced* QPJ (B78-51018)
Ostrander, Linda Woodaman. Creative piano : a modular approach for adult beginners. (Owyang, Lily Siao). *Houghton Mifflin. Unpriced* Q/AC (B78-50964) ISBN 0-395-25569-4
Ottaway, Hugh. Shostakovich symphonies. *British Broadcasting Corporation. £1.00* BSGRAMME (B78-28701) ISBN 0-563-12772-4
Our Gracie. *EMI. Unpriced* KDW/GB/AY (B78-50875)
Our love : a Marvin Yancy, Chuck Jackson songbook. (Yancy, Marvin). *Chappell. Unpriced* KDW/GB (B78-50871)
Out and about : 8 descriptive pieces for guitar. (Smith, Isabel). *Ricordi. Unpriced* TSPMJ (B78-50617)
Overture, Laurus cruentas. (Croft, William). *Oxford University Press. Unpriced* MRJ (B78-50195) ISBN 0-19-362424-9
Overture on a short theme. (Grundman, Clare). *Boosey and Hawkes. Unpriced* UMMJ (B78-51178)

Overture to youth. (Hughes, Eric). *Studio Music. Unpriced* WMJ (B78-51311)
Owen, Wilfred. Music : for 4-part choir of mixed voices unaccompanied. (Smith, Robert). *Roberton. £0.18* EZDW (B78-50053)
Owyang, Lily Siao. Creative piano : a modular approach for adult beginners. *Houghton Mifflin. Unpriced* Q/AC (B78-50964) ISBN 0-395-25569-4
Oxen : S.A.T.B. (Rorem, Ned). *Boosey Hawkes. Unpriced* EZDW/LF (B78-50803)
Oxford anthems.
Howells, Herbert. Come, my soul : SATB unacc. *Oxford University Press. Unpriced* EZDH (B78-50371)
Mathias, William. Arise, shine, for your light has come : S.A.T.B. *Oxford University Press. Unpriced* DK (B78-50732) ISBN 0-19-350367-0
Oxford book of English madrigals. *Oxford University Press. Unpriced* EZDU/AYD (B78-50792) ISBN 0-19-343664-7
Oxford choral songs.
Carter, Andrew. A maiden most gentle : (a Christmas carol) ; S.A.T.B., French tune. *Oxford University Press. Unpriced* DP/LF (B78-50737) ISBN 0-19-343067-3
Gardner, John. Sunny bank carol : S.A.T.B. (unacc.), opus 141. *Oxford University Press. Unpriced* EZDP/LF (B78-50785) ISBN 0-19-343063-0
Kelly, Bryan. Watt's cradle song : S.A.T.B. *Oxford University Press. Unpriced* DP/LF (B78-50739) ISBN 0-19-343065-7
Ledger, Philip. Two carols. *Oxford University Press. Unpriced* DP/LF (B78-50740) ISBN 0-19-343066-5
Mathias, William. Nativity carol : S.A.T.B. : by William Mathias. *Oxford University Press. Unpriced* DP/LF (B78-50741) ISBN 0-19-343064-9
Oxford Choral Songs. Parry, William Howard. The spiritual railway : two-part or unison with piano and optional instruments. *Oxford University Press. Unpriced* FDH (B78-50058) ISBN 0-19-341512-7
Oxford choral songs. Sternfeld, Frederick William. An old English carol. *arr.* An old English carol : old English ballad tune. *Oxford University Press. Unpriced* EZDP/LF (B78-50789) ISBN 0-19-343068-1
Oxford monographs on music. Deathridge, John. Wagner's 'Rienzi' : a reappraisal based on a study of the sketches and drafts. *Clarendon Press. £12.00 : CIP rev.* BWCAC (B77-08491) ISBN 0-19-816131-x
Oxford studies of composers. Macdonald, Hugh, *b.1940.* Skryabin. *Oxford University Press. £2.95* BSGNC (B78-35469) ISBN 0-19-315438-2
Paduana, galliarda .... Cantus 18. Canzon cornetto : for four trumpets. (Scheidt, Samuel). *Chester Music. Unpriced* WSNS (B78-51342)
Page, Jodi.
Fear not, for I have redeemed you. *Celebration Services. Unpriced* JDK (B78-50080)
On tiptoe. *Yeldall Manor, Hare Hatch, Reading : Celebration Services. Unpriced* JFDM (B78-50089)
Pageant of music : an introduction to the history of music. (Blackwood, Alan, *b.1932*). *Barrie and Jenkins. £3.95* A(X) (B78-04318) ISBN 0-214-20423-5
Pair of wings. (Sackman, Nicholas). *Schott. £5.00* JNFLDE/NYEXPNQDW (B78-50439)
Paleface. Buttons and bows. *arr.* Buttons and bows. (Livingston, Jay). *Warner : Blossom. Unpriced* UMMK/DW/JR (B78-51188)
Palestrina, Giovanni Pierluigi da.
Hodie Christus natus est. *Cathedral Music. Unpriced* GEZDGKJ/LF (B78-50411)
Motettorum ... portim quinis ... vocibus ... liber primus. O magnum mysterium. O magnum mysterium. *36 Ranelagh Gdns., W.6 : Cathedral Music. Unpriced* EZDGKH/LF (B78-50367)
Palm court waltz : for piano duet. (Berkeley, *Sir* Lennox). *Chester Music. Unpriced* QNVHW (B78-50987)
Palmer, Christopher. Herbert Howells : a study. *Novello. £1.20* BHS(N) (B78-33933)
Palmer, King. Music. 4th ed. *Teach Yourself Books. £1.50* A (B78-16899) ISBN 0-340-05666-5
Palmer, King. Teach yourself music. *For later edition see* Palmer, King. Music.
Palmer, Roy. Folk music in school. *Cambridge University Press. £4.95* A/G(VF) (B78-29835) ISBN 0-521-21595-1
Palmer, Trisha. The illustrated encyclopedia of jazz. (Case, Brian). *27 Old Gloucester St., WC1N 3AF : Salamander Books. £6.95* AMT(C) (B78-22169) ISBN 0-86101-013-2
Paloma blanca. *arr.* Paloma blanca. (Bouwens, J). *Chappell. Unpriced* NYFPK (B78-50513)
Panzergrenadiermarsch. (Stephan, Wilhelm). *Bote und Bock : Associated Music. £3.20* UMMGM (B78-50627)
'Par les fils de Mandrin'. *arr.* 'Par les fils de Mandrin'. (Ange). *Chappell. Unpriced* KDW/GB (B78-50123)
Paratum cor meum Deus. (Blow, John). *36 Ranelagh Gdns. W.6 : Cathedral Music. Unpriced* FLDJ (B78-50404)
Parfrey, Raymond. Three tunes for four clarinets. *EMI. Unpriced* VVNS (B78-51275)
Paris, Mike. Jimmie the Kid : the life of Jimmie Rodgers. *Eddison Press : 'Old time music' Magazine. £3.95* AKDW/GC/E(P) (B78-33931) ISBN 0-85649-019-9
Parisian chanson. Thirty chansons, 1529 : for three instruments or voices. *London Pro Musica. Unpriced* EZDU/AYH (B78-50384)
Parissi, Robert. Wild cherry. *arr.* Wild cherry : electrified funk. *Chappell. Unpriced* KDW/GB (B78-50137)
Parke, Dorothy.
Ostinati : for piano solo. *Banks Music. Unpriced* QPJ (B78-51018)
Prelude and burlesca : for piano solo. *Banks. Unpriced* QPJ (B78-51019)
Parker, Alice.
Songs for Sunday. Search me O God. Search me O God. *Roberton. £0.18* FDH (B78-50389)
Songs for Sunday. This joyful Eastertide. This joyful Eastertide : two seasonal carols of praise, for two-part choir and piano. *Roberton. £0.18* FDP/LL (B78-50391)
Parrott, Ian. The music of Rosemary Brown. *Regency Press. £2.40* A(Z) (B78-19809)
Parry, William Howard. The spiritual railway : two-part or unison with piano and optional instruments. *Oxford University Press. Unpriced* FDH (B78-50058) ISBN 0-19-341512-7
Partita canonica. (Feld, Jindřich). *Bärenreiter. £3.60* WNQG (B78-51335)
Pascall, Jeremy.
The illustrated history of rock music. *Hamlyn. £5.95* AKDW/HKR(X) (B78-39779) ISBN 0-600-37605-2
Paul McCartney & Wings. *Chartwell Books : Phoebus. £2.95* AKDW/GB/E(P) (B78-01677) ISBN 0-89009-125-0
Pasfield, William Reginald. Jillian of Berry : four part song for male voices T.T.B.B. *Edwin Ashdown. £0.20* GEZDW (B78-50829)
Pastoral symphony. (Vaughan Williams, Ralph). *Boosey and Hawkes. Unpriced* KFLE/MDX (B78-50175)
Pastoral theme : for 2 B flat cornets, E flat horn and euphonium. (Watters, Cyril). *Studio Music. Unpriced* WNS (B78-50690)
Pastorale and paean. (Kelly, Bryan). *Novello. £1.45* RJ (B78-50565)
Patey, Carole. Musical instruments at the Victoria & Albert Museum : an introduction. (Victoria and Albert Museum). *H.M.S.O. £0.95* AL/B(YDB) (B78-39230) ISBN 0-11-290274-x
'Path of the just' : poem, for chamber orchestra. (Newton, Rodney Stephen). *Composer Edition. Unpriced* MRJ (B78-50499)
Patrick, John, *b.1907.* Noah's animals : a musical allegory in three acts. *French. £1.65* BPECACM (B78-02612) ISBN 0-573-68078-7
Paulistana : piano. (Blanco, Billy). *Arapua : Essex Music. Unpriced* QPJ (B78-51008)
Paumgartner, Bernhard.
Sei sonate divise in studii e divertimenti. Sei sonate : (studii e divertimenti), per cembalo. (Durante, Francesco). *Bärenreiter. £4.80* QRPE (B78-51038)
Vita di Giuseppe Afflisio = Lebensgeschichte des Giuseppe Afflisio. (Afflisio, Giuseppe). *17 Bucklersbury, Hitchin, Herts. : Bärenreiter. £4.48* AC(WB/P) (B78-19963)
Pavane, 'Earl of Salisbury', virginals. *arr.* The 'Earl of Salisbury' carol, adapted from 'The Earl of Salisbury's Pavane', two-part. (Byrd, William). *Banks. Unpriced* FDP/LF (B78-50810)
Payne, Anthony.
A littel Ascensiontide cantata : for unaccompanied chorus SATB. *Chester Music. Unpriced* EZDE/LM (B78-50766)
A little Whitsuntide cantata : for unaccompanied chorus SATB. *Chester Music. Unpriced* EZDE/LN (B78-50767)
The world's winter : for soprano and instrumental ensemble. *Chester Music. Unpriced* KFLE/NVNNDX (B78-50894)
Payne, Harold. Music speaks louder than words. *arr.* Music speaks louder than words : SATB chorus and piano with optional guitar, bass and drums. *Warner : Blossom. Unpriced* DW (B78-50352)
Paynter, Elizabeth. Experiments in sound : new directions in musical education for young children. (Meyer-Denkmann, Gertrud). *Universal Edition. £3.50* A/D(VC) (B78-10119) ISBN 0-900938-49-8
Paynter, John.
Experiments in sound : new directions in musical education for young children. (Meyer-Denkmann, Gertrud). *Universal Edition. £3.50* A/D(VC) (B78-10119) ISBN 0-900938-49-8
Sound tracks
1: Pattern music. *Cambridge University Press. £1.95* A/D(VF) (B78-23589) ISBN 0-521-20581-6
2: Rites and ceremonies. *Cambridge University Press. £1.95* A/D(VF) (B78-23590) ISBN 0-521-20579-4
4: Magic songs. *Cambridge University Press. £1.95* A/D(VF) (B78-23592) ISBN 0-521-20578-6
Pearse, John. Frets and fingers : a guitar player's manual. *Paddington Press. £4.95* ATS/E (B78-34741) ISBN 0-7092-0625-9
Pearson, Johnny. All creatures great and small. *arr.* All creatures great and small. *EMI. £0.50* QPK/JS (B78-51035)
Pearson, Leslie. Hiplips . (Philip's) : for brass quintet. *Chester Music. Unpriced* WNR (B78-51337)
Pease, *III* Edgar. Music speaks louder than words. *arr.* Music speaks louder than words : SATB chorus and piano with optional guitar, bass and drums. (Payne, Harold). *Warner : Blossom. Unpriced* DW (B78-50352)
Pedrell, Felipe. Galician carol, Panxoliña sic de Nadal : for four-part chorus of mixed voices unaccompanied. (Wilkinson, Stephen). *Roberton. £0.18* EZDP/LF (B78-50048)
Pegge, Reginald Morley-. *See* Morley-Pegge, Reginald.
Pehkonen, Elis. Pop into the middle ages : new settings of medieval lyrics for group music making. *Novello. £0.94* ENYDDW (B78-50033)
Pelican originals.
Choral music : a symposium. *Penguin. £1.25* AD(X) (B78-35474) ISBN 0-14-020533-0
Swanston, Hamish. In defence of opera. *Penguin. £1.25* AC (B78-05403) ISBN 0-14-022005-4
Pelléas et Melisande. Op.80. Sicilienne. *arr.* Sicilienne from Pelléas et Melisande : for flute and piano. (Fauré, Gabriel). *Chester Music. Unpriced* VRPK/AHVQ/JM (B78-51221)
Penderecki, Krzysztof. Canticum canticorum Salomonis. Liberprimus : for 16-part vocal ensemble and orchestra. *Schott. £30.00* EMDE (B78-50030)
Penguin Australian song book. *Penguin Books. £1.25* JEZDW/AYX (B78-50085) ISBN 0-14-070004-8
Penguin book of folk ballads of the English-speaking world. *Penguin. £1.75* AKDW/K/G (B78-08525) ISBN 0-14-004241-5
Penguin stereo record guide. (Greenfield, Edward). 2nd ed. *Penguin. £4.50* A/FF(WT) (B78-23118)
Pennies from heaven : a selection of popular songs of the thirties as featured in the BBC TV series. *EMI. Unpriced* KDW/GB/AY (B78-50454)
Percussion. (Holland, James). *Macdonald and Jane's. £6.95* AX/B (B78-39787) ISBN 0-354-04173-8
Percussion Studio. Fink, Siegfried. Studien für Drum Set = Studies for drum set
Heft 2 = Vol.2: Mittelstufe = Intermediate. *Simrock. Unpriced* XQ/AF (B78-51363)
Percy French and his songs. (Healy, James N). *25 Lower Abbey St., Dublin 1 : Mercier Press. £1.70* BFUR(N) (B78-33936) ISBN 0-85342-394-6
Percy Grainger Society. The Grainger journal
No.1- ; Spring 1978-. *c/o D. Tall, 21 Laburnum Ave., Kenilworth, Warks CV8 2DR : Percy Grainger Society. Unpriced* BGRT(B) (B78-37094)

Periodicals:, *New periodicals and those issued with changed titles.*
Abba magazine
No.1- ; Dec. 1977-. *Poster Plus Ltd : Distributed by Seymour Press. £0.40* AKDW/GB/E(P/B) (B78-30832)
Black music & jazz review
Vol.1, issue 1- ; Apr. 1978-. *IPC Specialist and Professional Press. £0.40* AMT(YTLD/B) (B78-26878)
Box and fiddle
No.1- ; Oct. 1977-. *c/o The editor, 50 Mount Vernon Rd, Stranraer : National Association of Accordion and Fiddle Clubs. £0.10* ARS(B) (B78-03581)
Con brio
No.1- ; 1976-. *13 De Walden Court, 85 New Cavendish St., W.1 : New Philharmonia Club. Unpriced* AMM/E(QB/B) (B78-06990)
Country music round up
Vol.1, no.1- ; Dec. 1976-. *Country Music Round Up Publishing Co.; Roding Trading Estate, Barking, Essex : Distributed by A.M.D. Magazine Distributors Ltd. £0.20* A/GC(B) (B78-03571)
Deeper and deeper soul magazine
No.1- ; July 1977-. *18 Stretton Close, Holmlands Estate, Prenton, Birkenhead, Merseyside : K. Murray. £0.25* A/GBS(B) (B78-06258)
Electronic organ review
Nov.1976-. *Waldron, Heathfield, Sussex TN21 0QS Electronic Organ Review. £0.50(£5.00 yearly)* ARPV/B(B) (B78-11202)
Face out
No.1- ; Apr. 1978-. *c/o Chris Furse, 25 Lionel Ave., Wendover, Aylesbury, Bucks. : 'Face out'. Unpriced* AKDW/HKR(B) (B78-26879)
Folk news
Vol.1, no.1- ; June 1977-. *28 Gordon Mansions, Torrington Place, WC1E 7HF : Folk News Publications. £0.20* A/G(B) (B78-00387)
The Grainger journal
No.1- ; Spring 1978-. *c/o D. Tall, 21 Laburnum Ave., Kenilworth, Warks CV8 2DR : Percy Grainger Society. Unpriced* BGRT(B) (B78-37094)
Home organist and leisure music
Vol.1, no.1- ; Aug.-Sept. 1977-. *Cover Publications Ltd; 181 Queen Victoria St., EC4V 4DD : Distributed by Independent Magazines Ltd. £4.35 yearly* ARPV/E(B) (B78-06991)
The international piper
Vol.1, no.1- ; May 1978-. *Seton Works, Edinburgh Rd, Cockenzie, East Lothian EH32 0HQ : International Piper Ltd. £0.35* AVY/E(B) (B78-26248)
Liszt Society. The Liszt Society journal
Vol.1- ; 1975-. *78 Wimbledon Park Side, SW19 5LH : The Society. £3.50(for members)* BLJ(B) (B78-11193)
London Association of Organists. Newsletter
Issue no.1- ; 1976-. *c/o P. Lea-Cox, St Jude-on-the-Hill, Central Sq., N.W.11 : The Association. Unpriced* AR(YDB/B) (B78-09120)
Marching band news
No.1- ; Apr. 1978-. *64 London End, Beaconsfield, Bucks. : 'Marching band news'. £2.50 yearly* AUMM/E(B) (B78-26891)
Music in worship : a quarterly journal for Christians
No.1- ; Sept. 1977-. *c/o The editor, 78 Trevellance Way, Garston, Herts. WD2 6LZ : 'Music in worship'. £0.15* AD/LD(B) (B78-23593)
Rock on!
No.1- ; May 1978-. *IPC Magazines. £0.25* A/HKQ(B) (B78-26241)
Scottish National Orchestra. SNO scene
No.1- ; June 1977-. *150 Hope St., Glasgow G2 2TH : Scottish National Orchestra Society. £3.00 yearly* AMM/E(QB/B) (B78-06989)
Soul cargo
No.1-. *67 Albert Terrace, Wolstanton, Newcastle-under-Lyme, Staffs. : C. Savory. £0.30* A/GBS/FD(B) (B78-05414)
Trick
No.1- ; Nov. 1977-. *43 Bow La., EC4M 9DT : Wishcastle Ltd. £0.20* A/HKQ(B) (B78-02606)
Perite autem. Op.115, no.2. How brightly shine = Perite autem : for four part chorus of men's voices a cappella. (Mendelssohn, Felix). *Schirmer. £0.35* GEZDH/LF (B78-50420)
Perle, George.
Serial composition and atonality : an introduction to the music of Schoenberg, Berg and Webern. 4th ed., revised. *University of California Press. £8.75* A/PN (B78-16384) ISBN 0-520-03395-7
Twelve tonality. *University of California Press. £10.25* A/PN (B78-17614) ISBN 0-520-03387-6
Perlis, Vivian. An Ives celebration : papers and panels of the Charles Ives Centennial Festival-Conference. (Charles Ives Centennial Festival-Conference, *New York and New Haven, 1974*). *University of Illinois Press. £8.40* BIV (B78-16383) ISBN 0-252-00619-4
Persichetti, Vincent. Twentieth century harmony : creative aspects and practice. *Faber. £2.95* A/R(XMA60) (B78-11195) ISBN 0-571-11216-1
Pert, Margaret.
Dolly suite, op.56. Dolly. Op.36 sic : suite pour piano à 4 mains. (Fauré, Gabriel). *Cramer. £2.75* QNVG (B78-50521)
Faust. Ah! je ris. *arr.* Jewel song ... (Gounod, Charles). *Leonard, Gould and Bolttler. Unpriced* KDW (B78-50115)
Faust. Avant de quitter ces lieux. *arr.* Cavatina 'Avant de quitter ces lieux'. (Gounod, Charles). *Leonard, Gould & Bolttler. Unpriced* KDW (B78-50443)
Pert, Morris. Voyage in space : twenty pieces for solo piano. *Weinberger. Unpriced* QPJ (B78-50547)
Pescetti, Giovanni Battista. Sonata, organ, C minor. Sonata in C minor for organ. *Oxford University Press. Unpriced* RE (B78-50229) ISBN 0-19-375634-x
Peter, Johann Friedrich.
Herr, wie sind deine Werke so gross. *arr.* Lord, thy creations, how great they are = Herr, wie sind deine Werke so gross : S.A.T.B. with accompaniment. *Boosey and Hawkes. Unpriced* DH (B78-50339)
Ihre Priester will ich mit Heil kleiden. *arr.* I will clothe thy priests with salvation = Ihre Priester will ich mit Heil kleiden : S.A.T.B. with accompaniment. *Boosey and Hawkes. Unpriced* DH (B78-50340)
Kommt danket dem Helden. *arr.* Come thank now Jehovah = Kommt danket dem Helden : double chorus ; SATB with accompaniment. *Boosey and Hawkes. Unpriced* DH (B78-50341)
Unser Herr Jesus Christus. *arr.* Our dear Lord Jesus Christ = Unser Herr Jesus Christus : SATB with accompaniment. *Boosey and Hawkes. Unpriced* DH (B78-50342)
Petit concertiste. Mozart, Wolfgang Amadeus. Mozart : morçeaux choisis a l'usage des mains petites de la 2e année de piano (assez facile) a la moyenne difficulté. *Chappell. Unpriced* QPJ (B78-51015)
Petrokino, Paul.
Workers' carol. *arr.* The workers' carol. *Roberton. Unpriced* DP/LF (B78-50026)
Workers' carol. *arr.* The workers' carol. *Roberton. £0.12* JE/VSPDP/LF (B78-50426)
Petti, Anthony Gaetano.
Cantica sacra senis vocibus. Quem vidistis pastores? Quem vidistis pastores? : Motet for Christmas for six voices. (Dering, Richard). *Chester Music. Unpriced* DJ/LF (B78-50731)
The Chester books of motets : sacred renaissance motets with Latin texts
4: The German school for 4 voices. *Chester. Unpriced* EZDJ/AY (B78-50780)
5: The Flemish school for 4 voices. *Chester. Unpriced* EZDJ/AY (B78-50781)
The Western Wind mass. (Shepherd, John). *Chester Music. Unpriced* EZDG (B78-50768)
Peuerl, Paul. Newe Padouan, Intrada, Täntz unnd Galliarda. *Selections.* Four dances (1611). *Chester Music. Unpriced* WNSK/AH (B78-51340)
Pfitzner, Hans. Concerto, cello, A minor, op. posth, (1888). Konzert für Violoncello und Orchester (1888), Op. posth. *Schott. £6.00* MPSRF (B78-50935)
Phases, phases, phases, phases. *arr.* Phases, phases, phases, phases. (Wonder, Stevie). *Jobete Music : Chappell. Unpriced* KDW/GBS (B78-50155)
Phil the fluter's ball. *arr.* Phil the fluter's ball. (French, Percy). *Polyphonic Reproductions : Studio Music. Unpriced* WMK/DW (B78-50682)
Phillip, J B. On tiptoe. (Page, Jodi). *Yeldall Manor, Hare Hatch, Reading : Celebration Services. Unpriced* JFDM (B78-50089)
Phillips, Ivan C. Suite de pièces, 1st collection. Passacaille. *arr.* Passacaglia in G minor. (Handel, George Frideric). *Oxford University Press. Unpriced* UMMK/AHT (B78-50632)
Phillips, John Charles.
O waly waly : for SSA unaccompanied, Somerset folk song. *Roberton. £0.12* FEZDW (B78-50400)
O waly waly : for SSA unaccompanied, Somerset folk song. (Phillips, John Charles). *Roberton. £0.12* FEZDW (B78-50400)
Phoenix and the turtle. *Vocal score.* The phoenix and the turtle : for mezzo-soprano solo, SATB timpani (2) and string orchestra. (Hurd, Michael). *Novello. £0.78* DX (B78-50029)
Physics and the sound of music. (Rigden, John S). *Wiley. £8.85* A/B (B78-02609) ISBN 0-471-02433-3
Piano music. *Selections : arr.* Rags for guitar. (Joplin, Scott). *Schirmer. £1.50* TSPMK/AHXJ (B78-51167)
Pianoforte examinations, 1979
Grade 1: Lists A & B. (Associated Board of the Royal School of Music). *Associated Board of the Royal Schools of Music. £0.50* Q/AL (B78-50973)
Grade 2: Lists A & B. (Associated Board of the Royal School of Music). *Associated Board of the Royal School of Music. £0.50* Q/AL (B78-50974)
Grade 2: Lists A & B. (Associated Board of the Royal Schools of Music). *Associated Board of the Royal Schools of Music. £0.50* Q/AL (B78-50975)
Grade 3: Lists A & B. (Associated Board of the Royal Schools of Music). *Associated Board of the Royal Schools of Music. £0.50* Q/AL (B78-50976)
Grade 4: Lists A & B. (Associated Board of the Royal Schools of Music). *Associated Board of the Royal Schools of Music. £0.50* Q/AL (B78-50977)
Grade 5: List A. (Associated Board of the Royal Schools of Music). *Associated Board of the Royal Schools of Music. £0.50* Q/AL (B78-50978)
Grade 5: List B. (Associated Board of the Royal Schools of Music). *Associated Board of the Royal Schools of Music. £0.50* Q/AL (B78-50979)
Grade 6: List A. (Associated Board of the Royal Schools of Music). *Associated Board of the Royal Schools of Music. £0.50* Q/AL (B78-50980)
Grade 6: List B. (Associated Board of the Royal Schools of Music). *Associated Board of the Royal Schools of Music. £0.50* Q/AL (B78-50981)
Grade 7: List A. (Associated Board of the Royal Schools of Music). *Associated Board of the Royal Schools of Music. £0.50* Q/AL (B78-50982)
Grade 7: List B. (Associated Board of the Royal Schools of Music). *Associated Board of the Royal Schools of Music. £0.50* Q/AL (B78-50983)
Pianoforte scales and arpeggios
Grade 3. (Associated Board of the Royal Schools of Music). *Associated Board of the Royal Schools of Music. Unpriced* Q/AF (B78-50965)
Grade 4. (Associated Board of the Royal Schools of Music). *Associated Board of the Royal Schools of Music. Unpriced* Q/AF (B78-50966)
Grade 5. (Associated Board of the Royal Schools of Music). *Associated Board of the Royal Schools of Music. Unpriced* Q/AF (B78-50967)
Grade 6. (Associated Board of the Royal Schools of Music). *Associated Board of the Royal Schools of Music. Unpriced* Q/AF (B78-50968)
Grade 7. (Associated Board of the Royal Schools of Music). *Associated Board of the Royal Schools of Music. Unpriced* Q/AF (B78-50969)
Grade 8. (Associated Board of the Royal Schools of Music). *Associated Board of the Royal Schools of Music. Unpriced* Q/AF (B78-50970)
Pianoforte scales and broken chords
Grade 1. (Associated Board of the Royal Schools of Music). *Associated Board of the Royal Schools of Music. Unpriced* Q/AF (B78-50971)
Grade 2. (Associated Board of the Royal Schools of Music). *Associated Board of the Royal Schools of Music. Unpriced* Q/AF (B78-50972)
Pianos in practice. (Smith, Eric, *b.1940*). *Scolar Press. £8.00* AQ/BT (B78-28704) ISBN 0-85967-393-6
Pièce de resistance. (Orton, Richard). *Arts Lab Music. Unpriced* QPJ (B78-51017)
Pièces de violes, liv 4. Le Basque. *arr.* Le Basque : old French dance. (Marais, Marin). *116 Long Acre, W.C.2 : Paxman. Unpriced* WTPK/AH (B78-50316)
Pierpont, James S. Jingle bells. *EMI. Unpriced* KDW/LF (B78-50882)
Pierpont Morgan Library. Sir Arthur Sullivan : composer & personage. (Allen, Reginald). *Pierpont Morgan Library : Chappell. £12.95* BSW(N) (B78-05721) ISBN 0-87923-145-9
Pierre Boulez, conversations with Célestin Deliège. (Boulez, Pierre). *48 Great Marlborough St., W1V 2BN : Eulenburg Books. £3.00* BBRO (B78-11192) ISBN 0-903873-21-4
Piggott, Patrick. Rachmaninov. *Faber. £3.95 : CIP rev.* BRC(N) (B77-12592) ISBN 0-571-10265-4
Pilgrim : a musical morality in popular style for unison voices (with divisions) and piano with guitar chord symbols. (Hurd, Michael). *Novello. £0.86* DE (B78-50332)
Pilgrim. *Vocal score.* Pilgrim : a musical morality in popular style for unison voices (with divisions) and piano with guitar chord symbols. (Hurd, Michael). *Novello. £0.86* DE (B78-50332)
Pilkington, Michael.
Early Georgian songs
Book 1: Medium voice. *Stainer and Bell. £1.50* KDW/AYC (B78-50112) ISBN 0-85249-459-9
Book 2: Low voice. *Stainer and Bell. £1.50* KDW/AYC (B78-50113) ISBN 0-85249-460-2
Eight songs. (Eccles, John). *Stainer and Bell. £1.50* KDW (B78-50114) ISBN 0-85249-463-7
Piontek, Heinz. 4 Songs nach Texten von Hans-Jurgen Heise, Heinz Piontek, Hans Magnus Enzensberger und Ror Wolf für Singstimme, Klavier, Kontrabass und Schlagzeug. (Wimberger, Gerhard). *Bärenreiter. £2.50* KE/NYGDW (B78-50883)
Piramo e Tisbe. Tambourin. *arr.* Tambourin. (Hasse, Johann Adolf). *Lengnick. £0.60* VRPK/AHVQT (B78-51222)
Pitts, Michael R. Hollywood on record : the film stars' discography. *Scarecrow Press : Distributed by Bailey and Swinfen. £13.60* AKDW/JR/FD(YT/WT) (B78-27785) ISBN 0-8108-1093-x
Plain & easy introduction to the harpsichord. (Nurmi, Ruth). *University of New Mexico Press : Distributed by Heinemann. £9.50* AQR/E (B78-28705) ISBN 0-434-52470-0
Plaine and easy introduction to practicall musicke. O amica mea. *arr.* O amica mea. (Morley, Thomas). *Edizioni Pegasus : Peters. Unpriced* VSNRK/DJ (B78-50652)
Plaistow, Stephen. Catalogue of music broadcast on Radio 3 and Radio 4
1974. (British Broadcasting Corporation). *B.B.C. £4.00* A/JT(WT) (B78-20763) ISBN 0-563-17369-6
Platt, Richard.
Concerto, string orchestra, op.3, no.10, D minor. Concerto in D minor, opus 3, no.10, for strings and continuo. (Humphries, John). *Oxford University Press. Unpriced* RXMF (B78-50245) ISBN 0-19-364804-0
Concerto, trumpet & string orchestra, op.2, no.12, D major. Concerto in D major, for trumpet (or horn), strings and continuo. (Humphries, John). *Oxford University Press. Unpriced* RXMPWSF (B78-51075) ISBN 0-19-364797-4
Platti, Giovanni Benedetto. Sonata, flute, violin & continuo, G major. Triosonate, G-dur, G major, für Querflöte (Violine), Violine (Oboe) und B.C., for German flute (violin), violin (oboe) and b.c. Erstausgabe. *Heinrichshofen : Peters. Unpriced* NURNTE (B78-50501)
Platts, Kenneth. Sussex overture. Op.34. *Edwin Ashdown. £2.00* MJ (B78-50913)
Platz, Paul.
Marc Bolan : a tribute. *19 Poland St., W1V 3DD : Essex House Publishing : Springwood Books. £5.95* AKDW/HKR/E(P) (B78-39783) ISBN 0-906445-00-0
Marc Bolan : a tribute. *19 Poland St., W1V 3DD : Essex House Publishing. £2.95* AKDW/HKR/E(P) (B78-39784) ISBN 0-906445-01-9

Play a piece : easy solos in two books, guitar solo
Book 1. *Oxford University Press. Unpriced* TSPMK/AAY (B78-50621) ISBN 0-19-356796-2
Book 2. *Oxford University Press. Unpriced* TSPMK/AAY (B78-50622) ISBN 0-19-356797-0
Play the piano : a tutor for adults and late beginners. (Enoch, Yvonne). *Faber Music. Unpriced* Q/AC (B78-50960)
Player Piano Group. Membership list
Jan. 1977. *358 High St., Brentford, Middx : The Group. Unpriced* AQ/FH(Q/BC) (B78-01685)
Playing the horn : a practical guide. (Tuckwell, Barry). *Oxford University Press. Unpriced* WT/AC (B78-51349)

Playtime : Longman first recorder course
Stage 5. *Longman. Unpriced* VS/AC (B78-51237) ISBN 0-582-18526-2
Plomley, Roy. 'Desert island discs'. *Fontana. £0.85* A/FD/JT(P/X) (B78-08479) ISBN 0-00-634227-2
Ploughboy's glory : a selection of hitherto unpublished folk songs. *English Folk Dance and Song Society. Unpriced* KEZDW/G/AYD (B78-50467)
Plum stones : for piano. (Helyer, Marjorie). *Novello. Unpriced* QPJ (B78-50531)
Plumstead, Mary. They all were looking for a king : for four-part male voice choir unaccompanied. Revised ed. *Roberton. £0.15* GEZDP/LF (B78-50827)
Pockriss, Lee.
Happy birthday, Jesus. *arr.* Happy birthday, Jesus. *Chappell. Unpriced* DP/LF (B78-50742)
Happy birthday, Jesus. *arr.* Happy birthday, Jesus. *Chappell. Unpriced* FDP/LF (B78-50811)
Points and dances ... : for instrumental ensemble. (Davies, Peter Maxwell). *Boosey and Hawkes. Unpriced* LN (B78-50907)
Polonaise, Adagio und Finale : für vier Bläser (Oboe, Klarinette in B, Horn in F, Fagott) und Streichquintett (solistisch oder chorisch) = for four wind instruments (oboe, clarinet in B flat, horn in F, bassoon) and string quintet (solo or in chorus). (Egk, Werner). Neufassung. *Schott. £12.00* NWNM (B78-50947)
Polonaise, Adagio und Finale : für vier Bläser und Streichquintett = for four wind instruments and string quintet. (Egk, Werner). *Schott. Unpriced* NWNM (B78-50946)
Polonaise napolitana : piano solo. (Dale, Mervyn). *Edwin Ashdown. Unpriced* QPHVHM (B78-51001)
Polychromie : für Klavier und 10 Instrumente, Opus 38. (Steffen, Wolfgang). *Bote und Bock : Associated Music. £5.75* MPQ (B78-50496)
Polyhymnia caduceatrix et panegyrica. Wie schön leuchtet der Morgenstern. How brightly beams the morning star = Wie schön leuchtet der Morgenstern : for four-part chorus of mixed voices, five solo voices and optional keyboard accompaniment. (Praetorius, Michael). *Schirmer. £0.35* EZDH/LF (B78-50375)
Polyphonic music of the golden age. Byrd, Morley, Tallis : three-part vocal compositions. *Ricordi. Unpriced* VSNTK (B78-51247)
Pont, Kenneth. The lantern song : ten Chinese songs arranged for voices, recorders and percussion by Kenneth Pont. *Oxford University Press. Unpriced* JFE/NYHSDW (B78-50851) ISBN 0-19-330613-1
Ponte, Lorenzo da. *See* Da Ponte, Lorenzo.
Pooler, Marie. Three children's songs for three equal voices (SSA). (Lutoslawski, Witold). *Chester Music. Unpriced* FDW/GJ (B78-50816)
Poore, Melvyn. Vox superios : for solo tuba, 1976. *Arts Lab Music. Unpriced* WVPMJ (B78-51361)
Pop festivals and their problems : second report of the Working Group on Pop Festivals. (Great Britain. Working Group on Pop Festivals). *H.M.S.O. £0.85* A/GB(WE) (B78-16620) ISBN 0-11-751254-0
Pop goes the recorder : 20 great tunes with chord symbols for guitar
Book 1. *Chappell. Unpriced* VSPMK/DW/GB/AY (B78-50299)
Book 2. *Chappell. Unpriced* VSPMK/DW/GB/AY (B78-50300)
Book 3. *Chappell. Unpriced* VSPMK/DW/GB/AY (B78-51253)
Pop industry inside out. (Cable, Michael). *W.H. Allen. £4.95* A/GB/FD(XPQ22) (B78-03111) ISBN 0-491-02381-2
Pop into school.
Boswell, Eric. Little donkey. *arr.* Little donkey. *Chappell. Unpriced* NYDPK/DP/LF (B78-50950)
Bouwens, J. Paloma blanca. *arr.* Paloma blanca. *Chappell. Unpriced* NYFPK (B78-50513)
Davis, Katherine Kennicott. Carol of the drum. *arr.* The little drummer boy. *Chappell. Unpriced* NYDPK/DP/LF (B78-50951)
Hairston, Jester. Mary's boy child. *arr.* Mary's boy child. *Chappell. Unpriced* NYFPK/DW/LF (B78-50953)
Lennon, John. Yellow submarine. *arr.* Yellow submarine. *Chappell. Unpriced* NYFPK/DW (B78-50515)
Rodgers, Richard. The sound of music. Do-re-mi. *arr.* Do-re-mi. *Chappell. Unpriced* NYFPK/DW (B78-50516)
Trombey, Jack. Eye level. *arr.* Eye level. *Chappell. Unpriced* NYFPK (B78-50514)
Pop into the middle ages : new settings of medieval lyrics for group music making. (Pehkonen, Elis). *Novello. £0.94* ENYDDW (B78-50033)
Pop quest : so you think you know all about rock 'n' pop. (Tobler, John). *Independent Television Books : Arrow Books. £0.65* A/GB (B78-20431) ISBN 0-09-917570-3
Pop workbook. (Attwood, Tony). *Edward Arnold. £1.75 : CIP rev.* A/GB (B77-28559) ISBN 0-7131-0155-5
Pope, Alexander. Vital spark of heavenly flame. (The dying Christian to his soul) : for full chorus of mixed voices a cappella. (Chorbajian, John). *Schirmer. Unpriced* EZDH (B78-50043)
Popeye the sailor. I'm Popeye the sailor man. *arr.* I'm Popeye the sailor man. (Lerner, Sammy). *Warner Blossom. Unpriced* UMMK/DW/JR (B78-50636)
Popular Elizabethan tunes : for recorder and guitar. *Ariel : Music Sales. Unpriced* VSPLTSK (B78-51252) ISBN 0-86001-371-5
Popular music periodicals index
1976. *Scarecrow Press : Distributed by Bailey and Swinfen. £8.50* A/GB(DD/B/T) (B78-50320) ISBN 0-8108-1079-4
Popular music record reviews. Annual index to popular music record reviews
1976. *Scarecrow Press : Distributed by Bailey and Swinfen. £17.00* A/GB/FD(T) (B78-20767) ISBN 0-8108-1070-0
Popular song index
1st supplement. (Havlice, Patricia Pate). *Scarecrow Press Distributed by Bailey and Swinfen. £12.75* AKDW/GB(WT) (B78-27098) ISBN 0-8108-1099-9
Porgy and Bess. (Gershwin, George). *Chappell. Unpriced* KDW (B78-50442)
Porgy and Bess. *Selections : arr.* Porgy and Bess. (Gershwin, George). *Chappell. Unpriced* KDW (B78-50442)
Port, June G. The dictionary of composers and their music : every listener's companion arranged chronologically and alphabetically. (Gilder, Eric). *Paddington Press. £6.95* A/D(M/C) (B78-26881) ISBN 0-448-22364-3
Porter, Cole. The best of Cole Porter. *Chappell. Unpriced* KDW/GB (B78-50138)
Portsmouth : traditional. (Brand, Michael). *R. Smith. Unpriced* WMK/DW (B78-51323)
Pösch, Isaac. Newe Padouan, Intrada, Täntz unnd Galliarda. *Selections.* Four dances (1611). (Peuerl, Paul). *Chester Music. Unpriced* WNSK/AH (B78-51340)
Potter, Archibald James.
Lovelie Jemmie. *Ashdown. Unpriced* JFDW (B78-50092)
The storke : carol for S.A.T.B. *Edwin Ashdown. £0.20* EZDP/LF (B78-50787)
Potty pantomime. (Crocker, John, *b.1925*). *Evans Bros. £0.40* BCQRACPP (B78-37098) ISBN 0-237-75031-7
Poulenc, Francis.
My friends and myself : conversations with Francis Poulenc. (Audel, Stéphane). *Dobson. £4.95* BPO(N) (B78-39780) ISBN 0-234-77251-4
Sonata, clarinet & piano. Sonata for clarinet in B flat and piano. 5th ed. embodying corrections to the first ed., edited by Thea King and Georgina Dobree. *Chester Music. Unpriced* VVPE (B78-51283)
Poulton, Diana. Lute music. *Collections.* The collected lute music of John Dowland. (Dowland, John). 2nd ed. with 3 more pieces. *Faber Music. Unpriced* TW/AZ (B78-51171) ISBN 0-571-10024-4
Pound, Ezra. Ezra Pound and music : the complete criticism. *Faber. £25.00* A/CC(P) (B78-08474) ISBN 0-571-11233-1
Practical methods in choir training. (Nicholson, Sydney H). *Addington Palace, Croydon CR9 5AD : Royal School of Church Music. £0.65* AD/E (B78-01055) ISBN 0-85402-069-1
Pradère, O. Faust. Avant de quitter ces lieux. *arr.* Cavatina 'Avant de quitter ces lieux'. (Gounod, Charles). *Leonard, Gould & Bolttler. Unpriced* KDW (B78-50443)
Praetorius, Michael.
Musae Sioniae. Tl.2. *Selections.* Weihnachtskonzerte : für zwei vierstimmige Chöre. *Bärenreiter. £2.24* EWNDH/LF (B78-50360)
Musae Sioniae. Tl.2. *Selections.* Weihnachtskonzerte : für zwei vierstimmige Chöre. *Bärenreiter. £1.96* EZDH/LF (B78-50374)
Polyhymnia caduceatrix et panegyrica. Wie schön leuchtet der Morgenstern. How brightly beams the morning star = Wie schön leuchtet der Morgenstern : for four-part chorus of mixed voices, five solo voices and optional keyboard accompaniment. *Schirmer. £0.35* EZDH/LF (B78-50375)
Praise for today. *Psalms and Hymns Trust. Unpriced* DM/AY (B78-50734)
Praise God in his sanctuary : S.A.T.B. (Jackson, Francis). *Banks. Unpriced* DR (B78-50743)
Pratt, George. Six solos, Op.4 : for flute or violin and continuo. (Stanley, John). *Chester Music. Unpriced* VRPE (B78-51214)
Preces and responses for men's voices. (Jones, Michael Leighton). Revised ed. *36 Ranelagh Gdns., W.6 : Cathedral Music. Unpriced* GEZDGMM (B78-50414)
Preces and responses (SATB). (Doveton, Robin). *36 Ranelagh Gdns., W.6 : Cathedral Music. Unpriced* EZDGMM (B78-50368)
Prelude and burlesca : for piano solo. (Parke, Dorothy). *Banks. Unpriced* QPJ (B78-51019)
Prelude and idyll : for soprano and baritone with orchestra. (Delius, Frederick). *Boosey and Hawkes. Unpriced* JNEDX (B78-50438)
Prelude and march in canon : for French horn and piano. (Anderson, Muriel Bradford). *Boosey and Hawkes. Unpriced* WTPGM/X (B78-50315)
Prelude and march in canon : for viola and piano. (Anderson, Muriel Bradford). *Boosey and Hawkes. Unpriced* SQPGM/X (B78-50261)
Prelude for organ. (Thomson, Virgil). *Schirmer. £1.50* RJ (B78-50568)
Premier concert de chambre : for two descant recorders and keyboard. (Mouret, Jean Joseph). *Dolmetsch. Unpriced* VSRNTPWF (B78-51255)
Prentice-Hall history of music series.
Longyear, Rey Morgan. Nineteenth-century Romanticism in music. 2nd ed. *Prentice-Hall. £5.05* A(YB/XG101) (B78-22843) ISBN 0-13-622647-7
Malm, William Paul. Music cultures of the Pacific, the Near East, and Asia. 2nd ed. *Prentice-Hall. £7.95* BZB (B78-04322) ISBN 0-13-608000-6
Preston, Michael, *b.1945.* Music master
1978. *1 De Cham Ave., Hastings, Sussex : John Humphries. £30.00* A/FD(WT) (B78-11519) ISBN 0-904520-06-4
Pretender. (Browne, Jackson). *Warner : Blossom. Unpriced* KDW/HKR (B78-50160)
Previn, Dory. Midnight baby : an autobiography. *Corgi. £0.75* AKDW/GB/E(P/B) (B78-18542) ISBN 0-552-10643-7
Price, D I. Kemp's music & recording industry year book (international)
1978. *Kemps. £5.50* A/GB(YC/BC) (B78-09409) ISBN 0-905255-30-5
Primavera : for soprano and flute. (Musgrave, Thea). *Chester Music. Unpriced* KFLE/VRDW (B78-50896)
Prime Minister. *See* Great Britain. *Prime Minister.*
Primo libro a due voci. *Selections.* Nine fantasies : for two instruments. (Lupacchino, Bernadino). *London Pro Musica. Unpriced* LNU (B78-50909)
Primo libro delle canzoni a una, due, tre e quattro voci. *Selections.* Three canzonas for two treble, one bass instrument and continuo. (Frescobaldi, Girolamo). *London Pro Musica Edition. Unpriced* LNSPW (B78-50483)
Processional and prayer of Emperor of China on the Altar of Heaven, December 21, 1539. (Nelson, Ron). *Oxford University Press. Unpriced* EUMDE (B78-50041)
Prole do bebê no.1 : coleção completa, 8 peças para piano. (Villa-Lobos, Heitor). *Arthur Napoleão : Essex Music. Unpriced* QPJ (B78-50548)
Propulsions : concerts for percussion. (Bazelon, Irwin). *Boosey and Hawkes. £12.50* XNPF (B78-51362)
Psalm 100, Make a joyful noise unto the Lord. (Latrobe, Christian Ignatius). *Boosey and Hawkes. Unpriced* DR (B78-50346)
Psalmen Davids sampt etlichen Moteten und Concerten. Alleluia. Lobet den Herren = Alleluia. Worship Jehovah : for 8 solo voices and double choir, with instruments. (Schütz, Heinrich). *Oxford University Press. Unpriced* ENWXPDR (B78-50358) ISBN 0-19-338088-9
Psychology of music. (Davies, John Booth). *Hutchinson. £8.95* A/CS (B78-11194) ISBN 0-09-129500-9
Pub favourites
No.5. *Campbell, Connelly and Connelly. Unpriced* KDW/GB/AY (B78-50876)
Public Record Office. *MSS.(E101/369/6).* Menestrellorum multitudo : minstrels at a royal feast. (Bullock-Davies, Constance). *University of Wales Press. £7.50* AL/E(YD/XCKF) (B78-12983) ISBN 0-7083-0656-x
Pulkingham, Betty.
Be known to us : a collection of general anthems for mixed voices. *57 Dorchester Rd, Lytchett Minster : Celebration Publishing. Unpriced* DH/AY (B78-50727) ISBN 0-906309-03-4
Hail to the Lord's anointed. *57 Dorchester Rd. Lytchett Minister, Poole : Celebration Services. Unpriced* JDM (B78-50082)
Hosanna in the highest : a collection of descants for traditional hymns. *Dorchester Rd : Celebration Services. £1.50* FADM/AY (B78-50805) ISBN 0-906309-07-7
The King of glory : series 3 (mixolydian). *57 Dorchester Rd, Lytchett Minster, Poole : Celebration Services. Unpriced* ETSPLRDGS (B78-50040)
Puma, Joe. Carry me Bach : themes and variations on original classical and jazz themes for guitar solo. *Associated Music. £2.40* TSPM/T (B78-50611)
'Purbeck mail'. Edgar A. Lane : musician, 1865-1938 : memories of Edgar Alfred Lane. (Lane, Margaret, *b.1899*). *'Purbeck mail'. Unpriced* AD/E(P) (B78-09112)

Purcell, Henry.
Purcell for the guitar : five pieces ... *Oxford University Press. Unpriced* TSPMK (B78-51164) ISBN 0-19-358356-9
Sonatas in 4 parts, Z.802-811. Ten sonatas in four parts Nos. 1-6. *Eulenburg. £2.00* NXNSE (B78-50506)
Sonatas in 4 parts. Z.802-811. Ten sonatas in four parts Nos.7-10. *Eulenburg. £2.00* NXNSE (B78-50507)
The works of Henry Purcell
Volume 8: Ode on St Cecilia's Day, 1692 ; edited under the supervision of the Purcell Society by Peter Dennison. *Novello. £10.00* C/AZ (B78-50002)
Purcell for the guitar : five pieces ... (Purcell, Henry). *Oxford University Press. Unpriced* TSPMK (B78-51164) ISBN 0-19-358356-9
Pushover : a choral play in one act about Samson, Judge of Israel. (Easton, Ken). *French. £1.20* BSGNHACM (B78-03576) ISBN 0-573-62425-9
Q.M.B. Edition. Bernstein, Leonard. Slana!. *arr.* Slava! : a concert overture. *Amberson : Boosey and Hawkes Boosey and Hawkes. Unpriced* UMMK (B78-51186)
Q.M.B. edition.
Brunelli, Louis Jean. Chronicles. *Boosey and Hawkes. Unpriced* UMMJ (B78-50629)
Grundman, Clare. Overture on a short theme. *Boosey and Hawkes. Unpriced* UMMJ (B78-51178)

Q.M.B. Edition.
Jacob, Gordon. Tribute to Canterbury. *Boosey and Hawkes. Unpriced* UMMJ (B78-50281)
Mailman, Martin. A simple ceremony, 'In memorian John Barnes Chance', Op.53 : for symphonic band and unison

voices. *Boosey and Hawkes. Unpriced* JFE/UMMDGF (B78-50854)
Q.M.B. edition. Sparke, Philip. Gaudium : concert piece for wind symphony orchestra. *Boosey and Hawkes. Unpriced* UMMJ (B78-51183)
Q.M.B. Edition.
Tull, Fisher. Cryptic essay : for symphonic band. *Boosey and Hawkes. Unpriced* UMMJ (B78-50282)
Washburn, Robert. Trigon. *Boosey and Hawkes. £21.00* UMMJ (B78-51184)
Quando corpus ... : for four-part chorus of mixed voices. (Rossini, Gioacchino Antonio). *Roberton. £0.20* EZDJ/LK (B78-50783)
Quantum books. Conrad, Peter, *b.1948.* Romantic opera and literary form. *University of California Press. £5.50* AC(Z) (B78-12986) ISBN 0-520-03258-6
Quarles, Francis. Emblem XI. How shall my tongue express ...? : Motet. (Rubbra, Edmund). *Lengnick. £0.18* EZDH (B78-50372)
Quartet diversions. Hennessy, Val. In the gutter. *Quartet Books. £1.95* AKDW/HKQ (B78-24013) ISBN 0-7043-3230-2
Quasi improvvisando : pour ensemble à vent = für Bläserenseble. (Françaix, Jean). *Schott. £6.00* UMJ (B78-51174)
Quatermaine, Michael. 'Par les fils de Mandrin'. *arr.* 'Par les fils de Mandrin'. (Ange). *Chappell. Unpriced* KDW/GB (B78-50123)
Queen.
A day at the races. *arr.* A day at the races. *Beechwood Music : EMI. Unpriced* KDW/HKR (B78-50164)
News of the world. *EMI. Unpriced* KE/TSDW/HKR (B78-50173)
Queen's trumpeters : concert march. (Siebert, Edrich). *Harmer Music. Unpriced* WMGM (B78-50675)
Quem vidistis pastores? : Motet for Christmas for six voices. (Dering, Richard). *Chester Music. Unpriced* DJ/LF (B78-50731)
Quine, Hector.
Basque suite : for guitar and harpsichord (or piano). (Kelly, Bryan). *Oxford University Press. Unpriced* TSPJ (B78-50610) ISBN 0-19-357423-3
Pavane and galliard for solo guitar. (Wills, Arthur). *Ricordi. Unpriced* TSPMHVG (B78-50614)
Take two = A due = Für zwei : five guitar duets. (Dodgson, Stephen). *Ricordi. Unpriced* TSNU (B78-50609)
Quite piece for a violent time : orchestra. (Bazelon, Irwin). *Boosey and Hawkes. Unpriced* MMJ (B78-50187)
Race, Steve. The day of the donkey, and other songs of praise. *Vocal score.* The day of the donkey (and other songs of praise for juniors). *Weinberger. Unpriced* JFDM (B78-50839)
Rachmaninov. (Piggott, Patrick). *Faber. £3.95 : CIP rev.* BRC(N) (B77-12592) ISBN 0-571-10265-4
Radcliffe, Philip.
Beethoven's string quartets. 2nd ed. *Cambridge University Press. £6.95* BBJARXNS (B78-29840) ISBN 0-521-21963-9
Mozart piano concertos. *British Broadcasting Corporation. £1.00* BMSAMPQF (B78-33168) ISBN 0-563-12771-6
Ragossnig, Konrad. La guitarre royalle. *Selections.* Suite in A minor ... : guitar solo. (Corbetta, Francesco). *Universal. Unpriced* TSPMJ (B78-51153)
Rags for guitar. (Joplin, Scott). *Schirmer. £1.50* TSPMK/AHXJ (B78-51167)
Rail. Op.57. *arr.* Rail. (Josephs, Wilfred). *Galaxy : Stainer and Bell. Unpriced* UMMK (B78-50630)
"Raised on rock". *EMI Music. Unpriced* KDW/HK/AY (B78-50158)
Ramsbottom, Edward. Sounds and music. *Macmillan. £0.48* A (B78-18538) ISBN 0-333-23169-4
Rankin, Robert. Behind the Beatles songs. (Cowan, Philip). *159 Wardour St., W.1 : Polytantric Press. £2.50* AKDW/GB/E(P) (B78-28699) ISBN 0-905150-09-0
Raphael, Mark. Two Thomas Moore songs : for solo voice and piano. *Roberton. £0.50* KDW (B78-50445)
Ratcliffe, Desmond. Messe basse and other sacred works : for female or boys voices and organ or piano. (Fauré, Gabriel). *Novello. Unpriced* DFF (B78-50016)
Raven, Jon.
The urban & industrial songs of the Black Country and Birmingham. *68 Limes Rd, Tottenhall, Wolverhampton WV6 8RB : Broadside. £7.75* AKDW/G(YDHNB) (B78-20442) ISBN 0-9503722-2-6
Victoria's inferno : songs of the old mills, mines, manufactories, canals and railways. *68 Limes Rd, Tettenhall, Wolverhampton W. Midlands : Broadside. £0.95* AKDW/GM (B78-29838) ISBN 0-9503722-3-4
Ray, Robin. Robin Ray's music quiz. *Batsford. £3.50* A(DE) (B78-35466) ISBN 0-7134-1492-8
Raynor, Henry.
Mozart. *Macmillan. £5.95 : CIP rev.* BMS(N) (B77-22045) ISBN 0-333-21615-6
The orchestra : a history. *Scribner's : Hale. £4.50* AMM (B78-12988) ISBN 0-7091-6333-9
Read, Gardner. Music notation : a manual of modern practice. 2nd ed.. *Gollancz. £3.95* A(QU) (B78-30828) ISBN 0-575-02554-9
Ready to play : stories with percussion sounds. (Blades, James). *British Broadcasting Corporation. £1.50* AX/GR(VE) (B78-38609) ISBN 0-563-17610-5
Reaney, Gilbert. Two anonymous alleluias from the Worcester Fragments, (Worcester Cathedral Library, Add. ms. 68). *Antico Edition. Unpriced* EZDJ (B78-50045)
Rebuttal : two clarinets. (Kolb, Barbara). *Henmar Press : Peters : Peters. Unpriced* VVNU (B78-51278)
Recercari et canzoni francese. Libro primo. *Selections ; arr.* Ricercar et canzoni. (Frescobaldi, Girolamo). *Novello. £1.30* MRK (B78-50196)
Record of singing to 1914. (Scott, Michael). *Duckworth. £12.50* AK/FD(XM15) (B78-03582) ISBN 0-7156-1030-9
Recorder. (Goodyear, Stephen F). *Teach Yourself Books. £1.25 : CIP rev.* AVS/E (B78-25376) ISBN 0-340-22247-6
Recorder playing. (Rosenberg, Steve). *Prince Milburn Music : Boosey and Hawkes. Unpriced* VS/AC (B78-51238)
Recorder playing : for descant recorders
Junior book 2. *Chappell. Unpriced* VSRPMK/AAY (B78-51258)
Recorder tutor : for descant recorders. (Galloway, Malcolm). *Regina Music. Unpriced* VSR/AC (B78-51254)
Recordings of artists working in Scotland. (Scottish Arts Council). *19 Charlotte Sq., Edinburgh EH2 4DF : The Council. Unpriced* A/FD(YDL) (B78-35031) ISBN 0-902989-45-6
Recueil de vingt chansons et airs traditionnels. (Malicorne). *Chappell. Unpriced* KE/LDW/GB (B78-50167)
Red rose speedway. (McCartney, Paul). *MPL : Music Sales. Unpriced* KDW/GB (B78-50135) ISBN 0-86001-478-9
Red rose speedway. *arr.* Red rose speedway. (McCartney, Paul). *MPL : Music Sales. Unpriced* KDW/GB (B78-50135) ISBN 0-86001-478-9
Redel, Martin Christoph.
Interplay : für sieben Spieler, 1975. *Bote und Bock Associated Music. £7.70* NYDPNP (B78-50511)
Konfrontationen : für grosses Orchester, 1974. *Bote und Bock : Associated Music. £5.75* MMJ (B78-50494)
Mobile : für Oboe (Oboe d'amore ad lib.), Klarinette und Fagott, 1976. *Bote und Bock : Schirmer. £4.80* VNT (B78-51199)
Szenen : für Flöte und Klavier, Opus 26 (1977). *Bote und Bock : Schirmer. £4.80* VRPJ (B78-51218)
Redfern, Brian. Organising music in libraries
Vol.1: Arrangement and classification. Revised and rewritten ed. *Bingley etc.. £3.25* A(U) (B78-50319) ISBN 0-85157-231-6
Redmayne, Joan. Sounds and music. (Ramsbottom, Edward). *Macmillan. £0.48* A (B78-18538) ISBN 0-333-23169-4
Redwood, Dawn. Flecker and Delius : the making of 'Hassan'. *14 Barlby Rd, W10 6AR : Thames Publishing. £5.50* BDL/JM (B78-29853) ISBN 0-905210-06-9
Reed, John, *b.1909.* Schubert. *Faber. £3.95 : CIP rev.* BSF(N) (B77-22755) ISBN 0-571-10327-8
Reed, Les. The works of Les Reed. *EMI. Unpriced* KDW/GB (B78-50869)
Rees, Terence. Sing along with Sullivan : a new anthology of music for the voice. (Sullivan, *Sir* Arthur Seymour). *Cramer. Unpriced* KDW (B78-50447)
Reeve, Peter. Newe Padouan, Intrada, Täntz unnd Galliarda. *Selections.* Four dances (1611). (Peuerl, Paul). *Chester Music. Unpriced* WNSK/AH (B78-51340)
Reflections of Narziss and Goldmund : for two chamber groups, harp and piano or celesta. (Saxton, Robert). *Chester Music. Unpriced* MRJ (B78-50943)
Reflexionen : fünf Psychogramme für Flöte (Alt-Flöte), Violoncello und Klavier, 1975. (Ludewig, Wolfgang). *Bote und Bock : Associated Music. £3.85* NURNT (B78-50500)
Regan, Michael.
Four shanties : for guitar. *Schott. £0.70* TSPMJ (B78-51158)
Trio, guitars. Trio for three guitars. *Schott. Unpriced* TSNT (B78-51145)
Reger, Max. Dreissig kleine Choral-vorspiele zu den gebrauchlichsten Choralen, tür Orgel, Opus 135A. *Peters. Unpriced* RJ (B78-51052)
Regimental quick march of The Ulster Defence Regiment, 'The sprig of Shillelagh' 'Garry owen'. (Carson, D). *Boosey and Hawkes. Unpriced* UMMGM/KH (B78-50280)
Regina coeli. (White, Robert). *Oxenfor Imprint, dist. Blackwell's Music Shop. Unpriced* GEZDJ/LL (B78-50421)
Rehfeldt, Phillip. New directions for clarinet. *University of California Press. £10.50* AVV/E (B78-27527) ISBN 0-520-03379-5
Reicha, Joseph. Concerto, viola, op.2, no.1, E flat major. *arr.* Konzert Es-dur für Viola und Orchester = Concerto E-flat major for viola and orchestra. *Simrock. £5.50* SQPK/LF (B78-50596)
Reinhardt, Django. Django Reinhardt. *EMI. Unpriced* TSPMHX (B78-51151)
Reiser, Dave. 'Not the Count of Monte Cristo?!' : a musical comedy in three acts for 3 players and a piano. *French. £1.65* BSGNHACM (B78-12096) ISBN 0-573-68085-x
Remnant, Mary. Musical instruments of the West. *Batsford. £10.00* AL/B (B78-24452) ISBN 0-7134-0569-4
Rémy, Pierre Jean. Maria Callas : a tribute. *Macdonald and Jane's. £6.95* AKFL/E(P) (B78-35471) ISBN 0-354-04315-3
Rennicke, Klaus. Church sonata, violins (2), op.6, no.9, D minor. Sonata a tre, d-moll, d minor, op.VI, no.9, für zwei Sopranblockflöten und Basso continuo, for two soprano i.e. descent recorders and basso continuo. (Bononcini, Giovanni Maria). *Noetzel : Peters. Unpriced* VSRNTPWE (B78-50654)
Renwick, Roger de V. The British traditional ballad in North America. (Coffin, Tristram Potter). Revised ed reprinted. *University of Texas Press. £11.25* ADW/G(YT/TC) (B78-01317) ISBN 0-292-70719-3
Requiem, Op.48. (Fauré, Gabriel). *Eulenburg. Unpriced* EMDGKAV (B78-50031)
Resources of music.
Folk music in school. *Cambridge University Press. £4.95* A/G(VF) (B78-29835) ISBN 0-521-21595-1
Sawyer, David. Vibrations : making unorthodox musical instruments. *Cambridge University Press. £4.00* AY/BC (B78-04323) ISBN 0-521-20812-2
Resurrection jazz : a cantata for schools. (Cartwright, Kenneth). *Boosey and Hawkes. Unpriced* FDE/LL (B78-50388)
Reusner, Esaias. Neuen Lautenfrüchte. *Selections.* Two pieces ... : guitar solo. *Universal. Unpriced* TSPMK (B78-51165)
Reutter, Hermann. Tre notturni : drei Gedichte von Friedrich Nietzsche, für tiefe Männerstimme, Klavier und Bläser. *Schott. £6.00* KFXE/NWPNQDW (B78-50176)
Reynolds, Roger. Only now, and again : winds, piano and percussion (3). *Peters. Unpriced* UMPQ (B78-51191)
Rhodes, Michael.
RSCM chorister training scheme
Part 2. Handbook for ex-trebles and young choirmen. (Royal School of Church Music). *Addington Palace, Croydon, Surrey CR9 5AD : R.S.C.M.. £0.55* AD/LD/E (B78-22164) ISBN 0-85402-073-x
Part 2. Training for ex-trebles and young choirmen. (Royal School of Church Music). *Addington Palace, Croydon, Surrey CR9 5AD : R.S.C.M.. £0.80* AD/LD/E (B78-22165) ISBN 0-85402-071-3
Rice, Jo. The Guinness book of British hit singles : (the Guinness book of records records). *Guinness Superlatives. £4.95* AKDW/GB/FD(XPM16) (B78-02936) ISBN 0-900424-77-x
Rice, Tim. Evita. Evita : the legend of Eva Peron, 1919-1952. (Webber, Andrew Lloyd). *Elm Tree Books. £3.95 : CIP rev.* BWKRACM (B78-12401) ISBN 0-241-89890-0
Rice, Tim. The Guinness book of British hit singles : (the Guinness book of records records). (Rice, Jo). *Guinness Superlatives. £4.95* AKDW/GB/FD(XPM16) (B78-02936) ISBN 0-900424-77-x
Ricercar et canzoni. (Frescobaldi, Girolamo). *Novello. £1.30* MRK (B78-50196)
Ricercari, 'In memoriam Luigi Dallapiccola' : for 11 players. (Harper, Edward). *Oxford University Press. Unpriced* MRJ (B78-50941) ISBN 0-19-356888-8
Richards, Gavin. England expects : a musical entertainment for all those sick with sacrifice. *97 Ferme Park Rd, Crouch End, N8 9SA : Journeyman Press : Belt and Braces Roadshow Co. £1.20* BFKSACM (B78-01675) ISBN 0-904526-25-9
Richards, W Mansel. Dr Joseph Parry, 1841-1903. *c/o Town Hall, Merthyr Tydfil, M. Glam. : W.M. Richards. Unpriced* BPEB(N) (B78-03577)
Rick Wakeman's criminal record. (Wakeman, Rick). *Rondor Music : Music Sales. Unpriced* QPJ (B78-50224)
Rider-Meyer, Lucy. Jonah : spiritual for unaccompanied male choir or quartet. (Hughes, Brian). *Roberton. £0.12* GEZDW/LC (B78-50074)
Ridgeon, John. Brass for beginners : treble clef piston - valved brass instruments. *Boosey and Hawkes. £2.20* W/AC (B78-50309)
Ridgway, John, *b.1943.* The Sinatrafile
Part 2: Commercial. *Miramar, Rowney Green La., Alvechurch, Birmingham B48 7QF : John Ridgway Books. £14.00* AKDW/GB/FD(P) (B78-23594) ISBN 0-905808-02-9
Ridout, Alan.
Little sad sound : a melodrama for double bass and narrator. *Yorke. Unpriced* SSPMJ (B78-51131)
That virgin's child : for S.A.T.B. unacc. *Williams School of Church Music. Unpriced* EZDP/LF (B78-50047)
Riethmuller, Heinrich. Tempelhofer Messe. *Simrock. £4.96* ENYEXPDG (B78-50034)
Rigden, John S. Physics and the sound of music. *Wiley. £8.85* A/B (B78-02609) ISBN 0-471-02433-3
Rimmer, Joan. The Irish harp. 2nd ed. *4 Bridge St., Cork : Mercier Press for the Cultural Relations Committee. £1.50* ATQS/B (B78-35478) ISBN 0-85342-151-x
Ring bells ring. (Hughes, David E). *2 Highfield Close : David E. Hughes. Unpriced* DP/LF (B78-50738)
Ring des Nibelungen. Die Walküre. Die Walküre. (Wagner, Richard). *Dover : Constable. Unpriced* CQC (B78-50712) ISBN 0-486-23566-1
Ring of time : preludes and pageants for orchestra and bells. (Argento, Dominick). *Boosey and Hawkes. Unpriced* MMJ (B78-50186)
Ring out! : a book of bells. (Yolen, Jane). *Evans Bros. £3.50* AXS (B78-31602) ISBN 0-237-44875-0
Rinuccini, O. La Dafne. *Vocal score.* La Dafne. (Gagliano, Marco da). *Cathedral Music. Unpriced* CC (B78-50325)
Rizzo, Jacques.
African Sanctus. Lord's Prayer. *arr.* The Lord's Prayer ... : S.A.B. and piano with optional guitar and drums. (Fanshawe, David). *Chappell. Unpriced* DTF (B78-50348)
African Sanctus. Lord's Prayer. *arr.* The Lord's Prayer ... : S.A.T.B. and piano with optional guitar and drums. (Fanshawe, David). *Chappell. Unpriced* DTF (B78-50347)
African Sanctus. Lord's Prayer. *arr.* The Lord's Prayer ... : unison chorus and piano. (Fanshawe, David). *Chappell. Unpriced* JDTF (B78-50425)
Happy birthday, Jesus. *arr.* Happy birthday, Jesus. (Pockriss, Lee). *Chappell. Unpriced* DP/LF (B78-50742)
Happy birthday, Jesus. *arr.* Happy birthday, Jesus. (Pockriss, Lee). *Chappell. Unpriced* FDP/LF (B78-50811)
Road goes ever on : a song cycle : poemsby J.R.R. Tolkein. (Swann, Donald). 2nd ed. *Allen and Unwin. £4.75* KDW (B78-50863) ISBN 0-04-784011-0

Robert de Cormier choral series. De Cormier, Robert. She'll be comin' round the mountain : American folk song, for full chorus of mixed voices unaccompanied. *Roberton. £0.32* EZDW (B78-50051)

Roberton, *Sir* Hugh S. Iona boat song. For a dead king : traditional Scottish air for 4-part male chorus unaccompanied. (Lees, Heath). *Roberton. £0.15* GEZDW (B78-50828)

Roberton, *Sir* Hugh Stevenson. Two Scottish psalm tunes. *Roberton. £0.20* GDR (B78-50407)

Roberton male voice series. Roberton, *Sir* Hugh Stevenson. Two Scottish psalm tunes. *Roberton. £0.20* GDR (B78-50407)

Roberton mixed voice series. Tučapský, Antonin. Lands : two settings for unaccompanied mixed voice choir of poems by W.H. Auden, music by Antonin Tučapský. *Roberton. £0.32* EZDW (B78-50055)

Roberts, E Ernest. John Roberts, telynor Cymru. *Gwasg Gee. £1.50* ATQ/E(P) (B78-33170)

Roberts, Selyf. John Roberts, telynor Cymru. (Roberts, E Ernest). *Gwasg Gee. £1.50* ATQ/E(P) (B78-33170)

Robin, Jacqueline. Mozart : morçeaux choisis a l'usage des mains petites de la 2e année de piano (assez facile) a la moyenne difficulté. (Mozart, Wolfgang Amadeus). *Chappell. Unpriced* QPJ (B78-51015)

Robinson, Michael Finlay. Opera before Mozart. 3rd ed. *Hutchinson. £3.25* AC(XE182) (B78-40352)
ISBN 0-09-136221-0

Robinson, Paul. Stokowski. *Macdonald and Jane's. £4.95* A/EC(P) (B78-01681)   ISBN 0-354-04232-7

Robson, Alan. Newe teutsche Lieder, mit viern, fünff, und sechs Stimmen. *Selections.* Eight lieder, 1570 : for four voices or instruments, ATTBB. (Vento, Ivo de). *London Pro Musica. Unpriced* EZDU (B78-50383)

Roche, Renée la. Concerto, bassoon & string orchestra, C major. arr. Concerto C-dur für Fagott, Streicher und Basso continuo. (Fasch, Johann Friedrich). Ausgabe für Fagott und Klavier. *Noetzel : Peters. Unpriced* VWPK/LF (B78-50666)

Rock and roll-blues guitare. (Fanen, Pierre). *Chappell. Unpriced* TS/AC (B78-50268)

Rock music index. (Noyce, John Leonard). *Noyce. £1.20* A/HKR(T) (B78-02933)

Rock 'n roll circus : the illustrated rock concert. (Farren, Mick). *Pierrot Publishing Ltd; 219 Eversleigh Rd, SW11 5UY : Distributed by Big O Publishing Ltd. £3.95* AKDW/HKR/E(M) (B78-31595)   ISBN 0-905310-10-1

Rock of the westies. arr. Rock of the westies : songs from the album. (John, Elton). *Big Pig Music : Music Sales. £1.95* KDW/HKR (B78-50162)

Rock on!
No.1- ; May 1978-. *IPC Magazines. £0.25* A/HKQ(B) (B78-26241)

Rock record collectors guide. (Anderson, Ian, *b.1946). 77 New Bond St., W.1 : MRP Books. £2.99* A/HKR/FD(WT) (B78-02937)   ISBN 0-905590-04-x

Roddenberry, Gene.
Star trek. *Selections : arr.* Theme from 'Star Trek'. *Warner : Blossom. Unpriced* UMMK/JS (B78-50640)
Star trek. Theme. arr. Theme from Star trek. *Warner Blossom. Unpriced* UMMK/JS (B78-51189)

Rodgers, Richard.
Love me tonight. Mimi. arr. Mimi : SATB chorus and piano. *Warner : Blossom. Unpriced* DW (B78-50746)
The sound of music. Do-re-mi. arr. Do-re-mi. *Chappell. Unpriced* NYFPK/DW (B78-50516)

Rodwell, Bryan. Twelve melodies for organ : twelve favourite Lehár melodies. (Lehár, Franz). *Glocken Verlag. Unpriced* RPVK/DW (B78-51061)

Rogers, Richard. Love me tonight, Mimi. arr. Mimi. *Warner : Blossom. Unpriced* UMMK/DW (B78-50635)

Rognoni, Luigi. The second Vienna school : expressionism and dodecaphony. *J. Calder : Distributed by Calder and Boyars. £12.50* A/D(M/YEM/XLQ51) (B78-06256)
ISBN 0-7145-3528-1

Rolland, Douglas. Company section song book. (Boys' Brigade. *Glasgow Battalion*). *168 Bath St., G.2 : Boys' Brigade, Glasgow Battalion. Unpriced* JFVBDW/AY (B78-50856)

Rolling Thunder logbook. (Shepard, Sam). *Penguin. £1.75* AKDW/HKR/E(P/YT/XQQ) (B78-20439)
ISBN 0-14-004750-6

Romantic music for clarinet, including music by Baerman, Bruch, Gade, Spohr, Weber. *Boosey and Hawkes. Unpriced* VVPK/AAY (B78-50304)

Romantic opera and literary form. (Conrad, Peter, *b.1948). University of California Press. £5.50* AC(Z) (B78-12986)
ISBN 0-520-03258-6

Romantic pieces. Op.75. Four romantic pieces : for violin and piano. (Dvořák, Antonín). *Schirmer. £2.10* SPJ (B78-50589)

Romanza e danza : für Bläser - Oktett (nach J. Meyerbeer). (Bialas, Günter). *Bärenreiter. £3.92* UNN (B78-50641)

Romanzen für Frauenstimmen, Op.69. Tamburin schlägerin. The tambourine player = Tamburin schlägerin : for four-part chorus of women's voices a cappella. (Schumann, Robert). *Schirmer. £0.30* FEZDW (B78-50401)

Römische Orgel von Aquincum (3. Jahrhundert). (Kaba, Melinda). *Bärenreiter. £11.20* AR/B(YGB/XBH) (B78-03580)

Rondo from horn concerto no.3, K.447. (Mozart, Wolfgang Amadeus). *50 Ladbroke Grove, W.11 : Midland Music. Unpriced* WTPK/LW (B78-50317)

Rooley, Anthony. Six anonymous lute solos. *Novello. £0.72* TSPMK/AAY (B78-50623)

Rorem, Ned.
Book of hours : eight pieces for flute and harp. *Boosey and Hawkes. Unpriced* VRPLTQ (B78-51231)

Eight études : for piano. *Boosey and Hawkes. £3.25* QPG (B78-50217)

O magnum mysterium : S.A.T.B. *Boosey and Hawkes. Unpriced* EZDJ/LF (B78-50782)

The oxen : S.A.T.B. *Boosey Hawkes. Unpriced* EZDW/LF (B78-50803)

Shout the glad tidings : S.A.T.B. *Boosey and Hawkes. Unpriced* DM/LF (B78-50735)

Rosamunde. Ballet music. arr. Rosamunde ballet music, no.2. (Schubert, Franz). *Boosey and Hawkes. Unpriced* MK/AH/HM (B78-50183)

Rosamunde ballet music, no.2. (Schubert, Franz). *Boosey and Hawkes. Unpriced* MK/AH/HM (B78-50183)

Rosary songs = Rosenkranzlieder : three poems of Georg Trakl, for soprano, clarinet, viola and piano, Op.9. (Knussen, Oliver). *Faber Music. Unpriced* KFLE/NUVNTDW (B78-50893)

Rose, Al. New Orleans jazz : a family album. Revised ed.. *Louisiana State University Press. £17.50* AMT(YTRN/M) (B78-23597)   ISBN 0-8071-0374-8

Rose, Arnold. The singer and the voice : vocal physiology and technique for singers. 2nd ed. *Scolar Press. £8.00* AB/E (B78-36279)   ISBN 0-85967-446-0

Rosen, Jelka. Sea drift. (Delius, Frederick). *Boosey and Hawkes. Unpriced* EMDX (B78-50032)

Rosenberg, Steve. Recorder playing. *Prince Milburn Music : Boosey and Hawkes. Unpriced* VS/AC (B78-51238)

Rosina. *Selections : arr.* Four songs from 'Rosina'. (Shield, William). *Boosey and Hawkes. Unpriced* KFTDW (B78-50901)

Ross, Anne. Opera guide. (Westerman, Gerhart von). *Sphere. £0.90* AC (B78-05404)   ISBN 0-7221-9004-2

Rossetti, Christina. Singing together
The ferryman ; words by Christina Rossetti. (Wade, Darrell). *16 Anchor Way, Danes Green, Gnosall : Viking. Unpriced* JFDW (B78-50102)

Rossini, Gioacchino Antonio.
Sonata, harp. Sonata, für Harfe, for harp. *Schott. £2.40* TQPME (B78-51133)
Stabat mater. Quando corpus. Quando corpus ... : for four-part chorus of mixed voices. *Roberton. £0.20* EZDJ/LK (B78-50783)

Rota, Nino.
Death on the Nile. Love theme. arr. Love theme from Death on the Nile : piano solo. *EMI. Unpriced* QPK/JR (B78-51033)
The godfather. *Selections : arr.* Themes from The godfather and The godfather, part II. *Warner : Blossom. Unpriced* UMMK/JR (B78-50639)

Rothwell, Evelyn. Sonata, oboe & continuo, op.2, no.1, F major. Sonata no.1 in F for oboe and piano. (Tessarini, Carlo). *Chester Music. Unpriced* VTPE (B78-51266)

Rounds about rounds. *Franklin Watts. Unpriced* FDW/XC/AY (B78-50396)   ISBN 0-531-00125-3

Routh, Francis.
At the round earth's imagined corners : for unaccompanied voices S.M. S.A.T.B. *Radcliffe. Unpriced* EZDH (B78-50774)
Sonata, cello & piano, op.31. Sonata for violoncello and piano. *Arlington Park House, W.4 : Redcliffe Edition. Unpriced* SRPE (B78-51116)

Routley, Erik. The Church and music. Revised ed. *Duckworth. £12.50* AD/LD(X) (B78-30831)
ISBN 0-7156-0062-1

Rouzaud, René. Porgy and Bess. *Selections : arr.* Porgy and Bess. (Gershwin, George). *Chappell. Unpriced* KDW (B78-50442)

Rowland-Jones, A. Introduction to the recorder : a tutor for adults. *Oxford University Press. £1.95* AVS/E (B78-23598)   ISBN 0-19-322341-4

Royal, Timothy. Blues 1, 2 & 3 : for classical guitar. *16 Oldfield Place, Hotwells, Bristol 8 : Shed Music. £0.75* TSPMJ (B78-50272)

Royal Academy of Dancing
Andantino. (Higgins, Norman). *Royal Academy of Dancing. Unpriced* QPH/H (B78-50218)
Butterfly dance, and, Scherzo. (Higgins, Norman). *Royal Academy of Dancing. Unpriced* QPH/H (B78-50219)
Two folk melodies. (Higgins, Norman). *Royal Academy of Dancing. Unpriced* QPH/H (B78-50220)
Waltz in E. (Higgins, Norman). *Royal Academy of Dancing. Unpriced* QPHW/H (B78-50221)

Royal garland : for unaccompanied mixed voices, op.77. (Mathias, William). *Oxford University Press. Unpriced* EZDW (B78-50798)   ISBN 0-19-337440-4

Royal School of Church Music. English church music : a collection of essays
1978. *Addington Palace, Croydon CR9 5AD : Royal School of Church Music. £1.70* AD/LD(YD/D) (B78-29836)   ISBN 0-85402-075-6

Royal School of Church Music. Handbooks. Nicholson, Sydney H. Practical methods in choir training. *Addington Palace, Croydon CR9 5AD : Royal School of Church Music. £0.65* AD/E (B78-01055)
ISBN 0-85402-069-1

Royal School of Church Music.
RSCM chorister training scheme
Part 1. General outline and junior singer training. *Addington Palace, Croydon, Surrey CR9 5AD R.S.C.M.. £0.80* AD/LD/E (B78-22161)
ISBN 0-85402-070-5
Part 1. Senior singer training and chorister training. *Addington Palace, Croydon, Surrey CR9 5AD R.S.C.M.. £0.80* AD/LD/E (B78-22162)
ISBN 0-85402-074-8

Part 2. Handbook for ex-trebles and young choirmen.

Addington Palace, Croydon, Surrey CR9 5AD R.S.C.M.. £0.55 AD/LD/E (B78-22164)
ISBN 0-85402-073-x
Part 2. Training for ex-trebles and young choirmen. *Addington Palace, Croydon, Surrey CR9 5AD R.S.C.M.. £0.80* AD/LD/E (B78-22165)
ISBN 0-85402-071-3

Singing on Saturday : a selection of music and readings. *Royal School of Church Music. £1.90* DGM (B78-50335)

Royer, Alphonse. La favorita : drama in four acts. *140 Strand, WC2R 1HH : G. Schirmer. Unpriced* BDRAC (B78-26887)

RSCM chorister training scheme
Part 1. General outline and junior singer training. (Royal School of Church Music). *Addington Palace, Croydon, Surrey CR9 5AD : R.S.C.M.. £0.80* AD/LD/E (B78-22161)   ISBN 0-85402-070-5
Part 1. Senior singer training and chorister training. (Royal School of Church Music). *Addington Palace, Croydon, Surrey CR9 5AD : R.S.C.M.. £0.80* AD/LD/E (B78-22162)   ISBN 0-85402-074-8

Part 2. Handbook for ex-trebles and young choirmen. (Royal School of Church Music). *Addington Palace, Croydon, Surrey CR9 5AD : R.S.C.M.. £0.55* AD/LD/E (B78-22164)   ISBN 0-85402-073-x
Part 2. Training for ex-trebles and young choirmen. (Royal School of Church Music). *Addington Palace, Croydon, Surrey CR9 5AD : R.S.C.M.. £0.80* AD/LD/E (B78-22165)   ISBN 0-85402-071-3

Rubank symphonic band library.
Walters, Harold L. The third century : concert march. *Rubank : Novello. Unpriced* UMMGM (B78-50279)
Williams, Clifton. Songs of heritage : symphonic band. *Rubank : Novello. Unpriced* UMMJ (B78-51185)

Rubbra, Edmund.
Agnus Dei. Jesus, Lamb of God : op.143. *Lengnick. £0.12* EZDH (B78-50775)
Emblem XI. How shall my tongue express ...? : Motet. *Lengnick. £0.18* EZDH (B78-50372)
Meditations on a Byzantine hymn. Op.117a. arr. Meditations on a Byzantine hymn 'O quando in croce', op.117a. *Lengnick. Unpriced* SQNUK (B78-51108)
Symphony, no.10, op.145, 'Sinfonia da camera'. Sinfonia da camera. Symphony no.10 in one movement, op.145. *Lengnick. Unpriced* MME (B78-50919)

Rucker, Manuel. Doce canciones = Twelve songs : with guitar accompaniment. (Moretti, Federico). Complete facsimile ed. *Tecla. Unpriced* KE/TSDW (B78-50885)
ISBN 0-8494-0140-2

Runaways : a musical play for children. (Oliver, Donald). *Chappell. Unpriced* CN (B78-50707)

Running a disco. (Swindells, Adrienne P). *Hart-Davis Educational. £0.65* A/FF/ER (B78-15126)
ISBN 0-247-12630-6

Runswick, Daryl. 'Suite and low' : for double basses. *Yorke. Unpriced* SSNSG (B78-51123)

Rural Music Schools Association.
For joy that we are here : Rural Music Schools, 1929-1950. (Ibberson, Mary). *Bedford Square Press for the Rural Music Schools Association. £2.75* A(V/YD/XN31) (B78-03572)   ISBN 0-7199-0930-9
The Suzuki investigation in Hertfordshire : a report of the investigation, sponsored by the Calouste Gulbenkian Foundation and by the Leverhulme Trust, into the feasibility of introducing the Suzuki Talent Education method of teaching the violin into state schools in Britain. *Bedford Square Press. Unpriced* AS(VG/YDED) (B78-38994)   ISBN 0-7199-0941-4

Rush, Leonard.
The paleface. Buttons and bows. arr. Buttons and bows. (Livingston, Jay). *Warner : Blossom. Unpriced* UMMK/DW/JR (B78-51188)
Star trek. Theme. arr. Theme from Star trek. (Roddenberry, Gene). *Warner : Blossom. Unpriced* UMMK/JS (B78-51189)

Russell, Leslie. Rosina. *Selections : arr.* Four songs from 'Rosina'. (Shield, William). *Boosey and Hawkes. Unpriced* KFTDW (B78-50901)

Russell-Smith, Geoffry. Start making music : a primary teacher's guide : a complete self tutor for the absolute beginner - with instructional tape recording, reading, playing and teaching music for the non-specialist primary teacher. *Universal Edition. £6.00* AXT/E(VG) (B78-12102)   ISBN 0-900938-48-x

Russian school of piano playing
Vol.1. (Nikolaev, Aleksandr Aleksandrovich). English ed. *Boosey and Hawkes. Unpriced* Q/AC (B78-50962)
Vol.2. (Nikolaev, Aleksandr Aleksandrovich). English ed. *Boosey and Hawkes. Unpriced* Q/AC (B78-50963)

Rust, Brian Arthur Lovell. London musical shows on record, 1897-1976. *177 Kenton Rd, Harrow, Middx HA3 0HA : General Gramophone Publications Ltd. £11.00* ACM/FD(XL596) (B78-02935)   ISBN 0-902470-07-8

Rust, Friedrich Wilhelm.
Aria and variations, viola d'amore & cello, Czach 90, D major. Aria and VII variations : for viola d'amore and cello. *Little Margaret, Penmans Green, Chipperfield : Ian White. Unpriced* SQQPLSR/T (B78-50599)
Sonata, viola d'amore & keyboard, Czach 87, D major. Sonata for viola d'amore and harpsichord. *Little Margaret, Penmans Green, Chipperfield : Ian White. Unpriced* SQQPE (B78-50598)

Rutherford, Paris. Music speaks louder than words. arr. Music speaks louder than words : SATB chorus and piano with optional guitar, bass and drums. (Payne,

Harold). *Warner : Blossom. Unpriced* DW (B78-50352)
Rutherford, Pat. Love me tonight. Mimi. *arr.* Mimi : SATB chorus and piano. (Rodgers, Richard). *Warner : Blossom. Unpriced* DW (B78-50746)
Rutland, Jonathan Patrick. The clarinet. *F. Watts. £1.95* AVV/B (B78-50000) ISBN 0-85166-641-8
Rutter, John. Five traditional songs. *Oxford University Press. Unpriced* EZDW/AYC (B78-50800) ISBN 0-19-343717-1
Sachs, Harvey. Toscanini. *Weidenfeld and Nicolson. £10.00* A/EC(P) (B78-38607) ISBN 0-297-77492-1
Sackman, Nicholas. A pair of wings. *Schott. £5.00* JNFLDE/NYEXPNQDW (B78-50439)
Sacrae symphoniae. Bk.1. Sonata pian'e forte. Sonata pian'e forte : for brass octet. (Gabrieli, Giovanni). *Chester Music. Unpriced* WNNE (B78-51333)
Sadie, Stanley.
Fantasia and sonata, piano, K.475, K.457, C minor. Fantasia and sonata in C minor, K.475 and 457. (Mozart, Wolfgang Amadeus). *Associated Board of the Royal Schools of Music. Unpriced* QPE (B78-50993)
Sonata, piano, no.2, K.280, F major. Sonata in F. K.280. (Mozart, Wolfgang Amadeus). *Associated Board of the Royal Schools of Music. Unpriced* QPE (B78-50994)
Saffron Walden Society of Change Ringers. (Stacey, Harold Clifford). *Saffron Walden Society of Change Ringers; 36 Great Clarendon St., Oxford : Distributed by J. Hannon & Co. £3.50* AXSR/E(YDDES/QB) (B78-16903)
Saint Martha and the dragon. *Vocal score.* Saint Martha and the dragon : a dramatic legend set to music, for narrator, soprano and tenor soloists, chorus, children's chorus (with percussion) and chamber orchestra. (Tate, Phyllis). *Oxford University Press. Unpriced* DE (B78-50718) ISBN 0-19-338397-7
St Martin's organ series.
Charpentier, Marc Antoine. Te Deum, D major. Prelude. *arr.* Trumpet tune. *J.B. Cramer. £0.45* RK (B78-51054)
Marcello, Benedetto. Estro poetico-armonico. d Salmo 18. *arr.* 'The heavens devlare the glory of God'. *Cramer. Unpriced* RK/DR (B78-51056)
Saint-Saëns, Camille. Le carnaval des animaux. Le cygne. *arr.* The swan ... : violoncello and piano. *Leonard, Gould and Bolttler. £0.50* SRPK (B78-50266)
Salaman, William.
Class in concert : graded music for classroom orchestra
Grade A. *7 Garrick St., W.C.2 : Middle Eight Music. Unpriced* MJ (B78-50180)
Grade B. *7 Garrick St., W.C.2 : Middle Eight Music. Unpriced* MJ (B78-50178)
Grade C. *7 Garrick St., W.C.2 : Middle Eight Music. Unpriced* MJ (B78-50914)
Salamander books. Case, Brian. The illustrated encyclopedia of jazz. *27 Old Gloucester St., WC1N 3AF : Salamander Books. £6.95* AMT(C) (B78-22169) ISBN 0-86101-013-2
Sallager, Walter Hermann. Concerto, bassoon & string orchestra, C major. *arr.* Concerto C-dur für Fagott, Streicher und Basso continuo. (Fasch, Johann Friedrich). Ausgabe für Fagott und Klavier. *Noetzel : Peters. Unpriced* VWPK/LF (B78-50666)
Salomo : Solo für Alt-Flöte oder Grosse Flöte aus der Cantate "Der weise Mann" (1977-1978). (Yun, Isang). *Bote und Bock : Schirmer. £1.90* VRPMJ (B78-51235)
Salon Blumenkohl/Monsieur Choufleuri restera chez lui de ... : Buffo-Operette in einem Akt deutsch nach Karl Fr. Wiltmann von Heinz Balthes und Paul Vasil, opéra bouffe en un acte de St. Rémy, E. L'Epine, Hector Crémieux et Ludovic Halévy, musikalische Revision, neue Instrumentation und praktische Bearbeitung von Caspar Richter. (Offenbach, Jacques). *Bote und Bock Associated music. £11.50* CF (B78-50703)
Salvation Army Brass Band Journal (Festival series)
Nos 388-391: Saints of God : song arrangements, by James Curnew. Balm in Gilead : spiritual : by Donald Osgood. Through the Blood of the Lamb : rhapsody by Kenneth Downie. Selection from 'Spirit' arr. Ray Steadman-Allen. *Salvationist Publishing and Supplies. Unpriced* WM/AY (B78-51298)
Salvation Army Brass Band Journal (General series)
Nos 1697-1700: Here at the cross : meditation, by Roy Steadman-Allen. Camp Akatarawa, by Dean Goffin. The call of Christ : cornet solo by Norman Bearcroft, and Aria from concerto grosso. no.12 by Handel, arr. Michael Kenyon. In his hands : selection, by Erik Silfverberg. *Salvationist Publishing and Supplies. Unpriced* WM/AY (B78-50670)
Nos 1705-1708: St John's Citadel : march, by Eric O. Abbott. Christmas comes but once a year, by Brian Bowen. Prelude on 'Govaars', by Ray Steadman-Allen, melody by Gerrit Govaars. A joy untold : euphonium solo, by Terry Camsey. *Salvationist Publishing and Supplies. Unpriced* WM/AY (B78-51299)
Nos.1701-1704: Spirit divine : meditation by Leslie Condon. Selection from 'Glory', by Ray Steadman-Allen, (melodies, John Larsson), Stephanus : hymn-tune arrangement by J. Paul Green. Joyous proclamation : cornet quartet, by Norman Bearcroft. *Salvationist Publishing and Supplies. Unpriced* WM/AY (B78-51300)
Salvation Army Brass Band Journal (Triumph series)
Nos. 813-816: Joyful service : march by Edgar Grinsted. A little Mozart suite, by Ken Griffin. Whiter than snow : meditation by Terry Camsey. Thetford march : by Charles Craig. *Salvationist Publishing and Supplies. Unpriced* WM/AY (B78-50310)
Nos 821-824: Sing to God ; selection by Ralph Pearce. Kum ba yah ; spiritual by Ray Steadman-Allen. Listowel : march, by Dirk Krommenhoek. Forward to victory, by E.A. Smith. *Salvationist Publishing and Supplies. Unpriced* WM/AY (B78-51301)
Nos.817-820: When the glory gets into your soul, by John Larsson, arr. Ray Steadman-Allen. Variations on 'Duke Street', by Michael Kenyon. Our Father God : selection, by Derek Jordan. A song of fight : euphonium solo, by Erik Silferberg. *Salvationist Publishing and Supplies. Unpriced* WM/AY (B78-51302)
Sammlung kleiner Stücke für Violoncello = Collection of small pieces for violoncello : duets and solos from the 18th century
Vol.2: 1st to 4th position. *Schott. £4.00* SRNU/AY (B78-50264)
Sämtliche Kirchensonaten = Complete church sonatas III/IV: Zwei Sonaten in C für Orgel und Orchester, KV278 (271e), KV329 (317a) : Generalbassausetzung, Werner Bittinger. (Mozart, Wolfgang Amadeus). *Bärenreiter. £2.80* MPRE/AZ (B78-50498)
Sanctus : double chorus and piano or organ from the opera 'The masque of angels'. (Argento, Dominick). *Boosey and Hawkes. Unpriced* DGE (B78-50721)
Sander, Peter Southwell-. *See* Southwell-Sander, Peter.
Sándor, György. Sonata, violin. *Selections : arr.* Tempo di ciaccona and fuga. (Bartók, Béla). *Boosey and Hawkes. £3.00* QPK/AHJN (B78-50560)
Sappho. Notturni : für sechs Singstimmen, Violine, Klarinette, Schlaginstramente. (Terzakis, Dimitri). *Bärenreiter. £16.80* JNAZE/NYEVDW (B78-50437)
Sarabande and air : for keyboard. (Handel, George Frideric). *Banks Music. Unpriced* QPJ (B78-51012)
Sarabande and gavotte ... (Grieg, Edvard). *Banks Music. Unpriced* VSNSK/AH (B78-50296)
Sass im Wald ein Ungetier : Kinderschule für Gitarre
Band 1: Ein Lehr- und Spielbuch, für Kinder abs Jahven im Einzel-oder Gruppenunterricht. (Skiera, Ehrenhard). *Bärenreiter. £4.20* TS/AC (B78-51141)
Saudade : for guitar. (Branson, David). *Helicon. Unpriced* TSPMJ (B78-51152)
Sávic, Isaías. Luar do sertão. *arr.* Luar do sertão. (Cearense, Catallo da Paixão). *Arthur Napoleão : Essex Music. Unpriced* SPMK (B78-50594)
Sawyer, David. Vibrations : making unorthodox musical instruments. *Cambridge University Press. £4.00* AY/BC (B78-04323) ISBN 0-521-20812-2
Saxophone quartets
Vol.1. *Chester Music. Unpriced* VUNSK/AAY (B78-51272)
Saxton, Robert.
Reflections of Narziss and Goldmund : for two chamber groups, harp and piano or celesta. *Chester Music. Unpriced* MRJ (B78-50943)
What does the song hope for? : for soprano, ensemble and tape. *Chester Music. Unpriced* KFLE/NUPNPDX (B78-50892)
Sayer, Michael. BIOS journal
Vol.1 : 1977. (British Institute of Organ Studies). *130 Southfield Rd, Oxford OX4 1PA : Positif Press. Unpriced* AR(B) (B78-20443) ISBN 0-9503892-8-5
Scales and arpeggios (and how they are played) : for the guitar. (Wright, Francis). *Charnwood Music. Unpriced* TS/AF (B78-50604)
SCAM. *See* Standing Conference for Amateur Music.
Scanners. Swindells, Adrienne P. Running a disco. *Hart-Davis Educational. £0.65* A/FF/ER (B78-15126) ISBN 0-247-12630-6
Scarlatti, Alessandro. Il tigrane. *Selections : arr.* Suite ... for 2 descant, treble (or tenor) recorders. *Chester Music. Unpriced* VSNTK (B78-51249)
Scarpiello, Michael. Music speaks louder than words. *arr.* Music speaks louder than words : SATB chorus and piano with optional guitar, bass and drums. (Payne, Harold). *Warner : Blossom. Unpriced* DW (B78-50352)
Schaefer, Will. Fanfare and processional : for concert band. *Schirmer. £18.20* UMMJ (B78-51182)
Schafer, R Murray. Ezra Pound and music : the complete criticism. (Pound, Ezra). *Faber. £25.00* A/CC(P) (B78-08474) ISBN 0-571-11233-1
Scharnagl, August. Concerto, piano, no.1, op.20, C major. *arr.* Erstes Konzert C-Dur, Ut majeur, für Klavier mit 2 Oboen, 2 Hörnern und Streichern, op.20. (Sterkel, Franz Xaver). *Schott. £10.00* MPQF (B78-50192)
Scheidt, Samuel. Paduana, galliarda .... Cantus 18. Canzon cornetto : for four trumpets. *Chester Music. Unpriced* WSNS (B78-51342)
Scherzetto. (Wills, Arthur). *Cramer. Unpriced* RJ (B78-50231)
Schickhard, Johann Christian.
L'alphabet de la musique, Op.30 : 24 sonatas in all the keys for treble recorder and basso continuo in 6 volumes
Vol.1: Nos 1-4. *Musica rara. Unpriced* VSSPE (B78-50655)
L'alphabet de la musique. Op.30 : 24 sonatas in all the keys for treble recorder and basso continuo in 6 volumes
Vol.2: Sonatas 5-8. *Musica rara. £6.50* VSSPE (B78-51259)
Sonatas, treble recorder & continuo, op.17, nos 5,9. Sonatas op.17, nos 5 and 9 for treble recorder and basso continuo. *Musica rara. Unpriced* VSSPE (B78-50656)
Sonatas, treble recorder & continuo, op.17, nos 10,11. Sonatas op.17, nos 10 and 11 for treble recorder and basso continuo. *Musica rara. Unpriced* VSSPE (B78-50657)
Sonatas, treble recorder & continuo, op.17, nos.1-2. Sonatas op.17, nos 1 and 2, for treble recorder and basso continuo. *Musica rara. Unpriced* VSSPE (B78-50658)
Schirmer (G) *(Firm).* Collection of opera librettos. *See* G. Schirmer's collection of opera librettos.
Schirmer's edition of study scores of orchestral works and chamber music. Fussell, Charles. Three processionals : for orchestra. *Schirmer. £5.45* MMJ (B78-50490)
Schirmer's library of musical classics. Dvořák, Antonín. Romantic pieces. Op.75. Four romantic pieces : for violin and piano. *Schirmer. £2.10* SPJ (B78-50589)
Schirmer's singer's library : arias for baritone
Vol.1. *Schirmer. Unpriced* KGNDW/AY (B78-50478)
Schirmer's singer's library : arias for bass
Vol.1. *Schirmer. Unpriced* KGXDW/AY (B78-50480)
Schirmer's singer's library : arias for mezzo-soprano and alto
Vol.1. *Schirmer. Unpriced* KFNDW/AY (B78-50473)
Schirmer's singer's library : arias for soprano
Vol.1. *Schirmer. Unpriced* KFLDW/AY (B78-50470)
Schirmer's singer's library : arias for tenor
Vol.1. *Schirmer. Unpriced* KGHDW/AY (B78-50477)
Schlaginstrumente = Percussion instruments : a method of instruction
Teil 2: Pauken = Timpani. (Keune, Eckehardt). *Bärenreiter. £7.00* X/AC (B78-50696)
Schlumpf, Martin. Monolog 1 : für Violoncello solo (1976). *Bote und Bock : Schirmer. £5.75* SRPMJ (B78-51120)
Schmidt, Harvey. The fantasticks. *Vocal score.* The fantasticks : book and lyrics by Tom Jones. Revised ed. *Chappell. Unpriced* CM (B78-50327)
Schmitt, Meinrad. Trio, trumpet, bassoon & tuba. Trio für Trompete, Posaune und Tuba. *Bote und Bock Associated Music. £3.85* WNT (B78-50691)
Schneider, Willy. Ein Sommertag : Suite für Bläsorchester. *Schott. £20.00* UMMG (B78-51176)
Schoenberg, Arnold. Theory of harmony. *Faber : Faber Music. £22.50 : CIP rev.* A/R (B78-12985) ISBN 0-571-10933-0
Scholey, Arthur. Singalive! : twelve songs and a cakewalk. (Swann, Donald). *Collins. Unpriced* KDW (B78-50862) ISBN 0-00-599605-8
Schönster Schatz leb wohl eine Reise durch Deutschland mit Volksliedern und Tänzen : für Männerchor, zwei Klarinetten oder andere Holzbläser, Streicher oder Tasteninstrumente und Schlagzeug, Gitarre ad lib. *Schott. £5.20* GE/NYDPDW/G/AYE (B78-50071)
Schonthal, Ruth. Four epiphanies : for unaccompanied viola. *Oxford University Press. Unpriced* SQPMJ (B78-50262)
School Library Association. Book lists. Grindea, Carola. Music books for schools : an annotated list. *School Library Association. £1.30(£0.90 to members)* A(VC/T) (B78-18775) ISBN 0-900641-30-4
School of English Church Music. *See* Royal School of Church Music.
School of Oriental and African Studies. *See* University of London. *School of Oriental and African Studies.*
School recorder assembly book for pupils. *E.J. Arnold. Unpriced* VSRPMK/AAY (B78-51257) ISBN 0-560-00379-x
Schott (B.) *(Firm).* Lieder und Volksmusik aus der Tschechoslowakei : Materialien für den Musikunterricht in den Sekundarstufen. (Tschache, Helmut). *Schott. £4.80* AKDW/G(YF) (B78-33161)
Schott's Chorverlag. Schönster Schatz leb wohl eine Reise durch Deutschland mit Volksliedern und Tänzen : für Männerchor, zwei Klarinetten oder andere Holzbläser, Streicher oder Tasteninstrumente und Schlagzeug, Gitarre ad lib. *Schott. £5.20* GE/NYDPDW/G/AYE (B78-50071)
Schroeder, Felix.
Concerto, violins (2) & string orchestra, G minor. Concerto für zwei Violinen, Streicher und Basso continuo G moll. (Telemann, Georg Philipp). Zum ersten Mal herausgegeben von Felix Schroeder. *Litolff : Peters. Unpriced* RXMPSNUF (B78-50577)
Concerto, violins (2) & string orchestra, G minor. *arr.* Concerto für zwei Violinen, Streicher, und Basso continuo G-moll. (Telemann, Georg Philipp). Ausgabe für zwei Violinen und Klavier von Herausgeber. Zum ersten Mal herausgegeben von Felix Schroeder. *Litolff : Peters. Unpriced* SNTQK/LF (B78-50587)
Schubert, Franz.
3 Schubert dances. *7 Garrick St., W.C.2 : Middle Eight Music. Unpriced* VNSK/AH (B78-50287)
Das stille Lied : für vier Männerstimmen = for four men's voices. Erstausgabe. *Bärenreiter. £0.90* GEZDW (B78-50830)
Franz Schubert Lieder
Heft 3: Lieder nach Texten von Goethe, für mittlere Stimme. *Bärenreiter. £4.80* KFVDW (B78-50903)
Rosamunde. Ballet music. *arr.* Rosamunde ballet music, no.2. *Boosey and Hawkes. Unpriced* MK/AH/HM (B78-50183)
Sonatas, piano. Complete pianoforte sonatas, including the unfinished works
Vol.1. *Associated Board of the Royal Schools of Music. Unpriced* QPE/AZ (B78-50996)
Valses nobles, D.969. *Selections: arr.* Valses nobles, opus 77. *Schott. £4.65* RXMK/AHW (B78-50248)
Schumann, Robert.
Clavierstücke für die Jugend. Op.68. *Selections : arr.* A Schumann suite : seven pieces from 'Album for the young'. opus 68. *Novello. Unpriced* VVNSK (B78-51276)
Romanzen für Frauenstimmen, Op.69. Tamburin schlägerin. The tambourine player = Tamburin schlägerin : for four-part chorus of women's voices a cappella. *Schirmer. £0.30* FEZDW (B78-50401)
Schumann suite : seven pieces from 'Album for the young'. opus 68. (Schumann, Robert). *Novello. Unpriced* VVNSK (B78-51276)
Schütz, Heinrich. Psalmen Davids sampt etlichen Moteten und Concerten. Alleluia. Alleluia. Lobet den Herren = Alleluia. Worship Jehovah : for 8 solo voices and double choir, with instruments. *Oxford University Press. Unpriced* ENWXPDR (B78-50358) ISBN 0-19-338088-9

Schwartz, Arthur. That's entertainment. That's entertainment. *arr.* That's entertainment : S.S.A. with piano. *Chappell. Unpriced* FDW/JR (B78-50817)
Schwartz, Charles. Cole Porter : a biography. *W.H. Allen. £6.50* BPNN(N) (B78-22845) ISBN 0-491-02292-1
Schwartz, Stephen. The magic show. *Selections : arr.* The magic show : vocal selection ... *Belwin Mills. Unpriced* KDW (B78-50446)
Schweizer, Klaus. Klappentexte : für Flöte oder Piccolo und Oboe oder English Horn, 1976. *Bärenreiter. £8.96* VNU (B78-50647)
Schweizer, Rolf. Spirituals fur Blechbläser : bearbeitet von Rolf Schweizer. *Bärenreiter. £2.80* WNK/DW/LC (B78-50688)
Science at work. Kenney, A R. Sounds of music. *Nelson. £0.45* A/B (B78-29834) ISBN 0-17-438332-0
Scott, Jack Cassin-. *See* Cassin-Scott, Jack.
Scott, Michael. The record of singing to 1914. *Duckworth. £12.50* AK/FD(XM15) (B78-03582) ISBN 0-7156-1030-9
Scottish Arts Council. Recordings of artists working in Scotland. *19 Charlotte Sq., Edinburgh EH2 4DF : The Council. Unpriced* A/FD(YDL) (B78-35031) ISBN 0-902989-45-6
Scottish National Orchestra. SNO scene
No.1- ; June 1977-. *150 Hope St., Glasgow G2 2TH : Scottish National Orchestra Society. £3.00 yearly* AMM/E(QB/B) (B78-06989)
Scottish National Orchestra Society. SNO scene
No.1- ; June 1977-. (Scottish National Orchestra). *150 Hope St., Glasgow G2 2TH : Scottish National Orchestra Society. £3.00 yearly* AMM/E(QB/B) (B78-06989)
Sculthorpe, Peter.
Lament : for strings. *Faber Music. Unpriced* RXMJ (B78-51068)
Quartet, strings, no.8. String quartet, no.8. 2nd ed. *Faber Music. £2.00* RXNS (B78-50255)
Quartet, strings, no.9. String quartet no.9. *Faber Music. £2.00* RXNS (B78-51083)
Quartet, strings, no.9. String quartet no.9. *Faber Music. £6.00* RXNS (B78-51084)
Sea drift. (Delius, Frederick). *Boosey and Hawkes. Unpriced* EMDX (B78-50032)
Sea of faith, Dover Beach. (Hemingway, Roger). *Novello. £0.45* DH (B78-50726)
Sea pictures : fifteen easy piano duets in two sets
Set 1. (Wells, Elsie). *Oxford University Press. Unpriced* QNV (B78-50212) ISBN 0-19-373947-x
Set 2. (Wells, Elsie). *Oxford University Press. Unpriced* QNV (B78-50213) ISBN 0-19-373948-8
Sea shanties. (Hugill, Stan). *Barrie and Jenkins. £2.95* ADW/GMC (B78-01680) ISBN 0-214-20329-8
Search me O God. (Parker, Alice). *Roberton. £0.18* FDH (B78-50389)
Sechs Episoden aus einer unterbrochenen Chronik. 6 Episoden aus einer unterbrochenen Chronik = 6 episodes from a discontinued chronicle : Klavier = for piano : op.20. (Gruber, Heinz Karl). *Boosey and Hawkes. Unpriced* QPJ (B78-51011)
Sechs Stücke : für Kontrabass solo, Op.68. (Klebe, Giselher). *Bärenreiter. £2.70* SSPMJ (B78-51130)
Second book of Irish ballads. 3rd ed. *4 Bridge St., Cork : Mercier Press. £1.50* AKDW/K/G(YDM) (B78-37868) ISBN 0-85342-081-5
Second pocket organ tutor. The 2nd pocket organ tutor. (Ashburnham, George). *22 Effingham Close, Sutton, Surrey SM2 6AG : Ashburnham School of Music. £9.14* AR/E (B78-36280)
Second Vienna school : expressionism and dodecaphony. (Rognoni, Luigi). *J. Calder : Distributed by Calder and Boyars. £12.50* A/D(M/YEM/XLQ51) (B78-06256) ISBN 0-7145-3528-1
Secundus tomus musici operis. Ascendo ad Patrem meum. *arr.* Ascendo ad Patrem meum. (Handl, Jacob). *Cathedral Music. Unpriced* GEZDJ/LM (B78-50422)
Seeger, Charles. Studies in musicology, 1935-1975. *University of California Press. £11.75* A(VX/D) (B78-11189) ISBN 0-520-02000-6
Segovia technique. (Bobri, Vladimir). *Collier Books : Collier Macmillan. £4.50* ATS/CY (B78-01056) ISBN 0-02-079240-9
Sei sonate divise in studii e divertimenti. Sei sonate : (studii e divertimenti), per cembalo. (Durante, Francesco). *Bärenreiter. £4.80* QRPE (B78-51038)
Sei sonate : (studii e divertimenti), per cembalo. (Durante, Francesco). *Bärenreiter. £4.80* QRPE (B78-51038)
Selected solos and duets. (Handel, George Frideric). *Ariel Music Sales. £1.50* TSPMK (B78-51163) ISBN 0-86001-378-2
Selected works for one and two lutes with original lute tablature and transcription for the guitar. (Dowland, John). *Ariel : Music Sales. £1.95* TSPMK (B78-51162) ISBN 0-86001-294-8
Selected works : for piano solo. (Liszt, Franz). *Schirmer. £3.60* QPJ (B78-50541)
Selected works : for piano solo. (Mozart, Wolfgang Amadeus). *Schirmer. £3.60* QPJ (B78-50544)
Selection of musical instruments to make for children. (Goddard, Arthur). *Trident House, Brooks Mews, W1Y 2PN : Trident Television Ltd. £0.25* AX/BC (B78-05413)
Selections. *arr.* Capirola lute book : seven pieces, guitar solo. (Capirola, Vincenzo). *Universal. Unpriced* TSPMK (B78-51161)
Selections from the gutter : jazz portraits from the 'Jazz record'. *University of California Press. £8.75* AMT/FD(M) (B78-05409) ISBN 0-520-02999-2
Senior singer training and chorister training. RSCM chorister training scheme
Part 1. Senior singer training and chorister training. (Royal School of Church Music). *Addington Palace, Croydon, Surrey CR9 5AD : R.S.C.M.. £0.80* AD/LD/E (B78-22162) ISBN 0-85402-074-8
Sequence for All Saints : for SATB choir, baritone solo and organ, words from English Hymnal 731. (Leighton, Kenneth). *Roberton. £1.20* DE/LQ (B78-50719)
Serenade für Flöte und Gitarre. (Zehm, Friedrich). *Schott. £6.00* VRPLTS (B78-50293)
Serial composition and atonality : an introduction to the music of Schoenberg, Berg and Webern. (Perle, George). 4th ed., revised. *University of California Press. £8.75* A/PN (B78-16384) ISBN 0-520-03395-7
Series for school and amateur orchestra.
Latin-Americana : a selection of famous melodies and rhythms. *Bosworth and Co. £3.50* MK/AH/AYU (B78-50182)
Strauss, Johann, *b.1825.* Erinnerung an Covent Garden. Op.329. *arr.* Memories of Covent Garden = Erinnerung an Covent Garden : waltz, op.329, based on English music hall songs. *Bosworth & Co. Unpriced* MK/AHW (B78-50486)
Seven anthems. (Elgar, *Sir* Edward, *bart*). *Novello. £1.30* DH (B78-50725)
Seven part-songs for female voices and strings. (Holst, Gustav). Revised ed. 1973. *Novello. Unpriced* FE/RXNRDW (B78-50821)
Seven secular pieces : for four voices or instruments, ATTB. (Josquin des Prés). *London Pro Musica. Unpriced* EZDU (B78-50382)
Sex Pistols : the inside story. *Star Books. £0.75* AKDW/HKQ/E(P) (B78-35475) ISBN 0-426-18585-4
Shakespeare, William. The phoenix and the turtle. *Vocal score.* The phoenix and the turtle : for mezzo-soprano solo, SATB timpani (2) and string orchestra. (Hurd, Michael). *Novello. £0.78* DX (B78-50029)
Shapeshifter : for horn and piano. (McCabe, John). *Novello. £1.80* WTPJ (B78-51351)
Shaping forces in music : an inquiry into the nature of harmony, melody, counterpoint, form. (Toch, Ernst). 1st ed., reprinted. *Dover Publications : Constable. £2.50* A/LZ (B78-06255) ISBN 0-486-23346-4
Shapiro, Elliott. Handbook of early American sheet music, 1768-1889. (Dichter, Harry). *Dover Publications etc. : Constable. £4.70* A(TC/YT/XFYH22) (B78-30339) ISBN 0-486-23364-2
Shapiro, Nat. An encyclopedia of quotations about music. *David and Charles. £6.95 : CIP rev.* A(DD) (B78-19438) ISBN 0-7153-7611-x
Sharing sounds : musical experiences with young children. (Evans, David, *b.1940 (May)*). *Longman. Unpriced* A/GJ (B78-31364) ISBN 0-582-25006-4
Sharkey, Jack.
'Not the Count of Monte Cristo?!' : a musical comedy in three acts for 3 players and a piano. (Reiser, Dave). *French. £1.65* BSGNHACM (B78-12096) ISBN 0-573-68085-x
Pushover : a choral play in one act about Samson, Judge of Israel. (Easton, Ken). *French. £1.20* BSGNHACM (B78-03576) ISBN 0-573-62425-9
Turnabout : a musical version of the Book of Esther. (Easton, Ken). French's acting ed.. *French. £1.65* BSGNHACM (B78-20438) ISBN 0-573-62527-1
Sharp, Cecil. O waly waly : for SSA unaccompanied, Somerset folk song. (Phillips, John Charles). *Roberton. £0.12* FEZDW (B78-50400)
Sharpe, E P. Praise for today. *Psalms and Hymns Trust. Unpriced* DM/AY (B78-50734)
Shavitz, Carl.
Mirror of love : lute songs of love and lust. *Chester Music. Unpriced* KE/TWDW/AY (B78-50887)
What is love? : songs for voice, lute and viola da gamba. *Chester Music. Unpriced* KE/STPLTWDW (B78-50884)
Shaw, Watkins. God is gone up with a merry noise : full anthem with verse for SSAATB. (Croft, William). *Novello. £0.43* DK (B78-50343)
Shealy, Alexander.
Beloved Scotch & Irish songs & ballads. *Ashley : Phoenix. Unpriced* KDW/AYDM (B78-50120)
Das wohltemperirte Clavier. Well tempered clavier = Wohltemperiertes Clavier : forty-eight preludes and fugues, for the piano. (Bach, Johann Sebastian). *Ashley Phoenix. Unpriced* QP/Y (B78-50989)
Sheep may safely graze. (Bach, Johann Sebastian). *Oxford University Press. Unpriced* VRNTQK/DW (B78-50289) ISBN 0-19-355280-9
Sheldon, Robin. Anglican hymn book : Robin Sheldon, musical editor. Revised ed., with supplement. *Wine Office Court, E.C.4 : Vine Books. £4.85* DM/LSD/AY (B78-50736)
She'll be comin' round the mountain : American folk song, for full chorus of mixed voices unaccompanied. (De Cormier, Robert). *Roberton. £0.32* EZDW (B78-50051)
Shepard, Sam. Rolling Thunder logbook. *Penguin. £1.75* AKDW/HKR/E(P/YT/XQQ) (B78-20439) ISBN 0-14-004750-6
Shepherd, John. The Western Wind mass. *Chester Music. Unpriced* EZDG (B78-50768)
Shepherd, John, *b.1520.*
Haec dies. *Oxenford Imprint : Blackwell's Music Shop. Unpriced* EZDJ/LL (B78-50784)
Libera nos, salva nos : two settings. *Oxenford : Blackwell's Music Shop (dist.). Unpriced* EZDJ (B78-50778)
Paschal Kyrie. *Oxenford Imprint : Blackwell's Music Shop. Unpriced* EZDGB (B78-50770)
Shepherd, shepherd : spiritual for full chorus of mixed voices unaccompanied. (West, John A). *Roberton. £0.20* EZDW/LC (B78-50801)
Shepherd's calendar : choral symphony for baritone solo, SATB and orchestra. (Hurd, Michael). *Novello. £1.45* DX (B78-50354)
Shepherd's calendar. *Vocal score.* Shepherd's calendar : choral symphony for baritone solo, SATB and orchestra. (Hurd, Michael). *Novello. £1.45* DX (B78-50354)
Shield, William. Rosina. *Selections : arr.* Four songs from 'Rosina'. *Boosey and Hawkes. Unpriced* KFTDW (B78-50901)
Shields, Jim. Bob Dylan : an illustrated discography. (Hoggard, Stuart). *113 Thame Rd, Oxford : Transmedia Express. £1.90* AKDW/HKR/FD(P/WT) (B78-17915) ISBN 0-906344-00-x
Short Communion service : for ATB and organ. (Doveton, Robin). *Cathedral Music. Unpriced* GDGS (B78-50406)
Short service for men. Benedicite. Benedicite ... (Batten, Adrian). *36 Ranelagh Gdns., W.6 : Cathedral Music. Unpriced* GEZDGNR (B78-50415)
Short stories : für elf Bläser. (Wimberger, Gerhard). *Bärenreiter. £4.20* UMJ (B78-51175)
Shostakovich symphonies. (Ottaway, Hugh). *British Broadcasting Corporation. £1.00* BSGRAMME (B78-28701) ISBN 0-563-12772-4
Shout the glad tidings : S.A.T.B. (Rorem, Ned). *Boosey and Hawkes. Unpriced* DM/LF (B78-50735)
Showdown and other songs. (Gallagher, Benny). *Rondor Music : Music Sales. Unpriced* KDW/GB (B78-50128)
Sibley, R. With cheerful voice : hymns for children with melodies, descant recorder parts, and prayers. 2nd ed. revised and enlarged. *A. & C. Black. Unpriced* JFADM (B78-50086) ISBN 0-7136-1368-8
Sicilienne from Pelléas et Melisande : for flute and piano. (Fauré, Gabriel). *Chester Music. Unpriced* VRPK/AHVQ/JM (B78-51221)
Sidney Harrison adult piano tutor. (Harrison, Sidney). *Chappell. Unpriced* Q/AC (B78-50961)
Sieben Sterne : for organ. (Ferneyhough, Brian). *Peters. Unpriced* RJ (B78-50230)
Siebert, Edrich.
Bees-a-buzzin'. *Harmar : Studio Music. Unpriced* WMJ (B78-50678)
The bombastic bombardon : solo for E flat bass and brass band. *Harmer Music : Studio Music. Unpriced* WMPWX (B78-50686)
Le camp de Grand-Pré. Tambourin. *arr.* Tambourin : solo for B flat cornet. (Gossec, François Joseph). *Studio Music. Unpriced* WMPWRK/AHVQT (B78-51329)
Drummer's delight : drum feature. *Studio Music. Unpriced* WMJ (B78-51313)
Gipsy wedding. *Harmer Music : Studio Music. Unpriced* WMH (B78-50676)
The queen's trumpeters : concert march. *Harmer Music. Unpriced* WMGM (B78-50675)
Sunday morning. *Harmer : Studio Music. Unpriced* WMJ (B78-50679)
Warriors three : trio for B flat cornets and brass band. *Harmer : Studio Music. Unpriced* WMPWRNTHVH (B78-50684)
Siena : for cello and piano. (Heiden, Bernhard). *Associated Music. £3.05* SRPJ (B78-50601)
Sigurd Jorsalfar. Op.56. Homage march. *arr.* Homage march. (Grieg, Edvard). *Oxford University Press. Unpriced* MK/AGM (B78-50485) ISBN 0-19-363848-7
Silent night : all organ. (Gruber, Franz). *Chappell. Unpriced* RK/DP/LF (B78-50236)
Silly things to sing. (Smith, Pat). *E.J. Arnold. Unpriced* JFDW/GJ (B78-50846) ISBN 0-560-02726-5
'Silmarillion' : a symphonic prelude after J.R.R. Tolkien ; for orchestra. (Newton, Rodney Stephen). *13 Chetwynd Ave., East Barnet, Herts. : Composer Edition. Unpriced* MMJ (B78-50493)
Silver, Millicent.
Don Giovanni. Deh vieni alla finestra. *arr.* Canzonetta. (Mozart, Wolfgang Amadeus). *Lengnick. £0.60* VRPK/DW (B78-51224)
Drei Albumblätter, no.1. Albumblatt. (Busoni, Ferruccio). *Lengnick. £0.60* VRPK (B78-51219)
Piramo e Tisbe. Tambourin. *arr.* Tambourin. (Hasse, Johann Adolf). *Lengnick. £0.60* VRPK/AHVQT (B78-51222)
Die Zauberflöte. Wie stark ist nicht dein Zauberton. *arr.* Andante. (Mozart, Wolfgang Amadeus). *Lengnick. Unpriced* VRPK/DW (B78-51225)
Silver bells : SATB and piano. (Livingston, Jay). *Warner Blossom. Unpriced* DW (B78-50351)
Silverman, Jerry.
Jest 'fore Christmas. *Schirmer. Unpriced* KDW (B78-50116)
Jest 'fore Christmas : for two-part chorus of young voices with piano and guitar accompaniment. *Schirmer. Unpriced* FDW (B78-50063)
A visit from St Nicholas. (The night before Christmas). *Schirmer. Unpriced* KDW (B78-50117)
Simple ceremony, 'In memorian John Barnes Chance', Op.53 : for symphonic band and unison voices. (Mailman, Martin). *Boosey and Hawkes. Unpriced* JFE/UMMDGF (B78-50854)
Simple mass. Op.282 : for four-part unison chorus and soprano, alto, tenor and bass solos with organ accompaniment. (Hovhaness, Alan). *Associated Music. £1.80* DG (B78-50333)
Simple mass. Op.282. *Vocal score.* Simple mass. Op.282 : for four-part unison chorus and soprano, alto, tenor and bass solos with organ accompaniment. (Hovhaness, Alan). *Associated Music. £1.80* DG (B78-50333)
Simple samba : for descant 1, descant 2, and, or, treble recorder and piano. (Bonsor, Brian). *Schott. Unpriced* VSNTQHVKS (B78-51251)

Simple things : piano, vocal, chords. (King, Carole). *Colgems-EMI : EMI. Unpriced* KDW/GB (B78-50132)
Simpson, Dudley. Blakes 7. *arr.* Blakes 7. *Chappell. Unpriced* QPK/JS (B78-50228)
Simpson, Robert. The essence of Bruckner : an essay towards the understanding of his music. 2nd ed. *Gollancz. £4.95* BBUEAMME (B78-10360) ISBN 0-575-01189-0
Sinatra now. *Chappell. Unpriced* KDW/GB/AY (B78-50877)
Sinatrafile
Part 2: Commercial. (Ridgway, John, *b.1943*). *Miramar, Rowney Green La., Alvechurch, Birmingham B48 7QF : John Ridgway Books. £14.00* AKDW/GB/FD(P) (B78-23594) ISBN 0-905808-02-9
Sinfonia do Rio de Janeiro : piano. (Jobim, Antonio Carlos). *Arapua : Essex Music. Unpriced* QPE (B78-50995)
Sinfonia fidei. *Vocal score.* Sinfonia fidei : a cantata for soprano and tenor soloists, chorus and orchestra. (Hoddinott, Alan). *Oxford University Press. Unpriced* DE (B78-50716) ISBN 0-19-336842-0
Sinfonietta. Telemann, Georg Philipp. Concerto, violins (2) & string orchestra, G minor. Concerto für zwei Violinen, Streicher und Basso continuo G moll. Zum ersten Mal herausgegeben von Felix Schroeder. *Litolff : Peters. Unpriced* RXMPSNUF (B78-50577)
Sinful tunes and spirituals : black folk music to the Civil War. (Epstein, Dena J). *University of Illinois Press. £12.60* AKDW/G(YTLD/XA1867)(B78-15754) ISBN 0-252-00520-1
Sing along with Sullivan : a new anthology of music for the voice. (Sullivan, *Sir* Arthur Seymour). *Cramer. Unpriced* KDW (B78-50447)
Sing easy : twelve easy songs for mixed voices. *Oxford University Press. Unpriced* EZDW/AY (B78-50799) ISBN 0-19-330215-2
Sing for joy : ten Christmas carols. *Roberton. £0.28* FEZDP/LF (B78-50825)
Sing for pleasure. Sing easy : twelve easy songs for mixed voices. *Oxford University Press. Unpriced* EZDW/AY (B78-50799) ISBN 0-19-330215-2
Sing the happy song! : (a history of Salvation Army vocal music). (Boon, Brindley). *Salvationist Publishing and Supplies. Unpriced* AD/LSK(X) (B78-34738) ISBN 0-85412-321-0
Sing we now Christmas : traditional French carol for 4-part chorus of female voices unaccompanied. (Miller, Thomas E). *Roberton. £0.20* FEZDP/LF (B78-50399)
Singalive! : twelve songs and a cakewalk. (Swann, Donald). *Collins. Unpriced* KDW (B78-50862) ISBN 0-00-599605-8
Singer, Irving. Mozart & Beethoven : the concept of love in their operas. *Johns Hopkins University Press. £7.00* BMSAC(ZC) (B78-15123) ISBN 0-8018-1987-3
Singer and the voice : vocal physiology and technique for singers. (Rose, Arnold). 2nd ed. *Scolar Press. £8.00* AB/E (B78-36279) ISBN 0-85967-446-0
Singing and dancing games for the very young. (Nelson, Esther L). *Sterling etc. : Distributed by Ward Lock. £3.50* JFDW/GS (B78-50434) ISBN 0-7061-2558-4
Singing together
10 little chickadees. (Wade, Darrell). *16 Anchor Way, Danes Green, Gnosall : Viking. Unpriced* JFDW (B78-50093)
10 little chickadees. (Wade, Darrell). *16 Anchor Way, Danes Green, Gnosall : Viking. Unpriced* JFDW (B78-50432)
Bed in summer ; words by R.L. Stevenson. (Wade, Darrell). *16 Anchor Way, Danes Green, Gnosall : Viking. Unpriced* JFDW (B78-50094)
Bed in summer ; words by R.L. Stevenson. (Wade, Darrell). *16 Anchor Way, Danes Green, Gnosall : Viking. Unpriced* JFDW (B78-50095)
Little Indians all are we. (Wade, Darrell). *16 Anchor Way, Danes Green, Gnosall : Viking. Unpriced* JFDW (B78-50433)
Marching song ; words by R.L. Stevenson. (Wade, Darrell). *16 Anchor Way, Danes Green, Gnosall : Viking. Unpriced* JFDW (B78-50096)
Off to the circus. (Wade, Darrell). *16 Anchor Way, Danes Green, Gnosall : Viking. Unpriced* JFDW (B78-50097)
Rain ; words by R.L. Stevenson. (Wade, Darrell). *16 Anchor Way, Danes Green, Gnosall : Viking. Unpriced* JFDW (B78-50098)
Summer sun ; words by R.L. Stevenson. (Wade, Darrell). *16 Anchor Way, Danes Green, Gnosall : Viking. Unpriced* JFDW (B78-50099)
Swinging along. (Wade, Darrell). *16 Anchor Way, Danes Green, Gnosall : Viking. Unpriced* JFDW (B78-50100)
The 2 rats. (Wade, Darrell). *16 Anchor Way, Danes Green, Gnosall : Viking. Unpriced* JFDW (B78-50101)
The ferryman ; words by Christina Rossetti. (Wade, Darrell). *16 Anchor Way, Danes Green, Gnosall : Viking. Unpriced* JFDW (B78-50102)
The moon ; words by R.L. Stevenson. (Wade, Darrell). *16 Anchor Way, Danes Green, Gnosall : Viking. Unpriced* JFDW (B78-50103)
Window cleaning man ; words by M. Long. (Wade, Darrell). *16 Anchor Way, Danes Green, Gnosall : Viking. Unpriced* JFDW (B78-50104)
Sinner, please don't let this harvest pass : for four-part chorus of mixed voices a cappella. (West, John A). *Roberton. £0.20* EZDW/LC (B78-50802)
Sir Patrick Spens : a ballad for tenor and guitar. (Musgrave, Thea). *Chester Music. Unpriced* KGHE/TSDW (B78-50905)
Six airs irlandois nationales variées, Op.125. (Giuliani, Mauro). *Belwin Mills Music. £1.50* TSPM/T (B78-51147)
Six anonymous lute solos. *Novello. £0.72* TSPMK/AAY (B78-50623)
Six easy three-part anthems. *Royal School of Church Music. Unpriced* EZDH/AY (B78-50373)
Six-part masses. (Taverner, John). *Stainer and Bell. Unpriced* EZDG (B78-50769) ISBN 0-85249-477-7
Six pieces : for organ. (Inness, Peter). *Novello. £2.40* RJ (B78-51048)
Six pieces for the piano. 6 pieces for the piano. Polonaise napolitana. Polonaise napolitana : piano solo. (Dale, Mervyn). *Edwin Ashdown. Unpriced* QPHVHM (B78-51001)
Six pieces in the early grades. (Lambert, Sydney). *Associated Music. £1.20* QPJ (B78-50536)
Six rhymes from Mother Goose : for four-part chorus of mixed voices and piano accompaniment. (Lehár, Franz). *Schirmer. £1.60* DW (B78-50350)
Six solos, Op.4 : for flute or violin and continuo. (Stanley, John). *Chester Music. Unpriced* VRPE (B78-51214)
Six Susato dances : for brass band ... (Susato, Thielman). *Chester Music. Unpriced* WMK/AH (B78-51321)
Sixteen hymns of today for use as simple anthems. *Royal School of Church Music. Unpriced* DM/AY (B78-50345)
Skelton, Geoffrey. Cosima Wagner's diaries
Vol.1: 1869-1877. (Wagner, Cosima). *Collins. £15.00* BWC(N) (B78-34737) ISBN 0-00-216130-3
Skiera, Ehrenhard. Sass im Wald ein Ungetier : Kinderschule für Gitarre
Band 1: Ein Lehr- und Spielbuch, für Kinder abs Jahven im Einzel-oder Gruppenunterricht. *Bärenreiter. £4.20* TS/AC (B78-51141)
Skinner, Alison. Rock music index. (Noyce, John Leonard). *Noyce. £1.20* A/HKR(T) (B78-02933)
Skowronski, JoAnn. Women in American music : a bibliography. *Scarecrow Press : Distributed by Bailey and Swinfen. £6.80* A(Z/T) (B78-24791) ISBN 0-8108-1105-7
Slack, Roy. An introduction to the melodica : a beginner's guide to the melodica with well known tunes to play and sing. *EMI. Unpriced* VXR/AC (B78-51294)
Slana!. *arr.* Slava! : a concert overture. (Bernstein, Leonard). *Amberson : Boosey and Hawkes : Boosey and Hawkes. Unpriced* UMMK (B78-51186)
Slatford, Rodney.
Complete Bottesini
Vol.1: For two double basses and piano. (Bottesini, Giovanni). *Yorke. Unpriced* SS/AZ (B78-51121)
Duet no.2. Gran duetto 2 : for double basses. (Bottesini, Giovanni). *Yorke. Unpriced* SSNU (B78-51126)
Sonata, double bass, op.42. Sonata for unaccompanied double bass. (Ellis, David). *Yorke. Unpriced* SSPME (B78-51128)
Sonatas in canon. Op.5. Sonatas in canon : for bass instruments
Vol.3: Sonata in B flat major, Sonata in B flat minor no.4. (Telemann, Georg Philipp). *Yorke. Unpriced* LXNUE/X (B78-50910)
'Suite and low' : for double basses. (Runswick, Daryl). *Yorke. Unpriced* SSNSG (B78-51123)
Slavonic dance, no.8, op.46, no.8, G minor. *arr.* Slavonic dance, no.8. (Dvořák, Antonín). *Boosey and Hawkes. Unpriced* UNNK/AH (B78-50642)
Slavonic dance, no.9, op.72, no.1. *arr.* Slavonic dance no.9. (Dvořák, Antonín). *Boosey and Hawkes. Unpriced* UNNK/AH (B78-50643)
Slavonic dance, no.15, op.72, no.7, C major. *arr.* Slavonic dance, no.15. (Dvořák, Antonín). *Boosey and Hawkes. Unpriced* UNNK/AH (B78-50644)
Sleep = Cswg : for two-part choir and piano. (Hughes-Jones, Llifon). *Roberton. £0.20* FDW (B78-50815)
Sleigh ride = Schlittenfahrt. (Delius, Frederick). 1st ed. *Boosey and Hawkes. Unpriced* MJ (B78-50911)
Sleigh ride = Schlittenfahrt. (Delius, Frederick). 1st ed. *Boosey and Hawkes. Unpriced* MJ (B78-50912)
Slightly lightly Latin. (Littell, Barbara). *Warner : Blossom. Unpriced* UMMJ (B78-51181)
Sloane, Irving.
Classic guitar construction : diagrams, photographs and step-by-step instructions. *Omnibus Press. £2.95* ATS/BC (B78-01684) ISBN 0-86001-232-8
Guitar repair : a manual of repair for guitars and fretted instruments. *Omnibus Press. £2.95* ATS/BT (B78-19402) ISBN 0-86001-157-7
Small, Christopher, *b.1927*. Schoenberg. *Novello. £0.47* BSET(N) (B78-02607)
Smalley, Roger. Accord : for two pianists (1974-5). *Faber Music. Unpriced* QNU (B78-50985)
Smetana, Bedřich.
The bartered bride. *Vocal score.* The bartered bride : a comic opera in three acts. Revised English libretto. *Boosey and Hawkes. Unpriced* CC (B78-50702)
The dower. Die Mitgift und Gebet : zwei Männerchöre a cappella nach Texten von Josef Srb-Debrnov. *Bärenreiter. £0.70* GEZDW (B78-50423)
Smith, Doreen.
A cello sight-reading book : eighty studies
Part 1. *Oxford University Press. Unpriced* SR/EG (B78-51110) ISBN 0-19-358845-5
Part 2. *Oxford University Press. Unpriced* SR/EG (B78-51111) ISBN 0-19-358846-3
Four pieces for four cellos : Byrd, Tchaikovsky, Berlioz, Mozart. *Oxford University Press. Unpriced* SRNSK/AAY (B78-51112) ISBN 0-19-358850-1
Smith, Eric, *b.1940*. Pianos in practice. *Scolar Press. £8.00* AQ/BT (B78-28704) ISBN 0-85967-393-6
Smith, Geoffry Russell-. *See* Russell-Smith, Geoffry.
Smith, Isabel.
Out and about : 8 descriptive pieces for guitar. *Ricordi. Unpriced* TSPMJ (B78-50617)
Up the High Street with my guitar : 8 pieces for beginners. *Ricordi. Unpriced* TSPMJ (B78-50618)
Smith, Pat. Silly things to sing. *E.J. Arnold. Unpriced* JFDW/GJ (B78-50846) ISBN 0-560-02726-5
Smith, Peter Melville. Willowbrook suite : for descant, treble and tenor recorders. *Lengnick. £0.55* VSNTG (B78-51246)
Smith, Reginald Brindle. Canzona in 4 parts. (Merulo, Claudio). *Schott. Unpriced* TSNSK (B78-50607)
Smith, Robert.
Music : for 4-part choir of mixed voices unaccompanied. *Roberton. £0.18* EZDW (B78-50053)
Star of Bethlehem = Seren Bethlehem : three carols for S.A.T.B. unaccompanied. *Roberton. £0.48* EZDP/LF (B78-50788)
Smith, Robert F. In excelsis gloria : two carols for three-part female voice choir and piano with optional recorders. *Roberton. £0.28* FDP/LF (B78-50390)
Smokie's greatest hits. (Chapman, Mike). *Chappell. Unpriced* KDW/GB (B78-50127)
SNO scene
No.1- ; June 1977-. (Scottish National Orchestra). *150 Hope St., Glasgow G2 2TH : Scottish National Orchestra Society. £3.00 yearly* AMM/E(QB/B) (B78-06989)
Snow, George. Rock 'n roll circus : the illustrated rock concert. (Farren, Mick). *Pierrot Publishing Ltd; 219 Eversleigh Rd, SW11 5UY : Distributed by Big O Publishing Ltd. £3.95* AKDW/HKR/E(M) (B78-31595) ISBN 0-905310-10-1
SOAS. *See* University of London. *School of Oriental and African Studies.*
Soaster, Timothy. Heavy reductions : for tuba and tape, 1977. *Arts Lab Music. Unpriced* WV (B78-51358)
Sociology of rock. (Frith, Simon). *Constable. £7.50* AKDW/HKR(Z) (B78-31211) ISBN 0-09-460220-4
Soeyemund, Johann Georg. Das stille Lied : für vier Männerstimmen = for four men's voices. (Schubert, Franz). Erstausgabe. *Bärenreiter. £0.90* GEZDW (B78-50830)
Soldan, Kurt. Mass, no.2, E minor, (1896). *Vocal score.* Mass no.2, E minor, for eight part choir and wind instruments (1896 version). (Bruckner, Anton). Revised version of the edition of Kurt Soldan by James Erber. *Peters. Unpriced* DG (B78-50720)
Solomon, Maynard. Beethoven. *Cassell. £8.95* BBJ(N) (B78-26884) ISBN 0-304-30034-9
Sommer, Jürgen.
Kinderlieder in leichten Sätzen : elektronische Orgel (1 Manual). *Nagel : Bärenreiter. £3.36* RPVK/DW/GJ/AYE (B78-50573)
Volkslieder in leichten Sätzen : elektronische Orgel. *Nagel : Bärenreiter. £3.36* RPVK/DW/G/AYE (B78-50572)
Sommertag : Suite für Bläsorchester. (Schneider, Willy). *Schott. £20.00* UMMG (B78-51176)
Sonata da chiesa sopra un tema di Claudio Monteverdi. (Gardner, John). *Oxford University Press. Unpriced* WSNTR (B78-51343) ISBN 0-19-356713-x
Sonata on a motet. (McCabe, John). *Novello. £2.10* RXME (B78-50575)
Sonata pian'e forte : for brass octet. (Gabrieli, Giovanni). *Chester Music. Unpriced* WNNE (B78-51333)
Sonatas in canon : for bass instruments
Vol.3: Sonata in B flat major, Sonata in B flat minor no.4. (Telemann, Georg Philipp). *Yorke. Unpriced* LXNUE/X (B78-50910)
Sonatas, piano. Complete pianoforte sonatas, including the unfinished works
Vol.1. (Schubert, Franz). *Associated Board of the Royal Schools of Music. Unpriced* QPE/AZ (B78-50996)
Sonate e canzone a quatro. Canzone del terzo tuono : for recorder concert. (Neri, Massimiliano). *Dolmetsch : Chappell. Unpriced* VSN (B78-51239)
Sondards. (Sutermeister, Heinrich). *Schott. £0.20* GEZDW (B78-50073)
Song smith
No.1-. *495 Uttoxeter Rd., Meir, Stoke on Trent : Dave Wrench : Adrian Crosby. £1.00 for 4 issues* JEZDW/AY (B78-50429)
Song under the silver umbrella : for children's voices and accompaniment
1: The Christ-Child : (S.A. and piano or harp). (Binkerd, Gordon). *Boosey and Hawkes. Unpriced* FDP/LF (B78-50809)
2: Song of innocence : (three-part children's chorus). (Binkerd, Gordon). *Boosey and Hawkes. Unpriced* FEZDH (B78-50823)
3: An evening falls : (unison children's voices and piano). (Binkerd, Gordon). *Boosey and Hawkes. Unpriced* JFDW (B78-50841)
4: The merry man of Paris : (unison children's voices and piano). (Binkerd, Gordon). *Boosey and Hawkes. Unpriced* JFDW (B78-50842)
5: Child's song : (three-part children's chorus and piano). (Binkerd, Gordon). *Boosey and Hawkes. Unpriced* FDW (B78-50812)
6: White fields : (S.A. and piano). (Binkerd, Gordon). *Boosey and Hawkes. Unpriced* FDW (B78-50813)
Songs for Sunday. Search me O God. Search me O God. (Parker, Alice). *Roberton. £0.18* FDH (B78-50389)
Songs for Sunday. This joyful Eastertide. This joyful Eastertide : two seasonal carols of praise, for two-part choir and piano. (Parker, Alice). *Roberton. £0.18* FDP/LL (B78-50391)
Songs from Alice : Alice in Wonderland and Through the looking-glass. (Harper, Don). *Adam and Charles Black. Unpriced* JFDW (B78-50843) ISBN 0-7136-1879-5
Songs from 'One on one' : a Warner Bros. film. (Fox,

Charles). *Warner : Blossom. Unpriced* KDW/JR (B78-50166)
Songs of heritage : symphonic band. (Williams, Clifton). *Rubank : Novello. Unpriced* UMMJ (B78-51185)
Songs of London town. *Selections.* Highgate and The tower. (Burtch, Mervyn). *Roberton. £0.18* JFDW (B78-50090)
Songs of speech. (Spinks, Donald). *Morris Rd, Clarendon Pk : Taskmaster. Unpriced* JFDW/GJ (B78-50845)
Songs to sing in the bath : waterproof cartoons. (Baker, Nicholas). *Allison and Busby. £0.75* AKDW (B78-08476) ISBN 0-85031-190-x
Songsmiths. Reed, Les. The works of Les Reed. *EMI. Unpriced* KDW/GB (B78-50869)
Sonhar. Op.14. *arr.* Sonhar, Op.14. (Villa-Lobos, Heitor). *Arthur Napoleão : Essex Music. Unpriced* QPK (B78-50557)
Sophie : the Sophie Tucker story. (Freedland, Michael). *Woburn Press. £6.50* AKDW/GB/E(P) (B78-05406) ISBN 0-7130-0153-4
Sor, Fernando. Sonata, guitar, op.22, C major. *Selections.* Menuett und Rondo : für Gitarre. Revidierte Neuausgabe. *Schott. £3.20* TSPMJ (B78-50273)
Souchon, Edmond. New Orleans jazz : a family album. (Rose, Al). Revised ed.. *Louisiana State University Press. £17.50* AMT(YTRN/M) (B78-23597) ISBN 0-8071-0374-8
Soul cargo
No.1-. *67 Albert Terrace, Wolstanton, Newcastle-under-Lyme, Staffs. : C. Savory. £0.30* A/GBS/FD(B) (B78-05414)
Sound of their music : the story of Rodgers & Hammerstein. (Nolan, Frederick). *Dent. £6.50 : CIP rev.* BRK(N) (B78-09114) ISBN 0-460-04315-3
Sound piece no.6 : flute and clarinet. (Becker, John). *Peters. Unpriced* VRPLVV (B78-51232)
Sound tracks
1: Pattern music. (Paynter, John). *Cambridge University Press. £1.95* A/D(VF) (B78-23589) ISBN 0-521-20581-6
2: Rites and ceremonies. (Paynter, John). *Cambridge University Press. £1.95* A/D(VF) (B78-23590) ISBN 0-521-20579-4
4: Magic songs. (Paynter, John). *Cambridge University Press. £1.95* A/D(VF) (B78-23592) ISBN 0-521-20578-6
Sounds and music. (Ramsbottom, Edward). *Macmillan. £0.48* A (B78-18538) ISBN 0-333-23169-4
Sounds and music
Book 1. *Longman. Unpriced* JFE/LDW/AY (B78-50849) ISBN 0-582-24203-7
Sounds for swinging strings : four pieces in popular style for group music. (Evans, Colin). *Paxton. £1.32* NX (B78-50505)
Sounds fun 2 : a second book of musical games. (Wishart, Trevor). *Universal Edition. £0.75* A/GS (B78-11209) ISBN 0-900938-47-1
Sounds of music. (Kenney, A R). *Nelson. £0.45* A/B (B78-29834) ISBN 0-17-438332-0
Sounds sensational : piano or vocal
1. *Chappell. Unpriced* KDW/GB/AY (B78-50457)
2. *Chappell. Unpriced* KDW/GB/AY (B78-50456)
Southwell-Sander, Peter. Verdi : his life and times. *Midas Books. £6.50 : CIP rev.* BVE(N) (B78-03574) ISBN 0-85936-096-2
Space age suite : six easy guitar pieces for the young beginner. (Law, Leslie). *Charnwood Music. Unpriced* TSPMG (B78-50612)
Sparke, Philip.
Dolly. Op.56, no.1. Berceuse. *arr.* Berceuse. ('Listen with Mother' theme) ... (Fauré, Gabriel). *R. Smith. Unpriced* WMK (B78-51315)
Gaudium : concert piece for wind symphony orchestra. *Boosey and Hawkes. Unpriced* UMMJ (B78-51183)
Spass am Klavierspielen : Schule für Kinder aus Grund- un Früherziehungskursen. (Heilbut, Peter). *Bärenreiter. £4.20* Q/AC (B78-50518)
Spectrum : for orchestra. (Lees, Benjamin). *Boosey and Hawkes. Unpriced* MMJ (B78-50923)
Speer, Gotthard. Meilensteine eines Komponistenlebens : kleine Festschrift zum 70. Geburtstag von Günter Bialas. *32 Gt Titchfield St., W1P 7AD : Bärenreiter. £10.08* BBNO(D) (B78-19399)
Spektralanalytische Untersuchung der Bestandteile der Orgel von Aquincum. *See* Gegus, Erno.
Spencer, Roderick. Sing along with Sullivan : a new anthology of music for the voice. (Sullivan, *Sir* Arthur Seymour). *Cramer. Unpriced* KDW (B78-50447)
Spenser, Edmund.
Aubade, op.17 : for mixed chorus. (Brown, Christopher). *Chester Music. Unpriced* EZDW (B78-50795)
The hill of the graces : for unaccompanied chorus, SSAATTBB. (Berkeley, *Sir* Lennox). *Chester Music. Unpriced* EZDW (B78-50794)
Speranza : für fünfstimmigen gemischten Chor a cappella. (Killmayer, Wilhelm). *Schott. £0.72* EZDW (B78-50797)
Spero, James. The authentic Gilbert & Sullivan songbook : 92 unabridged selections from all 14 operas reproduced from early vocal scores. (Sullivan, *Sir* Arthur Seymour). *Dover : Constable. £5.35* DW (B78-50028) ISBN 0-486-23482-7
Spinks, Donald. Songs of speech. *Morris Rd, Clarendon Pk : Taskmaster. Unpriced* JFDW/GJ (B78-50845)
Spiritual railway : two-part or unison with piano and optional instruments. (Parry, William Howard). *Oxford University Press. Unpriced* FDH (B78-50058) ISBN 0-19-341512-7
Spirituals für Blechbläser : bearbeitet von Rolf Schweizer. *Bärenreiter. £2.80* WNK/DW/LC (B78-50688)
Sprechstücke : für Sprecher, Sprechchor und Schlagwerk. (Orff, Carl). *Schott. £7.20* HY (B78-50076)
Srb-Debrnov, Josef. The dower. Die Mitgift und Gebet : zwei Männerchöre a cappella nach Texten von Josef Srb-Debrnov. (Smetana, Bedřich). *Bärenreiter. £0.70* GEZDW (B78-50423)
Sretenskaya, N.
The Russian school of piano playing
Vol.1. (Nikolaev, Aleksandr Aleksandrovich). English ed. *Boosey and Hawkes. Unpriced* Q/AC (B78-50962)
Vol.2. (Nikolaev, Aleksandr Aleksandrovich). English ed. *Boosey and Hawkes. Unpriced* Q/AC (B78-50963)
St. Nicholas series. Rubbra, Edmund. Emblem XI. How shall my tongue express ...? : Motet. *Lengnick. £0.18* EZDH (B78-50372)
St. Paul's series.
Dearnley, Christopher. Let thy hand be strengthened. *Cathedral Music. Unpriced* EZDK (B78-50379)
McLeish, Craig. Preces and responses for trebles. *36 Ranelagh Gdns., W.6 : Cathedral Music. Unpriced* FLEZDGMM (B78-50405)
Stacey, Harold Clifford. The Saffron Walden Society of Change Ringers. *Saffron Walden Society of Change Ringers; 36 Great Clarendon St., Oxford : Distributed by J. Hannon & Co. £3.50* AXSR/E(YDDES/QB) (B78-16903)
Staempfli, Edward. Cinq préludes : pour piano. *Bote und Bock : Schirmer. £3.85* QPJ (B78-51020)
Standing Conference for Amateur Music. Music matters : a check-list for local music groups. (Crampton, Stephen). *26 Bedford Sq., WC1B 3HU : Standing Conference for Amateur Music. Unpriced* A(WB/WT) (B78-20433)
Stanley, John. Six solos, Op.4 : for flute or violin and continuo. *Chester Music. Unpriced* VRPE (B78-51214)
Star of Bethlehem = Seren Bethlehem : three carols for S.A.T.B. unaccompanied. (Smith, Robert). *Roberton. £0.48* EZDP/LF (B78-50788)
Star trek. *Selections : arr.* Theme from 'Star Trek'. (Roddenberry, Gene). *Warner : Blossom. Unpriced* UMMK/JS (B78-50640)
Star trek. Theme. *arr.* Theme from Star trek. (Roddenberry, Gene). *Warner : Blossom. Unpriced* UMMK/JS (B78-51189)
Starobin, David. Looking for Claudio : solo and tape. (Kolb, Barbara). *Boosey and Hawkes. Unpriced* TSPMJ (B78-51157)
Start making music : a primary teacher's guide : a complete self tutor for the absolute beginner - with instructional tape recording, reading, playing and teaching music for the non-specialist primary teacher. (Russell-Smith, Geoffry). *Universal Edition. £6.00* AXT/E(VG) (B78-12102) ISBN 0-900938-48-x
Starter's whistle, or, How to play the penny whistle. (Meiklem, Colin L). *Feldman. Unpriced* VSX/AC (B78-51262)
Stedman doubles : for clarinet and percussion. (Davies, Peter Maxwell). *Boosey and Hawkes. Unpriced* VVPLX (B78-50664)
Steffen, Wolfgang.
Music for piano and seven players = Musik für einen Pianisten und sieben Spieler, Opus 44. *Bote und Bock Associated Music. £5.75* NYDPNN (B78-50509)
Polychromie : für Klavier und 10 Instrumente, Opus 38. *Bote und Bock : Associated Music. £5.75* MPQ (B78-50496)
Tetraphonie : für Flöten (1 Spieler), (Altflöte, Grosse Flöte, Bassflöte ad libitum, Piccolo mit 2 Lotusflöten, Opus 42. *Bote und Bock : Schirmer. £3.85* VRPMJ (B78-51234)
Steinitz, Paul. Psalmen Davids sampt etlichen Moteten und Concerten. Alleluia. Alleluia. Lobet den Herren = Alleluia. Worship Jehovah : for 8 solo voices and double choir, with instruments. (Schütz, Heinrich). *Oxford University Press. Unpriced* ENWXPDR (B78-50358) ISBN 0-19-338088-9
Steinman, Jim. bat out of hell. *Dick James. Unpriced* KDW/HKR (B78-50880)
Stephan, Wilhelm.
Fahnengruss. *Bote und Bock : Associated Music. £1.60* UMMGM (B78-50626)
Panzergrenadiermarsch. *Bote und Bock : Associate Music. £3.20* UMMGM (B78-50627)
Stephens, Geoff. Dear anyone ... : a musical story of the agony behind the agony column ... from the concept album. *Dick James : Music Sales (dist.). Unpriced* KDW/GB (B78-50870)
Stephens, James.
Song under the silver umbrella : for children's voices and accompaniment
3: An evening falls : (unison children's voices and piano). (Binkerd, Gordon). *Boosey and Hawkes. Unpriced* JFDW (B78-50841)
6: White fields : (S.A. and piano). (Binkerd, Gordon). *Boosey and Hawkes. Unpriced* FDW (B78-50813)
Sterkel, Franz Xaver. Concerto, piano, no.1, op.20, C major. *arr.* Erstes Konzert C-Dur, Ut majeur, für Klavier mit 2 Oboen, 2 Hörnern und Streichern, op.20. *Schott. £10.00* MPQF (B78-50192)
Sterkel, Johann Franz Xaver. Concerto, piano, no.1, op.20, C major. *arr.* Erstes Konzert C-Dur, Ut majeur, C major, für Klavier mit 2 Oboen, 2 Hörnern und Streichern, Opus 20. *Schott. £10.00* QNUK/LF (B78-50211)
Sternfeld, Frederick William. An old English carol. *arr.* An old English carol : old English ballad tune. *Oxford University Press. Unpriced* EZDP/LF (B78-50789) ISBN 0-19-343068-1
Steurlein, Johann. Songs for Sunday. Search me O God. Search me O God. (Parker, Alice). *Roberton. £0.18* FDH (B78-50389)
Stevens, Cat.
Cat Stevens : hits. *Chappell. Unpriced* KDW/HKR (B78-50881)
Izitso. *arr.* Izitso. *Columbia Pictures Publications : EMI. Unpriced* KDW/GB (B78-50139)
Stevens, Denis.
Magnificat septimi toni for mixed voices and instruments. (Lasso, Orlando di). *Oxford University Press. Unpriced* EZDGKK (B78-50773) ISBN 0-19-337335-1
Recercari et canzoni francese. Libro primo. *Selections ; arr.* Ricercar et canzoni. (Frescobaldi, Girolamo). *Novello. £1.30* MRK (B78-50196)
Tenmadrigals : for mixed voices. (Monteverdi, Claudio). *Oxford University Press. Unpriced* EZDU (B78-50791) ISBN 0-19-343676-0
Venetian ceremonial motets. *Novello. £1.10* EWNDW (B78-50763)
Stevenson, Robert. Singing together
Marching song ; words by R.L. Stevenson. (Wade, Darrell). *16 Anchor Way, Danes Green, Gnosall : Viking. Unpriced* JFDW (B78-50096)
Stevenson, Robert Louis.
Singing together
Bed in summer ; words by R.L. Stevenson. (Wade, Darrell). *16 Anchor Way, Danes Green, Gnosall : Viking. Unpriced* JFDW (B78-50094)
Bed in summer ; words by R.L. Stevenson. (Wade, Darrell). *16 Anchor Way, Danes Green, Gnosall : Viking. Unpriced* JFDW (B78-50095)
Rain ; words by R.L. Stevenson. (Wade, Darrell). *16 Anchor Way, Danes Green, Gnosall : Viking. Unpriced* JFDW (B78-50098)
Summer sun ; words by R.L. Stevenson. (Wade, Darrell). *16 Anchor Way, Danes Green, Gnosall : Viking. Unpriced* JFDW (B78-50099)
The moon ; words by R.L. Stevenson. (Wade, Darrell). *16 Anchor Way, Danes Green, Gnosall : Viking. Unpriced* JFDW (B78-50103)
Stevie's ferry to Hoy : piano solo. (Davies, Peter Maxwell). *Boosey and Hawkes. Unpriced* QPJ (B78-50222)
Stewart, Al. Year of the cat. *arr.* Year of the cat. *71-75 New Oxford St., W.C.1 : Gwyneth Music. Unpriced* KDW/GB (B78-50140)
Stewart, John Lincoln. Horizons circled : reflections on my music. (Krenek, Ernst). *University of California Press. £6.80* BKTM (B78-06254) ISBN 0-520-02338-2
Stille Nacht, heilige Nacht. *arr.* Silent night : all organ. (Gruber, Franz). *Chappell. Unpriced* RK/DP/LF (B78-50236)
Stingl, Anton.
Lieder ohne Worte. *Selections: arr.* 6 Lieder ohne Worte. (Mendelssohn, Felix). *Schott. £4.80* TSPMK (B78-50275)
Serenade für Flöte und Gitarre. (Zehm, Friedrich). *Schott. £6.00* VRPLTS (B78-50293)
Stockert, Karl.
Klassische Tänze von Joseph Haydn und Wolfgang Amadeus Mozart : für Blockflöten - Ensemble ... Sopran, Alt, Tenor, Bass ... (Haydn, Joseph). *Schott. £3.20* VSNSK/AH (B78-50297)
Quartet, strings, no.3. Klassische Tanze von Joseph Haydn und Wolfgang Amadeus Mozart : für Blockflöten - Ensemble ... Sopran, Alt, Tenor, Bass ... (Haydn, Joseph). *Schott. £3.20* VSNSK/AH (B78-50298)
Stockmeier, Wolfgang. Zehn Chorale alter Meister für Posaune und Orgel. *Bärenreiter. £4.80* WUPLRK/DM/AYE (B78-51355)
Stockton, Robert. Let it shine : spiritual for 3-part chorus of female voices with piano and optional percussion. *Roberton. £0.18* FDW/LC (B78-50395)
Stoker, Richard. Trio, strings & piano, no.1, op.24. Piano trio no.1, opus 24, for violin, violoncello, and piano. *Peters. Unpriced* NXNT (B78-50206)
Stomping the blues. (Murray, Albert). *Quartet Books. £4.95* AKDW/HHW(X) (B78-22168) ISBN 0-7043-2172-6
Stone, Colin. Running a disco. (Swindells, Adrienne P). *Hart-Davis Educational. £0.65* A/FF/ER (B78-15126) ISBN 0-247-12630-6
Stone, David.
Rosamunde. Ballet music. *arr.* Rosamunde ballet music, no.2. (Schubert, Franz). *Boosey and Hawkes. Unpriced* MK/AH/HM (B78-50183)
Three chorales. (Bach, Johann Sebastian). *Boosey and Hawkes. Unpriced* MK/DM (B78-50184)
Variations, trumpet & piano. Variations for trumpet (or trombone) and piano. *Boosey and Hawkes. Unpriced* WSP/T (B78-51344)
Stone, Else. The writings of Elliott Carter : an American composer looks at modern music. (Carter, Elliott). *Indiana University Press. £12.95* A(D/XNS40) (B78-33159) ISBN 0-253-36720-4
Stone, Kurt. The writings of Elliott Carter : an American composer looks at modern music. (Carter, Elliott). *Indiana University Press. £12.95* A(D/XNS40) (B78-33159) ISBN 0-253-36720-4
Storke : carol for S.A.T.B. (Potter, Archibald James). *Edwin Ashdown. £0.20* EZDP/LF (B78-50787)
Storm in a teacup : a one act musical play for infants or lower juniors. (Wade, Darrell). *Viking. Unpriced* CN (B78-50708)
Story of jazz : from New Orleans to Rock Jazz. *Barrie and Jenkins etc.. £5.50* AMT(X) (B78-09118) ISBN 0-214-20379-4
Story of Stevie Wonder. (Haskins, James). *Panther. £0.65* AKDW/HKR/E(P) (B78-06263) ISBN 0-586-04541-4
Story of 'Tommy'. (Barnes, Richard). *The Boathouse, Ranelagh Drive, Twickenham, Middx TW1 1QZ : Eel Pie Publishing Ltd. £6.95* AKDW/HKR/E(P)

(B78-18545) ISBN 0-906008-02-6
Stout, Alan. 3 quarter-tone pieces. Quarter-tone chorale. *arr.* Quarter-tone chorale. (Ives, Charles). *Peters. Unpriced* RXMJ (B78-51067)
Stowe, Randolph. Miss Donnithorne's maggot : for mezzo-soprano and chamber ensemble. (Davies, Peter Maxwell). *Boosey and Hawkes. £7.00* C/J (B78-50003)
Strachan, Alan. The Mermaid's 'Cowardy custard' : an entertainment. (Frow, Gerald). *French. £1.80* BCMWACM (B78-21400) ISBN 0-573-68079-5
Strange encounters. (Balent, Andrew). *Warner : Blossom. Unpriced* UMMJ (B78-51177)
Stranz, Ulrich. Quartet, strings, no.1. 1. Streichquartett in vier Sätzen, 1976, von Ulrich Stranz. *Bärenreiter. £7.00* RXNS (B78-50583)
Straus, Oscar. Ein Walzertraum. *Vocal score.* A waltz dream : operetta in three acts. *Weinberger. Unpriced* CF (B78-50326)
Strauss, Johann, *b.1825.* Erinnerung an Covent Garden. Op.329. *arr.* Memories of Covent Garden = Erinnerung an Covent Garden : waltz, op.329, based on English music hall songs. *Bosworth & Co. Unpriced* MK/AHW (B78-50486)
Strauss, Richard.
Ariadne auf Naxos : Oper in einem Akt nebst einem Vorspiel. (Hofmannsthal, Hugo von). *Boosey and Hawkes. £0.85* BSUAC
A confidential matter : the letters of Richard Strauss and Stefan Zweig, 1931-1935. *University of California Press. £6.75* BSU(N/XNL5) (B78-04319) ISBN 0-520-03036-2
Elektra : tragedy in one act. (Hofmannsthal, Hugo von). *Boosey and Hawkes. £9.00* BSUAC
Strawberry fair. (Broadbent, Derek). *Logo Music : Studio Music. Unpriced* WMK/DW (B78-51325)
Street, Tison. Variations, flute, guitar & cello. Variations for flute, guitar and cello. *Schirmer. Unpriced* NVRNT (B78-50503)
String music of the second Elizabeth : twelve original pieces for string orchestra. *Belwin-Mills. Unpriced* RXM/AY (B78-50243)
'Stringing along' : a tutor for the first year schools' cello class. (Mish, Violet). *(16 Anchor Way, Danes Green, Gnosall) : Viking. Unpriced* SRN/AC (B78-50263)
Stringing along : a tutor for the second year school's violin class. (Wade, Darrell). *16 Anchor Way, Danes Green, Gnosall, Staffs. : Viking Publications. Unpriced* SN/AC (B78-50585)
Structure of atonal music. (Forte, Allen). *Yale University Press. £4.50* A/PN (B78-24451) ISBN 0-300-02120-8
Stuart, John.
Baby elephant walk. *arr.* Baby elephant walk. (Mancini, Henry). *Warner : Blossom. Unpriced* UMMK (B78-51187)
I'm Popeye the sailor man. *arr.* I'm Popeye the sailor man. (Lerner, Sammy). *Warner : Blossom. Unpriced* EWMDW/JR (B78-50762)
Stubbs, Leighton. Resurrection jazz : a cantata for schools. (Cartwright, Kenneth). *Boosey and Hawkes. Unpriced* FDE/LL (B78-50388)
Studien für Drum Set = Studies for drum set
Heft 2 = Vol.2: Mittelstufe = Intermediate. (Fink, Siegfried). *Simrock. Unpriced* XQ/AF (B78-51363)
Studien zur traditionellen Musik Japans. Giesen, Walter. Zur Geschichte des buddhistischen Ritualgesangs in Japan : Traktate des 9. bis 14. Jahrhunderts zum shomyo der Tendai-Sekte. *32 Gt Titchfield St., W1P 7AD : Bärenreiter. £12.60* BZHPADGVF (B78-35473)
Studies for string quartet. Op.34
Set 2: Fantasia, Aria (2) and Toccata. (Crosse, Gordon). *Oxford University Press. Unpriced* RXNS (B78-51078) ISBN 0-19-355974-9
Studies in musicology, 1935-1975. (Seeger, Charles). *University of California Press. £11.75* A(VX/D) (B78-11189) ISBN 0-520-02000-6
Studies in theology. Routley, Erik. The Church and music. Revised ed. *Duckworth. £12.50* AD/LD(X) (B78-30831) ISBN 0-7156-0062-1
Stumme, Wolfgang. Musikalische Grundausbildung in der Musikschule
Lehrerhandbuch. Teil 1 : Didaktik und Methodik. *Schott. £9.50* A(VF) (B78-33930)
Suidell, Padre. Credo. Crucifixus. *arr.* Crucifixus = (He was crucified) : for two-part chorus of women's voices with keyboard accompaniment. *Roberton. £0.15* FDJ (B78-50808)
'Suite and low' : for double basses. (Runswick, Daryl). *Yorke. Unpriced* SSNSG (B78-51123)
Suite de pièces, 1st collection. Passacaille. *arr.* Passacaglia in G minor. (Handel, George Frideric). *Oxford University Press. Unpriced* UMMK/AHT (B78-50632)
Suite de trois morçeaux : for flute and piano, op.116. (Godard, Benjamin). *Chester Music. Unpriced* VRPJ (B78-51217)
Suite for brass sextet. (Haan, Stefan de). *Chester Music. Unpriced* WNQ (B78-51334)
Suite in A minor ... : guitar solo. (Corbetta, Francesco). *Universal. Unpriced* TSPMJ (B78-51153)
Suite of dances. (Susato, Thielman). *Chester Music. Unpriced* WNK/AH (B78-51332)
Suite of dances : wind ensemble. (Lowe, Thomas). *Emerson. £3.50* UNNHG (B78-50285)
Sullivan, *Sir* Arthur Seymour.
The authentic Gilbert & Sullivan songbook : 92 unabridged selections from all 14 operas reproduced from early vocal scores. *Dover : Constable. £5.35* DW (B78-50028) ISBN 0-486-23482-7
Sing along with Sullivan : a new anthology of music for the voice. *Cramer. Unpriced* KDW (B78-50447)
Sullivan and his satellites : a survey of English operettas, 1860-1914. (Hyman, Alan). *Chappell : Elm Tree Books. £7.50* ACF(YD/XK55) (B78-26888) ISBN 0-903443-24-4
Sunday morning. (Siebert, Edrich). *Harmer : Studio Music. Unpriced* WMJ (B78-50679)
Sunny bank carol : S.A.T.B. (unacc.), opus 141. (Gardner, John). *Oxford University Press. Unpriced* EZDP/LF (B78-50785) ISBN 0-19-343063-0
Sunrise : voice, violin and piano. (Ives, Charles). *Peters. Unpriced* KE/SPDW (B78-50462)
Supersonic annual
1978. *IPC Magazines. £1.65* AKDW/GB/E(EM/M) (B78-02605) ISBN 0-85037-356-5
Supersound series for young bands.
Balent, Andrew. Strange encounters. *Warner : Blossom. Unpriced* UMMJ (B78-51177)
Lerner, Sammy. I'm Popeye the sailor man. *arr.* I'm Popeye the sailor man. *Warner : Blossom. Unpriced* EWMDW/JR (B78-50762)
Littell, Barbara. March for a free spirit. *Warner : Blossom. Unpriced* UMMJ (B78-51180)
Littell, Barbara. Slightly lightly Latin. *Warner : Blossom. Unpriced* UMMJ (B78-51181)
Livingston, Jay. The paleface. Buttons and bows. *arr.* Buttons and bows. *Warner : Blossom. Unpriced* UMMK/DW/JR (B78-51188)
Mancini, Henry. Baby elephant walk. *arr.* Baby elephant walk. *Warner : Blossom. Unpriced* UMMK (B78-51187)
Roddenberry, Gene. Star trek. Theme. *arr.* Theme from Star trek. *Warner : Blossom. Unpriced* UMMK/JS (B78-51189)
Supper, Walter. Die Orgeldisposition : eine Heranführung. Grossausgabe. *Bärenreiter. £13.44* AR/E (B78-01682)
Surinach, Carlos.
Celebraciones medievales : Spanish divertissements of the Middle Ages, for concert band with four-part chorus of mixed voices. *Associated Music. £4.55* EUMMDW (B78-50359)
Concerto, piano. *arr.* Concerto for piano and orchestra. *Associated Music. £4.55* QNUK/LF (B78-50520)
Susato, Thielman.
Het derde musyck boexken. *Selections : arr.* Six Susato dances : for brass band ... *Chester Music. Unpriced* WMK/AH (B78-51321)
A suite of dances. *Chester Music. Unpriced* WNK/AH (B78-51332)
Sussex overture. Op.34. (Platts, Kenneth). *Edwin Ashdown. £2.00* MJ (B78-50913)
Sutermeister, Heinrich. Les sondards. *Schott. £0.20* GEZDW (B78-50073)
Sutter, Robert. Sonata per orchestra in five parts. *Bärenreiter. £11.20* MME (B78-50487)
Sutton, Wadham. Werke für das Laufwerk. *Selections : arr.* Four clock pieces. (Haydn, Joseph). *Novello. Unpriced* VVNTK/B/FJ (B78-51277)
Suzuki investigation in Hertfordshire : a report of the investigation, sponsored by the Calouste Gulbenkian Foundation and by the Leverhulme Trust, into the feasibility of introducing the Suzuki Talent Education method of teaching the violin into state schools in Britain. (Rural Music Schools Association). *Bedford Square Press. Unpriced* AS(VG/YDED) (B78-38994) ISBN 0-7199-0941-4
Swan ... : violoncello and piano. (Saint-Saëns, Camille). *Leonard, Gould and Bolttler. £0.50* SRPK (B78-50266)
Swann, Donald.
The road goes ever on : a song cycle : poemsby J.R.R. Tolkein. 2nd ed. *Allen and Unwin. £4.75* KDW (B78-50863) ISBN 0-04-784011-0
Singalive! : twelve songs and a cakewalk. *Collins. Unpriced* KDW (B78-50862) ISBN 0-00-599605-8
Swanston, Hamish.
In defence of opera. *Penguin. £1.25* AC (B78-05403) ISBN 0-14-022005-4
In defence of opera. *Allen Lane. £6.50* AC (B78-09697) ISBN 0-7139-1063-1
Swarsenski, H. En blanc et noir : three pieces for two pianos. (Debussy, Claude). *Peters. Unpriced* QNU (B78-50984)
Swayne, Giles.
Alleluia!. *Vocal score.* Alleluia! : a Christmas sequence for speaker, female or boys' voices, harp, piano and percussion. *Novello. £1.05* FDE/LF (B78-50807)
Mary, Queen of Scots. *Vocal score.* Mary, Queen of Scots : opera in three acts. (Musgrave, Thea). *Novello. £15.00* CC (B78-50008)
Swindells, Adrienne P. Running a disco. *Hart-Davis Educational. £0.65* A/FF/ER (B78-15126) ISBN 0-247-12630-6
Symphonies of Havergal Brian
Vol.2: Symphonies 13-29. (MacDonald, Malcolm, *b.1948*). *Kahn and Averill. £6.25* BBTNAMME (B78-23596) ISBN 0-900707-43-7
Symphonische Ouverture für grosses Orchester (1942). (Hartmann, Karl Amadeus). *Schott. £14.00* MMJ (B78-50190)
Syrinx : for solo flute. (Debussy, Claude). *Chester Music. Unpriced* VRPMJ (B78-51233)
Szenen : für Flöte und Klavier, Opus 26 (1977). (Redel, Martin Christoph). *Bote und Bock : Schirmer. £4.80* VRPJ (B78-51218)
Ta-ra-ra boom-de-ay : songs for everyone. *A. and C. Black. Unpriced* JFADW/AY (B78-50837) ISBN 0-7136-1790-x
Take two = A due = Für zwei : five guitar duets. (Dodgson, Stephen). *Ricordi. Unpriced* TSNU (B78-50609)
'Talking machine review'. A catalogue of 'Clarion' & 'Ebonoid' records. (Carter, Sydney Horace). *19 Glendale Rd, Bournemouth BH6 4JA : 'Talking machine review'. £2.00* A/FD(QB/WT) (B78-20766) ISBN 0-902338-29-3
Tallis, Thomas.
Cantiones, 1575. Derelinquat impius. Derelinquat impius. *Cathedral Music. Unpriced* EZDJ (B78-50376)
Mass, Puer natus est nobis. *Oxenford Imprint : Dist. Blackwell's Music Shop. Unpriced* EZDG (B78-50365)
Tambourin : solo for B flat cornet. (Gossec, François Joseph). *Studio Music. Unpriced* WMPWRK/AHVQT (B78-51329)
Tambourine player = Tamburin schlägerin : for four-part chorus of women's voices a cappella. (Schumann, Robert). *Schirmer. £0.30* FEZDW (B78-50401)
Tammy Wynette's greatest hits. *EMI. Unpriced* KDW/GB/AY (B78-50458)
Tarrega, Francisco. Zwei spanische Stücke = Two Spanish pieces = Deux pièces espagnoles : für Gitarre ... Revidierte Neuausgabe. *Schott. £3.20* TSPMH (B78-50271)
Tate, Phyllis. Saint Martha and the dragon. *Vocal score.* Saint Martha and the dragon : a dramatic legend set to music, for narrator, soprano and tenor soloists, chorus, children's chorus (with percussion) and chamber orchestra. *Oxford University Press. Unpriced* DE (B78-50718) ISBN 0-19-338397-7
Taupin, Bernie.
Blue moves. *arr.* Blue moves. (John, Elton). *Big Pig Music : Music Sales. £4.95* KDW/HKR (B78-50161)
Rock of the westies. *arr.* Rock of the westies : songs from the album. (John, Elton). *Big Pig Music : Music Sales. £1.95* KDW/HKR (B78-50162)
Tavener, John.
Canticle of the Mother of God. *Chester Music. Unpriced* EZDE (B78-50764)
A gentle spirit : an opera in one act for soprano, tenor and chamber orchestra. *Chester Music. Unpriced* CQC (B78-50711)
Little requiem for Father Malachy Lynch. *Vocal score.* Little requiem for Father Malachy Lynch. *Chester Music. Unpriced* DGKAV (B78-50722)
Ultimos ritos. En honor de San Juan de la Cruz. *Chester Music. Unpriced* EMDH (B78-50750)
Taverner, John.
Six-part masses. *Stainer and Bell. Unpriced* EZDG (B78-50769) ISBN 0-85249-477-7
Te Deum. *Oxenford Imprint : Distributed by Blackwell's Music Shop. Unpriced* GEZDGKB (B78-50409)
Taverner. Dances. Points and dances ... : for instrumental ensemble. (Davies, Peter Maxwell). *Boosey and Hawkes. Unpriced* LN (B78-50907)
Taylor, David.
Augustine. *Choral score.* Augustine : an opera in one or two acts for children. (Boyle, Rory). *Chester Music. Unpriced* DACN (B78-50714)
Augustine. *Vocal score.* Augustine : an opera in one or two acts for children. (Boyle, Rory). *Chester Music. Unpriced* CN (B78-50704)
Teach me how to pray, Lord. (Chappell, Herbert). *Chappell. Unpriced* KDM (B78-50440)
Teach yourself books.
Goodyear, Stephen F. The recorder. *Teach Yourself Books. £1.25 : CIP rev.* AVS/E (B78-25376) ISBN 0-340-22247-6
Palmer, King. Music. 4th ed. *Teach Yourself Books. £1.50* A (B78-16899) ISBN 0-340-05666-5
Teach yourself music. Music. (Palmer, King). 4th ed. *Teach Yourself Books. £1.50* A (B78-16899) ISBN 0-340-05666-5
Techni-music series for the guitarist.
Wright, Francis. The capodastro and its use. *Charnwood Music. Unpriced* TS/PFT/AF (B78-50605)
Wright, Francis. Scales and arpeggios (and how they are played) : for the guitar. *Charnwood Music. Unpriced* TS/AF (B78-50604)
Telemann, Georg Philipp.
Concerto, flutes (2), E minor. *arr.* Concerto in E minor for two flutes and piano. *Schirmer. £2.75* VRNTQK/LF (B78-51202)
Concerto, violins (2) & string orchestra, G minor. Concerto für zwei Violinen, Streicher und Basso continuo G moll. Zum ersten Mal herausgegeben von Felix Schroeder. *Litolff : Peters. Unpriced* RXMPSNUF (B78-50577)
Concerto, violins (2) & string orchestra, G minor. *arr.* Concerto für zwei Violinen, Streicher, und Basso continuo G-moll. Ausgabe für zwei Violinen und Klavier von Herausgeber. Zum ersten Mal herausgegeben von Felix Schroeder. *Litolff : Peters. Unpriced* SNTQK/LF (B78-50587)
Neue Sonatinen, nos.2,5. Two new sonatinas, for treble recorder and basso continuo. 1st ed. *Musica rara. Unpriced* VSSPE (B78-51260)
Sonatas in canon. Op.5. Sonatas in canon : for bass instruments
Vol.3: Sonata in B flat major, Sonata in B flat minor no.4. *Yorke. Unpriced* LXNUE/X (B78-50910)
Telemann, Georg Phillip. Overture, orchestra, E flat major. *arr.* Overture in E flat. *Oxford University Press. Unpriced* QRPK/AG (B78-51041) ISBN 0-19-385586-0
Tempelhofer Messe. (Riethmuller, Heinrich). *Simrock. £4.96* ENYEXPDG (B78-50034)
Tempest. Incidental music. Incidental music for The tempest

: for strings and continuo. (Locke, Matthew). *Oxford University Press. Unpriced* RXM/JM (B78-50244)
ISBN 0-19-365350-8
Tempo di ciaccona and fuga. (Bartók, Béla). *Boosey and Hawkes. £3.00* QPK/AHJN (B78-50560)
Ten of the best : a selection of songs from Novello popular cantatas. *Novello. £1.20* JFDW (B78-50431)
Ten-string music : for cello and guitar. (Brindle, Reginald Smith). *Schott. Unpriced* SRPLTS (B78-51119)
Tennyson, Alfred, *Baron Tennyson.* The world's winter : for soprano and instrumental ensemble. (Payne, Anthony). *Chester Music. Unpriced* KFLE/NVNNDX (B78-50894)
Tensions in the performance of music : a symposium. *Kahn and Averill. £3.00* AL/CY (B78-16900)
ISBN 0-900707-44-5
Terzakis, Dimitri. Notturni : für sechs Singstimmen, Violine, Klarinette, Schlaginstramente. *Bärenreiter. £16.80* JNAZE/NYEVDW (B78-50437)
Terzetto (1925) : for flute, oboe and viola (or clarinet). (Holst, Gustav). 2nd revised ed. *Chester Music. Unpriced* VNT (B78-51198)
Terzi, Giovanni Antonio.
Canzona in 4 parts. (Merulo, Claudio). *Schott. Unpriced* TSNSK (B78-50607)
Intavolatura di liutto, lib.2. Canzona a 8. *arr.* Canzona in 8 parts. *Schott. £0.70* TSNSK (B78-50608)
Tessarini, Carlo. Sonata, oboe & continuo, op.2, no.1, F major. Sonata no.1 in F for oboe and piano. *Chester Music. Unpriced* VTPE (B78-51266)
Tetraphonie : für Flöten (1 Spieler), (Altflöte, Grosse Flöte, Bassflöte ad libitum, Piccolo mit 2 Lotusflöten, Opus 42. (Steffen, Wolfgang). *Bote und Bock : Schirmer. £3.85* VRPMJ (B78-51234)
Textures. Cadence IV. Cadence IV : for piano. (Lazarof, Henri). *Associated Music. £1.50* QPJ (B78-50540)
That time. (Fortner, Wolfgang). *Schott. £12.00* JNDE/NXNT (B78-50109)
That virgin's child : for S.A.T.B. unacc. (Ridout, Alan). *Williams School of Church Music. Unpriced* EZDP/LF (B78-50047)
Thatcher, David S. Musical settings of late Victorian and modern British literature : a catalogue. (Gooch, Bryan N S). *2 Holly Bush Hill, NW3 6SH : Garland Publishing, Inc. £55.35* AKDW(XKK101/T) (B78-14028)
ISBN 0-8240-9981-8
That's entertainment. That's entertainment. *arr.* That's entertainment : S.S.A. with piano. (Schwartz, Arthur). *Chappell. Unpriced* FDW/JR (B78-50817)
The best of Cole Porter. (Porter, Cole). *Chappell. Unpriced* KDW/GB (B78-50138)
The Hexamshire lass : ballads and folk songs from the North Country. *Curwen : Faber Music. Unpriced* KDW/G/AYDJ (B78-50450)
The lemon drop kid. Silver bells. *arr.* Silver bells : SATB and piano. (Livingston, Jay). *Warner : Blossom. Unpriced* DW (B78-50351)
The paleface. Buttons and bows. *arr.* Buttons and bows. (Livingston, Jay). *Warner : Blossom. Unpriced* UMMK/DW/JR (B78-50637)
The sound of music. Do-re-mi. *arr.* Do-re-mi. (Rodgers, Richard). *Chappell. Unpriced* NYFPK/DW (B78-50516)

Theme and variations 1-4. (Webber, Andrew Lloyd). *Chappell. Unpriced* QP/T (B78-50523)
Theme from 'Star Trek'. (Roddenberry, Gene). *Warner Blossom. Unpriced* UMMK/JS (B78-50640)
Theme from Z Cars ('Johnny Todd') : traditional. (Frazer, Alan). *7 Garrick St., W.C.2 : Middle Eight Music. Unpriced* MK/DW (B78-50916)
Themes from The godfather and The godfather, part II. (Rota, Nino). *Warner : Blossom. Unpriced* UMMK/JR (B78-50639)
Theory of harmony. (Schoenberg, Arnold). *Faber : Faber Music. £22.50 : CIP rev.* A/R (B78-12985)
ISBN 0-571-10933-0
They all were looking for a king : for four-part male voice choir unaccompanied. (Plumstead, Mary). Revised ed. *Roberton. £0.15* GEZDP/LF (B78-50827)
Third century : concert march. (Walters, Harold L). *Rubank : Novello. Unpriced* UMMGM (B78-50279)
Thirty chansons, 1529 : for three instruments or voices. *London Pro Musica. Unpriced* EZDU/AYH (B78-50384)
This is just to say : for tenor and piano. (Holloway, Robin). *Boosey and Hawkes. Unpriced* KGHDW (B78-50904)
This joyful Eastertide : two seasonal carols of praise, for two-part choir and piano. (Parker, Alice). *Roberton. £0.18* FDP/LL (B78-50391)
Thomas, Bernard.
Chester's piano book : for two instruments. (Barratt, Carol). *London Pro Musica. Unpriced* LNU (B78-50908)
Libro primo de canzoni da sonare. *Selections.* Five canzonas for four instruments SATB. (Maschera, Florentio). *London Pro Musica. Unpriced* LNS (B78-50482)
Primo libro a due voci. *Selections.* Nine fantasies : for two instruments. (Lupacchino, Bernardino). *London Pro Musica. Unpriced* LNU (B78-50909)
Il primo libro delle canzoni a una, due, tre e quattro voci. *Selections.* Three canzonas for two treble, one bass instrument and continuo. (Frescobaldi, Girolamo). *London Pro Musica Edition. Unpriced* LNSPW (B78-50483)
Thomas, Bob. The one and only Bing. *Joseph. £5.50* AKDW/GB/E(P) (B78-09699) ISBN 0-7181-1698-4
Thomas, Werner. Sprechstücke : für Sprecher, Sprechchor und Schlagwerk. (Orff, Carl). *Schott. £7.20* HY (B78-50076)
Thomas and Sally : dramatic pastoral in two acts. (Arne, Thomas Augustine). *Eulenburg. Unpriced* CQC (B78-50329)
Thomas and Sally. *Vocal score.* Thomas and Sally : a dramatic pastoral in two acts. (Arne, Thomas Augustine). *Schott. Unpriced* CC (B78-50323)
Thomatos, Spiro. Fantasia, flute & guitar, op.337. Fantasie, op.337, für Flöte und Gitarre. (Carulli, Ferdinando). *Heinrichshofen : Peters. Unpriced* VRPLTS (B78-50649)

Thompson, Charles. Bing. *For later edition see* Thompson, Charles. The complete Crosby.
Thompson, Charles.
Bing : the authorised biography. Large print ed.. *Magna Print Books. £4.75* AKDW/GB/E(P) (B78-04324)
ISBN 0-86009-048-5
The complete Crosby. Revised and augmented ed. *W.H. Allen. £5.95* AKDW/GB/E(P) (B78-20440)
ISBN 0-491-02335-9
Thompson, Charles Henry, *b.1910.* Antony Duddyngton, organ maker : the Duddyngton manuscripts at All Hallows-by-the-Tower, London. (Blewett, P R W). *22 Edgar Rd, Sanderstead, South Croydon CR2 0NG : Rev. P. Blewett. £0.50* AR/BC(P) (B78-33169)
ISBN 0-906257-00-x
Thompson, Roy. The illustrated encyclopedia of country music. (Dellar, Fred). *27 Old Gloucester St., WC1N 3AF : Salamander Books Ltd. £5.95* A/GC(C) (B78-05399)
ISBN 0-86101-004-3
Thomson, R W. Praise for today. *Psalms and Hymns Trust. Unpriced* DM/AY (B78-50734)
Thomson, Virgil.
The courtship of the Yongli Bongli Bo sic : for voice and piano. *Schirmer. £1.50* KDW (B78-50448)
Prelude for organ. *Schirmer. £1.50* RJ (B78-50568)
Thomson, William. Music for listeners. *Prentice-Hall. £8.70* A/C (B78-29828) ISBN 0-13-608026-x
Three. (Conyngham, Barry). *Universal. Unpriced* NYJNQ (B78-50955)
Three American choruses : for SATB voices, piano and optional brasses. (Bavicchi, John). *Oxford University Press. Unpriced* DW (B78-50027)
Three American choruses. *Vocal score.* Three American choruses : for SATB voices, piano and optional brasses. (Bavicchi, John). *Oxford University Press. Unpriced* DW (B78-50027)
Three canzonas for two treble, one bass instrument and continuo. (Frescobaldi, Girolamo). *London Pro Musica Edition. Unpriced* LNSPW (B78-50483)
Three children's songs for three equal voices (SSA). (Lutoslawski, Witold). *Chester Music. Unpriced* FDW/GJ (B78-50816)
Three chorales. (Bach, Johann Sebastian). *Boosey and Hawkes. Unpriced* MK/DM (B78-50184)
Three equali for four trombones. (Beethoven, Ludwig van). *Chester Music. Unpriced* WUNS (B78-51354)
Three nocturnes for harp. (Burgon, Geoffrey). *Chester Music. Unpriced* TQPMJ (B78-51135)
Three original pieces, composed for the sight-reading examinations at the Paris Conservatoire : for flute and piano. *Oxford University Press. Unpriced* VRP/AY (B78-50290)
Three pieces for keyboard. (Bach, Johann Sebastian). *Banks. Unpriced* QPK (B78-50225)
Three pigs : for group music making. (Winters, Geoffrey). *Novello. £1.20* CQN (B78-50330)
Three processionals : for orchestra. (Fussell, Charles). *Schirmer. £5.45* MMJ (B78-50490)
Three quarter-tone pieces. 3 quarter-tone pieces. Quarter-tone chorale. *arr.* Quarter-tone chorale. (Ives, Charles). *Peters. Unpriced* RXMJ (B78-51067)
Three rags for five. (Joplin, Scott). *Chester Music. Unpriced* WNRK/AHXJ (B78-51338)
Three sacred songs of Johannes Herbert. (Herbst, Johannes). *Boosey and Hawkes. Unpriced* KFTDH (B78-50899)
Three short sacred songs : for SSA chorus unaccompanied. (Weingarden, Louis). *Oxford University Press. Unpriced* FEZDW (B78-50402)
Three songs from 'A Shropshire lad' : for SATB choir unaccompanied with tenor solo. (Clark, Keith). *Roberton. £0.24* EZDW (B78-50386)
Three tunes for four clarinets. (Parfrey, Raymond). *EMI. Unpriced* VVNS (B78-51275)
Three Victorian scenes. (Leaper, Kenneth). *Chappell. Unpriced* JFE/NYHSDX (B78-50852)
Threlfall, Robert.
A catalogue of the compositions of Frederick Delius : sources and references. *Delius Trust : Distributed by Boosey and Hawkes. £10.00* BDL(TC) (B78-03908)
ISBN 0-85162-028-0
Delius : a life in pictures. *Oxford University Press. £6.95* BDL(N/EM) (B78-05402) ISBN 0-19-315437-4
Thrower, Arthur Harry. A brief history of the Middlesex Yeomanry (Duke of Cambridge's Hussars) Association Military Band. *44 South Easling Rd, W.5 : The author. Unpriced* AUMM(QB/X) (B78-30834)
Thurston, Frederick. Clarinet technique. 3rd ed. *Oxford University Press. £1.95* AVV/E (B78-05412)
ISBN 0-19-318610-1
Tigrane. *Selections : arr.* Suite ... for 2 descant, treble (or tenor) recorders. (Scarlatti, Alessandro). *Chester Music. Unpriced* VSNTK (B78-51249)
Tillett, Michael. The ice break. *Vocal score.* The ice break : an opera in three acts. (Tippett, *Sir* Michael). *Schott. £13.00* CC (B78-50009)
Time and motion study 2 : for solo 'cello and electronics'. (Ferneyhough, Brian). *Peters. Unpriced* SR (B78-51109)
Time and motion study I : solo bass clarinet. (Ferneyhough, Brian). *Peters. Unpriced* VVUPMJ (B78-50306)
Timmins, Donald Maxwell-. *See* Maxwell-Timmins, Donald.
Timms, Colin. Comus. Incidental music. Music for Comus : serenata a 9. (Handel, George Frideric). First modern ed. *23 Stanley Court, 1 Woodfield Rd, W.5 : Acca Music. Unpriced* JNDE/NXNQDW/JM (B78-50108)
Tippett, *Sir* Michael. The ice break. *Vocal score.* The ice break : an opera in three acts. *Schott. £13.00* CC (B78-50009)
Tobler, John.
Guitar heroes. *Marshall Cavendish. £2.95* ATS/E(M) (B78-39236) ISBN 0-85685-438-7
Pop quest : so you think you know all about rock 'n' pop. *Independent Television Books : Arrow Books. £0.65* A/GB (B78-20431) ISBN 0-09-917570-3
Toccata, nocturne and scherzo (1977) : for piano. (Matthews, Colin). *Faber Music. Unpriced* QPJ (B78-51014)
Toch, Ernst. The shaping forces in music : an inquiry into the nature of harmony, melody, counterpoint, form. 1st ed., reprinted. *Dover Publications : Constable. £2.50* A/LZ (B78-06255) ISBN 0-486-23346-4
Tolkien, John Ronald Reuel. The road goes ever on : a song cycle : poemsby J.R.R. Tolkein. (Swann, Donald). 2nd ed. *Allen and Unwin. £4.75* KDW (B78-50863)
ISBN 0-04-784011-0
Tolley, Bryan. Musical instruments. *Wayland. £1.75* AL/BC (B78-31598) ISBN 0-85340-529-8
Tomlinson, Ernest. String music of the second Elizabeth : twelve original pieces for string orchestra. *Belwin-Mills. Unpriced* RXM/AY (B78-50243)
Tony Macaulay songbook. (Macaulay, Tony). *Macaulay Music : Noel Gay Music. Unpriced* KDW/GB (B78-50866)
Top hat & tails : the story of Jack Buchanan. (Marshall, Michael, *b.1930*). *Elm Tree Books. £6.95 : CIP rev.* AKDW/GB/E(P) (B78-06268) ISBN 0-241-89602-9
Top pop scene. *Purnell. £1.00* AKDW/GB/E(M) (B78-04317) ISBN 0-361-03889-5
Top pop scene
1978. *Purnell. £1.35* AKDW/GB/E(M) (B78-26880)
ISBN 0-361-04141-1
Torelli, Giuseppe.
Sinfonia, trumpet & string orchestra, G.9, D major. Concerto D-Dur per tromba con archi e continuo. *Schott. £4.00* RXMPWSE (B78-50251)
Sinfonia, trumpet & string orchestra, G.9, D major. *arr.* Concerto D-Dur per tromba con archi e continuo. *Schott. £3.20* WSPK/LE (B78-50313)
Torok, Alan. Fantasia concertante no.5 : for solo guitar. (Camilleri, Charles). *Basil Ramsey : Roberton. £2.00* TSPMF (B78-51149)
Tortelier, Paul.
Tortelier cello book one : twleve classical and folk pieces. *Chester Music. Unpriced* SRNUK/AAY (B78-51114)
Tortelier cello book two : twelve classical and folk pieces. *Chester Music. Unpriced* SRPK/AAY (B78-51117)
Tortelier cello book one : twleve classical and folk pieces. *Chester Music. Unpriced* SRNUK/AAY (B78-51114)
Tortelier cello book two : twelve classical and folk pieces. *Chester Music. Unpriced* SRPK/AAY (B78-51117)
Tottcher, Hermann.
Concerto, oboe, no.1, D minor. Konzert No.1, d-Moll für Oboe und Orchester. (Lebrun, Ludwig August). *Schott. £11.00* MPVTF (B78-50194)
Concerto, oboe, no.1, D minor. *arr.* Konzert No.1, d-moll, für Oboe und Orchester. (Lebrun, Ludwig August). *Schott. £9.60* VTPK/LF (B78-50302)
Touchin, Roy. Erster Theil confortativae sacrae symphoniaceae. Wenn der Herr die Gefangnen Zion erlösen wird. *arr.* Motet, Wenn der Herr die Gefangnen Zion erlösen wird. (Hartmann, Heinrich). *Tomus. Unpriced* VSNQK/DJ (B78-51242)
Toussaint, or, The aristocracy of the skin : opera in 3 acts and 22 scenes. (Ward, Anthony). *Novello. £1.70* BBPLAC (B78-06260)
Townshend, Pete. The story of 'Tommy'. (Barnes, Richard). *The Boathouse, Ranelagh Drive, Twickenham, Middx TW1 1QZ : Eel Pie Publishing Ltd. £6.95* AKDW/HKR/E(P) (B78-18545) ISBN 0-906008-02-6
Toye, Wendy. The Mermaid's 'Cowardy custard' : an entertainment. (Frow, Gerald). *French. £1.80* BCMWACM (B78-21400) ISBN 0-573-68079-5
Tracey, Edmund. Ein Walzertraum. *Vocal score.* A waltz dream : operetta in three acts. (Straus, Oscar). *Weinberger. Unpriced* CF (B78-50326)
Traditional music in Ireland. (O Canainn, Tomás). *Routledge and Kegan Paul. £3.60 : CIP rev.* A/G(YDM) (B78-31597) ISBN 0-7100-0021-9
Traditional songs of the Maori. *A.H. and A.W. Reed. Unpriced* KDW/AYXR (B78-50449)
ISBN 0-589-00748-3
Training for ex-trebles and young choirmen. RSCM chorister training scheme
Part 2. Training for ex-trebles and young choirmen. (Royal School of Church Music). *Addington Palace, Croydon, Surrey CR9 5AD : R.S.C.M.. £0.80* AD/LD/E (B78-22165) ISBN 0-85402-071-3
Training musicians : a report to the Calouste Gulbenkian Foundation on the training of professional musicians. (Committee of Enquiry into the Training of Musicians). *98 Portland Place, W1N 4ET : The Foundation, UK and Commonwealth Branch. £1.50* A(VQ) (B78-18539)
ISBN 0-903319-11-x
Trakl, Georg.
Rosary songs = Rosenkranzlieder : three poems of Georg Trakl, for soprano, clarinet, viola and piano, Op.9. (Knussen, Oliver). *Faber Music. Unpriced* KFLE/NUVNTDW (B78-50893)

Trumpets : for soprano and three clarinets, op.12. (Knussen, Oliver). *Faber Music. Unpriced* KFLE/VVNTDW (B78-50897)

Transcriptions for organ. (Bach, Johann Sebastian). *Cramer. Unpriced* RK/AAY (B78-50570)

Transit : six solo voices and chamber orchestra. (Ferneyhough, Brian). *Peters. Unpriced* JNAZE/MRDW (B78-50107)

Travelling music show. *Selections : arr.* Leslie Bricusse and Anthony Newley's The travelling music show. (Bricusse, Leslie). *Tro-Essex. Unpriced* KDW (B78-50441)

Tre notturni : drei Gedichte von Friedrich Nietzsche, für tiefe Männerstimme, Klavier und Bläser. (Reutter, Hermann). *Schott. £6.00* KFXE/NWPNQDW (B78-50176)

Trend, J B. Galician carol, Panxoliña sic de Nadal : for four-part chorus of mixed voices unaccompanied. (Wilkinson, Stephen). *Roberton. £0.18* EZDP/LF (B78-50048)

Trevor, Caleb Henry. Music for memorial and thanksgiving services for manuals. *Elkin. £1.30* RK/AAY (B78-51055)

Tribute to Canterbury. (Jacob, Gordon). *Boosey and Hawkes. Unpriced* UMMJ (B78-50281)

Tribute to Elvis : 18 of his best loved songs. *Chappell. Unpriced* KDW/HK/AY (B78-50159)

Trick

No.1- ; Nov. 1977-. *43 Bow La., EC4M 9DT : Wishcastle Ltd. £0.20* A/HKQ(B) (B78-02606)

Trident Television. A selection of musical instruments to make for children. (Goddard, Arthur). *Trident House, Brooks Mews, W1Y 2PN : Trident Television Ltd. £0.25* AX/BC (B78-05413)

Trigon. (Washburn, Robert). *Boosey and Hawkes. £21.00* UMMJ (B78-51184)

Trio für Trompete, Posaune und Tuba. (Schmitt, Meinrad). *Bote und Bock : Associated Music. £3.85* WNT (B78-50691)

Triumph of Neptune. Suite. *arr.* The triumph of Neptune : suite for piano. (Tyrwhitt-Wilson, *Sir* Gerald Hugh, *14th Baron Berners*). *Chester Music. Unpriced* QPH/HM (B78-51000)

Triumph of Neptune : suite for piano. (Tyrwhitt-Wilson, *Sir* Gerald Hugh, *14th Baron Berners*). *Chester Music. Unpriced* QPH/HM (B78-51000)

Tromba. Torelli, Giuseppe. Sinfonia, trumpet & string orchestra, G.9, D major. *arr.* Concerto D-Dur per tromba con archi e continuo. *Schott. £3.20* WSPK/LE (B78-50313)

Trombey, Jack. Eye level. *arr.* Eye level. *Chappell. Unpriced* NYFPK (B78-50514)

Trowell, Brian. Invitation to medieval music

4: Music of the mid-fifteenth century (ii) : an advanced selection of 11 compositions for 1-3 voices and/or instruments newly transcribed and edited by Brian Trowell. *Stainer and Bell. £1.25* CB/AY(XCH 301) (B78-50004) ISBN 0-85249-317-7

Trubitt, Allen. What any lover learns : for four-part chorus of mixed voices a cappella. *Chappell. Unpriced* EZDW (B78-50054)

Trumpet and trombone : an outline of their history, development and construction. (Bate, Philip). 2nd ed. *E. Benn etc.. £8.50* AWS/B (B78-09121) ISBN 0-510-36412-8

Trumpet tune. (Charpentier, Marc Antoine). *J.B. Cramer. £0.45* RK (B78-51054)

Trumpets : for soprano and three clarinets, op.12. (Knussen, Oliver). *Faber Music. Unpriced* KFLE/VVNTDW (B78-50897)

Tschache, Helmut. Lieder und Volksmusik aus der Tschechoslowakei : Materialien für den Musikunterricht in den Sekundarstufen. *Schott. £4.80* AKDW/G(YF) (B78-33161)

Tuba tapestry : E flat bass solo. (Brand, Michael). *R. Smith. Unpriced* WMPWU (B78-50685)

Tučapský, Antonin. Lands : two settings for unaccompanied mixed voice choir of poems by W.H. Auden, music by Antonin Tučapský. *Roberton. £0.32* EZDW (B78-50055)

Tuckwell, Barry.

Fifty first exercises for horn. *Oxford University Press. Unpriced* WT/AF (B78-51350) ISBN 0-19-359150-2

Playing the horn : a practical guide. *Oxford University Press. Unpriced* WT/AC (B78-51349)

Tudor, Dean.

Annual index to popular music record reviews

1976. *Scarecrow Press : Distributed by Bailey and Swinfen. £17.00* A/GB/FD(T) (B78-20767) ISBN 0-8108-1070-0

Popular music periodicals index

1976. *Scarecrow Press : Distributed by Bailey and Swinfen. £8.50* A/GB(DD/B/T) (B78-50320) ISBN 0-8108-1079-4

Tudor, Nancy. Annual index to popular music record reviews

1976. *Scarecrow Press : Distributed by Bailey and Swinfen. £17.00* A/GB/FD(T) (B78-20767) ISBN 0-8108-1070-0

Tull, Fisher.

Cryptic essay : for symphonic band. *Boosey and Hawkes. Unpriced* UMMJ (B78-50282)

Cyclorama 1 : flute ensemble. *Boosey and Hawkes. Unpriced* VRN (B78-51201)

Tune a day : for classical guitar

Book 1. *Boston Music : Chappell. Unpriced* TS/AY (B78-51143)

Tune and repair your own piano : a practical and theoretical guide to the tuning of all keyboard stringed instruments, and to the running repair of the piano. (Johnson, Michael). *Harcourt Brace Jovanovich. Unpriced* AQ/BT (B78-24454) ISBN 0-15-191383-8

Turnabout : a musical version of the Book of Esther. (Easton, Ken). French's acting ed.. *French. £1.65* BSGNHACM (B78-20438) ISBN 0-573-62527-1

Turner, Steve. A decade of The Who : an authorised history in music, paintings, words and photographs. *Elm Tree Books for Fabulous Music Ltd. £4.50* AKDW/HKR/E(P) (B78-00388) ISBN 0-241-89809-9

Turok, Paul. Chorus of the frogs : for four-part chorus of mixed voices with piano accompaniment. *Schirmer. £0.45* DW (B78-50353)

Turpin, Tom. Piano music. *Selections : arr.* Rags for guitar. (Joplin, Scott). *Schirmer. £1.50* TSPMK/AHXJ (B78-51167)

Twelve melodies for organ : twelve favourite Lehár melodies. (Lehár, Franz). *Glocken Verlag. Unpriced* RPVK/DW (B78-51061)

Twelve Moravian songs : for voice and piano. (Husa, Karel). *Associated Music. £3.05* KDW (B78-50444)

Twelve tonality. (Perle, George). *University of California Press. £10.25* A/PN (B78-17614) ISBN 0-520-03387-6

Twelve tunes for violin : for groups of mixed ability. (Dale, Gordon). *EMI Music. Unpriced* SPMJ (B78-51106)

Twentieth century folk hymnal.

20th century folk hymnal

Vol.1. *55 Leigh Rd, Leigh-on-Sea : Kevin Mayhew. Unpriced* JEZDM/AY (B78-50427) ISBN 0-905725-27-1

Vol.3. *55 Leigh Rd, Leigh-on-Sea : Kevin Mayhew. Unpriced* JEZDM/AY (B78-50428) ISBN 0-905725-00-x

Twentieth century harmony : creative aspects and practice. (Persichetti, Vincent). *Faber. £2.95* A/R(XMA60) (B78-11195) ISBN 0-571-11216-1

Twenty British composers. *J. and W. Chester for the Feeney Trust. Unpriced* A(YC/XPQ17) (B78-33938) ISBN 0-9502767-3-1

Twenty elementary studies for the young violinist. (Wade, Darrell). *16 Anchor Way, Danes Green, Gnosall : Viking. Unpriced* S/AF (B78-50256)

Twenty-five etudes. (Giuliani, Mauro). *Ariel : Music Sales. £1.95* TSPMJ (B78-51156) ISBN 0-86001-372-3

Twenty years of British record charts, 1955-1975. British records charts, 1955-1978. Revised and updated ed.. *Macdonald and Jane's. £4.95* AKDW/GB/FD(XPQ24) (B78-37424) ISBN 0-354-08523-9

Two 14th-century motets in praise of music. (Bent, Margaret). *Newton Abbot. Unpriced* EZDW (B78-50793)

Two anonymous alleluias from the Worcester Fragments, (Worcester Cathedral Library, Add. ms. 68). (Reaney, Gilbert). *Antico Edition. Unpriced* EZDJ (B78-50045)

Two carols. (Ledger, Philip). *Oxford University Press. Unpriced* DP/LF (B78-50740) ISBN 0-19-343066-5

Two folk melodies. (Higgins, Norman). *Royal Academy of Dancing. Unpriced* QPH/H (B78-50220)

Two hand duos : nine pieces having equal interest for both hands. (Last, Joan). *Leonard, Gould and Bolttler. Unpriced* QPJ (B78-50539)

Two Old Testament spirituals. (Hughes, Brian). *Roberton. £0.18* EZDW/LC (B78-50057)

Two pieces, overture and foxtrot : for two pianos, four hands. (Martin, Frank). *Schirmer. £3.65* QNUHKEF (B78-50986)

Two plainsong preludes = Deux preludes de plain-chant = Zwei Choralmusik Vorspiele : for organ. (MacDonald, Peter). *64 Pineheath Rd., High Kelling, Holt, Nflk. : St Gregory. £1.25* RJ (B78-50566)

Two processional fanfares. (Howarth, Elgar). *Chester Music. Unpriced* WMGN (B78-51305)

Two Scottish psalm tunes. (Roberton, *Sir* Hugh Stevenson). *Roberton. £0.20* GDR (B78-50407)

Two Thomas Moore songs : for solo voice and piano. (Raphael, Mark). *Roberton. £0.50* KDW (B78-50445)

Tye, Christopher. English sacred music

Vol.1. *Stainer and Bell, for the British Academy. Unpriced* EZDK (B78-50046) ISBN 0-85249-449-1

Tyrwhitt-Wilson, *Sir* Gerald Hugh, *14th Baron Berners*. The triumph of Neptune. Suite. *arr.* The triumph of Neptune : suite for piano. *Chester Music. Unpriced* QPH/HM (B78-51000)

Tyson, Alan. Beethoven studies

2. *Oxford University Press. £9.50 : CIP rev.* BBJ(D) (B77-28782) ISBN 0-19-315315-7

Ultimos ritos. En honor de San Juan de la Cruz. (Tavener, John). *Chester Music. Unpriced* EMDH (B78-50750)

'Unforgettable' Nat 'King' Cole. *Chappell. Unpriced* KDW/GB/AY (B78-50878)

University of Essex. Carreras Arab lectures. *See* Carreras Arab lectures.

University of Keele. *Department of Music.* First American Music Conference held at Keele University, England, Friday, April 18-21, 1975. (American Music Conference, *1st, University of Keele, 1975*). *Keele, Staffs. ST5 5BG University of Keele, Department of Music. Unpriced* A(YT) (B78-30830)

University of London. *Birkbeck College. See* Birkbeck College.

University of London. *Institute of Education.* Music education review : a handbook for music teachers

Vol.1 : 1977. *Chappell. £5.95* A(VC)

University of London. *School of Oriental and African Studies.* London Oriental series. *See* London Oriental series.

Unser Herr Jesus Christus. *arr.* Our dear Lord Jesus Christ = Unser Herr Jesus Christus : SATB with accompaniment. (Peter, Johann Friedrich). *Boosey and Hawkes. Unpriced* DH (B78-50342)

Up the High Street with my guitar : 8 pieces for beginners. (Smith, Isabel). *Ricordi. Unpriced* TSPMJ (B78-50618)

Urban & industrial songs of the Black Country and Birmingham. (Raven, Jon). *68 Limes Rd, Tottenhall, Wolverhampton WV6 8RB : Broadside. £7.75* AKDW/G(YDHNB) (B78-20442) ISBN 0-9503722-2-6

Urwin, S George. A tune a day : for classical guitar

Book 1. *Boston Music : Chappell. Unpriced* TS/AY (B78-51143)

Utrecht Te Deum (1713) : for chorus of mixed voices and soloists with organ or piano accompaniment. (Handel, George Frideric). *Schirmer. £2.40* DGNQ (B78-50336)

Utrecht Te Deum. *Vocal score.* The Utrecht Te Deum (1713) : for chorus of mixed voices and soloists with organ or piano accompaniment. (Handel, George Frideric). *Schirmer. £2.40* DGNQ (B78-50336)

Vaëz, Gustave. La favorita : drama in four acts. (Royer, Alphonse). *140 Strand, WC2R 1HH : G. Schirmer. Unpriced* BDRAC (B78-26887)

Vallely, Eithne. Making music. The tin whistle. 2nd ed. *6 Dublin Rd, Belfast : Appletree Press. Unpriced* VSQW (B78-50301) ISBN 0-904651-19-3

Vallely, John. Making music. The tin whistle. (Vallely, Eithne). 2nd ed. *6 Dublin Rd, Belfast : Appletree Press. Unpriced* VSQW (B78-50301) ISBN 0-904651-19-3

Valls, Francisco. Missa scala aretina : para 11 voces in 3 cores, instrumentos y continuo = for 11 voices in 3 choirs, instruments and continuo. *Novello. £3.15* ENUDG (B78-50752)

Valsa de esquina : para violão. (Mignone, Francisco). *Arthur Napoleão : Essex Music. Unpriced* SPMHW (B78-50593)

Valse avec choeur = Walzermit Chor : pour choeur mixte et petit orchestra = für gemischten Chor und kleines Orchester. (Bizet, Georges). *Schott. £8.00* DW (B78-50744)

Valse avec choeur. *Vocal score.* Valse avec choeur = Walzermit Chor : pour choeur mixte et petit orchestra = für gemischten Chor und kleines Orchester. (Bizet, Georges). *Schott. £8.00* DW (B78-50744)

Valses nobles, D.969. *Selections: arr.* Valses nobles, opus 77. (Schubert, Franz). *Schott. £4.65* RXMK/AHW (B78-50248)

Valses nobles, opus 77. (Schubert, Franz). *Schott. £4.65* RXMK/AHW (B78-50248)

Van Beethoven, Ludwig. *See* Beethoven, Ludwig van.

Van Camp, Leonard. Stabat mater. Quando corpus. Quando corpus ... : for four-part chorus of mixed voices. (Rossini, Gioacchino Antonio). *Roberton. £0.20* EZDJ/LK (B78-50783)

Variaç ês. (Gomes, Antonio Carlos). *Arthur Napoleão Essex Music. Unpriced* QPK (B78-50550)

Variaç ões. *arr.* Variaç ês. (Gomes, Antonio Carlos). *Arthur Napoleão : Essex Music. Unpriced* QPK (B78-50550)

Variaç ões para violão sobro o tema 'Luar do sertão' de Catullo da Paixão Cearense. (Mignone, Francisco). *Arthur Napoleão : Essex Music. Unpriced* SPM/T (B78-50591)

Variationer über ein Thema von Tschaikowsky. (Rokoko Variationen) : für Violoncello und Klavier (1974). (Blacher, Boris). *Bote und Bock : Associated Music. £6.40* SRP/T (B78-50600)

Variations for solo tuba and nine horns. (Heiden, Bernhard). *Associated Music. £9.05* WN/T (B78-50687)

Variations on a theme by Alban Berg : piano solo. (Finney, Ross Lee). *Henmar Press : Peters : Peters. Unpriced* QP/T (B78-50215)

Variations on a theme of Tchaikovsky. Variationer über ein Thema von Tschaikowsky. (Rokoko Variationen) : für Violoncello und Klavier (1974). (Blacher, Boris). *Bote und Bock : Associated Music. £6.40* SRP/T (B78-50600)

Vasil, Paul. Monsieur Choufleuri restera chez lui de. *Vocal score.* Salon Blumenkohl/Monsieur Choufleuri restera chez lui de ... : Buffo-Operette in einem Akt deutsch nach Karl Fr. Wiltmann von Heinz Balthes und Paul Vasil, opéra bouffe en un acte de St. Rémy, E. L'Epine, Hector Crémieux et Ludovic Halévy, musikalische Revision, neue Instrumentation und praktische Bearbeitung von Caspar Richter. (Offenbach, Jacques). *Bote und Bock : Associated music. £11.50* CF (B78-50703)

Vaughan Williams, Ralph.

Hugh the drover. *Vocal score.* Hugh the drover or Love in the stocks : a romantic ballad opera in two acts. New ed. based on the 1959 edition as revised in accordance with the composer's directions .. *Curwen : Faber Music. Unpriced* CC (B78-50010)

Symphony no.3, 'Pastoral'. Pastoral symphony. *Boosey and Hawkes. Unpriced* KFLE/MDX (B78-50175)

Vendre le vent : für einen Pianisten, einen Schlagzeuger und neun Bläser. (Globokar, Vinko). *Litolff : Peters. Unpriced* UMPQ (B78-51190)

Venetian ceremonial motets. *Novello. £1.10* EWNDW (B78-50763)

Venetian instrumental music C.1600. Maschera, Florentio. Libro primo de canzoni da sonare. *Selections.* Five canzonas for four instruments SATB. *London Pro Musica. Unpriced* LNS (B78-50482)

Vento, Ivo de. Newe teutsche Lieder, mit viern, fünff, und sechs Stimmen. *Selections.* Eight lieder, 1570 : for four voices or instruments, ATTBB. *London Pro Musica. Unpriced* EZDU (B78-50383)

Verdi : his life and times. (Southwell-Sander, Peter). *Midas Books. £6.50 : CIP rev.* BVE(N) (B78-03574) ISBN 0-85936-096-2

Vermorel, Fred. The Sex Pistols : the inside story. *Star Books. £0.75* AKDW/HKQ/E(P) (B78-35475)
ISBN 0-426-18585-4
Vermorel, Judy. The Sex Pistols : the inside story. *Star Books. £0.75* AKDW/HKQ/E(P) (B78-35475)
ISBN 0-426-18585-4
Versalii icones : for dancer, solo cello and instrumental ensemble. (Davies, Peter Maxwell). *Boosey and Hawkes. Unpriced* NYDPNP (B78-50510)
Vibrations : making unorthodox musical instruments. (Sawyer, David). *Cambridge University Press. £4.00* AY/BC (B78-04323) ISBN 0-521-20812-2
Victoria, Tomás Luis de.
Jesu dulcis memoria. Jusu! the very thought is sweet : for 4-part female choir unaccompanied. *Roberton. £0.15* FEZDJ (B78-50824)
Liber primus qui missas ... aliaque cumplectitut, 1576. Nigra sum. Nigra sum de beata virgine : for six-part chorus of mixed voices unaccompanied. *Roberton. £0.20* EZDJ (B78-50779)
Motecta. Ave Maria. Ave Maria. In Annuntiationis B. Maria Virginis,. *36 Ranelagh Gdns. W.6 : Cathedral Music. Unpriced* EZDJ (B78-50377)
Motecta. Doctor bonus. Doctor bonus. In festo sancti Andreae. *Cathedral Music. Unpriced* EZDJ (B78-50378)

Victoria and Albert Museum.
Catalogue of musical instruments in the Victoria and Albert Museum
Vol.2: Non-keyboard instruments. 2nd ed. *H.M.S.O. £8.75* AL/B(WJ) (B78-36278) ISBN 0-11-290263-4
Musical instruments at the Victoria & Albert Museum : an introduction. *H.M.S.O. £0.95* AL/B(YDB) (B78-39230)
ISBN 0-11-290274-x
Victoria and Albert Museum. *Education Department.* Musical instruments at the Victoria & Albert Museum : an introduction. (Victoria and Albert Museum). *H.M.S.O. £0.95* AL/B(YDB) (B78-39230)
ISBN 0-11-290274-x
Victoria's inferno : songs of the old mills, mines, manufactories, canals and railways. *68 Limes Rd, Tettenhall, Wolverhampton W. Midlands : Broadside. £0.95* AKDW/GM (B78-29838) ISBN 0-9503722-3-4
Vierte Streichquartett. 4. Streichquartett = 4th string quartet (1976). (Henze, Hans Werner). *Schott. £12.00* RXNS (B78-51081)
Viking book of folk ballads of the English-speaking world. The Penguin book of folk ballads of the English-speaking world. *Penguin. £1.75* AKDW/K/G (B78-08525)
ISBN 0-14-004241-5
Villa-Lobos, Heitor.
Cantiga de roda. *arr.* Cantiga de roda. *Arthur Napoleão Essex Music. Unpriced* QPK (B78-50552)
Capricho, op.49. *arr.* Capricho, Op.49. *Arthur Napoleão Essex Music. Unpriced* QPK (B78-50553)
As criancas. *arr.* As criancas. *Arthur Napoleão : Essex Music. Unpriced* QPK (B78-50554)
Elegia. *arr.* Elegia. *Arthur Napoleão : Essex Music. Unpriced* QPK (B78-50555)
Prelude, cello & piano, op.20, no.2, F minor. *arr.* Prelúdio op.20, no.2 em lá bemol. *Arthur Napoleão : Essex Music. Unpriced* QPK (B78-50556)
Prole do bebê no.1 : coleção completa, 8 peças para piano. *Arthur Napoleão : Essex Music. Unpriced* QPJ (B78-50548)
Sonhar. Op.14. *arr.* Sonhar, Op.14. *Arthur Napoleão Essex Music. Unpriced* QPK (B78-50557)
Vingt-quatre préludes. 24 préludes : für Klavier (1974). (Blacher, Boris). *Bote und Bock : Schirmer. £7.70* QPJ (B78-51007)
Vinson, Johnnie. Baby elephant walk. *arr.* Baby elephant walk. (Mancini, Henry). *Warner : Blossom. Unpriced* UMMK (B78-50631)
Vinte obras para piano. 20 obras para piano
Album no.3. (Nazareth, Ernesto, *b.1863*). *Arthur Napoleão : Essex Music. Unpriced* QPJ (B78-51016)
Violin examinations, 1979 and 1980
Grade 1: Lists A & B. (Associated Board of the Royal Schools of Music). *Associated Board of the Royal Schools of Music. £1.00* S/AL (B78-51090)
Grade 2: Lists A & B. (Associated Board of the Royal Schools of Music). *Associated Board of the Royal Schools of Music. £1.00* S/AL (B78-51091)
Grade 3: Lists A & B. (Associated Board of the Royal Schools of Music). *Associated Board of the Royal Schools of Music. £1.00* S/AL (B78-51092)
Grade 4: Lists A & B. (Associated Board of the Royal Schools of Music). *Associated Board of the Royal Schools of Music. £1.00* S/AL (B78-51093)
Grade 5: Lists A & B. (Associated Board of the Royal Schools of Music). *Associated Board of the Royal Schools of Music. £1.00* S/AL (B78-51094)
Grade 6: Lists A & B. (Associated Board of the Royal Schools of Music). *Associated Board of the Royal Schools of Music. £1.00* S/AL (B78-51095)
Grade 7: Lists A & B. (Associated Board of the Royal Schools of Music). *Associated Board of the Royal Schools of Music. £1.00* S/AL (B78-51096)
Violin makers : portrait of a living craft. *Gollancz. £9.50* AS/BC(YD/M) (B78-28706) ISBN 0-575-02442-9
Vishnick, Martin. Four pieces for solo violin. *Edwin Ashdown. Unpriced* SPMJ (B78-51107)
Vision of Christ-phoenix : for organ. (Williamson, Malcolm). Revised version. *Boosey and Hawkes. Unpriced* RJ (B78-51053)
Visit from St Nicholas. (The night before Christmas). (Silverman, Jerry). *Schirmer. Unpriced* KDW (B78-50117)
Visocchi, Mark.
Children's overture : an introduction to music listening and creative musical activities for young children. (Jenkins, David, *b.1944*). *Oxford University Press. £2.75* AJFDW(VC) (B78-33673) ISBN 0-19-321388-5
Mendelssohn in Scotland. (Jenkins, David, *b.1944*). *Chappell : Elm Tree Books. £5.95* BMJ(N/YDL/XHJ) (B78-19674) ISBN 0-903443-18-x
Vita di Giuseppe Afflisio = Lebensgeschichte des Giuseppe Afflisio. (Afflisio, Giuseppe). *17 Bucklersbury, Hitchin, Herts. : Bärenreiter. £4.48* AC(WB/P) (B78-19963)
Vital spark of heavenly flame. (The dying Christian to his soul) : for full chorus of mixed voices a cappella. (Chorbajian, John). *Schirmer. Unpriced* EZDH (B78-50043)
Vivaldi, Antonio.
Concerto, trumpets (2), Ryom 537, C major. *arr.* Concerto in C, op.46, no.1, for two B flat trumpets and clarinet choir. *Associated Music. Score, £10.25, Parts, unpriced* UNPK/LF (B78-51192)
Concerto, viola d'amore, Ryom 540, D minor. Concerto con viola d'amor sic, e leuto sic e con tutti gl Isromti sordini. *Little Margaret, Penmans Green, Chipperfield : Ian White. Unpriced* RXMPSQQF (B78-50578)
Gloria. Gloria. Ryom 589. *Vocal score.* Gloria for SATB with keyboard or orchestra, from the cantata of the same name. *Roberton. £0.20* DH (B78-50020)
Vivat regina : suite for brass band. (Mathias, William). *Oxford University Press. Unpriced* WMG (B78-50672)
Vivat regina : suite for brass band, op.75. (Mathias, William). *Oxford University Press. Unpriced* WMG (B78-50673) ISBN 0-19-365694-9
Vocal refrain : an autobiography. (Lynn, *Dame* Vera). Large print ed. *Magna Print Books. £4.25* AKDW/GB/E(P) (B78-05405) ISBN 0-86009-046-9
Voce e tuba : gesammelte Reden und Aufsätze, 1934-1974. (Ehmann, Wilhelm). *32 Great Titchfield St., W.1 : Bärenreiter Kassel. Unpriced* A(D) (B78-03573)
Voces musicales.
Tallis, Thomas. Mass, Puer natus est nobis. *Oxenford Imprint : Dist. Blackwell's Music Shop. Unpriced* EZDG (B78-50365)
White, Robert. Magnificat. *Oxenford Imprint : Blackwell's Music Shop. Unpriced* EZDGKK (B78-50772)
White, Robert. Regina coeli. *Oxenfor Imprint, dist. Blackwell's Music Shop. Unpriced* GEZDJ/LL (B78-50421)
Voces musicales series. Taverner, John. Te Deum. *Oxenford Imprint : Distributed by Blackwell's Music Shop. Unpriced* GEZDGKB (B78-50409)
Vogel, Gunther. dtv-Atlas zur Musik : Tafeln und Texte Bd 1. Systematischer Teil ; und, Historischer Teil: Von den Anfängen bis zur Renaissance. (Michels, Ulrich). 2.Aufl. *Bärenreiter etc.. £3.58* A(C) (B78-19397)
Vogt, Hans. Sonata, violin & double bass, (1976). Sonatina per violino & contrabasso (1976). *Bote und Bock : Yorke. Unpriced* SPLSSEM (B78-51101)
Voices of the night : for orchestra. (Berkeley, *Sir* Lennox). *Chester Music. Unpriced* MMJ (B78-50920)
Volkslieder in leichten Sätzen : elektronische Orgel. *Nagel Bärenreiter. £3.36* RPVK/DW/G/AYE (B78-50572)
Voluntary, organ, no.6, B flat major. *arr.* Voluntary in C major, for descant, treble and tenor recorders. (Greene, Maurice). *Chester Music. Unpriced* VSNTK (B78-51248)
Von Einem, Gottfried. *See* Einem, Gottfried von.
Von Einem, Gottfried von. *See* Einem, Gottfried von.
Von Goethe, Johann Wolfgang. *See* Goethe, Johann Wolfgang von.
Von Herder, Johann. *See* Herder, Johann von.
Von Hofmannsthal, Hugo. *See* Hofmannsthal, Hugo von.
Von Westerman, Gerhart. *See* Westerman, Gerhart von.
Vox superios : for solo tuba, 1976. (Poore, Melvyn). *Arts Lab Music. Unpriced* WVPMJ (B78-51361)
Voxman, Himie.
Concertino, flute & oboe, F major. *arr.* Concertino for flute, oboe and orchestra. (Kalliwoda, Jan Vaclav). *Musica rara. Unpriced* NWPNTK/LF (B78-50202)
Concerto, bassoon & string orchestra, B flat major. *arr.* Concerto in B flat for bassoon, strings and basso continuo. (Hertel, Johann Wilhelm). *Musica rara. Unpriced* VWPK/LF (B78-51291)
Concerto, bassoon, C major. *arr.* Concerto in C for bassoon and orchestra. (Kozeluch, Johann Anton). *Musica rara. Unpriced* VWPK/LF (B78-51292)
Trio concertans, flute, oboe & bassoon, op.45, no.6. Trio op.45, no.6 for flute, oboe and bassoon. (Cambini, Giuseppe). *Musica rara. Unpriced* VNTF (B78-51200)
Voyage in space : twenty pieces for solo piano. (Pert, Morris). *Weinberger. Unpriced* QPJ (B78-50547)
Wade, Darrell.
'11 minutes' : for the junior string orchestra. *16 Anchor Way, Danes Green : Viking. Unpriced* RXMJ (B78-51069)
'11 minutes' : for the junior string orchestra. *16 Anchor Way, Danes Green : Viking. Unpriced* RXMJ (B78-51070)
A Christmas collection : for the junior school orchestra. *16 Anchor Way, Danes Green : Viking. Unpriced* MK/DP/LF/AY (B78-50915)
Dismal land and the giant : a one act musical play for juniors. *(16 Anchor Way, Danes Green, Gnosall) : Viking. Unpriced* CN (B78-50011)
Fanfare. Fanfare, Lullaby, Cherokee war dance. *16 Anchor Way, Danes Green, Gnosall : Viking. Unpriced* MJ (B78-50181)
'Getting together' : a collection devised for the junior and middle school. *16 Anchor Way, Danes Green, Gnosall : Viking. Unpriced* NYDS (B78-50208)
Mr Mulberry's toyshop : a one act musical play for infants or lower juniors. *16 Anchor Way, Danes Green, Gnosall : Viking. Unpriced* CN (B78-50012)
Mrs Pennyweather's garden : a musical play for infants (with optional percussion). *16 Anchor Way, Danes Green, Gnosall : Viking. Unpriced* CN (B78-50328)
Singing together
10 little chickadees. *16 Anchor Way, Danes Green, Gnosall : Viking. Unpriced* JFDW (B78-50093)
10 little chickadees. *16 Anchor Way, Danes Green, Gnosall : Viking. Unpriced* JFDW (B78-50432)
Bed in summer ; words by R.L. Stevenson. *16 Anchor Way, Danes Green, Gnosall : Viking. Unpriced* JFDW (B78-50094)
Bed in summer ; words by R.L. Stevenson. *16 Anchor Way, Danes Green, Gnosall : Viking. Unpriced* JFDW (B78-50095)
Little Indians all are we. *16 Anchor Way, Danes Green, Gnosall : Viking. Unpriced* JFDW (B78-50433)
Marching song ; words by R.L. Stevenson. *16 Anchor Way, Danes Green, Gnosall : Viking. Unpriced* JFDW (B78-50096)
Off to the circus. *16 Anchor Way, Danes Green, Gnosall : Viking. Unpriced* JFDW (B78-50097)
Rain ; words by R.L. Stevenson. *16 Anchor Way, Danes Green, Gnosall : Viking. Unpriced* JFDW (B78-50098)
Summer sun ; words by R.L. Stevenson. *16 Anchor Way, Danes Green, Gnosall : Viking. Unpriced* JFDW (B78-50099)
Swinging along. *16 Anchor Way, Danes Green, Gnosall : Viking. Unpriced* JFDW (B78-50100)
The 2 rats. *16 Anchor Way, Danes Green, Gnosall : Viking. Unpriced* JFDW (B78-50101)
The ferryman ; words by Christina Rossetti. *16 Anchor Way, Danes Green, Gnosall : Viking. Unpriced* JFDW (B78-50102)
The moon ; words by R.L. Stevenson. *16 Anchor Way, Danes Green, Gnosall : Viking. Unpriced* JFDW (B78-50103)
Window cleaning man ; words by M. Long. *16 Anchor Way, Danes Green, Gnosall : Viking. Unpriced* JFDW (B78-50104)
A storm in a teacup : a one act musical play for infants or lower juniors. *Viking. Unpriced* CN (B78-50708)
Stringing along : a tutor for the second year school's violin class. *16 Anchor Way, Danes Green, Gnosall, Staffs. : Viking Publications. Unpriced* SN/AC (B78-50585)
Twenty elementary studies for the young violinist. *16 Anchor Way, Danes Green, Gnosall : Viking. Unpriced* S/AF (B78-50256)
Wagner, Cosima. Cosima Wagner's diaries
Vol.1: 1869-1877. *Collins. £15.00* BWC(N) (B78-34737)
ISBN 0-00-216130-3
Wagner, Hans. Vita di Giuseppe Afflisio = Lebensgeschichte des Giuseppe Afflisio. (Afflisio, Giuseppe). *17 Bucklersbury, Hitchin, Herts. : Bärenreiter. £4.48* AC(WB/P) (B78-19963)
Wagner, Richard. Der Ring des Nibelungen. Die Walküre. Die Walküre. *Dover : Constable. Unpriced* CQC (B78-50712) ISBN 0-486-23566-1
Wagner and Nietzsche. (Fischer-Dieskau, Dietrich). *Sidgwick and Jackson. £7.50* BWC(Z) (B78-39782)
ISBN 0-283-98434-1
Wagner the dramatist. (Garten, Hugh Frederic). *J. Calder. £5.95* BWCAC (B78-09113) ISBN 0-7145-3620-2
Wagner's 'Rienzi' : a reappraisal based on a study of the sketches and drafts. (Deathridge, John). *Clarendon Press. £12.00 : CIP rev.* BWCAC (B77-08491)
ISBN 0-19-816131-x
Wahren, Karl Heinz. Entrerue : für Flöte und Orgel, 1976, 1977. *Bote und Bock : Schirmer. £4.30* VRPLR (B78-51228)
Wake up, Jacob : negro spiritual. (Dexter, Harry). *Edwin Ashdown. £0.20* FDW/LC (B78-50819)
Wakeman, Rick. Rick Wakeman's criminal record. *Rondor Music : Music Sales. Unpriced* QPJ (B78-50224)
Walckiers, Robert. Flute duets
Vol.3: Six easy duos for two flutes. *Chester Music. Unpriced* VRNU (B78-51203)
Waldmusik : für Orchester und Soloinstrumente. (Bialas, Günter). *Bärenreiter. £8.40* MMJ (B78-50489)
Walker, James. À la russe : for bassoon & piano, based on a theme by Moscheles. *Weinberger. Unpriced* VWPJ (B78-50665)
Walker, Richard, *b.1925.* Edmund Rubbra : composer-essays. *22 Pheasant Way, Rickmansworth, Herts. : Triad Press. £9.95 : CIP rev.* BRU (B77-18309)
ISBN 0-902070-21-5
Walker, Sue. The day the world was born. *Mayhew McCrimmon. £1.10* FDE (B78-50806)
ISBN 0-85597-271-8
Walker, Timothy.
African light suite. *Belwin Mills. Unpriced* TSPMG (B78-50613)
Étude. *Belwin Mills. £0.50* TSPMJ (B78-50619)
Fantasia celestina. *Belwin Mills Music. £0.80* TSPMJ (B78-51159)
Prelude, guitar. Prelude. *Belwin Mills Music. £0.50* TSPMJ (B78-51160)
Six airs irlandois nationales variées, Op.125. (Giuliani, Mauro). *Belwin Mills Music. £1.50* TSPM/T (B78-51147)
Walküre. (Wagner, Richard). *Dover : Constable. Unpriced* CQC (B78-50712) ISBN 0-486-23566-1
Walt Disney's musical colouring book. *Wise. Unpriced* JFDW/JR/AY (B78-50848) ISBN 0-86001-484-3
Walter, Christopher. Music books for schools : an annotated list. (Grindea, Carola). *School Library Association. £1.30(£0.90 to members)* A(VC/T) (B78-18775)
ISBN 0-900641-30-4

Walters, Gareth. Invocation and toccata : guitar. *Oxford University Press. Unpriced* TSPMJ (B78-50274) ISBN 0-19-359380-7
Walters, Harold L. The third century : concert march. *Rubank : Novello. Unpriced* UMMGM (B78-50279)
Walton, *Sir* William. Antiphon : S.A.T.B. *Oxford University Press. Unpriced* DH (B78-50021) ISBN 0-19-350366-2
Waltz dream : operetta in three acts. (Straus, Oscar). *Weinberger. Unpriced* CF (B78-50326)
Waltz-impromptu : for guitar. (Branson, David). *Helicon. Unpriced* TSPMHW (B78-51150)
Walzertraum. *Vocal score.* A waltz dream : operetta in three acts. (Straus, Oscar). *Weinberger. Unpriced* CF (B78-50326)
Ward, Anthony. Toussaint, or, The aristocracy of the skin : opera in 3 acts and 22 scenes. *Novello. £1.70* BBPLAC (B78-06260)
Ward, Carole. Ready to play : stories with percussion sounds. (Blades, James). *British Broadcasting Corporation. £1.50* AX/GR(VE) (B78-38609) ISBN 0-563-17610-5
Warlock, Peter. *See* Heseltine, Philip.
Warriors three : trio for B flat cornets and brass band. (Siebert, Edrich). *Harmer : Studio Music. Unpriced* WMPWRNTHVH (B78-50684)
Washburn, Robert.
Elegy : for orchestra. *Boosey and Hawkes. Unpriced* MMJ (B78-50924)
Trigon. *Boosey and Hawkes. £21.00* UMMJ (B78-51184)
Wastall, Peter.
Baroque music for clarinet : including music by Couperin, Handel, Molter, Pokorny, Stamitz. *Boosey and Hawkes. Unpriced* VVPK/AAY (B78-51286)
Classical music for clarinet, including music by Beethoven, Grétry, Haydn, Mozart, Stamitz. *Boosey and Hawkes. Unpriced* VVPK/AAY (B78-50303)
Divertimento, woodwind quartet, Hob.II, no.7, C major. Feld-Parthie in C for wind ensemble. (Haydn, Joseph). *Boosey and Hawkes. Unpriced* UNN (B78-50284)
Feld-Parthie in F, for wind ensemble. (Haydn, Joseph). *Boosey and Hawkes. Unpriced* UNQ (B78-51193)
Romantic music for clarinet, including music by Baerman, Bruch, Gade, Spohr, Weber. *Boosey and Hawkes. Unpriced* VVPK/AAY (B78-50304)
Serenade, wind sextet, no.11, K.375, E flat major. Adagio. Adagio ... for wind ensemble. (Mozart, Wolfgang Amadeus). *Boosey and Hawkes. Unpriced* UNQ (B78-51194)
Water ... footsteps ... time. (Conyngham, Barry). *Universal. Unpriced* MMJ (B78-50921)

Watkins, David. Three nocturnes for harp. (Burgon, Geoffrey). *Chester Music. Unpriced* TQPMJ (B78-51135)
Watkins, Michael Blake. Japanese fragments : for soprano, viola and guitar. (Williams, Graham). *Chester Music. Unpriced* KFLE/SQPLTSDW (B78-50895)
Watson, Pat. Inside the pop scene. *Thornhill Press. £1.50* AKDW/GB/E(M) (B78-14832) ISBN 0-904110-57-5
Watson, Ronald. All my hope on God is founded. *Deacon House, Brundall : Braydeston Press : William Elkin. Unpriced* DH (B78-50022)
Watters, Cyril. Pastoral theme : for 2 B flat cornets, E flat horn and euphonium. *Studio Music. Unpriced* WNS (B78-50690)
Watters, Harold. Songs of heritage : symphonic band. (Williams, Clifton). *Rubank : Novello. Unpriced* UMMJ (B78-51185)
Watts, Isaac. Watt's cradle song : S.A.T.B. (Kelly, Bryan). *Oxford University Press. Unpriced* DP/LF (B78-50739) ISBN 0-19-343065-7
Watt's cradle song : S.A.T.B. (Kelly, Bryan). *Oxford University Press. Unpriced* DP/LF (B78-50739) ISBN 0-19-343065-7
Way out west. (Crookes, Brian). *50 Ladbroke Grove, W.11 : Midland Music. Unpriced* WMJ (B78-50311)
WB easy marching bands series.
Fox, Charles. Happy days. *arr.* Happy days : from the Paramount TV series 'Happy days'. *Warner : Blossom. Unpriced* UMMK/DW/JS (B78-50638)
Hartford, John. Gentle on my mind. *arr.* Gentle on my mind. *Warner : Blossom. Unpriced* UMMK/DW (B78-50634)
Lerner, Sammy. Popeye the sailor. I'm Popeye the sailor man. *arr.* I'm Popeye the sailor man. *Warner : Blossom. Unpriced* UMMK/DW/JR (B78-50636)
Livingston, Jay. The paleface. Buttons and bows. *arr.* Buttons and bows. *Warner : Blossom. Unpriced* UMMK/DW/JR (B78-50637)
Mancini, Henry. Baby elephant walk. *arr.* Baby elephant walk. *Warner : Blossom. Unpriced* UMMK (B78-50631)

Roddenberry, Gene. Star trek. *Selections : arr.* Theme from 'Star Trek'. *Warner : Blossom. Unpriced* UMMK/JS (B78-50640)
Rota, Nino. The godfather. *Selections : arr.* Themes from The godfather and The godfather, part II. *Warner : Blossom. Unpriced* UMMK/JR (B78-50639)
We piano teachers. (Booth, Victor). Revised ed.. *Hutchinson. £2.95* AQ/E(VC) (B78-40354) ISBN 0-09-106191-1
We really want to thank you, Lord. (Baggett, Ed). *Yeldall Manor, Hare Hatch, Reading : Celebration Services. Unpriced* JFDM (B78-50087)
Weaver, William, *b.1923.*
La favorita : drama in four acts. (Royer, Alphonse). *140 Strand, WC2R 1HH : G. Schirmer. Unpriced* BDRAC (B78-26887)
Puccini : the man and his music. *Hutchinson. £5.50* BPU(N) (B78-20437) ISBN 0-09-132380-0
Webber, Andrew Lloyd.
Argentine melody. *arr.* Argentine melody = Canción de Argentina : official BBC tv World Cup theme. *Chappell. Unpriced* QPK/JS (B78-51036)
Evita : the legend of Eva Peron, 1919-1952. *Elm Tree Books. £3.95 : CIP rev.* BWKRACM (B78-12401) ISBN 0-241-89890-0
Theme and variations 1-4. *Chappell. Unpriced* QP/T (B78-50523)
Variations, cello & piano. Variations. *Chappell. Unpriced* SRP/T (B78-51115)
Weber, Carl Maria von, *Freiherr.* Trio, flute, cello & piano, J. 259, G minor. Trio for flute, cello and piano in G minor, J.259. *Eulenburg. Unpriced* NURNT (B78-50198)
Weihnachtskonzerte : für zwei vierstimmige Chöre. (Praetorius, Michael). *Bärenreiter. £2.24* EWNDH/LF (B78-50360)
Weihnachtskonzerte : für zwei vierstimmige Chöre. (Praetorius, Michael). *Bärenreiter. £1.96* EZDH/LF (B78-50374)
Weiner, Stanley.
Sonatina, violin & piano, op.69. Sonatina for violin and piano, op.69. *Bote und Bock : Associated Music. £7.70* SPEM (B78-50588)
Sonatinas, viola, op.70, nos 1-3. 3 Sonatinen für Viola solo, op.70. *Bote und Bock : Associated Music. £4.80* SQPMEM (B78-50597)
Weingarden, Louis. Three short sacred songs : for SSA chorus unaccompanied. *Oxford University Press. Unpriced* FEZDW (B78-50402)
Weinzweig, John.
Divertimento 1 for flute and string orchestra. *Boosey and Hawkes. Unpriced* RXMPVR (B78-51073)
Divertimento, oboe & string orchestra, no.2. Divertimento 2 for oboe and string orchestra. *Boosey and Hawkes. Unpriced* RXMPVT (B78-51074)
Weise Mann. Salomo. Salomo : Solo für Alt-Flöte oder Grosse Flöte aus der Cantate "Der weise Mann" (1977-1978). (Yun, Isang). *Bote und Bock : Schirmer. £1.90* VRPMJ (B78-51235)
Weiss, Donn. De tierra lejana venimos. *Roberton. £0.24* EZDP/LF (B78-50790)
Weiss, Sylvias Leopold. Zwei Menuette = Two minuets. *Schott. £2.00* TSPMK/AHR (B78-51166)
Weiss, Sylvius Leopold. Duet, lute. *arr.* Duett für Gitarren = Duet for guitars. *Schott. £2.00* TSNU (B78-51146)
Weisse, Fritz. Valse avec choeur. *Vocal score.* Valse avec choeur = Walzermit Chor : pour choeur mixte et petit orchestra = für gemischten Chor und kleines Orchester. (Bizet, Georges). *Schott. £8.00* DW (B78-50744)
Welcome home : piano, vocal, chords. (King, Carole). *Colgems-EMI Music : EMI. Unpriced* KDW/GB (B78-50865)
Well tempered clavier = Wohltemperiertes Clavier : forty-eight preludes and fugues, for the piano. (Bach, Johann Sebastian). *Ashley : Phoenix. Unpriced* QP/Y (B78-50989)
Wells, Elsie.
Sea pictures : fifteen easy piano duets in two sets
Set 1. *Oxford University Press. Unpriced* QNV (B78-50212) ISBN 0-19-373947-x
Set 2. *Oxford University Press. Unpriced* QNV (B78-50213) ISBN 0-19-373948-8
Welsh Amateur Music Federation. The amateur singer : a series of practical hints on the use of the voice for conductors, soloists and choristers. (Linwood-Christopher, Mabel). *9 Museum Place, Cardiff : Welsh Amateur Music Federation. Unpriced* AB/E (B78-06264)
Welsh Arts Council.
Alun Hoddinott. (Deane, Basil). *University of Wales Pres for the Welsh Arts Council. £1.50* BHND (B78-39781) ISBN 0-7083-0695-0
William Mathias. (Boyd, Malcolm, *b.1932*). *University of Wales Press for the Welsh Arts Council. Unpriced* BMGH (B78-15753) ISBN 0-7083-0672-1
Welsh National Opera Company. Opera at Llandudno. (Jones, Ivor Wynne). *c/o I.W. Jones, 'Pegasus', 71 Llandudno Rd, Penrhyn Bay, Llandudno, Gwynedd LL30 3HN : Welsh National Opera Company. Unpriced* AC/E(YDKPL) (B78-28696)
Werke für das Laufwerk. *Selections : arr.* Four clock pieces. (Haydn, Joseph). *Novello. Unpriced* VVNTK/B/FJ (B78-51277)
Werkreihe für Bläser und Sanger. Praetorius, Michael. Musae Sioniae. Tl.2. *Selections.* Weihnachtskonzerte : für zwei vierstimmige Chöre. *Bärenreiter. £2.24* EWNDH/LF (B78-50360)
West, John A.
Shepherd, shepherd : spiritual for full chorus of mixed voices unaccompanied. *Roberton. £0.20* EZDW/LC (B78-50801)
Sinner, please don't let this harvest pass : for four-part chorus of mixed voices a cappella. *Roberton. £0.20* EZDW/LC (B78-50802)
Westcott, Frederick. With cheerful voice : hymns for children with melodies, descant recorder parts, and prayers. 2nd ed. revised and enlarged. *A. & C. Black. Unpriced* JFADM (B78-50086) ISBN 0-7136-1368-8
Westerman, Gerhart von.
Concert guide : a handbook for music-lovers. *Sphere. £0.90* A (B78-09117) ISBN 0-7221-9003-4
Opera guide. *Sphere. £0.90* AC (B78-05404) ISBN 0-7221-9004-2
Western Wind mass. (Shepherd, John). *Chester Music. Unpriced* EZDG (B78-50768)
Weston, Pamela. More clarinet virtuosi of the past. *1 Rockland Rd, SW15 2LN : The author. £5.40* AVV/E(M) (B78-00390)
What any lover learns : for four-part chorus of mixed voices a cappella. (Trubitt, Allen). *Chappell. Unpriced* EZDW (B78-50054)
What does the song hope for? : for soprano, ensemble and tape. (Saxton, Robert). *Chester Music. Unpriced* KFLE/NUPNPDX (B78-50892)
What is love? : songs for voice, lute and viola da gamba. *Chester Music. Unpriced* KE/STPLTWDW (B78-50884)
Wheatley, Dorothy. Silly things to sing. (Smith, Pat). *E.J. Arnold. Unpriced* JFDW/GJ (B78-50846) ISBN 0-560-02726-5
Whelan, Carys.
Carol y doethion. Carol y doethion = Carol of the kings a Cysgu yn y gwair = Lord Emmanuel. (Whelan, E L). *Hafod, St. Hilary, Cowbridge : E.L. Whelan. £0.25* FDP/LF (B78-50060)
Clychau'r nadolig. Clychau'r nadolig = Christmas bells a Bethlehem. (Whelan, E L). *Hafod, St. Hilary, Cowbridge : E.L. Whelan. £0.25* FDP/LF (B78-50061)
Whelan, E L.
Carol y doethion. Carol y doethion = Carol of the kings a Cysgu yn y gwair = Lord Emmanuel. *Hafod, St. Hilary, Cowbridge : E.L. Whelan. £0.25* FDP/LF (B78-50060)
Clychau'r nadolig. Clychau'r nadolig = Christmas bells a Bethlehem. *Hafod, St. Hilary, Cowbridge : E.L. Whelan. £0.25* FDP/LF (B78-50061)
When the kye comes home : T.T.B.B. unacc. (Johnston, Peter Fyfe). *Banks Music. Unpriced* GEZDW (B78-50072)
Where the palm trees grow : six pieces for the young pianist. (Alt, Hansi). *Oxford University Press. Unpriced* QPJ (B78-51003)
Whipple, James. Terzetto (1925) : for flute, oboe and viola (or clarinet). (Holst, Gustav). 2nd revised ed. *Chester Music. Unpriced* VNT (B78-51198)
Whipple, Tim. The celebration song. (Asprey, Jonathan). *57 Dorchester Rd, Lychett Minster, Poole : Celebration Services. Unpriced* FDM (B78-50059)
White, Geoff. Big red songbook. *Unit 10, Specner Court, Chalcot Rd, N.W.1 : Plato Press. £1.00* JEZDW/AY (B78-50835) ISBN 0-904383-12-1
White, Ian.
Aria and variations, viola d'amore & cello, Czach 90, D major. Aria and VII variations : for viola d'amore and cello. (Rust, Friedrich Wilhelm). *Little Margaret, Penmans Green, Chipperfield : Ian White. Unpriced* SQQPLSR/T (B78-50599)
Concerto, viola d'amore, Ryom 540, D minor. Concerto con viola d'amor sic, e leuto sic e con tutti gl Isromti sordini. (Vivaldi, Antonio). *Little Margaret, Penmans Green, Chipperfield : Ian White. Unpriced* RXMPSQQF (B78-50578)
Parthia, viola d'amore, gamba & harpsichord, C minor. Parthia in C minor for viola d'amore, gamba & harpsichord. (Grabe). *Little Margaret, Penmans Green, Chipperfield : Ian White. Unpriced* NXNTG (B78-50508)
Quartet, recorder, viola d'amore, violin & cello, D major. Quartetto in D for viola d'amore, recorder, violino con sordino and basso. (Hoffmeister, Franz Anton). *Little Margaret, Penmans Green, Chipperfield, Kings Langley : E.L. White. Unpriced* NVSNS (B78-50200)
Sonata, viola d'amore & keyboard, Czach 87, D major. Sonata for viola d'amore and harpsichord. (Rust, Friedrich Wilhelm). *Little Margaret, Penmans Green, Chipperfield : Ian White. Unpriced* SQQPE (B78-50598)

White, Mark.
The observer's book of big bands. *F. Warne. £1.25* AMT(M) (B78-37101) ISBN 0-7232-1589-8
The observer's book of jazz. *F. Warne. £1.25* AMT(C) (B78-35477) ISBN 0-7232-1588-x
White, Robert.
Magnificat. *Oxenford Imprint : Blackwell's Music Shop. Unpriced* EZDGKK (B78-50772)
Regina coeli. *Oxenfor Imprint, dist. Blackwell's Music Shop. Unpriced* GEZDJ/LL (B78-50421)
White Christmas. (Berlin, Irving). *Chappell. Unpriced* NYFPK/DW/JR/LF (B78-50952)
Whitfield, John. String music of the second Elizabeth : twelve original pieces for string orchestra. *Belwin-Mills. Unpriced* RXM/AY (B78-50243)
Whitman, Walt.
Idyll 'Once I passed through a populous city'. *Vocal score.* Prelude and idyll : for soprano and baritone with orchestra. (Delius, Frederick). *Boosey and Hawkes. Unpriced* JNEDX (B78-50438)
Sea drift. (Delius, Frederick). *Boosey and Hawkes. Unpriced* EMDX (B78-50032)
Whittaker, William Gillies.
The cantatas of Johann Sebastian Bach : sacred and secular
Vol.1. *Oxford University Press. £6.95(set of 2 vols)* BBCADE (B78-39233) ISBN 0-19-315238-x
The Hexamshire lass : ballads and folk songs from the North Country. *Curwen : Faber Music. Unpriced* KDW/G/AYDJ (B78-50450)
Whitworth, John. First guitar pieces. (Garcia, Gerald). *Holley Music. Unpriced* TSPMJ (B78-51154)
WHO. A decade of The Who : an authorised history in music, paintings, words and photographs. *Fabulous Music : Music Sales. Unpriced* KE/TSDW/HKR (B78-50172) ISBN 0-8256-2670-6
Wiegenlied : for mixed chorus and piano four hands. (Brahms, Johannes). *Boosey and Hawkes. Unpriced* DW

(B78-50349)
Wiegold, Mary. Catalogue of music broadcast on Radio 3 and Radio 4
1974. (British Broadcasting Corporation). *B.B.C. £4.00* A/JT(WT) (B78-20763) ISBN 0-563-17369-6
Wiener Symphonie, Opus 49. (Einem, Gottfried von). *Bote und Bock : Schirmer. £14.40* MME (B78-50918)
Wiggins, Bram. Giles Farnaby suite. (Farnaby, Giles). *Oxford University Press. Unpriced* UMMK (B78-50283)

Wild cherry. *arr.* Wild cherry : electrified funk. (Parissi, Robert). *Chappell. Unpriced* KDW/GB (B78-50137)
Wild cherry : electrified funk. (Parissi, Robert). *Chappell. Unpriced* KDW/GB (B78-50137)
Wilkinson, Philip George. Clavierstücke für die Jugend. Op.68. *Selections : arr.* A Schumann suite : seven pieces from 'Album for the young'. opus 68. (Schumann, Robert). *Novello. Unpriced* VVNSK (B78-51276)
Wilkinson, Stephen. Galician carol, Panxoliña sic de Nadal : for four-part chorus of mixed voices unaccompanied. *Roberton. £0.18* EZDP/LF (B78-50048)
Wilkinson, Thomas Turner. Ballads and songs of Lancashire
Part 2: Modern. 3rd ed. *EP Publishing. £5.25* AKDW/K/G(YDJD) (B78-02615) ISBN 0-7158-1182-7
Williams, Aaron. Byrd, Morley, Tallis : three-part vocal compositions. *Ricordi. Unpriced* VSNTK (B78-51247)
Williams, Clifton. Songs of heritage : symphonic band. *Rubank : Novello. Unpriced* UMMJ (B78-51185)
Williams, Graham. Japanese fragments : for soprano, viola and guitar. *Chester Music. Unpriced* KFLE/SQPLTSDW (B78-50895)
Williams, Hank. 20 greatest hits. *Acuff-Rose : Chappell. Unpriced* KDW/GC (B78-50156)
Williams, Paul. One on one. *Selections: arr.* Songs from 'One on one' : a Warner Bros. film. (Fox, Charles). *Warner Blossom. Unpriced* KDW/JR (B78-50166)
Williams, Peter.
Concerto, organ, op.4, no.1, G minor. Organ concerto, G minor, Op.4, no.1. (Handel, George Frideric). *Eulenburg. Unpriced* MPRF (B78-50926)
Concerto, organ, op.4, no.2, B flat major. Organ concerto, B flat major, Op.4, no.2. (Handel, George Frideric). *Eulenburg. Unpriced* MPRF (B78-50927)
Concerto, organ, op.4, no.3, G minor. Organ concerto, G minor, Op.4, no.3. (Handel, George Frideric). *Eulenburg. Unpriced* MPRF (B78-50928)
Concerto, organ, op.4, no.4, F major. Organ concerto, F major, Op.4, no.4. (Handel, George Frideric). *Eulenburg. Unpriced* MPRF (B78-50929)
Concerto, organ, op.4, no.5, F major. Organ concerto, F major, Op.4, no.5. (Handel, George Frideric). *Eulenburg. Unpriced* MPRF (B78-50930)
Concerto, organ, op.4, no.6, B flat major, 'Harp'. Organ concerto, (Harp concerto), B flat major, Op.4, no.6. (Handel, George Frideric). *Eulenburg. Unpriced* MPRF (B78-50931)
Williams, Ralph Vaughan. *See* Vaughan Williams, Ralph.
Williams, William Carlos. This is just to say : for tenor and piano. (Holloway, Robin). *Boosey and Hawkes. Unpriced* KGHDW (B78-50904)
Williamson, Malcolm. Vision of Christ-phoenix : for organ. Revised version. *Boosey and Hawkes. Unpriced* RJ (B78-51053)
Williamson, *Sir* Malcolm. String music of the second Elizabeth : twelve original pieces for string orchestra. *Belwin-Mills. Unpriced* RXM/AY (B78-50243)
Willowbrook suite : for descant, treble and tenor recorders. (Smith, Peter Melville). *Lengnick. £0.55* VSNTG (B78-51246)
Wills, Arthur.
Pavane and galliard for solo guitar. *Ricordi. Unpriced* TSPMHVG (B78-50614)
Scherzetto. *Cramer. Unpriced* RJ (B78-50231)
Willson, Robina Beckles. Musical merry-go-round : musical activities for the very young. *Heinemann. £3.50* A/GR (B78-01459) ISBN 0-434-97257-6
Wilmer, Valerie.
As serious as your life : the story of the new jazz. *Quartet Books. £2.95* AMT(M/YTLD) (B78-05410) ISBN 0-7043-3164-0
As serious as your life : the story of the new jazz. *Allison and Busby. £6.50* AMT(M/XQ18) (B78-11201) ISBN 0-85031-224-8
Wilson, Christopher Robert. An old English carol. *arr.* An old English carol : old English ballad tune. (Sternfeld, Frederick William). *Oxford University Press. Unpriced* EZDP/LF (B78-50789) ISBN 0-19-343068-1
Wilson, Earl. Sinatra. *Star Books. £1.25* AKDW/GB/E(P) (B78-22166) ISBN 0-352-30194-5
Wilson, John. Sixteen hymns of today for use as simple anthems. *Royal School of Church Music. Unpriced* DM/AY (B78-50345)
Wilson-Dickson, Andrew. Sonata, organ, no.1. Sonata no.1 for organ. *Banks. Unpriced* RE (B78-51047)
Wiltshire Library and Museum Service. Music for orchestras. *Bythesea Rd, Trowbridge, Wilts. : Wiltshire County Council Library and Museum Service. £0.20* A(TC) (B78-23116) ISBN 0-86080-010-5
Wimberger, Gerhard.
4 Songs nach Texten von Hans-Jurgen Heise, Heinz Piontek, Hans Magnus Enzensberger und Ror Wolf für Singstimme, Klavier, Kontrabass und Schlagzeug. *Bärenreiter. £2.50* KE/NYGDW (B78-50883)
Memento vivere : für Mezzosopran, Bariton, 3 Sprechstimmen, gemischten Chor und Orchester. *Bärenreiter. £12.60* EMDX (B78-50356)
Short stories : für elf Bläser. *Bärenreiter. £4.20* UMJ (B78-51175)

Windsor series of old music for recorders. Morley, Thomas. A plaine and easy introduction to practicall musicke. O amica mea. *arr.* O amica mea. *Edizioni Pegasus : Peters. Unpriced* VSNRK/DJ (B78-50652)
Winfrey, Robert. Let's build a city : for two-part chorus of young voices with piano accompaniment. *Schirmer. Unpriced* FDW (B78-50064)
Winterhoff, Hans-Jürgen. Meilensteine eines Komponistenlebens : kleine Festschrift zum 70. Geburtstag von Günter Bialas. *32 Gt Titchfield St., W1P 7AD : Bärenreiter. £10.08* BBNO(D) (B78-19399)
Winters, Geoffrey.
Sounds and music
Book 1. *Longman. Unpriced* JFE/LDW/AY (B78-50849) ISBN 0-582-24203-7
The three pigs : for group music making. *Novello. £1.20* CQN (B78-50330)
Wishart, Trevor. Sounds fun 2 : a second book of musical games. *Universal Edition. £0.75* A/GS (B78-11209) ISBN 0-900938-47-1
Wishbone Ash. Classic Ash. *EMI. Unpriced* KE/TSDW/GB (B78-50170)
With a joyful voice : a collection of anthems. *Novello. £1.45* DH/AY (B78-50729)
With cheerful voice : hymns for children with melodies, descant recorder parts, and prayers. 2nd ed. revised and enlarged. *A. & C. Black. Unpriced* JFADM (B78-50086) ISBN 0-7136-1368-8
Wittmann, Karl Friedrich. Monsieur Choufleuri restera chez lui de. *Vocal score.* Salon Blumenkohl/Monsieur Choufleuri restera chez lui de ... : Buffo-Operette in einem Akt deutsch nach Karl Fr. Wiltmann von Heinz Balthes und Paul Vasil, opéra bouffe en un acte de St. Rémy, E. L'Epine, Hector Crémieux et Ludovic Halévy, musikalische Revision, neue Instrumentation und praktische Bearbeitung von Caspar Richter. (Offenbach, Jacques). *Bote und Bock : Associated music. £11.50* CF (B78-50703)
Woffinden, Bob.
The illustrated 'New musical express' encyclopedia of rock. (Logan, Nick). 1978 ed.. *27 Old Gloucester St., WC1N 3AF : Salamander Books Limited. £3.95* A/HKR(C) (B78-12095) ISBN 0-86101-009-4
The illustrated 'New musical express' encyclopedia of rock. (Logan, Nick). Revised ed. *Hamlyn. £5.95* AKDW/HKR(C) (B78-15752) ISBN 0-600-33171-7
Wohltemperirte Clavier. Well tempered clavier = Wohltemperiertes Clavier : forty-eight preludes and fugues, for the piano. (Bach, Johann Sebastian). *Ashley Phoenix. Unpriced* QP/Y (B78-50989)
Wolf, Ror. 4 Songs nach Texten von Hans-Jurgen Heise, Heinz Piontek, Hans Magnus Enzensberger und Ror Wolf für Singstimme, Klavier, Kontrabass und Schlagzeug. (Wimberger, Gerhard). *Bärenreiter. £2.50* KE/NYGDW (B78-50883)
Wolf-Ferrari, Ermanno. Italian intermezzo : six pieces. *Weinberger. Unpriced* VRPLTSK (B78-50650)
Wolfgang Amadeus Mozart, Chronik eines Lebens. (Eibl, Joseph Heinz). 2.Aufl. *Bärenreiter etc.. £1.90* BMS(N) (B78-21399)
Women in American music : a bibliography. (Skowronski, JoAnn). *Scarecrow Press : Distributed by Bailey and Swinfen. £6.80* A(Z/T) (B78-24791) ISBN 0-8108-1105-7
Wonder, Stevie. Phases, phases, phases, phases. *arr.* Phases, phases, phases, phases. *Jobete Music : Chappell. Unpriced* KDW/GBS (B78-50155)
Wood, David, *b.1944.* Old Father Time : a family musical. *French. £1.20* BWPDACN (B78-39232) ISBN 0-573-05046-5
Wood, Gareth. Introduction and allegro. *R. Smith. Unpriced* WMJ (B78-50680)
Wood, Hugh.
Concerto, violin, op.17. Violin concerto, op.17. *Chester Music. Unpriced* MPSF (B78-50933)
Quartet, strings, no.2. String quartet no.2. *Chester Music. Unpriced* RXNS (B78-51085)
Wood, Roger. The making of an opera : 'Don Giovanni' at Glyndebourne. (Higgins, John, *b.1934*). *Secker and Warburg. £7.95* BMSAC/E (B78-33162) ISBN 0-436-19595-x
Woodford, Peggy. Schubert : his life and times. *Midas Books etc.. £6.50* BSF(N) (B78-40351) ISBN 0-85936-095-4
Wooding, Dan. Rick Wakeman : the caped crusader. *Hale. £4.95* AKDW/HKR/E(P) (B78-22170) ISBN 0-7091-6487-4
Woodrow, Martin. Make your own musical instruments : a bibliography. *14 Wisden Rd, Stevenage, Herts. : Clover Publications. £2.40* AL/BC(T)
Woods, Stanley. Cornet cosmology : for brass band. *Chester Music. Unpriced* WMJ (B78-51314)
Wootton, Richard. Honky tonkin' : a guide to music USA. 2nd ed. *21 Melbourne Court, Anerley Rd, Penge, S.E.20 : The author. £2.50* A/GB(YT/BC) (B78-28695) ISBN 0-9506108-0-1
Workers' carol. (Petrokino, Paul). *Roberton. Unpriced* DP/LF (B78-50026)
Workers' carol. (Petrokino, Paul). *Roberton. £0.12* JE/VSPDP/LF (B78-50426)
Workers' carol. *arr.* The workers' carol. (Petrokino, Paul). *Roberton. Unpriced* DP/LF (B78-50026)
Workers' carol. *arr.* The workers' carol. (Petrokino, Paul). *Roberton. £0.12* JE/VSPDP/LF (B78-50426)
Working Group on Pop Festivals. *See* Great Britain. *Working Group on Pop Festivals.*
Works. Der musikalische Nachlass. (Nietzsche, Friedrich). *Bärenreiter. Unpriced* C/AZ (B78-50699)
Works. Der musikalische Nachlass. (Nietzsche, Friedrich). *Bärenreiter. Unpriced* C/AZ (B78-50700)

Works of Henry Purcell
Volume 8: Ode on St Cecilia's Day, 1692 ; edited under the supervision of the Purcell Society by Peter Dennison. (Purcell, Henry). *Novello. £10.00* C/AZ (B78-50002)
Works of Jimmy Kennedy. (Kennedy, Jimmy). *EMI. Unpriced* KDW/GB (B78-50872)
Works of Les Reed. (Reed, Les). *EMI. Unpriced* KDW/GB (B78-50869)
World is mad : song, for voice, clarinet and piano. (Head, Michael). *Emerson. Unpriced* KE/VVPDW (B78-50466)

World of art library. Griffiths, Paul. A concise history of modern music from Debussy to Boulez. *Thames and Hudson. £5.50* A(XLK88) (B78-21398) ISBN 0-500-18167-5
World's favorite folk explosion : for all fretted instruments, guitar, banjo, ukulele, mandolin, tenor banjo, tenor guitar, baritone uke. *Ashley : Phoenix. Unpriced* TPMK/DW/G/AYT (B78-50267)
World's favorite popular classics for organ and other favorites
Vol.1. *Ashley : Phoenix. Unpriced* RK/AAY (B78-50234)

Vol.2 ; arranged by Lawrence Grant. *Ashley : Phoenix. Unpriced* RK/AAY (B78-50235)
World's favorite selected masterpieces : for classic guitar
Vol.3 : compiled and edited by Frantz Cassens. *Ashley Phoenix. Unpriced* TSPMK/AAY (B78-50276)
World's favorite series.
Bach, Johann Sebastian. Das wohltemperirte Clavier. Well tempered clavier = Wohltemperiertes Clavier : forty-eight preludes and fugues, for the piano. *Ashley Phoenix. Unpriced* QP/Y (B78-50989)
Beloved Scotch & Irish songs & ballads. *Ashley : Phoenix. Unpriced* KDW/AYDM (B78-50120)
World's favorite folk explosion : for all fretted instruments, guitar, banjo, ukulele, mandolin, tenor banjo, tenor guitar, baritone uke. *Ashley : Phoenix. Unpriced* TPMK/DW/G/AYT (B78-50267)
World's favorite popular classics for organ and other favorites
Vol.1. *Ashley : Phoenix. Unpriced* RK/AAY (B78-50234)

World's favorite popular classics for organ and other favorites
Vol.2 ; arranged by Lawrence Grant. *Ashley : Phoenix. Unpriced* RK/AAY (B78-50235)
World's favorite selected masterpieces : for classic guitar
Vol.3 : compiled and edited by Frantz Cassens. *Ashley Phoenix. Unpriced* TSPMK/AAY (B78-50276)
World's favourite series. Five greatest symphonies : for piano, two hands. *Ashley : Phoenix. Unpriced* QPK/AE/AY (B78-51024)
World's winter : for soprano and instrumental ensemble. (Payne, Anthony). *Chester Music. Unpriced* KFLE/NVNNDX (B78-50894)
Would I might go far over sea : for four-part chorus of mixed voices a cappella. (George, Thom Ritter). *Chappell. Unpriced* EZDW (B78-50387)
Wright, Francis.
The capodastro and its use. *Charnwood Music. Unpriced* TS/PFT/AF (B78-50605)
Scales and arpeggios (and how they are played) : for the guitar. *Charnwood Music. Unpriced* TS/AF (B78-50604)

Wright, O. The modal system of Arab and Persian music, AD 1250-1300. *Oxford University Press. £32.00 : CIP rev.* BZCW/PR (B77-07528) ISBN 0-19-713575-7
Wulstan, David.
Haec dies. (Shepherd, John, *b.1520*). *Oxenford Imprint : Blackwell's Music Shop. Unpriced* EZDJ/LL (B78-50784)
Libera nos, salva nos : two settings. (Shepherd, John, *b.1520*). *Oxenford : Blackwell's Music Shop (dist.). Unpriced* EZDJ (B78-50778)
Mass, Puer natus est nobis. (Tallis, Thomas). *Oxenford Imprint : Dist. Blackwell's Music Shop. Unpriced* EZDG (B78-50365)
Paschal Kyrie. (Shepherd, John, *b.1520*). *Oxenford Imprint : Blackwell's Music Shop. Unpriced* EZDGB (B78-50770)
Te Deum. (Taverner, John). *Oxenford Imprint : Distributed by Blackwell's Music Shop. Unpriced* GEZDGKB (B78-50409)
Wurzels song book. *EMI. Unpriced* KE/TSDW/GB/AY (B78-50171)
Wye, Trevor.
Le carnival de Venice. Op.14. Carnival of Venice : for flute and piano. (Genin, P A). *Chester Music. Unpriced* VRP/T (B78-51210)
Fantaisie pastorale hongroise. Op.26. Hungarian pastoral fantasy : for flute and piano. (Doppler, Franz). *Chester Music. Unpriced* VRPJ (B78-51215)
Flute duets
Vol.1: Thirty duets by Devienne, Berbiguier, Boismortier, Loeillet, Naudot, Tulou, Kohler and Mozart. *Chester Music. Unpriced* VRNU/AY (B78-51205)

Vol.2. *Chester Music. Unpriced* VRNU/AY (B78-51204)
Vol.3: Six easy duos for two flutes. *Chester Music. Unpriced* VRNU (B78-51203)
Flute solos with piano accompaniment
Vol.3. *Chester Music. Unpriced* VRPK/AAY (B78-51220)

Syrinx : for solo flute. (Debussy, Claude). *Chester Music. Unpriced* VRPMJ (B78-51233)

Wyn, Hefin. Doedd neb yn becso dam : hanes, lluniau a
chaneuon Edward H. Dafis. *Ffordd Llanllyfni,
Penygroes, Gwynedd LL54 6DB : Sain (Recordiau) Cyf.*.
£1.50 AKDW/GB/E(P) (B78-09115)

Wyton, Alec. A hymne to God the Father. *Novello. £0.47*
EXRPLRDH (B78-50363)

Yakeley, June. Guitar masters of the 19th century : Italian
masters, 19 original easy pieces, collected, edited and
arranged in progressive order by June Yakeley. *Ricordi.
Unpriced* TSPMJ (B78-50616)

Yancey, Becky. My life with Elvis. *W.H. Allen. £5.95*
AKDW/HK/E(P) (B78-01678)   ISBN 0-491-02084-8

Yancy, Marvin. Our love : a Marvin Yancy, Chuck Jackson
songbook. *Chappell. Unpriced* KDW/GB (B78-50871)

Yankee ingenuity : a musical. (Bimonte, Richard). *French's
acting ed. French. £1.65* BWNTSACM (B78-12987)
     ISBN 0-573-68082-5

Yankel, der Heizeriker. *See* Gottlieb, Jacob.

Yantra : für Klavier, Violine und Violoncello, Opus 41
(1974). (Michael, Frank). *Bote und Bock : Schirmer.
£15.35* NXNT (B78-50949)

Yates, Charles Dwight. Concerto, trumpets (2), Ryom 537,
C major. *arr.* Concerto in C, op.46, no.1, for two B flat
trumpets and clarinet choir. (Vivaldi, Antonio).
Associated Music. Score, *£10.25*, Parts, *unpriced*
UNPK/LF (B78-51192)

Year book
1978. (British Federation of Music Festivals). *106
Gloucester Place, W1H 3DB : The Federation. £1.50*
A(YC/WE/Q) (B78-17612)

Year of the cat. (Stewart, Al). *71-75 New Oxford St., W.C.1
: Gwyneth Music. Unpriced* KDW/GB (B78-50140)

Year of the cat. *arr.* Year of the cat. (Stewart, Al). *71-75
New Oxford St., W.C.1 : Gwyneth Music. Unpriced*
KDW/GB (B78-50140)

Yearbook
1978. (British Country Music Association). *PO Box 2,
Newton Abbot, Devon TQ12 4HT : The Association.
Unpriced* AKDW/GCW(BC) (B78-21397)

Yehudi Menuhin music guides. Holland, James. Percussion.
Macdonald and Jane's. £6.95 AX/B (B78-39787)
     ISBN 0-354-04173-8

Yeldall carol, This is the day. (Davis, Diane). *Yeldall
Manor, Hare Hatch, Reading : Celebration Services.
Unpriced* DP/LF (B78-50025)

Yellow submarine. *arr.* Yellow submarine. (Lennon, John).
Chappell. Unpriced NYFPK/DW (B78-50515)

Yes.
Going for the one. *arr.* Going for the one. *Warner
Blossom. Unpriced* KDW/HKR (B78-50165)
Yes. *Chappell. Unpriced* KDW/GB (B78-50141)

Yes. (Yes). *Chappell. Unpriced* KDW/GB (B78-50141)

Yolen, Jane.
Ring out! : a book of bells. *Evans Bros. £3.50* AXS
(B78-31602)   ISBN 0-237-44875-0
Rounds about rounds. *Franklin Watts. Unpriced*
FDW/XC/AY (B78-50396)   ISBN 0-531-00125-3

York Minster. *Library.* A catalogue of the printed music
published before 1850 in York Minster Library. *Dean's
Park, York YO1 2JD : The Library. £1.50* A(TC)
(B78-20765)

Yorkshire Television.
Pop quest : so you think you know all about rock 'n' pop.
(Tobler, John). *Independent Television Books : Arrow
Books. £0.65* A/GB (B78-20431)   ISBN 0-09-917570-3
A selection of musical instruments to make for children.
(Goddard, Arthur). *Trident House, Brooks Mews, W1Y
2PN : Trident Television Ltd. £0.25* AX/BC
(B78-05413)

Young, Percy Marshall. Alice Elgar : enigma of a Victorian
lady. *Dobson. £7.50* BEP(N/XLJ32) (B78-35468)
     ISBN 0-234-77482-7

Young, *Sir* Robin Mackworth-. *See* Mackworth-Young, *Sir*
Robin.

Yun, Isang.
Concerto, flute, (1977). Konzert für Flöte und kleiner
Orchester (1977). *Bote und Bock : Schirmer. £8.65*
MPVRF (B78-50937)
Double concerto, oboe & harp. Doppelkonzert für Oboe
und Harfe mit kleinem Orchester, 1977. *Bote und Bock :
Schirmer. £14.40* MPVTPLTQF (B78-50938)
Fragment für Orgel, 1975. *Bote und Bock : Associated
Music. £2.40* RJ (B78-50569)
Königliches Thema : für Violine solo, 1976. *Bote und Bock
: Associated Music. £2.40* SPM/T (B78-50592)
Der weise Mann. Salomo. Salomo : Solo für Alt-Flöte oder
Grosse Flöte aus der Cantate "Der weise Mann"
(1977-1978). *Bote und Bock : Schirmer. £1.90* VRPMJ
(B78-51235)

Zauberflöte. Wie stark ist nicht dein Zauberton. *arr.*
Andante. (Mozart, Wolfgang Amadeus). *Lengnick.
Unpriced* VRPK/DW (B78-51225)

Zehm, Friedrich.
Serenade für Flöte und Gitarre. *Schott. £6.00* VRPLTS
(B78-50293)
Sinfonia, trumpet & string orchestra, G.9, D major. *arr.*
Concerto D-Dur per tromba con archi e continuo.
(Torelli, Giuseppe). *Schott. £3.20* WSPK/LE
(B78-50313)

Zehn Chorale alter Meister für Posaune und Orgel.
Bärenreiter. £4.80 WUPLRK/DM/AYE (B78-51355)

Zeitströme : für Orchester, 1974. (Zender, Hans). *Bote und
Bock : Associated Music. £7.70* MMJ (B78-50495)

Zender, Hans.
Chiffren : für Cembalo, (1976). *Bote und Bock : Schirmer.
£2.40* QRPJ (B78-51040)
Litanei : für 3 Violoncello (1976). *Bote und Bock
Schirmer. £5.75* SRNT (B78-51113)
Zeitströme : für Orchester, 1974. *Bote und Bock*

Associated Music. £7.70 MMJ (B78-50495)

Zickler, Heinz.
Sinfonia, trumpet & string orchestra, G.9, D major.
Concerto D-Dur per tromba con archi e continuo.
(Torelli, Giuseppe). *Schott. £4.00* RXMPWSE
(B78-50251)
Sinfonia, trumpet & string orchestra, G.9, D major. *arr.*
Concerto D-Dur per tromba con archi e continuo.
(Torelli, Giuseppe). *Schott. £3.20* WSPK/LE
(B78-50313)

Zimmer, Ulrich W. Nun jauchzt dem Herren, alle Welt :
Chorsätze zu Gemeinsamen Kirchenliedern. *Bärenreiter.
£3.20* EZDM/AYE (B78-50381)

Zodiac : orchestra. (Bennett, Richard Rodney). *Novello.
£3.15* MMJ (B78-50188)

Zodiac trio, op.70 : for flute, viola, and harp. (Mathias,
William). *Oxford University Press. Unpriced* NVRNT
(B78-50199)   ISBN 0-19-335774-7

Zodiac : twelve pieces for clarinet in B flat and piano, in
two sets
Set 1. (Kelly, Bryan). *Oxford University Press. Unpriced*
VVPJ (B78-51284)   ISBN 0-19-357442-x
Set 2. (Kelly, Bryan). *Oxford University Press. Unpriced*
VVPJ (B78-51285)   ISBN 0-19-357443-8

Zodiacs. (Moroder, Giorgio). *Hansa Productions : ATV
Music : Music Sales. Unpriced* KFDW (B78-50174)

Zukofsky, Paul. All-interval scale book, including a chart of
harmonics for the violin. *Schirmer. £3.65* S/AF
(B78-50584)

Zur Geschichte des buddhistischen Ritualgesangs in Japan :
Traktate des 9. bis 14. Jahrhunderts zum shomyo der
Tendai-Sekte. (Giesen, Walter). *32 Gt Titchfield St., W1P
7AD : Bärenreiter. £12.60* BZHPADGVF (B78-35473)

Zwei Menuette = Two minuets. (Weiss, Sylvias Leopold).
Schott. £2.00 TSPMK/AHR (B78-51166)

Zwei spanische Stücke = Two Spanish pieces = Deux
pièces espagnoles : für Gitarre ... (Tarrega, Francisco).
Revidierte Neuausgabe. *Schott. £3.20* TSPMH
(B78-50271)

Zweig, Stefan. A confidential matter : the letters of Richard
Strauss and Stefan Zweig, 1931-1935. (Strauss, Richard).
University of California Press. £6.75 BSU(N/XNL5)
(B78-04319)   ISBN 0-520-03036-2

Subject Index

Sextets: Brass, strings, keyboard & percussion:
Accompanying soprano trio
JNFLDE/WYEXPNQ
Sextets: Recorder   VSNQ
Sextets: Strings & keyboard: Accompanying vocal trio
JNDE/NXNQ
Sextets: Strings & percussion   NYJNQ
Sextets: Trumpet, strings & keyboard   NUXSNQ
Sextets: Vocal ensembles   JNAZ
Sextets: Wind & keyboard   NWNQ
Sextets: Wind ensemble   UNQ
Sextets: Woodwind & keyboard: Accompanying low voice
KFXE/NWPNQ
Sextets: Woodwind, strings & percussion   NYEPNQ
Sextets: Woodwind, strings, keyboard & percussion:
Accompanying mezzo-soprano voice
KFNE/NYDNQ
Shanties: Arrangements for woodwind quartet
VNSK/DW/GMC
Sharkey, Jack: Books   BSGNH
Shostakovich, Dmitri Dmitrievich: Books   BSGR
Sicilianos: Arrangements for flute & piano
VRPK/AHVQT
Sight reading: Cello   SR/EG
Sinatra, Frank: Books   AKDW/GB/E(P)
Sinatra, Frank: Recorded music: Books
AKDW/GR/FD(P)
Singers: Baritone voice: Books   AKGN/E(M)
Singers: Country 'n' western songs: Books
AKDW/GCW/E(M)
Singers: Opera: Books   AC/E(M)
Singers: Popular music: Books AKDW/GB/E(M)
Singers: Rock 'n' roll: Songs: Solo voice: Books
AKDW/HK/E(M)
Singers: Soprano voice: Books   AKFL/E(M)
Singers: Soul music: Books   AKDW/GBS/E(M)
Singing: Books   AB/E
Skye: Folk songs   ADW/G(YDLZS)
Social aspects: Books   A/KD
Solo voice   KDH
Solos Guitar   TSPM
Solos: Organ   R
Solos: Piano   QP
Solos: Vihuela   TVPM
Solos: Viola   SQPM
Solos: Violin   SPM
Solos: Vocal music   K
Solos: Vocal music: Books   AK
Solos: Voice   KEZ
Solos, Unaccompanied: Bass clarinet   VVUPM
Solos, Unaccompanied: Bassoon   VWPM
Solos, Unaccompanied: Cello   SRPM
Solos, Unaccompanied: Clarinet   VVPM
Solos, Unaccompanied: Descant recorder   VSRPM
Solos, Unaccompanied: Double bass   SSPM
Solos, Unaccompanied: Flute   VRPM
Solos, Unaccompanied: Harp   TQPM
Solos, Unaccompanied: Lute   TWPM
Solos, Unaccompanied: Trumpet   WSPM
Solos, Unaccompanied: Tuba   WVPM
Sonatas: Alto flute & cello   VRSPLSRE
Sonatas: Arrangements for clarinet & piano
VVPK/AE
Sonatas: Arrangements for trumpet & piano
WSPK/AE
Sonatas: Bass instrument duet   LXNUE
Sonatas: Cello & piano   SRPE
Sonatas: Clarinet & piano   VVPE
Sonatas: Double bass   SSPME
Sonatas: Flute & piano   VRPE
Sonatas: Flute, strings & keyboard trio   NURNTE
Sonatas: Guitar solo   TSPME
Sonatas: Harp solo   TQPME
Sonatas: Keyboard & descant recorders (2)
VSRNTPWE
Sonatas: Oboe & piano   VTPE
Sonatas: Organ   RE
Sonatas: Piano solos   QPE
Sonatas: Pianos (2), 4 hands   QNUE
Sonatas: Strings & keyboard quartet   NXNSE
Sonatas: Trumpet, strings & keyboard sextet
NUYSNQE
Sonatas: Treble recorder & piano   VSSPE
Sonatas: Trumpet & string orchestra   RXMPWSE
Sonatas: Trumpet, strings & keyboard septet
NUXSNPE
Sonatas: Trumpets (2) & string orchestra
RXMPWSNUE
Sonatas: Viola d'amore & piano   SQQPE
Sonatas: Violin & piano   SPE
Sonatas: Violin solos   SPME
Sonatas: Violins (2) & keyboard   SNTPWE
Sonatinas: Double bass & violin   SPLSSEM
Sonatinas: Piano solo   QPEM
Sonatinas: Saxophone & piano   VUPEM
Sonatinas: Viola, unaccompanied   SQPMEM
Sonatinas: Violin & piano   SPEM
Songs: Accompanied by brass band   EWMDW
Songs: Accompanied by brass ensemble   EWNDW
Songs: Accompanied by clarinet & piano
KE/VVPDW
Songs: Accompanied by instrument(s)   KE/LDW
Songs: Accompanied by string quintet
FE/RXNRDW
Songs: Accompanied by trumpet & piano
EWSPDW
Songs: Accompanied by wind, strings, keyboard &
percussion   ENYDDW

Songs: Arrangements for brass band   WMK/DW
Songs: Arrangements for brass ensemble   WNK/DW
Songs: Arrangements for chord organ   RPVCK/DW
Songs: Arrangements for electronic organ
RPVK/DW
Songs: Arrangements for flute & piano   VRPK/DW
Songs: Arrangements for flutes (2) & piano
VRNTQK/DW
Songs: Arrangements for guitar solo   TSPMK/DW
Songs: Arrangements for military band
UMMK/DW
Songs: Arrangements for organ   RK/DW
Songs: Arrangements for piano solo   QPK/DW
Songs: Arrangements for plucked string instrument
TPMK/DW
Songs: Arrangements for recorder ensemble
VSNK/DW
Songs: Arrangements for recorder quartet
VSNSK/DW
Songs: Arrangements for recorder solo
VSPMK/DW
Songs: Arrangements for trumpet, unaccompanied
WSPMK/DW
Songs: Arrangements for unaccompanied bassoon
VWPMK/DW
Songs: Arrangements for unaccompanied clarinet
VVPMK/DW
Songs: Arrangements for woodwind keyboard &
percussion   NYFPK/DW
Songs: Arrangements for woodwind quartet
VNSK/DW
Songs: Baritone voice   KGNDW
Songs: Baritone voice: Accompanied by orchestra
KGNE/MDW
Songs: Bass voice   KGXDW
Songs: Books   ADW
Songs: Boys voices   JFVBDW
Songs: Choral music   DW
Songs: Choral music: Accompanied by keyboard &
percussion   ENYLDW
Songs: Choral music: Accompanied by military band
EUMMDW
Songs: Choral music: Unaccompanied works
EZDW
Songs: Female voice, Child's voice   KFDW
Songs: Female voices, Children's voices: Unison
JFDW
Songs: Female voices, Children's voices: Unison:
Accompanied by guitar   JFE/TSDW
Songs: Female voices, Children's voices: Unison:
Accompanied by percussion ensemble
JFE/XNDW
Songs: Female voices, Children's voices: Unison:
Accompanied by recorders & percussion
JFE/NYHSDW
Songs: Female voices, Children's voices: Unison:
Accompanied by various instruments
JFE/LDW
Songs: Female voices, Children's voices: Unison:
Accompanied by woodwind, strings & percussion
JFE/NYEPDW
Songs: Female voices, Children's voices: Unison: Books
AJFDW
Songs: Female voices, Children's voices: Unison: Voice
parts   JFDADW
Songs: High voice   KFTDW
Songs: High voice: Accompanied by harp
KFTE/TQWD
Songs: Low voice: Accompanied by woodwind & keyboard
sextet   KFXE/NWPNQDW
Songs: Male voices: Accompanied by woodwind, strings,
keyboard & percussion   GE/NYDPDW
Songs: Mezzo-soprano voice   KFNDW
Songs: Mezzo-soprano voice: Accompanied by flute
KFLE/VRDW
Songs: Middle voice   KFVDW
Songs: Mozart, W. A.: Books   BMSADW
Songs: Solo voice   KDW
Songs: Solo voice: Accompanied by guitar
KE/TSDW
Songs: Solo voice: Accompanied by lute
KE/TWDW
Songs: Solo voice: Accompanied by strings, keyboard &
percussion   KE/NYGDW
Songs: Solo voice: Accompanied by viol & lute
KE/STPLTWDW
Songs: Solo voice: Books   AKDW
Songs: Soprano trio: Accompanied by brass, strings,
keyboard & percussion sextet
JNFLDE/NYEXPNQDW
Songs: Soprano voice: Accompanied by clarinet trio
KFLE/VVNTDW
Songs: Soprano voice: Accompanied by viola & guitar
KFLE/SQPLTSDW
Songs: Soprano voices: Accompanied by keyboard &
percussion   FLE/NYLDW
Songs: Tenor voice   KGHDW
Songs: Tenor voice: Accompanied by guitar
KGHE/TSDW
Songs: Unaccompanied female voices, children's
voices   FEZDW
Songs: Unaccompanied female voices, children's voices:
Unison   JFEZDW
Songs: Unaccompanied solo voice   KEZDW
Songs: Unaccompanied works: Unison   JEZDW
Songs: Unison   JDW
Songs: Vocal duets   JNEDW

Songs: Vocal sextet: Accompanied by chamber orchestra
JNAZE/MRDW
Songs: Vocal sextet: Accompanied by clarinet, strings &
percussion   JNAZE/NYEVDW
Songs: Vocal solo: Accompanied by violin & piano
KE/SPDW
Soprano voice: Books   AKFL
Soprano voices: Choral works   FL
Soul: Songs: Vocal solo   KDW/GBS
Soul music: Books   A/GBS
Soul music: Songs: Books   AKDW/GBS
Spain: Collections: Arrangements for guitar
TSPMK/AYK
Speaking chorus   HY
Spirituals: Arrangements for brass ensemble
WNK/DW/LC
Spirituals: Choral music   DW/LC
Spirituals: Female voices, Children's voices
FDW/LC
Spirituals: Unaccompanied works   EZDW/LC
Spirituals: Vocal solos   KDW/LC
Stage music: Vocal music   CB/J
Stereophonic records: Books   A/FF
Stewart, Rod: Books   AKDW/HKR/E(P)
Stokowski, Leopold: Books   A/EC(P)
Stories: Librettos: Musical plays   ACMBN
Strauss, Richard: Books   BSU
Stravinsky, Ïgor: Books   BSV
String bass   SS
String instruments: Accompanying female voices,
children's voices   FE/RW
String instruments: Accompanying unison choral works
JE/RW
Strings & keyboard: Accompanying vocal trio
JNDE/NX
Strings & keyboard: Ensembles: Chamber music
NX
Strings & wind: Ensembles: Accompanying soprano voice
KFLE/NV
Strings & woodwind: Ensembles: Chamber music
NVP
Strings & wind: Ensembles: Chamber music   NV
Strings, brass & keyboard: Ensembles: Accompanying
choral works   ENUXP
Strings, brass & percussion: Accompanying choral works
ENYEXP
Strings, keyboard & percussion: Ensembles:
Accompanying solo voice   KE/NYG
Strings, trumpet & keyboard: Chamber music
NUXS
Strings, wind & keyboard: Ensembles: Accompanying
choral works   ENU
Strings, wind & keyboard: Ensembles: Accompanying
soprano voice   KFLE/NU
Strings, wind & keyboard: Ensembles: Chamber music
NU
Strings, wind & percussion: Accompanying vocal sextet
JNAZE/NYE
Strings, wind & percussion: Ensembles: Accompanying
soprano voice   KFLE/NYE
Strings, wind & percussion: Ensembles: Chamber music
NYE
Strings, wind, keyboard & percussion: Ensembles:
Accompanying mezzo-soprano voice
KFNE/NYD
Strings, wind, keyboard & percussion: Ensembles:
Chamber music   NYD
Strings, woodwind & percussion: Ensembles:
Accompanying soprano voice
KFLE/NYEP
Strings, woodwind & keyboard: Ensembles:
Accompanying soprano voice   KFLE/NUP
Suites: Arrangements for descant recorder & piano
VSRPK/AG
Suites: Brass band   WMG
Suites: Brass sextet   WNQG
Suites: Double bass quartet   SSNSG
Suites: Guitar duet   TSNUG
Suites: Guitar solo   TSPMG
Suites: Military band   UMMG
Suites: Organ   RG
Suites: Piano duets, 4 hands   QNVG
Suites: Piano solo   QPG
Suites: Recorder ensemble   VSNG
Suites: Recorder trio   VSNTG
Suites: String & keyboard trio   NXNTG
Sullivan, Sir Arthur Seymour: Books   BSW
Symphonies   MME
Symphonies: Arrangements for brass band
WMK/AE
Symphonies: Arrangements for piano solo   QPK/AE
Symphonies: Arrangements for trumpet & piano
WSPK/LE
Symphonies: Brian, H.: Books   BBTNAMME
Symphonies: Bruckner, A.   BBUEAMME
Symphonies: Dvořák, A.: Books   BDXAMME
Symphonies: Organ & orchestra   MPRE
Symphonies: Shostakovich D. D.   BSGRAMME
Symphonies: String orchestra   RXME
Symphonies: Toy instruments: Orchestra   MVE
Symphony orchestra   MM
Symphony orchestra: Books   AMM
Syro-Maronite liturgy: Books   ADGTCX

List of Music Publishers

While every effort has been made to check the information given in this list with the publishers concerned, the British Library cannot hold itself responsible for any errors or omissions.

ACUFF-ROSE Music Ltd. 50 New Bond St.,
London W1. *Tel:* 01-629-0392.
Grams: Acufrose London.

AFFILIATED MUSIC Publishers Ltd.
138 Charing Cross Rd, London WC2H 0LD.
Tel: 01-836-9351.

AMERICAN UNIVERSITY PUBLISHERS Group,
Ltd. 70 Great Russell St., London WC1B 3BY.
Tel: 01-405-0182. *Grams:* Amunpress.

ANTICO Edition. North Harton, Lustleigh,
Newton Abbot, Devon TQ13 9SG.
Tel: Lustleigh (064-77)-260.

ARDMORE AND BEECHWOOD, Ltd.
21 Denmark St., London WC2H 8WE
Tel: 01-836-3856.

ARNOLD. E.J. Arnold & Son Ltd. Butterley St.,
Leeds LS10 1AX.

ARS VIVA. 48 Great Marlborough St.,
London W1V 2BN.

ASCHERBURG, HOPWOOD AND CREW, Ltd.
50 New Bond St., London W1A 2BR.
Tel: 01-629-7600. *Grams:* Symphony London.

ASHDOWN. Edwin, Ltd.
275-281 Cricklewood Broadway,
London NW2 6QR. *Tel:* 01-450-5237.

ASHLEY-FIELDS Music, Ltd. 61 Frith St.,
London W1V 5TA. *Tel:* 01-734-7462.
Grams: Fieldmus London.

ASSOCIATED BOARD OF THE ROYAL SCHOOLS
OF MUSIC. (Publications Dept), 14 Bedford Sq.,
London WC1B 3JG. *Tel:* 01-636-6919.
Grams: Musexam London WC1.

ASSOCIATED MUSIC Publishers, Inc. c/o G.
Schirmer Ltd, 140 Strand, London WC2R 1HH.
Tel: 01-836-4011.

BANKS and Son (Music) Ltd. Stonegate, York.

BARENREITER Ltd. 17-18 Bucklersbury,
Hitchin, Herts. 3G5 1BB. *Tel:* 0462-57535.

BAYLEY AND FERGUSON, Ltd. 65 Berkeley St.,
Glasgow C3. *Tel:* Central 7240.
Grams: Bayley Glasgow.

B.B.C. *See* British Broadcasting Corporation.

BELWIN-MILLS Music, Ltd. 250 Purley Way,
Croydon CR9 4QD. *Tel:* 01-681-0855.
Grams: Belmilmus Croydon.

BERRY MUSIC Co. Ltd. 10 Denmark St.,
London WC2H 8LU. *Tel:* 01-836-1653.

BLOSSOM Music, Ltd. 80a Vivian Ave.
London NW4. *Tel:* 01-202-5736.
Grams: Leedsmusik London.

BODLEY HEAD. The Bodley Head, Ltd. 9 Bow
St., London WC2E 7AL. *Tel:* 01-836 9081.
Grams: Bodleian London WC2.

BOELKE-BOMART. *See* Kalmus

BOONIN. *See* Kalmus

BOOSEY AND HAWKES Music Publishers, Ltd.
295 Regent St., London W1A 1BR.
Tel: 01-580-2060.
Grams: Sonorous London W1.
Trade: The Hyde, Edgware Rd,
London NW9 6JN. *Tel:* 01-305-3861.
Grams: Sonorous London NW9.

BOSWORTH and Co., Ltd. 14-18 Heddon St.,
London W1R 8DP. *Tel:* 01-734-0475.
Grams: Bosedition London W1.

BOURNE MUSIC Ltd. 34/36 Maddox St.,
London W1R 9PD. *Tel:* 01-493-6412.
Grams: Bournemusic London W1.

BREGMAN VOCCO AND CONN, Ltd.
50 New Bond St., London W1A 1BR.
Tel: 01-629-7600. *Grams:* Symphony London.

BREITKOPF AND HARTEL (London) Ltd.
8 Horse and Dolphin Yard, London W1V 7LG.
Tel: 01-437-3342.
Grams: Breitkopfs London W1.

BRITISH AND CONTINENTAL Music Agencies,
Ltd. 8 Horse and Dolphin Yard,
London W1V 7LG. *Tel:* 01-437-3342.

BRITISH BROADCASTING CORPORATION.
BBC Publications, 35 Marylebone High St.,
London W1M 4AA. *Tel:* 01-580-5577.
Grams: Broadcasts London. *Telex:* 265781.

CAMBRIDGE UNIVERSITY PRESS. Bentley House,
P.O. Box 92, 200 Euston Rd., London NW1
2DB.
Tel: 01-387-5030.
Grams: Cantabrigia London NW1.
Telex: 27335.
Editorial and Production: The Pitt Building,
Trumpington St., Cambridge CB2 1RP.
Tel: Cambridge 58331. *Grams:* Unipress
Cambs.
Telex: 817256.

CAMPBELL CONNELLY and Co., Ltd.
10 Denmark St., London WC2.
Tel: 01-863-1653.

CARY. L.J. Cary and Co., Ltd. 50 New Bond St.,
London W1A 2BR. *Tel:* 01-629-7600.
Grams: Symphony London W1.

CENTRAL COUNCIL OF CHURCH BELL
RINGERS. c/o "Monsal", Bredon, Tewkesbury,
Glos. GL20 7LY.

CHAPPELL and Co., Ltd. 50 New Bond St.,
London W1A 1DR. *Tel:* 01-629-7600.
Grams: Symphony London. *Telex:* 268403.

CHARNWOOD MUSIC Publishing Co.
5 University Rd, Leicester.

CHESTER. J. and W. Chester/Edition Wilhelm
Hansen London Ltd. Eagle Court,
London EC1M 5QD. *Tel:* 01-253-6947
Grams: Guarnerius London EC1.

CLIFFORD ESSEX Music Co. Ltd.
20 Earlham St., London WC2 *Tel:* 01-836-2810.
Grams: Triomphe London WC2.

COLLIER MACMILLAN Publishers.
Division of Cassell and Collier Macmillan
Publishers Ltd., 35 Red Lion Sq.,
London WC1R 4SG. *Tel:* 01-831-6100.

CONNELLY, CAMPBELL and Co., Ltd. *See*
Campbell Connelly.

CONSTABLE and Co., Ltd. 10 Orange St.,
London WC2H 7EG. *Tel:* 01-930-0801.
Grams: Dhagoba London WC2H 7EG.
Trade: Tiptree, Essex. *Tel:* 0621-81-6362.

COPPENRATH. *See* Kalmus.

CRAMER. J.B. Cramer and Co., Ltd.
99 St. Martin's Lane, London WC2N 4AZ.
Tel: 01-240-1612.

CURWEN. J. Curwen and Sons, Ltd. *See* Faber
Music.

DAVID AND CHARLES (Publishers) Ltd.
South Devon House, Railway Station,
Newton Abbot, Devon TQ12 2BP.
Tel: 0626-3521. *Telex:* 42904.

DE WOLFE, Ltd. 80-82 Wardour St.,
London W1V 3LF. *Tel:* 01-437-4933.
Grams: Musicall London.

DICK JAMES MUSIC Ltd. 71 New Oxford St.,
London WC1A 1DP. *Tel:* 01-836-4864.

EFDS. *See* English Folk Dance and Song Society.

ELKIN and Co., Ltd. Borough Green, Sevenoaks,
Kent. *Tel:* 0732-88-3261.
Grams: Novellos Sevenoaks.

EMERSON. June Emerson Wind Music.
Windmill Farm, Ampleforth, York.

EMI MUSIC. 20 Manchester Sq., London W1.
Tel: 01-486-4488.

ENGLISH FOLK DANCE AND SONG SOCIETY.
Cecil Sharp House, 2 Regent's Park Rd,
London NW1 7AY. *Tel:* 01-485-2206.

EP PUBLISHING. EP Group of Companies.
Bradford Rd. East Ardsley, Wakefield,
Yorkshire. *Tel:* Wakefield 823971 (0924).
Grams: Edpro Wakefield.
London Office: 27 Maunsel St.,
London SW1P 2QS. *Tel:* 01-834-1067.

ESSEX, C. Clifford Essex Music Co. Ltd.
See Clifford Essex.

ESSEX MUSIC Group. 19 Poland St.
London W1. *Tel:* 01-734-8121.
Grams: Sexmus London.
Trade: Music Sales Ltd, 78 Newman St.,
London W1.

EULENBURG. Ernst, Ltd.
48 Great Marlborough St., London W1V 2BN.
Tel: 01-437-1246.

EUROPEAN AMERICAN MUSIC.
See Kalmus.

FABER MUSIC, Ltd. 3 Queen Sq.,
London WC1B 5DA. *Tel:* 01-278-6881.
Grams: Fabbaf London WC1.

FAMOUS CHAPPELL, Ltd. 50 New Bond St.,
London W1A 2BR. *Tel:* 01-629-7600.
Grams: Symphony London.

FELDMAN. B. Feldman and Co. Ltd.
64 Dean St., London W1. *Tel:* 01-437-9336.
Grams: Humfriv London WC2.

FENETTE MUSIC. 138-140 Charing Cross Rd,
London WC2H 0LD.

FORSYTH Brothers, Ltd. 190 Grays Inn Rd, London WC1X 8EW. *Tel:* 01-837-4768.

FOX. SAM FOX PUBLISHING Co. (London) Ltd. *See* Sam Fox.

FRANCIS, DAY AND HUNTER, Ltd. 138 Charing Cross Rd, London WC2H 0LD. *Tel:* 01-836-6699. *Grams:* Arpeggio London WC2.

FRANK MUSIC Co., Ltd. 50 New Bond St., London W1A 2BR. *Tel:* 01-629-7600. *Grams:* Symphony London.

FREEMAN. H. Freeman, Ltd. 64 Dean St., London W1. *Tel:* 01-437-9336.

GALAXY MUSIC. *See* Stainer and Bell.

GALLIARD. *See* Stainer and Bell.

GLOCKEN Verlag, Ltd. 10-16 Rathbone St., London W1P 2BJ. *Tel:* 01-580-2827. *Grams:* Operetta London W1.

GOOD NEWS CRUSADE. 32a Fore St., St Austell, Cornwall PL25 5EP. *Tel:* St Austell 2716.

GRAHAM. Frank Graham. 6 Queen's Terrace, Newcastle upon Tyne. *Tel:* Newcastle upon Tyne 813067.

GWASG PRIFYSGOL CYMRU. *See* University of Wales Press.

HANSEN. Edition Wilhelm Hansen London Ltd. *See* Chester.

HANSEN Publications Ltd. 21-25 Earle St., London EC2. *Tel:* 01-267-0237.

HART. F. PITMAN HART and Co., Ltd. *See* Pitman Hart.

HORTON TRUST. 1 Sherbourne Rd, Great Horton, Bradford, West Yorkshire BD7 1RB. *Tel:* Bradford (0274) 26975. *Grams:* Hortrust Bradford.

HUGHES A'I FAB. (Hughes and Son) Publishers, Ltd. 29 Rivulet Rd, Wrexham, Clwyd. *Tel:* Wrexham 4340.

IMPERIA MUSIC CO. Ltd. 21 Denmark St., London WC2. *Tel:* 01-836-6699. *Grams:* Maritunes London WC2.

INTER-ART Music Publishers. 10-16 Rathbone St. London W1P 2BJ. *Tel:* 01-580-2827. *Grams:* Operetta London W1.

JAMES. Dick James Music Ltd. *See* Dick James Music.

KALMUS. Alfred A. Kalmus, Ltd. 2-3 Fareham St., London W1V 4DU. *Tel:* 01-437-5203. *Grams:* Alkamus London W1.

KEITH PROWSE MUSIC Publishing Co., Ltd. 21 Denmark St., London WC2H 8NE. *Tel:* 01-836-5501.

LEEDS MUSIC, Ltd. 139 Piccadilly, London W1. *Tel:* 01-629-7211. *Grams:* Leedsmusik London.

LENGNICK. Alfred Lengnick and Co., Ltd. Purley Oaks Studios, 421a Brighton Rd, South Croydon, Surrey CR2 6YR. *Tel:* 01-660-7646.

LEONARD, GOULD AND BOLTTLER. 99 St Martin's Lane, London WC2N 4AZ. *Tel:* 01-240-1612.

LONDON PRO MUSICA. 42 Christchurch Ave., London NW6.

LONGMAN Group Ltd. Longman House, Burnt Mill, Harlow, Essex. *Tel:* Harlow 26721. *Trade:* Pinnacles, Harlow, Essex. *Tel:* Harlow 29655. *Grams:* 81259.

MOBART. *See* Kalmus.

MORRIS. Edwin H. Morris and Co., Ltd. 52 Maddox St., London W1. *Tel:* 01-629-7600.

MOZART EDITION (Great Britain) Ltd. 199 Wardour St., London W1V 3FA. *Tel:* 01-734-3711.

MUSIC SALES Ltd. 78 Newman St., London W1. *Tel:* 01-636-9033.

MUSICA RARA. 2 Great Marlborough St., London W1. *Tel:* 01-437-1576.

MUSICA VIVA. 558 Galleywood Rd, Chelmsford, Essex CM2 8BX.

NATIONAL FEDERATION OF WOMEN'S INSTITUTES. 39 Eccleston St., London SW1W 9NT. *Tel:* 01-730-7212. *Grams:* Fedinsti London SW1.

NOVELLO and Co., Ltd. Borough Green, Sevenoaks, Kent TN15 8DT. *Tel:* 0732-88-3261. *Grams:* Novellos Sevenoaks.

OCTAVA Music Co., Ltd. *See* Weinberger.

OXFORD UNIVERSITY PRESS (Music Department). 44 Conduit St., London W1R 0DE. *Tel:* 01-734-5364. *Grams:* Fulscore London W1.

PATERSON. Paterson's Publications, Ltd. 38 Wigmore St., London W1H 0EX. *Tel:* 01-935-3551. *Grams:* Paterwia London W1.

PAXTON. Borough Green, Sevenoaks, Kent TN15 8DT.

PENQUIN Books, Ltd. Bath Rd, Harmondsworth, Middx. *Tel:* 01-759-1984. *Grams:* Penquinook West Drayton. *Telex:* 263130. *London Office:* 17 Grosvenor Gardens, London SW1.

PETERS Edition. 10 Baches St., London N1 6DN. *Tel:* 01-253-1638. *Grams:* Musipeters London.

PHOENIX. 61 Frith St., London W1V 5TA.

PITMAN HART. F. Pitman Hart, and Co., Ltd. 99 St Martin's Lane, London WC2N 4AZ. *Tel:* 01-240-1612.

PRO MUSICA. *See* London Pro Musica.

PROWSE. Keith Prowse Music Publishing Co. Ltd. *See* Keith Prowse Music.

R. SMITH and Co. Ltd. P.O. Box 210, Watford, Herts.

RAHTER. D. Rahter. Lyra House, 67 Belsize La., London NW3. *Tel:* 01-794-8038.

REGINA MUSIC Publishing Co., Ltd. Old Fun Rd, Leeds LS10 2AA. *Tel:* Leeds 700527.

RICORDI. G. Ricordi and Co. (London), Ltd. The Bury, Church St., Chesham, Bucks HP5 1JG. *Tel:* Chesham 3311. *Grams:* Ricordi Chesham. *Sales:* see Belwin-Mills.

ROBBINS Music Corporation, Ltd. 138 Charing Cross Rd, London WC2H 0LD. *Tel:* 01-836-6699.

ROBERTON Publications. The Windmill, Wendover, Aylesbury, Bucks. HP22 6JJ. *Tel:* Wendover (0296) 623107.

ROYAL SCHOOL OF CHURCH MUSIC. Addington Palace, Croydon CR9 5AD. *Tel:* 01-654-7676. *Grams:* Cantoris Croydon.

ROYAL SCOTTISH COUNTRY DANCE SOCIETY. 12 Coates Cres., Edinburgh EH3 7AF. *Tel:* 031-225-3854.

RUBANK. *See* Novello.

SALVATIONIST PUBLISHING AND SUPPLIES, Ltd. 117 Judd St., London WC1H 9NN. *Tel:* 01-387-1656. *Grams:* Savingly London WC1.

SAM FOX Publishing Co. (London) Ltd. 21 Denmark St., London WC2H 8NE. *Tel:* 01-836-6699.

SCHAUER AND MAY, 67 Belsize La., London NW3. *Tel:* 01-794-8038.

SCHIRMER. G. Schirmer Ltd. (Music Publishers). 140 Strand, London WC2R 1HH. *Tel:* 01-836-4011.

SCHOFIELD AND SIMS, Ltd. 35 St John's Rd, Huddersfield, Yorkshire HD1 5DT. *Tel:* Huddersfield 30684. *Grams:* Schosims Huddersfield.

SCHOOLMASTER PUBLISHING Co. Ltd. Derbyshire House, Lower St., Kettering, Northants. NN16 8BB. *Tel:* 053687-3407.

SCHOTT and Co. Ltd. 48 Great Marlborough St., London W1V 2BN. *Tel:* 01-437-1246. *Grams:* Shotanco London.

SCHROEDER, A.A. Schroeder Music Publishing Co., Ltd. 15 Berkeley St., London W1. *Tel:* 01-493-2506.

SCHROEDER AND GUNTHER Inc. c/o G. Schirmer Ltd., 140 Strand, London WC2R 1HH. *Tel:* 01-836-4011.

SIKORSKI. *See* Belwin-Mills.

SIMROCK. N. Simrock. Lyra House, 67 Belsize La., London NW3 5AX. *Tel:* 01-749 8038.

SMITH. R. Smith and Co. Ltd. *See* R. Smith.

ST GREGORY PUBLISHING Co. 64 Pineheath Rd., High Kelling, Holt, Norfolk.

SOUTHERN MUSIC, TEXAS. *See* Belwin-Mills.

STAINER AND BELL Ltd. 82 High Rd, London N2 9PW. *Tel:* 01-444-9135.

STUDIO MUSIC Co. 77-79 Dudden Hill La., London NW10 2UA.

THAMES MUSIC. 1st Floor, 117 Church Road, Barnes, London, SW13. *Tel:* 01-741 2406.

THAMES PUBLISHING. 14 Barlby Rd, London W10 6AR. *Tel:* 01-969-3579.

TOMUS Publications. Carne House, Parsons La., Bury, Lancs. BL9 0JT. *Tel:* 061-764-1099.

UNITED MUSIC Publishers Ltd. 1 Montague St., London WC1B 5BS. *Tel:* 01-636-5171.

UNIVERSAL Edition (London), Ltd. 2 Fareham St., London W1V 4DU. *Tel:* 01-437-5203. *Grams:* Alkamus London W1.

UNIVERSITY IF ILLINOIS PRESS. *See* American University Publishers.

UNIVERSITY OF TEXAS PRESS, Ltd. *See* American University Publishers.

UNIVERSITY OF WALES PRESS. Merthyr House, James St., Cardiff CF1 6EU. *Tel:* Cardiff 31919.

VANGUARD MUSIC Ltd. 12 Portland Rd., London SE25. *Tel:* 01-654-4017.

WEINBERGER. Joseph Weinberger Ltd. 10-16 Rathbone St., London W1P 2BJ. *Tel:* 01-580-2827. *Grams:* Operetta London W1.

WISE Publications. 78 Newman St., London W1. *Tel:* 01-636-0933.

WOLFE Publishing, Ltd. 10 Earlham St., London WC2H 9LP. *Tel:* 01-240-2935.